The *New* **Birds**
of the **West Midlands**

covering

Staffordshire, Warwickshire, Worcestershire and the former West Midlands county

Dedicated to everyone, past and present, who over the years have diligently submitted records of birds they have seen in the region, without which this book could not have been written.

The *New* Birds
of the West Midlands

covering
Staffordshire, Warwickshire, Worcestershire
and the former West Midlands county

Graham and Janet Harrison

with contributions from

Alan Richards
Jim Winsper
Bert Coleman

Line drawings by Steve Cale
Maps by Andy Lawrence
Migration data by Peter Rollin

**Published by The West Midland Bird Club
in celebration of its 75th Anniversary.**

First published 2005 by the West Midland Bird Club,
PO Box 1, Studley, Warwickshire B80 7JG.
www.westmidlandbirdclub.com

Registered Charity No 213311

ISBN 0-9507881-2-0

British Library Cataloguing in Publication Data.
A catalogue record for this book is available from the British Library.

The text for this book is printed on environmental-friendly paper produced from wood taken from sawmill residues, forest thinnings and sustainable forests. The pulps used are ECF (Elemental Chlorine Free).

Printed in Great Britain by Goodman Baylis Ltd, Worcester.

Contents

Foreword

by

Bill Oddie OBE
President, West Midland Bird Club

Ah the memories!

Between the age of 7 and 22 I lived on the edge of Birmingham. If you must know, that means between 1948 and 1963. So, it was in the West Midlands that I discovered birds, and bird watching. Fortunately, I am blessed with a pretty much photographic memory—or perhaps that should be a 'video memory', since my recollections definitely move; or rather fly, flit, flap, swim, dive or perch. I only have to close my eyes to be able to re-run a miscellany of magic moments. Climbing up into a soggy hawthorn tree in pouring rain to get at my first Chaffinch's nest, in the Leasowes woods in Quinton. (Yes, I was a schoolboy egg collector, but then so were half the committee of the WMBC I dare say). My very first visit to the god-forsaken concrete mere that is Bartley Reservoir—on October 28th, of a year before I kept proper notes—and 'lucking in' on a mixed wildfowl flock that included male Pintail, male Common Scoter, and a Black-necked Grebe. I never saw the like again, though I watched that place for ten years after. My first Smew: two 'redheads' in a snow flurry, across the other side of bleak Shustoke Reservoir. Upper Bittell, on a crisp December morning, with a Snow Bunting tinkling along the shore, and a Red Kite soaring overhead (a real wild Welsh one, no wing tags in those days!) A disappearing wader over Blithfield calling 'prrp prrp', which I now know was a Pectoral Sandpiper. A breeding plumaged Water Pipit, in early April at Belvide, one of the prettiest birds I have ever seen. And Upton Warren, which I *thought* I had 'discovered' by browsing through pre-war WMBC annual reports, and then by following a small party of Bewick's Swans which appeared to crash land in a field. In fact, they landed on the shallow pools where—a few years later—I saw my first Temminck's Stints. It was also at Upton that I *thought* I'd found a superb male Blue-winged Teal in the early 1960s. As it happens, both Upton and the teal should really be credited to Arthur Jacobs, who, in both cases, had got there before me. But yes, happy memories indeed.

I no longer belong to the West Midlands, but Arthur still does, and indeed so do all the above named places. Except that the names have sometimes changed. In many cases, so have the places, but the satisfying fact is that the changes have without doubt been for the better. A great deal of my birding back in the 1950s involved trespassing, which in turn involved the danger of snaring delicate bits of my anatomy on barbed wire or iron spiked railings, or—at the very least—being yelled at, chased and possibly assaulted by irate landowners, water bailiffs and farmers. Youngsters today simply have no idea of the risks we old 'uns had to take when we went birding when we were lads. Nowadays, it's all so easy. Instead of having to track Bewick's Swans, or cut through wire fences, all that present day birders have to do is buy a copy of *Where to Watch Birds in the West Midlands*. They will then be encouraged—nay invited—to explore many of the places I had to sneak or break into. They will be directed down nature trails, and maybe even offered little leaflets telling them what they are likely to see. Everything is laid on!

Thus, the almost secret Upton Warren of my day, has become the magnificent Worcestershire Trust Nature Reserve, complete with paths and signs leading you to the Moors Pool and The Flashes, and even cozy covered hides. Hides!? For heaven's sake, how wet can you get? Very, in my young shelterless days. The then barricaded Shustoke Reservoir may still be pretty inhospitable, but instead you can spend a whole day checking out the nearby Ladywalk Reserve, and the Kingsbury Water Park. Belvide, Blithfield and Bittell are still all thriving, with the immense added advantage that areas are specially designated for birds and birdwatchers. Arguably Bartley is much the same as when I were a lad, though even there, there are a few notice boards acknowledging that you may see some wildlife round the reservoir—if you are *very* lucky.

It is thanks to the efforts of the WMBC and the County Wildlife Trusts, and the co-operation of various water companies, that most of the sites where I birded in the old days are now properly protected and managed; and in addition many excellent new areas have been discovered or developed.

Things are pretty good for birdwatchers, but how about the birds? Well, surely the very existence of this book implies the answer to that question. I confess that when I first saw the title, I misread it as meaning 'new birds' of the West Midlands. Silly mistake, you may think, but then again, I dare say there have been so many species added to the West Midlands list during recent years that it may indeed merit a whole book just about the 'new ones'. Of course, what you actually get is a much better deal. The *new* 'Birds of the West Midlands'. An update of everything birdy.

I have been based in London for the past 40 years, but just now and again, I get back to the West Midlands; usually to open a new hide, or even a new reserve. I confess that on such occasions (which I enjoy immensely) I always harbour a secret wish that I might get lucky and spot something really good, preferably new for the site or—even better—for the whole region. The best I've managed so far is a Bittern at Ladywalk a couple of autumns ago. OK, not exactly a 'crippler' I know, but I like to think that I may have made a tiny contribution to what you are about to read. I dare say that many of *you* have made a much greater contribution. Satisfying isn't it?

Enjoy, and be inspired.

Bill Oddie OBE

Acknowledgements

A book of this kind could not have been produced without assistance from a great many people and the authors are deeply indebted to everyone who has helped or passed on information in any way whatsoever, whether they are mentioned by name below or not.

We are especially grateful to Bert Coleman, Alan Richards and Jim Winsper, who not only wrote their individual chapters, but undertook a great many other tasks, too numerous to list completely. These included reading and commenting on manuscripts and helping to gather together and select the photographs. Both Jim and Alan helped with the production of publicity material and Alan compiled the long list of Exotic Species, assisted with obtaining printing estimates and made first contact with the chosen printers. Bert has provided all the ringing data for the individual species and collected volumes of wildfowl counts from Maurice Arnold, to whom we are in turn grateful for lending this material which he has collated so meticulously over many years.

We are so thankful that we have someone in the Bird Club, namely Andy Lawrence, who can produce such excellent maps. He also understands computers much better than we do and was most willing to advise and assist in preparing material for the printers.

We owe especial debts to Mike Warren for his stunning jacket illustration, to his son Simon for the jacket typography and to Steve Cale for his delightful line drawings. The book is also much enhanced by the individually credited photographs of Charles Brown, Bert Coleman, Andy Hale, Mike Lane, Richard Mills, Keith Stone, Phill Ward, Keith Warmington and Mike Wilkes, to whom we are very grateful.

Peter Rollin has analysed all the first and last dates for migratory birds and has also produced the regional distribution maps for a number of species. Paul Goode and Nigel Palmer inputted much data for raptors and waders, and for wildfowl respectively, onto computer spreadsheets from ten years of Annual Reports—a somewhat boring job! Alan Dean made particularly helpful comments on the drafts of several species accounts and added some very useful passages to the gull species. Lilian Winsper has undertaken to receive all orders for the book and organise their dispatch. We are most grateful to these five people.

We would like to thank those who commented on manuscripts relating to areas they know well. They are Frank Gribble, who also provided reports, documents and snippets from his store of knowledge; Jonathan Bowley and Kevin Clements, who also supplied information from their respective Tetrad Atlas work; David Emley; Richard Harbird; Tim Hextell; Mike Inskip; Andy Lawrence; and Andy Warr, who also loaned annual site reports. Others who kindly loaned site reports were Steve Cawthray, Peter Dedicoat, Ted Jury and Alban Wincott. Milan Tursner provided information on a Kestrel nest box scheme, Rob Skeates did likewise on Firecrest records and Andy Mabbett publicised the book on the Club's website.

We are most grateful to the British Trust for Ornithology (BTO) for providing local data from the Common Bird Census (CBC) and Breeding Bird Survey (BBS) sites and to the Royal Society for the Protection of Birds (RSPB) for their assistance. In particular we very much appreciate the information received from all their staff at Sandwell Valley, Nicholas Chambers at Coombes Valley, Anna Sugrue about the North Staffordshire Moors, and Kirsty Meadows and Anna Broszkeiwicz from the Central England Regional Office. The various Wildlife Trust offices kindly provided details of their nature reserves and Warwickshire Wildlife Trust and Sara Carvalho from EcoRecord also supplied habitat statistics. We should like to thank Anton Irving at English Nature for his prompt response in obtaining various data, Ewan Calcott of the Forestry Commission for woodland statistics and the English Nature and Forestry Commission staff at Wyre Forest. We must also thank Valerie and Colin Shawyer of the Hawk and Owl Trust for information on Barn Owl nest box schemes and David Sims for kindly extracting records from the Warwick Natural History Society's archives.

Both past and present County recorders and Annual Report Editors have made a huge contribution in enabling us to extract all the information required from the Annuals Reports they have produced over the years. The work of the ringing groups and individuals, which in turn has provided data for the book, is also acknowledged.

All maps are based on Ordnance Survey maps and are reproduced by kind permission of the Ordnance Survey, © Crown copyright NC/04/33918.

Last, but not least, we are most grateful for the help and advice we received from the staff at the printers, Goodman Baylis Ltd, and especially to Michael Cawley.

There are likely to be others who have passed on information that has reached us through some of the above people and there are many hundreds who have submitted their bird records over the years and given us all this valuable material—to you all a very big thank you. We can only apologise if we have forgotten to mention anyone specifically.

Finally, even our daughters have been inveigled into helping and we should like to thank Sue for compiling the list of plants and Jenny for the proof reading she has promised to do when she comes home at Christmas. So, to our family and friends who have had to put up with being virtually ignored for at least the last two years—we are very sorry!

Graham and Janet Harrison

Abbreviations

Below are abbreviations used in the text, other than ones found in a standard dictionary.

AONB	Area of Outstanding Natural Beauty	km^2	square kilometre
BAP	Biodiversity Action Plan	km/h	kilometres per hour
BB or	British Birds	LBAP	Local Biodiversity Action Plan
Brit. Birds		LNR	Local Nature Reserve
BBRC	British Birds Rarities Committee	mph	miles per hour
BBS	Breeding Bird Survey	nk	not known
BBCBBS	Birmingham and Black Country Breed-	NNR	National Nature Reserve
	ing Bird Survey	*op cit.*	in the work already quoted
BOU	British Ornithologists' Union	*pers. comm.*	personal communication
BOURC	British Ornithologists' Union Records	RBBP	Rare Breeding Birds Panel
	Committee	RSPB	Royal Society for the Protection of
BSE	Bovine Spongiform Encephalitis		Birds
BTO	British Trust for Ornithology	SAC	Special Area of Conservation
CA	Countryside Agency	SPA	Special Protection Area
CAP	Common Agricultural Policy	SSSI	Site of Special Scientific Interest
CBC	Common Bird Census	Staffs	Staffordshire
CES	Constant Effort Site	STW	Severn Trent Water
cf.	compare	SWT	Staffordshire Wildlife Trust
CP	Country Park	UP	Urban Park
DEFRA	Department for Environment, Food and	Warks	Warwickshire
	Rural Affairs	WaWT	Warwickshire Wildlife Trust
EA	Environment Agency	WBS	Waterways Bird Survey
EN	English Nature	WBBS	Waterways Breeding Bird Survey
ESA	Environmentally Sensitive Area	WeBS	Wetland Bird Survey
et al.	and others	WMBC	West Midland Bird Club
EU	European Union	W Mid	West Midlands
FC	Forestry Commission	Worcs	Worcestershire
FE	Forest Enterprise	WoWT	Worcestershire Wildlife Trust
GM	genetically modified	WP	Water Park
GP	gravel pit	WTA	Warwickshire Tetrad Atlas
ha	hectares	WWT	Wildfowl and Wetlands Trust
JNCC	Joint Nature Conservancy Committee		

The following abbreviated forms of titles are used for frequently cited works of reference:

Breeding Atlas Gibbons D.W., Reid J.B. and Chapman R.A. (Eds). 1993. *The New Atlas of Breeding Birds in Britain and Ireland: 1988-1991*. BTO, T. & A.D. Poyser, London.

BWM Harrison G.R., Dean A.R., Richards A.J. and Smallshire D. 1982. *The Birds of the West Midlands*. West Midland Bird Club, Studley.

BWP Cramp S. *et al.* (Eds). 1977-1994. *Handbook of the Birds of Europe, the Middle East and North Africa: The Birds of the Western Palearctic*. Vols I-IX. OUP, Oxford.

Character Area Countryside Agency 1999. *Countryside Character Volume 5: West Midlands. The character of England's natural and man-made landscape*. Countryside Agency, Cheltenham.

Natural Areas English Nature 1998. *Natural Areas* Nature conservation in context. (CD-ROM). Version 1.1. Peterborough: English Nature. Available from: www. english-nature.org.uk

Winter Atlas Lack P. 1986. *The Atlas of Wintering Birds in Britain and Ireland*. BTO, Poyser, Calton.

Tetrad Atlases Refers to the Birmingham and Black Country Breeding Bird Survey and the Warwickshire Tetrad Atlas survey, both of which are in the course of preparation.

Migration Atlas Wernham C.V. *et al.* 2002. *The Migration Atlas: movements of the birds of Britain and Ireland*. BTO, T. & A.D. Poyser, London.

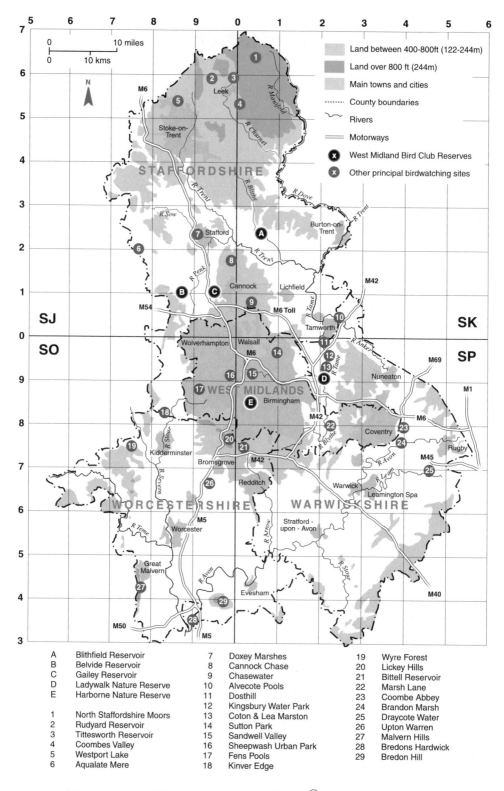

		0	10 miles	
		0	10 kms	

Land between 400-800ft (122-244m)
Land over 800 ft (244m)
Main towns and cities
County boundaries
Rivers
Motorways
X West Midland Bird Club Reserves
x Other principal birdwatching sites

A	Blithfield Reservoir	7	Doxey Marshes	19	Wyre Forest
B	Belvide Reservoir	8	Cannock Chase	20	Lickey Hills
C	Gailey Reservoir	9	Chasewater	21	Bittell Reservoir
D	Ladywalk Nature Reserve	10	Alvecote Pools	22	Marsh Lane
E	Harborne Nature Reserve	11	Dosthill	23	Coombe Abbey
		12	Kingsbury Water Park	24	Brandon Marsh
1	North Staffordshire Moors	13	Coton & Lea Marston	25	Draycote Water
2	Rudyard Reservoir	14	Sutton Park	26	Upton Warren
3	Tittesworth Reservoir	15	Sandwell Valley	27	Malvern Hills
4	Coombes Valley	16	Sheepwash Urban Park	28	Bredons Hardwick
5	Westport Lake	17	Fens Pools	29	Bredon Hill
6	Aqualate Mere	18	Kinver Edge		

Map reproduced by kind permission of Ordnance Survey. © Crown copyright NC/04/33918

Introduction

The production of this book is timely for two reasons. Firstly, the seventy-fifth anniversary is an appropriate occasion to look back and reflect on the West Midland Bird Club's (WMBC's) considerable achievements, as the first chapter does. Secondly, as we move into a new Millennium it is appropriate to take stock of how and why our birdlife is changing. The West Midlands may not be regarded as an especially bird-rich area in the national context, but it is nevertheless surprising just how much variety there is. Many of our birds travel great distances in order to spend the summer or winter here, whilst others arrive by accident during bad weather. Before presenting the individual species accounts in the Systematic List, we have therefore tried to set the region in its global context by including chapters on Birds, Climate and Weather and the Movements of Birds to and from the West Midlands. We have then followed these by a profile of the region and its main habitats, with more detailed descriptions of the physical features, landscape character and key habitats for each of eleven sub-regions. These sub-regions broadly correspond to those used in the *Birds of the West Midlands* (*BWM*), but have been slightly revised to take account of the *Character of England* map produced jointly by English Nature (EN) and the Countryside Agency (CA), formerly the Countryside Commission (Countryside Agency 2000).

For our purposes the West Midland Region, hereafter generally referred to as the region, comprises Staffordshire, Warwickshire, Worcestershire and the former county of the West Midlands (now the seven Metropolitan areas of Birmingham, Coventry, Dudley, Sandwell, Solihull, Walsall and Wolverhampton). These are the four counties covered by the West Midland Bird Club and on which its recording system is based. Herefordshire and Shropshire are excluded since, though they are part of the West Midlands for governmental purposes, they are covered by separate ornithological societies. The WMBC's region covers 7,354 km^2 and is home to 4.8 million people, so the pressures on its wildlife are considerable.

Several earlier avifaunas have covered various parts of this region. The oldest is Smith's *Birds of Staffordshire*, published in 1938 but updated by Lord and Blake in their *Birds of Staffordshire* in 1962. Harthan produced his *Birds of Worcestershire* in 1946 and subsequently updated it in 1961 and Norris published the *Birds of Warwickshire* in 1947. However, the first comprehensive avifauna for the region was *BWM*, which covered the period up to 1978 and was published by the West Midland Bird Club in 1982 to mark its fiftieth anniversary. This present book provides a comprehensive analysis of all the birds that occurred during 1979-2001. In addition it lists all records of birds that are rare visitors to the region, including those post 2001 which we know have been authenticated.

Barely a quarter of a century has passed since then, yet even in that short space of time it is amazing just how much has changed. The two recessions of the 1980s and 1990s brought about the collapse of many traditional manufacturing industries, since when the region has been trying to shed its traditional 'metal bashing' image and forge a new identity. Birmingham, in particular, has led the way by transforming itself from the 'workshop of the world' into a 'world-class city'. The countryside, too, has suffered many painful changes, particularly in agriculture, where the Common Agricultural Policy (CAP), the aftermath of various food scares and the outbreak of Foot and Mouth disease in 2001 has left British farming reeling. As a result, the need for economic regeneration and diversification have become imperatives for rural as well as urban life. On top of this we have witnessed pressures for further development and entered an era of climate change.

All this upheaval has had a profound effect on our birdlife. Much of this can be attributed to changes in farming and the climate. Over the last two decades we have lost Marsh Warblers and Black Grouse and now some species of farmland birds, for example the Grey Partridge, could be on the verge of extinction. Indeed, many birds living in the general countryside are in a sorry plight. On the other hand, some seem to have turned the corner. Mute Swans and Eurasian Sparrowhawks, for example, have recovered from the effects of poisons in the environment, whilst many more species are thriving in the relative sanctity of the growing number of nature reserves. Common Terns have spread in this way, Wood Larks have returned after a long absence and European Nightjars are responding well to the sympathetic management of heathland on Cannock Chase. Raptors have also spread, especially the Common Buzzard, no doubt helped by less persecution.

Birdwatching has changed too. To begin with, more people are taking it up, many perhaps inspired by our President's natural history programmes on the television. Yet the number contributing records is only 25% higher than it was twenty-five years ago. People are also working less regular hours and retiring early, so the weekend bias, very evident in past records, is now much less noticeable. With the aid of better field guides and optics, identification skills have also improved, whilst birding hotlines, pagers, mobile phones and internet websites all put today's birders in instant touch with what is about. This encourages them to go 'twitching' where they *know* the birds are, rather than visiting a local spot in the *hope* of an unexpected discovery. As a result, there is less 'local patch' recording of the commoner species. Nevertheless, a dedicated band of volunteers still brave all weathers to count wildfowl and waders, carry out ringing, or help with the various breeding bird and other surveys. So the Club continues to gather an ever-increasing archive of valuable data about the region's birdlife.

Even so, the number of people interested in birds means there must still be records of which we are unaware. To those whose records do not appear, we can only apologise, but there is a wealth of data stored in innumerable places, many of them unknown to us. To have tried to hunt these down would have been an impossible task, so we have restricted our analyses to those records that have been published in authoritative ornithological publications. Almost exclusively, we have only included records of nationally rare birds when they have been accepted by the British Birds Rarities Committee (BBRC). Likewise, records of regionally rare species are included only if they have been accepted by the WMBC's county records committees. On the one or two occasions when we have departed from these rules, this is clearly stated.

Some readers may be unfamiliar with the bird names used in this book. Regrettably, there is no universally agreed list of English bird names, but we have adopted those used by *British Birds* (*BB*) magazine (*Brit. Birds* 1997 and *Brit. Birds* 97: 2-5). Scientific names and, where relevant, alternative English ones can be found under the individual species accounts in the Systematic List. Since this is a bird book, we have also elected to use initial capitals for specific bird names in order to help them stand out on the page, but for other fauna and flora we have followed the more usual convention by putting names in lower case.

Inevitably, a book of this nature contains many references to other publications, organisations, surveys and techniques. To aid understanding, save space and avoid breaking up the text too much, we have used acronyms for organisations and abbreviated references for standard works as set out on page 11. For the same reasons, not every article or book is specifically acknowledged in the text, but we hope we have included all in the Bibliography. We apologise to the authors concerned, but trust they will understand our reasons. Tetrads and 10-km squares are frequently referred to in the text and an explanation of these terms can be found in the introduction to the Systematic List. Finally, we would stress that the mention of places in the text does not imply there is public access. However, there are many sites open to the public and others can be visited through membership of various organisations, purchase of permits, or payment of entrance fees or just car parking charges.

The West Midland Bird Club:
seventy-five years of progress

by

Alan Richards,

Vice President, West Midland Bird Club

On November 1st 1929, Wellington Ernest Groves, then 60 years old, invited four friends to his house at 4, Lyttleton Road, Edgbaston and proposed the formation of a bird club. 'The Birmingham Bird Club', so named, comprised Horace Alexander, Charles Wallis, Dr Henry and Miss Celia James. The prime mover of such an elite group of birdwatchers of its day was then Chief Engineer of the Birmingham Electric Company that had been instrumental in bringing electric power to the city at the end of the 1800s. Wellington Ernest Groves had had a life long interest in wild birds, but, like so many nineteenth century ornithologists, it involved egg collecting, much of it in his native county of Essex. After giving up this increasingly frowned upon pursuit in favour of watching birds and recording their occurrences in and around his adopted city, his collection was donated to the Birmingham Natural History Museum.

Mr Charles Wallis and Dr Henry were both on the staff of Birmingham University at Edgbaston, but nothing more is known about them. Horace Alexander, then 40, was already recognised as one of the 'new breed' of field ornithologists even before he moved to the Birmingham area in 1919, leaving a teaching post at Cranbook School, Kent, to further the interests of his Quaker faith. He would go on to be a major influence, not only in the development of The Birmingham Bird Club, but on British ornithology in general, for the next fifty years.

Miss Celia James, who lived at Barnt Green, regularly watched birds at Bittell Reservoirs, which along with nearby Lickey Woods, were within easy reach of Birmingham. All of the above went birdwatching there individually and, no doubt, on occasions together. The Club's Annual Report for 1936 carried an article on the birds of Bittell Reservoirs, highlighting their importance for the avifauna of the area. During the Club's early years, regular meetings were first held at Lyttleton Road and later in a room of the Grand Hotel, Colmore Row, in the city centre. Its members also kept in touch by telephone to advise each other of any interesting sightings they made, so that all might enjoy each other's finds! No minutes or records of these first meetings were kept and the Club remained a very private affair. It was generally known that W. E. Groves did not want to see any expansion of 'his bird club'! However, as the growing number of birdwatchers in the area learned of its existence, pressure grew for it to admit new members. Persuaded by Horace Alexander that it was the way to go, he finally bowed to pressure and in 1934 a decision was made to invite anyone interested in birds to become an associate by the payment of an annual subscription of five shillings. By the time the Club's second annual report was published in 1935 there were 33 members and associates. Among this number, as well as W. E. Groves of course, who was briefly the Treasurer and later a Vice President from 1947-57, there was Horace Alexander who became the President during the period 1946-59. Some of the Club's other early stalwarts included F.R. Barlow, C.W.K. Cornwallis, F. Fincher, A.J. Harthan, who was report editor during the war years, a Vice President from 1959-64 and author of *The Birds of Worcestershire* (1946), Miss Celia James, a committee member from 1946-51, the brothers W.E. and H. Kenrick and Duncan Wood, author of *Horace Alexander—Birds and Binoculars* (2003). All contributed greatly to its development as an active and effective bird club. By 1938 membership had grown to 78. However, further expansion was curtailed by the start of the Second World War, but the Club continued to publish modest annual reports of birds seen in the area during the years of hostilities.

In 1945 the Club changed its name to The Birmingham and District Bird Club to reflect its now wider coverage of activities in the area. A junior member class was also established in that year. By then the membership had risen to 92. At the end of the war the Club was fortunate in having an enthusiastic core of members, mostly comprising professional people and businessmen who were able to provide administrative expertise and logistical support for a rapidly expanding club. In 1947 it changed its name again, to The Birmingham and West Midland Bird Club, with membership passing the 200 mark at that time.

Under the Chairmanship of W.E. Kenrick (1947-52), and with C.A. (Tony) Norris as Secretary (1947-52), the Club flourished. Tony Norris became Chairman in 1953 to be joined by the redoubtable A.R.M. (Tony) Blake as Secretary in 1954. He was ably supported by Assistant Secretaries D.J. Mirams (1953-56) and J.N. Sears (1953-75) and they led the Club through a decade of further development and innovation. This continued from 1963-67 under the chairmanship of P.W. Hinde. During the period 1949-54 the honorary post of Treasurer was in the safe hands of G.C. (Cecil) Lambourne. Of those who followed in this office, Norman Swindells, Ken Thomas, John Ridley and Ken Webb all served for more than five years.

Cecil Lambourne later became Chairman of the Studley Branch and the Club's first Conservation Officer. For many years he also maintained the Club's mailing list and provided addressed envelopes for the then monthly Bulletins. These were first introduced in 1948 by Tony Norris, who until 1953 also wrote and compiled them. The early Bulletins were a single duplicated foolscap sheet, with details of future meetings and, most importantly, the latest bird sightings! Tony Blake took over its production in 1954 and over the next decade it grew to three or four pages as sightings increased. When I became Secretary in 1964 the job included producing the Bulletins, compiling bird notes—receiving eighty or more letters a month— and issuing reserve permits. In 1974 Eric Clare took over the bird notes and he dealt expertly with this important task for ten years. Others involved with the Bulletin over long periods have included George and Maurice Arnold, Peter Dedicoat and Paul South. The latter introduced the A5 format we enjoy today, now under the very able editorship of Andy Lawrence.

The Club's other major publication is its Annual Report, which grew from 31 pages in the first edition in 1934 to 50 or more pages by the 1950s as ever more records were received from the growing membership. Today it comprises 200 plus pages and has an editor supported by four county recorders and their teams—a far cry from earlier times when it was the work of one man, John Lord, who was editor for eighteen years from 1953-71. Successive editors have added their mark, continuing to improve both the content and presentation. It is currently in the capable hands of David Emley, who in 2000 introduced colour throughout.

In the late 1940s, indoor meetings, held in the City of Birmingham Art Gallery, were attracting audiences of eighty or more, while field meetings were becoming increasingly popular with full coach loads travelling to such places as Northampton sewage farm and Slimbridge. Many members will certainly have fond memories of such outings that Talbot Clay led as Field Meetings Secretary from 1949-60. Equally, there will be those who will recall with great pleasure the many field meetings Arthur Jacobs organised, both near and far, over the following fourteen years. Arthur was a hard act to follow, but his successors have served us well, especially Stan Young who did so for eleven years. Talbot Clay later became Club Chairman in 1968, sadly dying whilst in office in 1977. He was succeeded by Tony Blake, whom I followed in 1983 before handing over to the current chairman, Jim Winsper, in 1999. During my term I was fortunate to have Hugh MacGregor as Secretary from 1987-98.

To satisfy the demands of an increasing membership, the Club established branches at Kidderminster and Studley in 1948 and in East Warwickshire in 1949. In 1957 a Stafford Branch was formed and, under the leadership of E.W. (Eric) Longman and N.R. (Roy) Went, it very soon began to play a major role in the study of bird life in that area. Later, other Stafford Branch members, such as Bevan Craddock, Peter Dedicoat and Frank Gribble, played key roles (and still do) in the administration and survey work undertaken by the Branch. Frank Gribble, awarded an MBE for services to nature conservation in 1996, was Branch Chairman from 1993-99 and has been a Vice President of the WMBC since 1991.

Subsequently new branches were formed at Solihull, Tamworth and Leamington Spa (Coventry and Warwickshire), the Kidderminster Branch was revived after being dormant for a period and the meetings previously run by the parent Club were devolved to a newly constituted Birmingham Branch. Many people have served these branches well, but special mention should be made of George Morley, John Sears, Barbara Stubbs and Tony Kettle.

Members of the Club have been involved in ringing birds from the earliest times, with bat fowling nets used to catch Common Starlings at a roost near Stratford-on-Avon in the late 1940s, whilst a Heligoland trap was constructed at Bartley in 1950. However, it was not until 1962 that a Ringing Secretary was appointed to liaise with the various ringing groups in the region. Dr. C.D.T. (Clive) Minton was first to hold this post, which he did until he moved to Australia in 1969. He was succeeded by E.J. Pratley (1970-75) and Philip Ireland (1976-82). Since then the post has been held for over twenty years by A.E. (Bert) Coleman BEM, a ringer of international repute who is particularly known for his study of the Mute Swan. Our members have also been involved in one of the longest standing studies of Grey Herons in the UK, namely at Gailey which has now been running for over 40 years.

In 1952 Tony Norris, along with the West Wales Field Society, was instrumental in setting up a Bird Observatory on the island of Bardsey, with the WMBC helping with its administration. Cecil Lambourne and W.E. (Bill) Condry were also very involved at this time and later such Club stalwarts as Nick Barlow, Bevan Craddock, George Lewis, Bob and Alicia Normand and Mike West have played key roles in its running through to the present day.

1954 saw the 25th Anniversary of the founding of the Club. To mark the occasion it was agreed to construct a hide ('the gazebo') at Belvide Reservoir, formerly called 'Bellfields'. Raised on stilts and with straw-filled wire-netting walls, it was completed in 1956. Following negotiations with the owners, British Waterways, Belvide became a Club reserve, which was inaugurated in 1978 by Sir Peter Scott, who also opened a second hide. David Smallshire, the first Honorary Warden, played a major role in making it one of the top Midlands wetlands it is today, now with Trevor Hardiman in this post.

Equally important is the Ladywalk Nature Reserve. Harry Lees and Ken Darlow first recognised the area's potential when they discovered breeding Little Ringed Plovers there in the 1960s. The Club eventually persuaded the Central Electricity Generating Board to designate it as a reserve in 1970. It was inaugurated by Max Nicholson CBE the following year and visited by HRH The Duke of Edinburgh in 1973. Its first honorary warden, Brian Kington, has now been succeeded by Steve Cawthray. The Club's third major reserve is Blithfield Reservoir. This was established by arrangement with the South Staffordshire Water plc in 1968 and here our interests are looked after by Charles Brown and Eric Clare. A fourth reserve is Harborne, where, through the good offices of Derek Brown who is now honorary warden, the Club negotiated an agreement with Birmingham City Council in 1993 to run an urban bird reserve on former allotments. All our reserves are managed by dedicated volunteers. By 1973 the Club was issuing 1,000 reserve visiting permits a year. I was more than delighted when Mrs. Cicily Randall relieved me of this task. In 1979 Miss Margaret Surman became the first official Permit Secretary—a job she still does twenty-six years later, making her the longest serving officer in a single post.

In 1959 the Club changed its name yet again, to The West Midland Bird Club, which title remains to this day. The next year, The Lord Hurcomb became President, and he remained in office for thirteen years. Tony Norris then followed in his father-in-law's footsteps as the Club's President from 1977 to 1998. The Club is now honoured and delighted to have another of its famous sons, Bill Oddie OBE, as its current President.

In 1969 the Club enrolled its 1,000th member. By 1972 it was clear the Treasurer needed help with membership applications, so Derek Thomas was appointed as the first Membership Secretary, followed by David Hawker, Jean Nicholls, Dai Evans and currently John Reeves.

Bird surveys were a prime concern of the Club from its earliest days and the Research Committee, set up in 1947, became the catalyst for all future surveys and enquiries. The first meeting comprised Tony Norris as Chairman, I.L. Forster, G.C. Lambourne and G.W. Rayner, and later included H.E. Kenrick, C. Cadbury and L. Salmon. By 1949 upwards of a dozen members had been invited to join this elite group. Over the years this grew to around twenty attending its monthly meetings. At most of its earlier meetings members and experts presented papers, or spoke, on their theories or findings. The Committee organised field surveys, notably the Common Starling counts in Birmingham City Centre and single species surveys, such as rookery counts. Much time was spent organising fieldwork for both the Club's *Breeding Atlas* and, together with the BTO representatives, the national atlases. Other long-serving chairmen included Professor W.B. Yapp, Talbot Clay, Graham Harrison and Jim Winsper. From 1960-78, Arthur Cundall assiduously minuted meetings, providing a definitive history in his own inimitable and humorous style over the eighteen years that he wielded his secretarial pen.

A major landmark in the Club's history was the publication of *The Atlas of Breeding Birds of the West Midlands* (Lord and Munns 1970). This mapped the distribution of breeding birds using pioneering survey techniques based on the Ordnance Survey 10-km square system—a method later adopted worldwide for similar surveys. An earlier ground-breaking survey deserving mention was that compiled and produced for private circulation by Tony Norris in 1951. This showed, in tabular form, the breeding distribution and status of 100 bird species in the region, with distribution maps for fourteen of them printed in six colours!

Over the years, several Research Committee members have gone on to make names for themselves within the ornithological world, such as George Evans, one-time warden on Bardsey and later at Gibraltar Point; Harry Green, Vice President of the Worcestershire Wildlife Trust; Joe Hardman of the Arden Ringing Group; Rob Hume, currently editor of the RSPB *Birds* magazine; John Nelder, whose statistical evidence revealed the scandal of the 'Hastings Rarities'; and M.J. Rogers, Secretary of the British Birds Rarities Committee.

In 1971 the Club staged an Open Day at the Carr's Lane Church Centre, Birmingham, in conjunction with the RSPB, when over 1,000 people attended. This was the forerunner of other day events held during 1970s and 1980s, pre-dating today's 'Bird Fairs' by two decades! We could not have run these events without our team of willing volunteers, so ably led by Daphne Dunstan, who for very many years was a great ambassador for both the WMBC and the RSPB. Other landmarks in the Club's history must include its 50th Anniversary Reception in 1979, held in the Banqueting Suite of the Council House, Birmingham; the publication of *The Birds of the West Midlands* in 1982; the introduction of a telephone 'hot-line' in 1986, manned and up-dated by Eric Clare (and still going strong today!); and the enrolment of the 2,000th member in 1990. Moving with the times, the WMBC now has its own, highly regarded website, www.westmidlandbirdclub.com, which is managed by Andy Mabbett and includes over 700 pages about the Club and its activities.

Over the 75 years of its existence The West Midland Bird Club has established itself as one of Britain's most innovative and leading provincial bird clubs. Throughout this time many members have given freely of their time and expertise in helping to run the WMBC. Regrettably space does not allow them all to be mentioned and I apologise to anyone who feels they have been overlooked. It is hoped this imbalance can be redressed with a fuller history to be published at some later date.

We must record here Alan Richards' own immense contribution to the WMBC. He has been a member for around 55 years and a serving officer for over 40 continuous years. After twenty-one years as Secretary he then became Chairman for another sixteen years. He was made a Vice President in 1999, but has continued to serve as Press Officer and later established the Coventry and Warwickshire Branch, of which he is Chairman. He has worked tirelessly for the Club and introduced very many new initiatives and we are all greatly indebted to him.

Graham and Janet Harrison

Birds, Climate and Weather

by

Jim Winsper

Chairman, West Midland Bird Club

In order to understand the region's birdlife, it is necessary to understand those factors that affect the environment in which they live. None are more important than climate and weather, since between them these have a profound influence on life on earth, none more so than on the vegetation and hence the habitats that are available. They are also global and beyond man's ability to control, though not his ability to influence. It is important to distinguish between the two.

Weather is the fluctuating state of the atmosphere around us. As we know only too well, it can change dramatically, from warm, dry and calm to cold, wet and windy in a short period of time. These changes are largely the result of moving air masses and changes in pressure and they affect our birds in many ways. A cold, wet spring often results in a poor breeding season, while a wet winter with resulting flooding can be a bonanza for wildfowl. On the other hand a long, dry summer might be beneficial to some birds, but not others, while a prolonged cold spell in winter can be devastating. Birds on the move can also be blown off course by strong winds, forced to land by heavy rain and disorientated in fog. Climate describes the prevailing weather and is normally defined by averages and extremes of temperature, rainfall, wind, sunshine and humidity. These are governed by global movements of air masses and pressure systems, the penetration of the atmosphere by heat and light and the chemical reactions that release gases such as carbon dioxide, methane and ozone. Climate also incorporates the influences that our oceans, land masses, ice sheets and sea ice impart upon the atmosphere. Long term changes in weather patterns that eventually affect the seasons are changes that are potentially the most damaging, or beneficial, of all.

Britain experiences a cool temperate climate, ameliorated by the strong maritime influence of the Gulf Stream, or North Atlantic Drift—a current of warm water that emanates in the Caribbean, passes up the eastern coast of North America and is then swept across the Atlantic by the prevailing westerly winds. Without the Gulf Stream, our winters would be much colder than they are. As it is, our climate is cool to mild, with frequent cloud and rain interspersed with occasional settled spells. The weather, however, is notoriously variable, changing from day to day (Pearce and Smith 1998). Here in the West Midlands our land-locked situation means we derive less benefit than coastal areas from the surrounding seas. So in summer our days may get uncomfortably hot and humid, whilst in winter our nights can be very cold.

Mean temperatures at Birmingham over the past thirty years have ranged from 3°C in January to 16°C in July, whilst the annual rainfall was about 660 mm. The main features are that, on average, winter temperatures remain above freezing, even at night, while summers are generally cool. Rainfall is spread throughout the year, though spring tends to be the driest season and autumn the wettest. Rain also falls on virtually every other day in each month. Across the region as a whole, altitude has the greatest influence on climate, with the temperatures on the higher ground of north Staffordshire being as much as 5°C lower than in the favoured Severn and Avon valleys, whilst rainfall, at around 1,300 mm, is twice as high. Despite these variations, at no place or season is our climate hostile enough to present long-term problems to our birds and up until now they have only had to contend with the short-term fluctuations inflicted by the vagaries of the weather.

However, things might be starting to change. In the twenty-three year period covered by this book, the world has experienced the commencement of a climatic change that has surpassed any other of its kind in modern history. This phase, known generally as 'Global Warming' is attributed, in the main, to man's interference with the natural balance of the earth's atmosphere by producing abnormally high quantities of ozone depleting gases, namely Chlorofluorocarbons (CFCs). Likewise, Carbon Dioxide (CO_2) emissions, heightened by the combustion of fossil fuels, vehicle emissions and deforestation of many of the world's great rain forests, are causing great concern because they further this climatic imbalance. The impact of this phenomenon upon wild birds has come to be recognised in both phenological and ornithological studies. In respect to the birds of our region, then those species that would normally suffer in prolonged hard weather spells of sub-zero temperatures have clearly benefited from an almost total lack of such a weather feature. As an example, the abundance of Grey Herons, Wrens, Goldcrests and Long-tailed Tits is naturally controlled by long spells of severely cold weather, but all four species are now showing a marked increase in their numbers and distribution. Such gains without doubt result from years of favourable weather conditions that have contributed to the overall survival rate and consequent breeding success.

Up until 1993, both Blackcap and Common Chiffchaff were described as summer visitors and scarce winter visitors in WMBC *Annual Reports*. Clearly, for several years prior to 1993 there had been overwhelming evidence that both species were wintering in our region in ever increasing numbers. Irrespective of whether these birds were over-wintering, winter visitors or more likely a mixture of both categories, the common factor was that both species now found many regions within the United Kingdom (UK) perfectly suited to sustain their needs throughout our winters. This period of time, from the mid-1980s to the early 1990s, drew us to make a direct comparison between our findings and the meteorological and scientific evidence that we were witnessing a definite rise in mean global temperatures and entering a phase of warming (see accompanying chart).

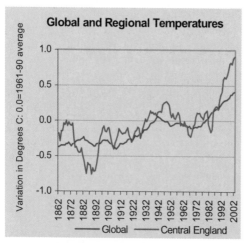

Annual difference in average surface temperature compared to 1961-1990 average (0.0 on chart). Compiled with data from the Meteorological Office and reproduced by kind permission of the Hadley Centre for Climate Prediction and Research.

In the main, the 23 years 1979-2001 were uneventful weather wise, in so much as no one particular feature prevailed over a lengthy period. Indeed, most cold spells were only short lived and had little bearing, or most importantly, lasting affect on bird populations. Until recently, the summer months, for that matter, had a tendency to be a little cooler and rather wetter than we might expect. In this entire period, only three of these years, 1979, 1981 and 1995, would qualify as weather event years.

While this rather mundane weather pattern seems harmless on the face of things, there is a more sinister side to the climatic changes that underlie it. Seasons have not only jelled into an uneventful pattern, but unseasonable features have occurred when least expected, with potentially disastrous effects on the region's birds.

At the onset of the period, 1978/9 began in dramatic fashion with a winter of almost comparable severity to those of 1947 and 1963. Intermittent thaws between heavy snow falls and sub-zero conditions was the pattern in January, while a building anticyclone was developing over Scandinavian countries, bringing Arctic conditions across the near Continent. This in turn brought blizzards to much of the UK and particularly to our region in mid-February. This Arctic weather dominated the scene through to May, with further snow at the beginning of this month. Benefits to birders came in the form of 13 Red-necked Grebes within the space of just a few days in February and a Dusky Thrush that preceded the arrival of a finch flock containing at least 1,000 Bramblings and 1,200 Linnets. For a fuller description of the weather patterns leading up to this influx see Moss (1995 pp 108-110). The real cost, however, came in the form of exceptional losses to those species mentioned previously which are most susceptible to such conditions.

Snow and severe cold weather were again the main feature early in 1981. These were followed by snow and glazed ice in late April, with disastrous effects upon a breeding population that had just begun to show signs of a recovery from the hard weather of 1979. Heavy snow and sub-zero temperatures dominated again in December, to be followed in January 1982 by more heavy snow and night-time temperatures down to –25° C. This second period of harsh weather followed a cool, wet summer and an autumn period that had given little respite from a spring that had offered such inhospitable breeding conditions for our resident and summering birds.

There then followed a period of 13 years when, in general, our climate saw real changes by lacking any distinction between the four seasons. By the late eighties it was obvious that reports of global climatic change were being substantiated by hard evidence. Even so, 1995 began in what had become typical fashion, mild and wet. There was little sign that this year would end the run of our somewhat prosaic annual weather conditions. After a traditional spring there followed a long hot summer, with temperatures equalling the highest on record. This period in turn gave way to an 'Indian Summer', with October temperatures exceeding any within the past 300 years. The year closed with December frosts and heavy snow, so in many ways 1995 had reverted to, and even surpassed, an annual weather pattern that was linked to the past.

Added to these three notable years, there were individual weather events that had varying degrees of impact on a number of bird species within the region. In 1987 hurricane force winds wreaked havoc amongst leaf-clad trees in the south-east of England. Likewise its peripheral winds had a similar impact upon trees in our region. Many migratory birds moving through the area on return passage met their doom on October 16th as the relentless blasts, some well in excess of 120 km/h (75 mph), spared little in their path. The resulting damage to trees and woodland would take effect the following year on arboreal nesting species, particularly where traditional nest sites had been wiped out. Despite this 'one off' event, 1987 proved to be a record year for birds, with 236 species being recorded. Further hints of climatic change were again apparent in 1988, when both winter periods were relatively mild, while the intermediate summer months were cooler and considerably wetter than might be expected. Such weather patterns were coming to be regarded as typical. The young of many small passerine species, and those also of ground nesting birds, suffered during the protracted cool, wet spring and summer periods. However, the milder less severe winter periods saw a greater survival rate of those species that would normally suffer at this time of year. So a balance of sorts had become evident, with breeding failure being compensated by winter survival.

On Maundy Thursday in 1998 the worst flooding for 100 years resulted from a stationary, and particularly deep, depression located over the south Midlands. An incessant deluge, with 75 mm (3 inches) of rain recorded, saw large areas of land under water as the Rivers Avon and Severn, together with many tributaries, shed water across much of south Warwickshire and Worcestershire, devastating the breeding attempts of many riparian nesting species. The intensity of this deluge was such that many areas away from our river systems also succumbed to heavy flooding. Extreme weather events such as these have been notable and are thought likely to be indicative of a changing climate. Many such events that have occurred during the two plus decades covered by this book have broken long-standing records.

As weather conditions exert such a dominant force upon wild birds, then with the changes witnessed over the past two decades, it is quite reasonable to expect some changes in the avifauna of our region. It is, of course, quite natural to encounter occurrences of species that are purely the result of weather happenings that have absolutely nothing to do with possible climate change. The vagaries of the planet's weather will always dictate such events, whether they arise locally or from much further a field. Added to such occurrences are those birds, mostly migratory, that overshoot or become disorientated from their desired route or destination. A good example of overshoooting occurred on May 2nd 1990, when an anticyclone over south-west Britain caused a massive overshoot of Black Terns that brought over 1,100 to the region. Vagrancy is a common occurrence that may be attributed to weather conditions, or simply to a bird, or birds, particularly juvenile birds of the year, that have got it wrong. However, these accidental arrivals often form the nucleus of a variation to normal migratory routes or to the colonisation of new areas.

Wild birds are great opportunists, ready to exploit any niche that offers a habitat and climate suited to their existence and reproductive programme. What we are witnessing may well be neither accidental, nor the result of adverse or freak weather conditions, but a range expansion by certain species that are taking full advantage of their preferred habitat, together with a climatic change that has transformed the UK into an environmental region that is suitable to their existence. The diverse, patchwork habitat of the British Isles may well prove suitable to a variety of birds which now find that our winters are bearable. Conversely, we could lose certain species if our climate becomes unsuited to their needs. For example, some of the moorland species that are at the southern edge of their range in Britain might well retreat northwards. Indeed, many such species are already in decline and, whilst this is thought to be largely due to habitat change and disturbance from recreational activity, climate change might well be an added factor. Equally, if the shifts in climate affect the Gulf Stream, then 'global warming' could lead to 'local cooling', causing a gain in northerly species and a loss in southerly ones.

There are many uncertainties, but the mid-1980s again proved to be crucial in our unfolding knowledge of the immediate effects of a warming climate and the adaptation to this by certain bird species. A Little Egret at Coton in the Middle Tame Valley on May 20th 1965 was only the second Warwickshire record and the fourth for our region. In *BWM*, Harrison (1982) evaluated this bird as a rare vagrant to the region, with just seven records up to 1978, four of which were prior to 1836. There were no surprises in finding this rare bird at such a location as the vast wetland habitat of the Middle Tame Valley at a time when increasing numbers were occurring on Britain's south coast and speculation was rife as to its future British status. With growing UK records it was a little surprising that a gap of five years would occur before the species was again recorded in our region. The sighting of a bird at Brandon Marsh in 1991 saw the beginning of this species' foothold in the Midlands. Since then, and including the 1991 bird, Little Egrets have been recorded annually in our region up to the present year. The probability that no fewer than 38 birds were recorded in the region during 2001 is proof that colonisation of the UK by this extremely attractive bird is well underway.

Also of note is the first record for the region of Great White Egret in 1992, since when this species has been recorded in four of the ten years 1992-2001. This most cosmopolitan of herons certainly has the potential to follow in its close relative's tracks, though its European numbers are relatively low in comparison to those of Little Egret. However, we cannot escape the fact that it is also finding the UK a more hospitable place than ever before.

Certainly one of the most notable changes in a species, in both abundance and distribution, is that of Common Buzzard. Harrison (*op. cit.*) described this bird in *BWM* as mainly scarce, but the same cannot be said of it now. Common Buzzard records have increased dramatically throughout the whole region, particularly as a breeding species. Its range expansion can sensibly be attributed to continued breeding success and a natural dispersion of birds from over populated areas. This in turn may well be attributed to a continuation of suitable weather conditions that provide food items in abundance, while favourably warm winters see a high survival rate in young birds. While on the face of things Common Buzzard may seem to be an unlikely candidate to benefit from such conditions, certainly to the degree that we have experienced, we must take a closer look at the bird's feeding habits to make critical links with favourable winter weather conditions.

A vital proportion of the Common Buzzard's diet is made up of invertebrates, particularly earthworms. Juvenile birds in particular, which are less skilled in hunting down prey and are generally last in the pecking order over carrion, are particularly dependent upon the much easier pickings of invertebrates. This is especially true during their early lives, when they first become independent of their parents. It is, then, highly likely that the milder, wetter winters that have predominated in the UK over the last twenty years have seen this particular food source become far more accessible, leading to a higher survival rate amongst young Common Buzzards than we have previously experienced. Frost free ground is a major factor in the survival of many birds and the UK has now experienced milder weather conditions for a lengthy period of time. As a result, the soft, unfrozen soil and ice-free water have been paramount to the successful survival rate of many bird species, in particular young Common Buzzards.

The years of 1994 and 1996 both stand out as being ones that attracted a record number of species to the region. In 1994 there were 240 species recorded, but that record was short lived as 1996 saw our highest ever total of 242. While these years stand out bird wise, they were quite unremarkable weather wise. The quite mundane pattern of milder, wetter seasons, with no dominant or prolonged spells of weather, was the feature of both years. So why these years were so productive in terms of species may never be fully understood, but the factor of birdwatchers being in the right place at the right time may well have been the reason in both instances. However, one must look at what part the weather played during these years and it may well be that the overcast, wet periods of weather during the seasons of migration had some bearing on these figures. Included in the 240 species recorded in 1994 were two new birds to the region, Collared Pratincole and Red-throated Pipit; together with Night Heron, Cattle Egret, Purple Heron, American Wigeon, Buff-breasted Sandpiper, Long-tailed Skua, Sabine's and Bonaparte's Gulls, Whiskered Tern, Alpine Swift, Shore Lark, Richard's Pipit, Bluethroat, Savi's and Yellow-browed Warblers and Little Bunting. A hugely impressive list of birds, many of which, under suitable weather conditions of clear, cloudless night skies, might well have over-flown the region undetected. This, however, was not the case and the now typical conditions of overcast, wet weather during periods of migration and movement resulted in a hindrance to the birds' journeys and a crucial stop over, while those who watch and record them benefited in their delay. Much the same could be said about 1996. However, on this occasion no fewer than six firsts for the region were recorded, namely Baird's Sandpiper, Desert Wheatear, River, Melodious and Dusky Warblers and Pine Bunting. All these species had the potential to fly through our region and may well do so more frequently than we realise. All would be considered as extremely rare visitors to the region however, and many were grounded by what has become a common and frequent weather pattern during migratory periods, that of poor visibility brought about by heavy cloud cover and persistent rain.

The potential for good bird watching in poor weather conditions is highlighted by these two years, while the margin between good and average years in terms of species and numbers may well hinge on just such a spell of inclement weather at a critical time, coupled with the fortune of birds and birdwatchers coming together. By way of example, stationary weather fronts across the region halted the progress of at least 1,350 Arctic Terns on May 2nd 1983 and around 500 Kittiwakes on March 12th and 13th 1988.

Seldom a year passes without the effects of ocean storms adding to the diversity of the region's birdlife. Strictly maritime species, such as the auks, petrels, Manx Shearwater, Northern Gannet and, in particular, Kittiwake can all be forced inland as a result of gales. The auks—the least aerial of species—are often found grounded through exhaustion and discovered in bizarre circumstances, with recoveries from such locations as urban gardens not unknown. Kittiwakes, on the other hand, though masters of the air, can be driven inland and under such circumstances may be found at the larger bodies of water in reasonable numbers. Storms sometimes bring a minor influx of a particular species that happens to be passing when the storm strikes. This happened during September 8th-10th 1989, when 19 Great Skuas passed through the region during a spell of gale force winds.

Wild birds are quite used to coping with weather conditions of all forms. However, changes in climate are now taking on far more significance within their lives. The climatic regions of the world are associated, in ornithology, with the range of wild birds that have adapted to live there. Such regions form barriers that species which survive happily within them are unwilling to cross. Their very existence is thus dependent upon a climate that benefits their well being. As the world teeters on the threshold of potentially dramatic changes, there are initial, yet discernible indications that some bird species might be reacting to changes within their geographical range.

However, most wild birds are highly mobile and have few, if any, physical geographical barriers, so we cannot yet be sure that these reactions are directly linked to climatic change. The circumstantial evidence suggests they are, but they might simply be the consequence of their mobility, natural opportunism or misfortune. The twenty years or so that we, as a regional bird club, have had to examine and begin to understand such changes are a mere drop in the ocean in terms of the transformation and adaptation in the lives of birds and it may well be an equally considerable amount of time before we even begin to have definitive answers.

Here, in the middle of Great Britain our geographical location may have a little less significance than its geographical features, bird wise. However, in both instances there is a definite north-south divide that contributes to quite diverse weather features, with mean temperatures on the moorlands of north Staffordshire noticeably lower than those for the lower Severn and Avon valleys, where the effects of the Gulf Stream are most noticeable.

Likewise, Great Britain itself is subject to massive and frequent changes in its weather conditions, as many islands are. Influenced, weather wise, in the main by the Atlantic Ocean to the west, this can be transformed by weather effects from the massive Continent to the east, the near Arctic to the north and a Mediterranean impact from the south. Wild birds may converge on our island from all points of the compass and national and local weather patterns have a strong influence as to where these birds are found. If the warming of our planet does influence our climate and the *fauna* and *flora* of our region reacts to such changes, then the sequel to this book in around twenty years time might well record Little Egret as a Midland breeding species, or that the great divide from the near Continent formed by the English Channel and North Sea has been breached by more species which find our climate, and particularly our mild winters, more suited to their needs. Likewise, those birds that frequent our region during the summer months may relinquish the need to travel south in the autumn. But will those summer visitors that depend upon finding food available at the critical times when they reach this region be able to react in tune with evolving adaptations of their prey?

Birds, climate and weather and the convergence of all three embrace a new generation of study that will be governed by time, with perhaps, an involvement by mankind.

The Movement of Birds
to and from the West Midlands

by

A.E.Coleman BEM

Ringing Secretary of the West Midland Bird Club

The previous chapter showed how climate and weather affect our birdlife and here we explore further how our birds respond to that in their seasonal movements and migrations. The birdlife of the West Midlands is both varied and dynamic and every year many hundreds of thousands of migrants take up residence alongside our resident birds. Winter migrants arrive in late summer or early autumn seeking refuge from the harsh winters of their northern breeding latitudes. These include thrushes, finches and starlings from Scandinavia and ducks, geese and swans from the high Arctic regions. Summer migrants arrive the following spring, replacing the winter migrants as they return to their northern breeding grounds. They include the warblers, flycatchers and hirundines coming from Africa to exploit not only the great surge of insect life that accompanies our spring vegetation, but also the extended hours of daylight of our long summer days for feeding their young. Some birds reach us by chance, especially young gulls as they disperse widely from their natal sites, while others simply use the region for refuelling and, once they have accumulated sufficient fat to sustain them for the remainder of their migratory journey, they move on to their wintering or breeding grounds. Our resident birds are with us throughout the year, but during the winter months even they will often make local movements in response to severe weather.

One way of finding out more about these movements is by ringing birds. This has taken place in the West Midlands for many years and has enabled us to document precisely the movements of our birds through the seasons. In addition it has also provided a great deal of data relating to their longevity, site fidelity, condition and breeding behaviour. The earliest known recovery of a bird ringed in the West Midlands relates to an Eurasian Teal ringed in 1910 and recovered the following year in Kopparberg, Sweden. Since then large numbers of birds of many species have been ringed in the region and over the years a considerable data bank of information has accrued.

Rings are made from a light metal alloy and vary in size according to the size of the bird when it is fully grown. Each one is engraved with a unique number, rather like a car registration plate, to enable individual birds to be identified. In the case of many species, especially small passerines, these numbers are difficult to read in the field, so positive identifications of individual birds can only be made if the bird is re-caught or found dead—often as a result of collisions with obstacles, or being killed by predators or, in the case of water birds, found oiled or entangled in discarded material. However, with the help of modern high-tech optics, some people are now able to read the ring numbers of finches and tits visiting garden feeders and also waders and gulls as they stand on concrete embankments and ramps. The use of lightweight, coloured, plastic Darvic rings, each engraved with an individual alfanumeric code, has also enabled positive identifications of individual birds of some species to be made in the field without having to re-catch them.

Canada Geese, Greylag Geese and Mute Swans have been studied intensively within the region for many years and the introduction of the Darvic ring has enabled individual birds to be monitored throughout their lives. Small numbers of geese are caught individually throughout the year, but most fully-grown birds are caught in late June during their moult period, when, like other waterfowl, they shed their flight feathers simultaneously and become flightless for a few weeks until they grow new primaries. Large creches of goslings in the process of growing their flight feathers are often included in such catches. Fully-grown Mute Swans moult later, during July and August, on their moulting sites and during this period large herds of these flightless birds can be gently herded into pens for ringing (Coleman *et al.* 1998). Moulting herds can be spectacular sights, often with between 150-300 individuals moving to destinations such as Belvide and Blithfield Reservoirs, Chasewater, Westport Lake and the river at Burton-on-Trent in Staffordshire; Alvecote Pools, Kingsbury Water Park and Strat-ford-on-Avon in Warwickshire; and at Worcester. Late July and August is the time when fam-ily parties of Mute Swans are located for cygnet ringing. Recording ring numbers has shown that both swans and geese tend to follow river valley systems. Swans in particular prefer to avoid ground above 150m (500 ft.) and move through gaps between areas of high ground into adjacent valleys. The Trent, Avon and Severn valley systems are the main flyways within the region. Birds using these corridors have been recorded in Shropshire, Wales and the northern counties of Cheshire, Lancashire, Derbyshire, Nottinghamshire and Yorkshire, while those travelling south along the River Severn have been sighted in Gloucestershire and Somerset. Highest mortalities in Mute Swans are recorded during the first two years of life, with the chief known cause of death being collisions with obstacles—especially overhead wires. In contrast, a high percentage of geese are shot, with the highest mortalities again occurring in young birds. Studies of Canada Geese have to date been confined to analysing movement and mortality data (Clifton *et al.* 2001), but the breeding biology in Mute Swans has also been studied in detail. Locating pairs of swans each year and reading Darvic rings has shown that although some birds remain paired to the same mate for life, others will divorce, with one or both birds taking a new partner during the current or following season. New mates may also be taken if a member of a pair is killed. Longevity records have been surprising, with male and female Mute Swans recorded breeding at 18 years of age, whilst the oldest recorded Canada Goose was 24 years of age.

Gulls figure very prominently in the West Midland avifauna. In addition to using landfill sites as a plentiful and consistent source of food and reservoirs as safe roosting sites at night, they also exploit ledges on city buildings and gravel pit complexes as breeding sites. Black-headed Gull nestlings, or pulli, are regularly ringed at nesting colonies on the great chain of gravel pits in the Trent and Tame valleys, while adults, together with adult Lesser Black-backed Gulls and Herring Gulls, are netted and ringed on landfill sites in Staffordshire, War-wickshire and Worcestershire. Recoveries of ringed birds provide a wealth of data on their origins and destinations. Juvenile gulls tend to disperse from their natal sites quite early in their lives and many Black-headed Gulls and Lesser Black-backed Gulls ringed as nestlings in the Netherlands, Poland, Finland and Russia appear in the region the following November/ December and January/February. Our only record for a Common Gull is a bird ringed as a nestling in Norway in July 1984 and recovered at Draycote Water in March 1985—it had trav-elled a distance of 1,082 km. Black-headed Gulls ringed as pulli in the region show a similar pattern, with birds moving to Scandinavia, western Europe, northern and southern England and Wales during their first autumn and winter. Large numbers of adult and nestling gulls are also colour-ringed, both in this country and on the Continent, and many observers record their movements through the region. In some cases the rings are plain coloured and indicate only the colony from which the birds have dispersed, but others carry a unique alphanumeric code that enable the birds to be recognised as individuals. Such observations, together with recover-ies, again show the cosmopolitan nature of the gulls we find in the West Midlands, many of them moving to and from western Europe, Scandinavia and northern Africa, in some cases flying thousands of miles from their ringing site.

Except for the occasional adult rescued from entanglement in fishing line, Grey Herons are ringed as nestlings. They are early nesters and the young birds are ringed mostly during April. Heronries tend to be in tall trees and most are inaccessible to ringers, but there are a few he-ronries within the region that are easily accessible and enable chicks to be ringed. The heronry at Gailey Reservoir has been ringed since the early 1960s and, because all the birds ringed are pulli, recoveries provide immensely valuable information on the routes taken when birds first disperse, together with data on their longevity and causes of death. Analysis of such data from the Gailey heronry shows an apparent correlation between the average number of young produced per nest and the colony density—the higher the density the lower the brood size (Minton 1970 & Coleman and Coleman 1994). Grey Herons can be long lived, with ages of 12 and 13 years being recorded. There is, however, a high winter mortality in first year birds, probably due to a lack of feeding skills coupled with progressively shorter day length in which to feed during their first winter. The pattern of movements suggest that Grey Herons travel along river valleys. The more random distribution of fledged birds from the Gailey heronry may be the result of easier access to several river systems via the Trent and Severn valleys, both of which are within easy reach of the heronry, whereas Worcestershire birds from the Grimley heronry mainly use the Severn valley system. Recoveries from all heronries ringed within the area show large numbers of birds moving to Wales and there appears to be a definite link between the Severn Valley and the distribution of birds in Wales, where they penetrate deeply into the Welsh rivers adjacent to the Severn flyway. Several long distance movements have been recorded, with birds ringed as pulli in Scandinavia and the Low Countries sighted in the region, while nestlings from the West Midlands have been recorded in France and Iberia.

Great Cormorants are also mostly ringed as nestlings and, although none has been ringed in the region to date, there have been sightings of colour-ringed birds from some of the large inland and coastal breeding colonies. Many of these coloured Darvic rings are engraved with alphanumeric characters and can be read in the field with binoculars enabling positive identifications to be made. They show birds from Anglesey, Dyfed, the Orkneys and the Farne Islands appearing in Staffordshire, while nestlings ringed at the inland breeding colonies of Abberton in Essex and Rutland Water in Leicestershire have been sighted at Brandon Marsh.

Another coastal bird that now breeds regularly in the region is the Common Tern. Many pairs take up residence on former gravel pit complexes and at some sites large artificial rafts are provided in an attempt to encourage nesting. Warwickshire has one of the largest inland breeding colonies of Common Terns in the country and each year the nestlings are colour-ringed in order that their movements can be traced. Sightings already indicate a clear link between dispersing juveniles and the Lancashire coastline. Terns are reputed to travel huge distances and nestlings ringed at Branston and at Kingsbury Water Park have been recorded in Ghana and Senegal, distances of 5,235 and 4,476 km respectively from their natal sites—truly remarkable journeys.

Very few species of duck have been ringed in any numbers within the region, with the exception of Eurasian Wigeon, which are regularly caught at two major sites, namely Blithfield Reservoir and Bredon's Hardwick. A large number of these have been recovered after being shot as they made their way to and from their breeding grounds in Arctic Russia—many of the movements recorded being in excess of 4,000 km. Although the ringing of other species has not been prolific, the limited number of recoveries from eastern and southern Europe and Scandinavia of Midland ringed Mallard, Eurasian Teal, Common Pochard and Shoveler indicates that there is a great deal still to be explored.

Winter migrants also include finches, thrushes and starlings from eastern Europe, Scandinavia and Russia. They are most easily caught when they congregate at roosts to spend the night together. Wing measurements and weights taken from birds carrying foreign rings show a tendency for migrant birds to be larger than resident ones of the same species and it is often possible to separate them using this criterion. Measurements taken from birds ringed here and later controlled during migration, or on their continental breeding grounds, also confirm this to be true.

Ringing Redwings and Fieldfares at West Midland roosts not only shows movements back to Scandinavia and Russia the following spring, but also indicates that many of them winter elsewhere in subsequent seasons (Minton 1969)—as evidenced by one Redwing that wintered in Warwickshire in 1974 and was caught again the following winter in Iran. Some Redwings were shown to use the West Midlands only as a refuelling site before moving on to winter in Wales and Ireland, whereas others moved further south to winter in Iberia. Recently large numbers of Fieldfares have been ringed in a Worcestershire orchard and future recoveries will undoubtedly improve our understanding of these wintering thrushes (Brown and Skeates 2001).

Unlike Redwings, the Common Starlings that come from a wide area of the Continent to winter in the region tend to remain faithful to their wintering sites, with few birds changing areas from one year to the next. Common Starlings ringed here as nestlings have been shown to be mainly resident (Thomas and Minton 1976). Large numbers of Blackbirds wintering in the West Midlands come from Scandinavia and the Low Countries and tend to stay for the winter, but ringing has shown that many of the Song Thrushes, which also come to us from the Low Countries, pass through the region to winter elsewhere (Minton 1969).

In the case of Common Chaffinches, although the birds ringed here as nestlings remain resident throughout the year, large numbers of our wintering birds originate chiefly from southern Scandinavia. Ringing recoveries indicate a migration route through Denmark, north Germany, the Netherlands and Belgium before crossing into Britain (Coleman 1987). Wintering Common Chaffinches are partial migrants, the birds representing only the migratory segment of the Scandinavian population. Ringing has also established a general northerly movement of Lesser Redpolls and Siskins through the West Midlands during the early spring, with birds returning to southern regions in late summer and early autumn and some over-wintering on the Continent. Also in late summer and early autumn hirundines begin to congregate in large numbers prior to their return journey to southerly wintering grounds in Africa. These pre-migratory congregations can be several hundred strong and ringing has documented the remarkable journeys undertaken by these birds. Roosts of Barn Swallows occur in all counties within the region and ringing has shown that large numbers of birds make the south-easterly journey of 246 km to Icklesham in Sussex, where they join with thousands more birds from other parts of the country prior to moving across the English Channel onto the European mainland. Barn Swallow roosts have traditionally been over water in reedbeds, but recently many hundreds of birds have taken to using maize as an alternative roosting site. Probably the most famous roost was at Bedworth Slough, where many thousands of Barn Swallows were ringed. Recoveries from this roost provided spectacular examples of movements, with birds recorded later in the same year in France, Morocco, Nigeria, the Congo, Uganda and right down into Cape Province in South Africa. Interestingly, many of the birds ringed at this roost as juveniles were recorded during the following breeding season in Norway, the Netherlands, Belgium and Italy. Sand Martins also congregate in pre-migratory roosts in reedbeds and ringing has also demonstrated the link between birds in this area and Icklesham. In addition to roost netting, many juvenile Sand Martins are also caught at their colonies. Again birds ringed in the West Midlands and recovered during the same year have shown movements through France and Spain into Africa, with some recoveries south of the Sahara. In the 1980s an analysis of Sand Martins ringed and recovered in the same year showed an influx from the north into West Midland roosts, with birds coming from as far afield as Ayr, Fife and Perthshire, while many more were from Cheshire, Lancashire and Cumbria.

Warblers are summer migrants enjoyed by all for the quality and variety of their song. Ringing them is challenging because they occupy a wide variety of habitats, including woodland, reedbeds, hedgerows and scrub vegetation. Our records show that fourteen species of warbler have been ringed within the region and recoveries from these birds have provided a wealth of information.

They have revealed many examples of site fidelity, with Reed Warblers, Willow Warblers and Sedge Warblers returning in the next or subsequent years to the reedbeds where they were originally ringed as juveniles. One male Marsh Warbler, ringed as a juvenile, returned to the same site for five consecutive seasons. Warblers are African in origin and there are many examples of long distance movements, with Blackcaps, Reed Warblers and Common Whitethroats travelling over two thousand kilometres into Morocco, Garden Warblers travelling over five thousand kilometres to Nigeria and a Reed Warbler travelling over four thousand kilometres to the Senegal. They are not large birds, the tiny Willow Warbler weighing only about nine grammes, and yet one such bird moved over five thousand kilometres to the Ivory Coast. Because they are small and make such incredible journeys most are not long lived. Our most remarkable longevity record involved a Reed Warbler ringed at Brandon Marsh in 1990 and recorded on the marsh again just six days short of achieving nine years of age. Originally ringed as a nestling in the East Marsh Ditch, it had returned to breed in the same ditch every year since 1993. When last re-trapped it had made sixteen trips to and from its wintering quarters in Africa, south of the Sahara, covering a total distance of at least forty-eight thousand miles. Reed Warblers appear to be remarkably long lived for a small migrant, with two birds at Brandon of eight years (one of which was an adult when ringed), six birds of seven years and six birds of six years of age being recorded. Recoveries for many species of warbler also show how they too move in a south-easterly direction to Icklesham prior to moving onto the mainland of Europe. In recent years Blackcaps have been observed, and some have been caught, in the West Midlands during the winter months. Originally it was thought that these were over-wintering birds that had bred here during the summer, but they are now thought to be of northern European origin. An example is shown by an adult female ringed in Hertfordshire in November 1999 and killed by traffic in Warwickshire in January 2004. In all probability this bird regularly over-wintered in this country.

Common Swifts are undoubtedly the most aerial of all our summer migrants and are normally caught as they fly low over gravel pit sandbanks, when low cloud forces the insect plumes on which they feed to appear at lower altitudes. Ringing recoveries show many of them to be long lived, several being recovered alive and well eleven, twelve and thirteen years after ringing. Interestingly 78% of all recoveries in the region are of birds originally ringed here.

A large number of woodland birds are hole nesting, so nest-box schemes, in addition to providing extra nesting sites in woodlands for both resident and summer migrants, also enable large numbers of nestlings to be ringed each year. Several schemes operate within the West Midlands and most target specific species, such as Pied Flycatcher and Common Redstart. However, each year many of these boxes are taken over by Blue Tits, Great Tits and Eurasian Nuthatches. Similarly, boxes provided for Barn Owls are often occupied by Stock Doves, Common Kestrels, or Little and Tawny Owls. Ringing nestlings provides valuable information because, if the birds are re-caught at a later date, they can be precisely aged. Such schemes are meticulously monitored every year and in addition to the ringing aspect, data on brood sizes enables comparisons of productivity between seasons to be made. Long standing nest-box schemes in the Wyre Forest and at Midsummer Hill and Coombes Valley have made a real contribution to the number and survival of the Pied Flycatcher in the region. Recoveries of birds ringed in Worcestershire have also provided excellent examples of natal site fidelity, with a number of birds returning to the coppice where they were ringed in the previous season. Although Common Redstarts are ringed in relatively low numbers, they have provided a number of examples of migratory movements, with pulli from nest-boxes in the Wyre Forest and Cheadle being recovered a few months later in the Basse Pyrenees in France and the Algarve in Portugal—clearly on route to their wintering quarters in Africa.

Ringing broods of Blue Tits and Great Tits, whose parents have 'hijacked' nest-boxes intended for Pied Flycatchers and Common Redstarts, shows that these species have low survival rates and tend to be very local in their movements—most birds being recovered within a few kilometres of their ringing site and surviving for only one or two years. The Eurasian Nuthatch is more robust than any of the tits and one would expect greater longevity records, but our recoveries from birds ringed in nest-boxes show little difference in results to those obtained for the tits.

Resident birds such as the Wren and Greenfinch are with us all the year round. However, recoveries for these birds show significant movements in response to local weather conditions. For example, some of the Wrens ringed in the region during the summer were recovered further south a few months later, during the winter, while two birds, respectively ringed 90 km and 75 km north of the West Midlands during the summer months, were recovered here during the following winter. The Greenfinch provides a further example, with many birds ringed in the region being recovered on the warmer West Coast during the winter months.

Very few corvids have been ringed in the West Midlands and, apart from recoveries of Rooks ringed as pulli in Warwickshire and Worcestershire rookeries, most are caught accidentally during normal mist netting sessions. Only two of the recoveries give indications of longevity—a 14 year old Eurasian Jay and an 11 year old Carrion Crow. All recoveries showed small movements.

Ringing therefore provides an important tool in attempting to unravel the mysteries of bird movements and behaviour. Our knowledge of avian biology is constantly being challenged and even the common birds continue to provide questions that need answering. One such example comes from the declining Reed Bunting. This is a species that used to form large winter roosts in our reedbeds and several hundred individual birds were known to have used one such roost, less than ten miles from the centre of Birmingham, during the winter, though at any one time there were always less than 150 birds. Little is known of where these birds came from or what was their future destination—so there is still much to be learnt.

The Changing Profile of the West Midlands

The West Midlands is a very diverse region. For some it will always be inseparable from Birmingham and the motor car, either as a centre of manufacture or through the sheer frustration of motorway traffic jams. For others it rekindles memories of belching chimneys in the Black Country or bottle kilns in the Potteries. Still more recall its wealth of historical and cultural associations and especially its connections with Shakespeare. Yet some of England's finest countryside can also be found amidst the dales and wild moors of north Staffordshire, the lush valleys of the Avon and Severn, or along the rugged ridge of the Malverns and the softer sweep of the Cotswolds. Within this countryside, and indeed the urban areas too, a surprising variety of birdlife awaits those who have the interest and patience to search and discover it. In today's rapidly changing world, this countryside and its birds are threatened as never before. Agricultural changes, new development, infrastructure improvements and leisure pursuits all continue to gnaw steadily away at our natural habitats, leaving them ever more isolated and fragmented. Meanwhile, climate change poses unknown implications for our wildlife.

Nature Conservation and Sustainable Development

Since 1980 our approach to nature conservation has fundamentally changed as we have come to appreciate the contribution that wildlife makes to our quality of life. The event that did most to change attitudes was the United Nations Conference on Environment and Development—the 'Earth Summit'—held at Rio de Janeiro in 1992. This saw governments, including our own, commit nations worldwide to the principle of 'sustainable development'—that is "development that meets the needs of the present without compromising the ability of future generations to meet their own needs." A major outcome of the Summit was the Biodiversity Convention—an agreement between countries about how to protect the diversity of species and habitats in the world. As part of its commitment, the British government followed this up by publishing its own proposals in *Biodiversity: The UK Action Plan* (DoE 1994b).

For the first time, conserving biodiversity became a prime objective of the Government, with birds standing alongside economic and social criteria as one of its headline indicators of sustainable development—the so-called 'happiness index'. (DETR 1998 and Noble and Robinson 2000). This raised the profile of nature conservation, introduced the concept of *red* and *amber alert lists* and greatly enhanced the importance of monitoring undertaken by members of the BTO, RSPB and WMBC. Moreover, for the first time ever, conserving biodiversity was to be regarded as important, not just on designated sites, but throughout the whole environment. The first national Biodiversity Action Plan (BAP) was published in 1995 (UK Biodiversity Steering Group 1995) and this has since been followed by a frenzy of activity as each county has produced its complementary Local Biodiversity Action Plan (LBAP).

The 'Earth Summit' also included a commitment to combat the effects of climate change, which many authorities believe poses the greatest threat to our wildlife. Already our resident birds are nesting earlier (Crick 1999). With regard to summer migrants, the WMBC has been recording the first arrival and last departure dates since 1934. Analysis of this data by P. Rollin (*pers. comm.*) has shown arrival dates getting earlier and departures dates later. This analysis covers sixteen species of summer visitors and, as the following charts show, their combined average arrival date advanced by nearly two weeks. Furthermore much of that advancement has occurred since 1990. As observers have always been keen to note the earliest dates, particularly for obvious species such as Common Cuckoo and Barn Swallow, this data is likely to indicate a real shift in timing. Also, the average departure date has receded, by over three weeks, but in this case the change mostly occurred before 1980 and could be partially due to increased observer coverage. Taken in combination, these changes suggest that our

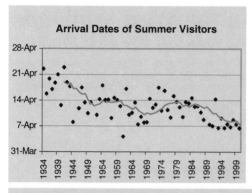

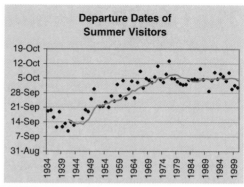

Note: Points denote the means of the first arrival and last departure dates for sixteen species of summer visitors. Trend lines show the eight-yearly running means.

summer visitors could be spending anything from two to five weeks more in the region.

Most conservation bodies agree that the present network of Sites of Special Scientific Interest (SSSIs) is too small and fragmented for our flora and fauna to withstand climate change, so they are seeking to create large areas for conservation. Three of the most important habitat creation schemes in this region involve extending the heathland on Cannock Chase, re-flooding Longdon Marsh in the Severn Valley and creating the National Forest. The potential impacts of climate change are complex, but we believe the issue is of crucial importance, which is why we have devoted a chapter specifically to Birds, Climate and Weather.

In theory, the statutory SSSI system also provides the legislative framework necessary to protect our most important habitats and species and the Government has charged English Nature with getting all SSSIs into a 'favourable', or good condition. In some cases, this designation has been further enhanced by declaring the South Pennine Moors as a Special Protection Area (SPA) under the European Birds Directive and areas such as Cannock Chase and the dales of north Staffordshire as candidates for inclusion as Special Areas for Conservation (SACs) under the European Habitats and Species Directive. Whilst this framework may be sound, its implementation sometimes fails to match expectations.

Meanwhile, on the ground, many of the region's best sites and habitats are more secure now than they were two to three decades ago. The RSPB has established its Sandwell Valley reserve, English Nature has declared Sutton Park a National Nature Reserve (NNR), the WMBC has secured a lease on its Ladywalk reserve, the Wildlife Trusts have acquired several important new reserves, local authorities have designated more Local Nature Reserves (LNRs) and a few private nature reserves, such as Marsh Lane, have been created.

In summary, the fragments of protected habitats and the birds living in them are generally more secure now than they were twenty-five years ago, but those living outside reserves, in what is termed the wider countryside, are much less secure—but public opinion is changing.

The Farmed Environment

The plight of our farmland birds has been headline news for some time now, with several species showing dramatic declines. Familiar birds such as Northern Lapwing, Sky Lark, Common Starling, Linnet and Bullfinch all showed national declines of more than a half during 1974-99, but the biggest declines were suffered by farmland specialists such as Turtle Dove (69%), Grey Partridge (84%), Corn Bunting (89%) and Tree Sparrow (95%) (Gregory *et al.* 2002). Moreover, two-thirds of this region is farmed, so it is easily our most extensive habitat.

To understand why these changes have occurred we need to take a long-term perspective. Ever since our ancestors began to clear the wildwood, man has shaped the countryside and its habitats to meet his own needs. For centuries this process was slow, allowing our wildlife plenty of time to adapt and our farmland bird communities contain many species of woodland origin, such as the Blackbird and Robin. The enclosures and major drainage schemes of the eighteenth and nineteenth centuries brought widespread changes. In this region particularly, they introduced hedgerows, which became a surrogate habitat for woodland birds. At the same time a new way of farming evolved. This was 'high' farming, or a four-year rotation of root crops, oats or barley, grass ley and wheat. The root crops provided winter feed for the live-stock on the farm, which in turn manured the ground for the benefit of next seasons crops. This sustainable system of farming prevailed until the 1940s, providing food in stubbles and stack yards that tided huge numbers of birds over the winter (Shrubb 2003).

With the burgeoning population of the Industrial Revolution to feed, more land was brought into cultivation and this increased until the 1870s. Then, unable to compete with cheap imports from abroad, British agriculture entered a depression that, apart from brief res-pites during the two world wars, lasted until the 1950s. Marginal land reverted to permanent pastures or rough grazing, buildings became decrepit, hedges were overgrown, ditches blocked and stocking levels low. This was inefficient farming, with three-quarters of the region's land permanently under grass. But the naturally fertilised hay meadows, washlands and old pas-tures were valuable breeding sites for waders and Sky Larks, feeding areas for Northern Lap-wings and winter thrushes and hunting grounds for Common Kestrels and Barn Owls.

The post-war era changed all that. Mechanisation enabled previously unworkable, flower-rich grasslands to be ploughed, wetlands to be drained and hedges removed. The agrochemical industries waged war with fertilisers, herbicides and insecticides. These infiltrated food chains and the former led to nutrient enrichment in many streams and rivers. New disease-free crop strains were developed, nature's clock was advanced by winter sowing and the first trials of genetically modified (GM) crops took place. In short, farming was working against nature rather than with it and the consequence was a series of crises ranging from salmonella in eggs to BSE in cattle and the devastating outbreak of Foot and Mouth Disease in 2001.

The first problem faced by our birds was the build-up of pesticides through the food chain, which culminated in sterility amongst top predators such as the Eurasian Sparrowhawk. Thankfully, this has now been overcome. But they now face an even more serious problem—a critical shortage of food. Shrubb (2003) identified four crucial developments since the 1970s that were disadvantageous to birds. These were the revolution in grassland management; the development of herbicides, particularly pre-emergent treatments; changes in harvesting meth-ods; and the loss of undersown leys.

All these have had a significant impact on the region's farmland as a habitat for birds. Whilst the proportion of land that is farmed has remained fairly constant for the last thirty years at around two-thirds, the percentage that is either permanent or temporary grassland has fallen from 62% to 49%. Moreover, almost all has been agriculturally 'improved' by chemical dressings, re-seeding and drainage to support higher stocking rates. As a result invertebrate populations have plummeted and, with no food, birds such as the Sky Lark and Common Star-ling have dramatically declined. In addition, earlier and more frequent cutting for silage has seriously reduced the breeding success of ground-nesting birds. For waders, this has been fur-ther exacerbated by drainage, which has led to serious declines in Northern Lapwings, Com-mon Snipe and Eurasian Curlew even on the moors of north Staffordshire. With very few ex-ceptions, Common Snipe no longer nest in river valleys and Yellow Wagtails and Reed Bun-tings have become much scarcer. Today the distribution of grassland largely reflects altitude, with 51% of Staffordshire still permanent grassland or rough grazing, compared to 38% in Worcestershire and 29% in Warwickshire. Wet grassland and marshy ground are now con-fined to a few fragments in the Avon, Churnet, Severn and Sow valleys and to a few urban sites. However, with the threat of increased flooding from climate change, steps are being taken to restore some flood plains to their traditional role, most notably by the Worcestershire Wildlife Trust (WoWT) at Longdon Marsh. Such initiatives will help to redress the loss of wet

Percentage Breakdown of Agricultural Land by Use 1973 and 2003

	1973	2003				
		Region	*Staffs*	*Warks*	*Worcs*	*W Mid*
Percentage of Land Area	c 67.0	65.4	70.2	76.1	71.0	16.0
Arable	53.4	53.9	43.1	66.1	56.6	49.0
Crops and Fallow		39.2	28.3	51.0	42.0	36.6
Wheat	10.7	14.2	11.9	28.1	19.4	12.4
Barley	16.6	6.2	6.6	6.5	5.4	6.4
Oats	2.3	1.2	0.9	1.5	1.4	0.8
Temporary Grass	15.3	9.0	11.1	6.5	9.0	8.5
Set aside	-	5.7	3.7	8.6	5.6	3.9
Permanent grass	46.6	39.8	50.5	28.7	37.4	36.1
Other	8.5	6.3	6.4	5.2	6.0	14.9

Notes: Only selected crops are shown, so arable percentages do not total 100.
Permanent grass also includes rough grazing.

Data Sources: 1973 *BWM*: 2003 DEFRA www.defra.gov.uk

grassland and hopefully benefit wintering waterfowl and bring back breeding waders.

The lower lying counties have become the region's arable strongholds, with 66% of the farmland in Warwickshire and 57% of that in Worcestershire under cultivation or in set-aside, compared to 47% in Staffordshire. Many of the most damaging changes on arable land have stemmed from the use of pre-emergent herbicides, applied before the crop appears. These have virtually eradicated arable weeds by preventing flowering and seeding. As a result there are very few seeds left to provide winter feed for sparrows, finches and buntings. This has also broken food chains. For example, the herbicides killed off the knotgrass that was the sole food plant of a small leaf-beetle whose larva formed an important part of the diet of Grey Partridge chicks (Marren 2002). In addition their use has facilitated autumn sowing, which has increased threefold since the 1960s. The consequential reduction in spring cultivation has meant less food for birds at a critical time of year, and this has affected Linnets in particular (O'Connor and Shrubb 1986). It has also deprived Northern Lapwings of their nest sites, so they have vanished from many areas, and further diminished winter stubbles, again to the detriment of seed-eaters. The move to monocultures spelt the end of under-sowing cereals with grass or clover and that, too, has led to a loss of stubbles to the detriment of species such as Grey Partridge. Moreover, grubbing up hedges and trees to make large enough fields for sprayers and combine harvesters to manoeuvre has also removed food, cover and nest sites for a whole range of birds, notably Tree Sparrows, Linnets and Yellowhammers, whilst combines and drying barns have resulted in more efficient harvesting and storage of grain.

The pattern of farming varies noticeably across the region. Cattle and sheep are generally widespread from the lowlands to the uplands, but other types tend to be more localised. Warwickshire, for example, is the main arable centre, with two-thirds of the land under cultivation, mainly in the Dunsmore and Feldon districts, along the Cotswold Fringe and in parts of Tame Valley and Arden. Most dairy farming, on the other hand, is in Staffordshire and especially in the Meres and Mosses, Potteries and Churnet and Needwood districts. Elsewhere in this county, pigs and poultry are important in the Tamworth district, whilst the lighter soils around Lichfield are widely cultivated for a variety of crops. In Worcestershire, horticulture and fruit growing are dominant in the Vale of Evesham and in parts of the Severn and Teme valleys.

There is much less farming in the heavily urbanised West Midlands county, but arable and pasture are more balanced here with neither dominant. The mixed farm holdings that provide an all the year round habitat for birds are confined to a very few, well isolated pockets (Countryside Agency 2000). However, the mosaic of cereal fields and sheep and cattle pastures found in south-east Warwickshire still seems to support good populations of several declining farmland species, notably Turtle Doves, Yellow Wagtails and Tree Sparrows.

Undoubtedly a mixed farming habitat would suit our birds better than the specialist monocultures of today. The Northern Lapwing seems to epitomise the problem, with everything— drainage, over-grazing, cutting for silage and autumn sowing—combining against it, even on the moorlands of north Staffordshire. By the end of the 1980s the prospects for most of our farmland birds were looking very grim indeed.

The irony was that Government subsidies funded these changes, which were designed to increase productivity and make farming more profitable, but paid little heed to the environmental consequences and the effect on wildlife. However, as Oliver Rackham (1986) said, the end result was somewhat different, as "we contrived at the same time to subsidise agriculture *and* to have expensive food *and* to ravage the countryside." The consequence was massive over-production across the European Community, with butter mountains, wine lakes and grain surpluses. The first signs of change came in the mid-1980s, when the European Commission (EC) responded by introducing milk quotas. Had stocking rates been reduced as a result, then wildlife might have benefited, but the reality was worse as many dairy farmers switched to growing cereals instead. In the process, more wet pastures were drained and permanent grassland ploughed, again to the detriment of breeding waders and birds such as Yellow Wagtail and Reed Bunting. The mid 1980s also saw the introduction of Environmentally Sensitive Areas (ESAs)—a scheme which pays farmers to manage their land in ways which will benefit wildlife—but the only ESA within this region is in north Staffordshire and that came too late to prevent the earlier damage inflicted to the moors by improved drainage and overstocking.

Then, in 1989, 'set-aside' was introduced and farmers were compensated for taking land out of production each year, either on a rotational or long-term basis. Although not intended as an environmental measure, wildlife did benefit from new woods, hedges and headlands. Most farmers, however, opted for 'rotational set-aside', which gave insufficient time for plant communities and seed banks to develop. Some ground nesting birds, notably Sky Larks, did benefit by moving into this new habitat, though sadly some found their nests sprayed or ploughed as the grant was conditional on keeping down arable weeds (Marren 2002).

The most popular scheme was Countryside Stewardship, introduced in 1990 to combine wildlife and amenity interests with farming through a trade-off between incentives and concessions. Linked to habitats rather than areas, this scheme has brought benefits, though its popularity has led to its being over-subscribed. From 2005, it and the ESAs are to be replaced by a new scheme of Environmental Stewardship, details of which were not available at the time of writing. Other incentives included the Farm Woodlands and the Hedgerow Incentive Schemes, the latter providing grants for new hedges to replace those removed with earlier grants! Finally, in 1999 a new set of CAP reforms was agreed, offering some hope for a more integrated rural policy, though to what extent agriculture will outweigh other interests remains to be seen. Meanwhile organic farming is on the increase, but the future for hill farming and stock rearing remains bleak and many are leaving farming altogether, whilst others seek to diversify.

A thriving farming industry is vital to the wider countryside and its wildlife. Without it, the alternatives might be even more dire. Since the mid 1980s an increasing amount of agricultural support has been switched from production into environmental schemes and this seems set to continue. Much research is also being undertaken into practical ways of making farming economical, yet more environmentally friendly (Henderson 2004, Atkinson *et al.* 2004), so the outlook for our farmland birds seems brighter. But whether these changes will be in time to save the Turtle Dove, Grey Partridge, Corn Bunting and Tree Sparrow only time will tell.

The Urban Influence

Data on the extent of urbanisation is scarce, but new buildings and roads have continued to erode the region's landscape and probably now cover 15-20% of the land. The rate of encroachment into the countryside has slowed since the 1960s and 1970s, however, as growing traffic congestion and its contribution to greenhouse gases have shifted the emphasis to building on previously developed sites within our towns and cities. Fortuitously, the collapse of so much manufacturing industry created a plentiful supply of these 'brownfield', or 'post-industrial', sites, but this supply could dwindle in the future. In the past such sites were often left for nature to reclaim and many, such as Fens Pools, eventually became outstanding wild-life sites. It would be tragic if, by recycling them, we deny future generations the chance to enjoy the splendour of a rich and varied wildlife just to save open fields that modern agriculture has turned into wildlife deserts.

Meanwhile, the brownfield sites created through industrial restructuring in Birmingham created a wealth of opportunities for Black Redstarts, which reached their peak in the late 1980s. Newcomers to the city centre are Lesser Black-backed and Herring Gulls, which now nest on roof-tops, whilst Peregrine Falcons have joined Common Kestrels and Eurasian Sparrowhawks as urban predators. On the debit side, House Sparrows and Common Swifts have declined, possibly due to the loss of nest sites through redevelopment, and the great night-time roosts of Common Starlings have become a distant memory. However, Pied Wagtails still roost in city trees close to the warmth of street lights (A. Mabbett *pers. comm.*).

Gardens, too, are becoming more valuable to birds as the vogue for planting shrubs and trees provides more food and nest sites. Ornamental conifers have certainly aided the expansion of Collared Doves and Coal Tits and increasing numbers of people are now feeding birds with specially formulated foods rather than the conventional stale bread and peanuts. Nest-boxes also help and, despite the deprivations caused by cars, cats, grey squirrels, Magpies and windows, the region's gardens now support a substantial and growing population of birds.

The infrastructure needed to support our urbanised society is a mixed blessing for birds. Overhead wires, for example, kill many swans and geese, but the pylons supporting them provide Common Kestrels, Carrion Crows and Rooks with nest sites. Peregrine Falcons have even nested on cooling towers, but most of the coal-fired power stations are now near the end of their lives and may be replaced by smaller, gas-fired stations, such as that at Hams Hall. Similarly, gulls, Common Starlings and corvids are opportunists and they quickly learnt to exploit the feeding opportunities at rubbish tips, or landfill sites. With more stringent regulations and the Government's current drive to reduce the amount of waste going to landfill, however, this might prove to be a diminishing bonanza.

One of the biggest changes over the past twenty-five years has been the inexorable growth in road traffic. All attempts to restrict this have failed and, despite building new roads such as the M40 and M6 Toll motorways, congestion has worsened. Now it is planned to extend the M6 Toll to Manchester. Common Kestrels are one of the few birds to have benefited from motorways and the Department of Transport and the Forestry Commission have erected nest-boxes for them along the M40. Generally, new roads destroy precious habitats, whilst more traffic means more wildlife casualties, particular amongst Barn Owls, which are just beginning to recover in numbers. Even along country lanes, traffic noise and turbulence are making hedges less tenable for birds.

More threatening than roads are the proposed airport expansions. Although the idea of a major new airport between Coventry and Rugby has been dropped, the Government's White Paper on air transport proposes an expansion of Birmingham Airport, whilst both Coventry Airport and Halfpenny Green, near Wolverhampton, are independently seeking to expand their operations. Because of the danger of bird strikes, particularly with gulls and other large birds such as Canada Geese, the relevant authorities are scrutinising every change within the vicinity of airports.

Woodland, Parkland and Orchards

Over the period 1965-1997 woodland increased in extent by a third and now covers just over 6% of the region's land area. Around three-quarters of this increase has occurred since 1980. One very significant change revealed in the following table is in the type of woodland to be found in the region. Back in 1965 broad-leaved and coniferous woods occurred in roughly equal proportions, whilst the high percentage of other woodland comprised mainly scrub. Today almost two-thirds of the woodland is broad-leaved, but only a fifth coniferous. Even allowing for the fact that 'scrubby' vegetation (which is mostly broad-leaved) is no longer included as a separate category, but is now incorporated into one of the three main types, this represents a significant shift away from conifers towards broad-leaved trees.

	1965	1997				
		Region	*Staffs*	*Warks*	*Worcs*	*W Mid*
Percentage of land cover	4.6	6.2	7.8	4.7	7.0	3.1
Coniferous	32.5	19.0	26.2	10.1	16.8	4.4
Broad-leaved	33.2	63.4	59.2	66.7	63.6	82.7
Mixed	-	8.6	6.6	10.5	11.1	6.1
Other	34.3	9.0	8.0	12.7	8..5	6.8

Extent and Structure of Woodland in 1965 and 1997

Note: Figures for Worcestershire have been apportioned from the combined Hereford-Worcester data on the basis of total land area and percentage of woodland cover.
Sources: 1965 *BWM.* 1997 Forestry Commission , www.forestry.gov.uk

Despite this increased coverage, compared to the national coverage of 10% the proportion of the region that is wooded remains relatively modest. Furthermore, it is not evenly distributed, with Staffordshire having almost 8% coverage, but Warwickshire less than 5%. However, the region does contain a good proportion of England's broad-leaved woodland and this provides a home not only for birds, but also for a wide range of woodland flowers, fungi, insects and mammals. There is also a wide range, from the archetypal Midland pedunculate oakwoods of Warwickshire and Worcestershire to the sessile oakwoods of the Staffordshire uplands and west Worcestershire; and from the upland mixed ashwoods of the Dales to lowland beech and yew woods along the Malverns and Teme Valley. Birchwoods also occur on the thirsty sandstone soils, particularly in Staffordshire, while wet woods of alder and willow are common along many valleys. Some, such as parts of the Churnet Valley, Sutton Park, Ufton and Long Itchington Wood and, in particular, the Wyre Forest, are of national, if not international, importance (West Midlands Wildlife Trusts 2001).

Nationally, several woodland birds declined significantly during 1966-99 and Fuller (2004) listed seven possible causes for this, namely pressures on the winter grounds or on migration, climate change on the breeding grounds, reduction in invertebrates, impacts at the woodland edge, reduction in woodland management, intensified pressure from deer and competition or predation.

Within this region much depends on management. 'Coppice with standards' were once widespread, but except at a few Wildlife Trust reserves such as Hornhill Coppice, most have now been abandoned and allowed to develop into high forest. This excludes light and so diminishes the richness of the flora and invertebrate life. Browsing by a growing deer population has the same effect, with the consequence that there is less food for species such as Tree Pipit, Dunnock, Common Nightingale, Song Thrush, Marsh and Willow Tits, Bullfinch and warblers such as Garden and Willow Warblers. The removal of dead and decaying wood for safety and insurance reasons also reduces the food supply available to woodpeckers and Willow Tits.

Even the better managed woods cannot escape the threats from acid rain, climate change and browsing deer, all of which are preventing natural regeneration.

Many broad-leaved woods have also suffered partial felling and replanting with conifers. In their early years these often attracted Tree Pipits and Lesser Redpolls, but these have gone as the plantations have matured leaving little but Goldcrests, Coal Tits and perhaps Common Crossbills in irruption years. However, sympathetic management of the plantations on Cannock Chase by Forest Enterprise (FE) is benefiting European Nightjars, Wood Larks and Tree Pipits by providing a continuous supply of clear fell areas. Fortunately extensive plantations such as these permit felling in rotation, which enables a varied age structure to be maintained whilst still retaining areas large enough to provide territories for Northern Goshawks and Long-eared Owls. Smaller plantations seldom allow the economics of good forestry and the interests of nature conservation to be combined to such good effect.

The forest strategy component of sustainable development, combined with the need for agricultural diversification, has aroused new interest in tree planting among public bodies and private landowners (particularly as grants or tax incentives are often available). Environment and conservation form one of the four programmes in the Government's England Forest Strategy and the Forestry Commission's (FC's) Woodland Grant Scheme supports the implementation of this. In some areas agricultural land is being planted to produce Christmas trees. In the short-term at least, these plantations are used by Song Thrushes, Willow Warblers and Common Whitethroats. Interest is also being shown in growing crops such as willow on a short-rotation (biomass) to provide a renewable source of energy. Suitably managed, such habitats could replace the old coppiced woods, providing a niche for scrub species such as Garden Warblers, Bullfinches and maybe even Common Nightingales.

If the region lacks its share of woodland, it is certainly well endowed with parklands. Some date back to medieval times and the enclosure of wood pastures, but most were fashioned during the eighteenth century by designers such as Lancelot 'Capability' Brown to give the large estates of the landed gentry a 'natural' setting. By far the most important features are the veteran trees that provide the decaying and fallen timber on which many fungi and insects, such as the stag and violet click beetles, depend. The holes and cavities in these old trees also harbour bats and a range of hole-nesting birds, from tits and Eurasian Nuthatches to Stock Doves, Tawny Owls and Western Jackdaws. Apart from the old trees, most parklands comprise grasslands grazed by sheep or deer, scrub, woods and open water and this combination of habitats further enhances their wildlife value.

Most parklands form part of large country estates, or belong to bodies such as the National Trust, and are managed along traditional lines and show few outward signs of change. As more are opened up to the public, however, so the landowners' responsibilities change, resulting in the removal of more decaying and dead timber, both on safety grounds and as part of a general desire to maintain a tidy appearance. Grazing and browsing also threaten the long-term future by inhibiting the natural regeneration of trees. The region's parklands, in particular Warwick Castle Park and Croome Court, are of considerable historical importance. Equally, there are excellent examples of wood pasture on Bredon Hill and at Brocton Coppice. On Cannock Chase, Staffordshire County Council is also gradually thinning the conifers in Haywood Park, adjacent to Brocton Coppice, to restore the area to wood pasture.

Orchards were once familiar features of the countryside, especially in the Vale of Evesham, around the Malverns and along the Teme Valley. Many comprised old trees that were encrusted with lichens and festooned with mistletoe and these harboured many insects and birds, notably Green Woodpeckers. Bullfinches, too, used to visit them in spring to strip the blossom, whilst Hawfinches feasted on the crops of cherries. Most of the orchards we see today have been replanted with new, low-growing varieties of tree and many are netted to prevent attack by birds, but the Wildlife Trusts are seeking to have 100 ha managed in the traditional way by 2005 (West Midlands Wildlife Trusts 2001).

Lowland Heath

Britain's lowland heaths have been steadily disappearing for centuries and within this region only isolated fragments of the once extensive cover remain. Yet Staffordshire still has 3.5% of what little remains of this internationally important habitat in Britain, principally on Cannock Chase. Other important heaths are also found in Sutton Park, in the Enville-Kinver area and south of Kidderminster. Most lowland heath developed when woodland was cleared for agriculture, but it was later found that the poor, freely draining soils would support nothing but rough grazing. It consists of dwarf shrubs, notably ling and heather, in association with gorse, bilberry, crowberry and cowberry and relies on low intensity grazing. Scattered trees, often of birch or pine, are important to birds as they provide song posts and a sanctuary from ground predators. As well as some specialist birds, heathland also supports many lichens and mosses, moths and butterflies, and reptiles such as the adder and common lizard.

Unfortunately, few heaths, apart from Sutton Park, are still grazed, so many are steadily reverting to woodland. On Cannock Chase, Staffordshire County Council has embarked upon a programme of heathland restoration that involves extensive bracken and scrub control, together with some clearance of trees. Already the number of European Nightjars has increased, Tree Pipits and Wood Larks are flourishing and the populations of characteristic heathland birds such as Sky Larks, Meadow Pipits and Common Stonechats have stabilised.

Moorland

The moorland that covers the southernmost tip of the Pennines in north Staffordshire is one of the region's most important habitats for birds. Regrettably, most of its special birds are in severe decline and at least one, the Black Grouse, has been lost, probably because the habitat mosaic had become too fragmented. Many of the problems that beset this area have already been referred to in the section on agriculture. Basically, they include drainage and overstocking of the upland pastures and making silage rather than hay, both of which have been to the detriment of breeding waders such as Northern Lapwing, Common Snipe and Eurasian Curlew. Reduced management of the heather moor itself has also contributed to the decline of Red Grouse and Twite, whilst Ring Ouzels have suffered from increased disturbance from recreational activities, particularly rock climbing. Indeed, the only characteristic species of the area to be stable or increasing are Whinchat and Northern Wheatear—the latter aided by the short swards created by the spread of rabbits following their recovery after myxomatosis.

Wetlands

Although widely distributed, wetlands are the least extensive of the main habitats. Nevertheless they attract a wide range of birds. The habitat includes both running and still water, from small streams and tiny ponds to large rivers, lakes and meres and includes man-made features such as canals, reservoirs and gravel pits. Here wetlands are also taken to embrace associated aquatic habitats such as reedbeds, marshland and wet grassland. Within this broad definition there is considerable variety, from the fast-flowing upland streams of the north and west, which are home to Dippers; to the sluggish lowland rivers of the Avon, Severn and Trent, which are the haunt of Common Kingfishers. Some flow swiftly between high banks that occasionally contain colonies of Sand Martins, whilst others meander gently across wide flood plains where flocks of swans, geese, ducks and waders gather in times of flood. In addition to birds, otters are gradually re-colonising many rivers, but water voles are sadly fast disappearing, largely due to predation by mink.

All these species rely on a healthy aquatic environment and much has been done in recent years to improve the water quality of our rivers, most notably on the Tame where fish have now returned to the reaches downstream of the purification lakes at Lea Marston. Nonetheless, many watercourses are suffering nutrient enrichment caused by nitrate run-off from agricultural fertilisers and the danger of accidental chemical or oil spills is ever present. Further threats to their birdlife come from the proposals to open up the River Avon for navigation between Stratford and Warwick and the River Arrow upstream to Alcester.

On the brighter side, the area of water continues to increase, largely through the creation of new gravel pits. Although only transitory, these provide open water and bare, disturbed ground that attracts a wide range of birds from waterfowl, waders and gulls to finches and buntings. Most hold breeding Little Ringed Plovers and perhaps Common Redshank, but few seem to have the once characteristic colonies of Sand Martins. Food surpluses mean there is no longer an imperative to restore exhausted pits to agriculture, so more are being kept as wetlands and some are even being specially restored as nature reserves. The region's best example of habitat creation from gravel extraction is the chain of wetlands along the Middle Tame Valley, which includes the river purification scheme at Lea Marston and Coton, Kingsbury Water Park and the WMBC reserve at Ladywalk. Between them, these waters hold nationally important numbers of wintering waterfowl and regionally important populations of waders and Common Terns. Fortunately many of the sites now have fairly secure futures, but the loss of Dosthill Lake to summer water skiing serves to underline the competing and conflicting interests of recreation and nature conservation.

Unusually for a habitat dominated by a single species, reedbeds support a wide variety of wildlife, including several special species, such as the Eurasian Bittern, which is now an established winter visitor in small numbers. Apart from the Staffordshire Meres, Brandon Marsh and Ladywalk, the region's reedbeds are few and mostly small, with only 26 ha in the whole of Worcestershire, for example. Often they comprise little more than narrow strips along the margins of rivers and canals, but a substantial bed with a large Reed Warbler colony did exist along the abandoned Droitwich canal. Now that the canal is being restored, however, much of this has been cleared. However, two major reedbeds have recently been planted, namely 10 ha at the Gwen Finch Reserve and an additional 8 ha at Brandon Marsh. In time these will provide food and cover for waterfowl and maybe even entice Eurasian Bittern, Marsh Harrier and Bearded Tit to breed in the region.

On the whole, our wetlands are better protected now than they were twenty years or so ago. Many are scheduled SSSIs and some of our most special areas, notably the Staffordshire meres and the valleys of the Dove, Hamps and Manifold, have additionally been included within candidate SACs. Others are secure in the hands of authorities such as Severn Trent Water (STW) and the Environment Agency (EA), form features in Country Parks or have been incorporated into nature reserves.

Sub-regions

To assist in understanding this diverse region, we have divided it into eleven sub-regions. These broadly correspond with those used in *BWM*, but we have made some changes to boundaries and nomenclature to take account of English Nature's *Natural Areas* (English Nature 1998) and the Countryside Agency's *Character Areas* as defined on the *Character of England Map* (Countryside Agency 1999). We have also drawn heavily on these sources in compiling the following chapters, which describe the physical structure, landscape character and key habitats of each sub-region. We have also used a variety of other publications, including site leaflets and Wildlife Trust books. The descriptions aim to provide a flavour of each area and its wildlife, focussing as much on what is typical as on what is special. The sites covered and the species mentioned are by no means exhaustive and their selection was very much a personal choice.

The Midland Plateau

General Description

This low plateau occupies the central third of the region, stretching almost 80 km (50 miles) from Stafford in the north to Stratford-upon-Avon in the south and 65 km (40 miles) from the Wyre Forest in the west to Coventry in the east. It covers 2,504 km^2 and includes the whole of the former West Midlands County along with much of southern Staffordshire, north-east Worcestershire and northern Warwickshire. At its widest point, it virtually cuts the region into two.

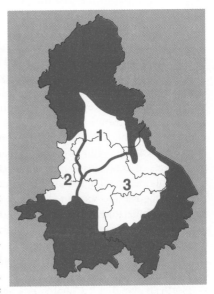

The dominant features are the developed areas. At the centre is the West Midlands Conurbation, which has a population of 2.6 million within its constituent cities of Birmingham and Wolverhampton and the Metropolitan Boroughs of Dudley, Sandwell, Solihull and Walsall. To the east, the city of Coventry, together with the towns of Nuneaton, Bedworth and Kenilworth, form another major urban corridor. Thus, 40% of the plateau is urbanised and few parts have escaped the influence of buildings, roads, railways, power stations, gravel pits, landfill sites and the general paraphernalia of modern living. Moreover, these extensive built-up areas even influence the climate, with Birmingham and the Black Country creating a heat island some 4°C warmer than the surrounding rural districts. Time was when this attracted large numbers of Common Starlings to roost in the city on cold winter nights, but this is a phenomenon of the past.

The whole area falls within the *Midland Plateau Natural Area*. However, because of its large size, it is convenient to sub-divide it into three parts, based on the *Character Areas*, but we have chosen slightly different names to those used by the Countryside Agency (shown in italics below) in order to clarify where the main urban areas fall, namely:

1. Black Country and Cannock Chase   *Cannock Chase and Cank Wood*
2. Mid-Severn Sandstone Plateau   *Mid-Severn Sandstone Plateau*
3. Birmingham, Coventry and Arden   *Arden*

These sub-divisions are based on differences in the landscape that arise from the underlying geology and the boundaries that separate them broadly coincide with the high ground within the West Midlands conurbation that forms the watersheds between the Trent, Severn and Avon catchment areas.

The Black Country and Cannock Chase

Physical Features

This broadly triangular tract of land is bounded by Stafford, Tamworth and Dudley and covers 743 km^2, or 10% of the total regional area—the seemingly unlikely link between the Black Country and Cannock Chase arising from the similarity of the underlying geology and natural vegetation.

For the most part it consists of a level, or gently undulating, plateau that reaches 243m above sea level on the Chase, though to the south-west a broken line of hills rises above the plateau, reaching 267m on Turners Hill at Rowley Regis. To the west and north-east the edge of the plateau is well-defined by scarp slopes that drop abruptly down into the Penk, Sow and Trent valleys, but to the east the ground slopes more gradually into the Tame valley. Southwards, the merger with Arden is largely imperceptible as any vestige of physical difference has been largely obliterated by the sprawling suburbs of Birmingham.

The southern part of this triangle is occupied by Sandwell, Walsall, most of Dudley and eastern Wolverhampton, which formed the core of the Black Country, along with the northern suburbs of Birmingham. The prosperity of the area was based largely on an uplifted block of Upper Carboniferous coal measures, which brought the seams of coal, fireclay and iron ore in the South Staffordshire coalfield near the surface and spawned the exploitation that made such a significant contribution to the Industrial Revolution. The multitude of mines and quarries left a legacy of derelict land, whilst the settlements that grew up around them gradually spread outwards, leaving behind pockets of isolated countryside. Both the reclaimed derelict land and the pockets of countryside now act as green oases. Within the coalfield, the line of prominent hills mentioned earlier marks the watershed between the Severn and Trent catchment areas. The hills themselves vary in character, with Wren's Nest and Castle Hill at Dudley composed of Silurian limestone, while igneous intrusions form the hills in the Rowley Regis area. These rocks, too, have been exploited for their minerals. Indeed, Rowley Regis is still being quarried for hard rock. A layer of glacial till covers most of the coalfield, yielding heavy, poorly drained soils that were once covered in heathland, remnants of which survive around Brownhills and in parts of Dudley.

North of the Black Country is Cannock Chase itself. This is underlain by down-faulted younger rocks of the Permo-Triassic period, including 'Bunter Pebble Beds' from the Sherwood Sandstone Group, which act as valuable aquifers. Exploitation of the thinner coal seams beneath these beds came much later than in the Black Country. Further south, the same sandstone and pebble beds also underlie Sutton Park. Around the margins of the Chase the pebble beds are replaced by buffish red sandstone, which in turn gives way to red mudstones of the Mercia Mudstones Group. To the west these Triassic rocks are overlain by glacial drift, but to the east they outcrop to give the fertile, easily worked soils around Lichfield. One result of past glaciation is the dry valleys that occur across parts of the Chase. Otherwise drainage is through small streams that radiate outwards from the plateau summits to the surrounding rivers Penk, Sow, Trent, Tame and Stour.

Landscape Character

The appearance of today's landscape owes much to its past history as former forest and chase, though in the south this typical landscape has been covered by the urban development that followed exploitation of the coalfield.

Cannock Chase is the dominant landscape feature, rising above the conglomeration of the Black Country and the surrounding towns of Cannock, Stafford and Rugeley. The Chase is an Area of Outstanding Natural Beauty (AONB) and much of it is also a Country Park, an SSSI and a candidate SAC. Due to its proximity to the West Midlands Conurbation, it is heavily used for recreation, but still manages to remain one of the most important habitats for birds in the whole region. The unenclosed, heavily wooded landscape has a varied, often steeply-sloping surface on which the large, sombre conifer plantations are complemented by broad swathes of heathland. There are expansive views, usually to wooded horizons, but sometimes to the lower ground around, which emphasise the elevation. The many valleys, known locally as slades, are very varied, though Sherbrook Valley perhaps has most interest. The wild character of the heaths, dotted with patches of pine and birch and dominated by heather and bracken, makes a stark contrast with the surrounding cultivated ground and built-up areas. The wildness is emphasised by the small pockets of enclosed agricultural land within the heaths. South of the Chase, the settlements, tips, open-cast sites and reclaimed areas of the coalfield, such as Bleak House, dominate the scene. The settlements tend to sprawl, not least because they extended along the straight roads and field boundaries of the nineteenth century enclosures, which paid little regard to landform. Red-brick terraced houses and high-density post-war development tend to predominate.

Although much derelict and open-cast land has been reclaimed, this has not always been successful and there is a large urban fringe around the settlements that contains a mosaic of actively farmed land, rushy pastures and unenclosed land. The more rural parts south-east of the Chase, around Chorley, are now mainly used for stock-rearing and have an irregular pattern of small to medium sized fields enclosed by hedgerows with mature oaks. Small woodlands, narrow sunken lanes and clustered red-brick and whitewashed farmsteads give this landscape a very rural feel—its pattern quite different to the larger-scale straight line development of the nineteenth century landscape found elsewhere.

Still further east, towards Lichfield, and also westwards into the Penk Valley, the scenery becomes gently undulating, with large arable fields, game coverts and belts of trees. The good quality soils here are predominantly under cultivation, but the area's former heathland origins are still evident from the vegetation in the hedgerows and small woodlands. Hedges and hedgerow trees have often been reduced or removed, giving some arable areas an almost prairie-like appearance. Settlements are generally very sparse. In contrast, northwards towards Stafford the villages are older, though some, such as Brocton and Milford, have expanded into virtual suburbs. Here the hedges are generally better, but the landscape remains predominantly open and arable. Historic parks, such as Beaudesert, Teddesley and Wolseley, are clustered on the edge of the Chase, with Shugborough Park a particularly fine example of an eighteenth century designed landscape.

The Black Country has a complex structure within which it is still possible to find traces of the original landscape. The sense of identity in some settlements, such as Dudley, with its castle, wooded hill, medieval street plan and Georgian buildings, is very strong. To varying degrees, this also applies to the other older settlements, such as Wednesbury. But for others, like Tipton with its uniform rows of terraced houses, it is far less clear. Separating the multitude of settlements are pockets of derelict and un-reclaimed land, subsidence ponds, fragments of farmland and patches of naturally regenerated scrub and young woodland. These, plus the parks, golf courses and urban open spaces, combine to provide much valuable green space. Within this mosaic, the canals and disused railway lines are also significant landscape and ecological features.

The fragmented pockets of countryside to the north of Birmingham and West Bromwich consist of medium-sized fields enclosed by good quality hedgerows, patches of ancient enclosure fields and a mixture of semi-natural vegetation including acid grassland, pools, fens and fragments of ancient woodland. Narrow, hedged lanes often survive and there is a real feeling of detachment despite the proximity of built-up areas all around. Even within the confines of the Conurbation there are substantial oases of open land, such as Sutton Park, Barr Beacon, Sandwell Valley, Sheepwash Urban Park, Fens Pools and Saltwells Wood/Doulton's Claypit— all of them valuable habitats for birds.

Key Habitats
Heathland and woodland are the most important habitats, the former often exhibiting a transition from lowlands to uplands in their character. Also of significance for birds are some of the man-made freshwater habitats, most noticeably Chasewater and Sandwell Valley. Most of the area has been included as an Area for Concentrated Biodiversity Enhancement in the recently approved Regional Planning Guidance (ODPM 2004).

The two prime habitats occur together on Cannock Chase, where 67 km^2 of lowland heath, ancient and semi-natural broad-leaved woodland and conifer plantations are owned and managed by Forest Enterprise and Staffordshire County Council. This represents one of the most extensive and important natural resources in the whole region.

Lowland heath is one of Britain's scarcest and most threatened habitats, so the 6 km^2 on the Chase are especially precious. Although officially classed by English Nature as lowland heath, it exhibits a transition into upland heath and is well known amongst botanists for having the best population in Britain of the hybrid bilberry—a cross between bilberry and cowberry. Large stands of coniferous woodland are interspersed with the heaths, creating a mosaic that favours many birds.

Surveys undertaken by the Staffordshire Branch of the WMBC give a good idea of its birdlife (Baskerville 1992, Harbird and Gribble 1997 and Bennett *et al.* 2002). The most important species is the European Nightjar, whose numbers increased from around 30 territories in 1992 to 75 in 2002—the majority of them in clearings or young plantations. Aside from European Nightjars, the Chase is also important for several other species. Tree Pipits, for example, seem to have been declining across the region, yet here their numbers showed a remarkable increase from 95 singing males in 1992 to 179 in 1997. By 2002, though, this figure had fallen to 119, with the losses mostly on the heaths. Another species closely associated with the mix of heath and conifer plantations is Woodcock, of which there appear to be somewhere around 15-20 roding birds. More good news was the recent discovery of Wood Larks in 1994, after a long absence from the region. By 1997 there were seven singing males and this had increased to 26 by 2002. Hobbies and Common Stonechats have both increased, too, whilst Common Ravens are new colonists. The most productive part of the Chase for heathland birds is the Brocton Field-Katyn Memorial-Sherbrook Valley area.

Other species have not been so fortunate, however, with Whinchats having disappeared, while Grasshopper Warblers and Reed Buntings continue to decline. Passage usually brings a scatter of Northern Wheatears and a few Ring Ouzels, especially in autumn. The latter often feast on the harvest of berries to be found in valleys such as Oldacre, as do the autumn flocks of Redwings and Fieldfares. The winter months bring Siskins and Lesser Redpolls to the alders and birches along Sherbrook Valley and the 1996 invasion brought up to six Arctic Redpolls. In winter, the heathland sometimes attracts a Hen Harrier and is also one of the most favoured areas in the region for a Great Grey Shrike.

The semi-natural sessile oak-birch woods, particularly those in the Brocton Coppice-Seven Springs area, hold variable numbers of Common Redstarts, Wood Warblers and Pied Flycatchers, although the small populations of the latter two give cause for concern. The three woodpeckers are also present, but, with just three territories, the Lesser Spotted Woodpecker is very scarce. The extensive conifer plantations also have their interest, with Brambling, Siskin and Common Crossbill all regular visitors in their appropriate seasons. Common Buzzards, Northern Goshawks, Long-eared Owls and Siskins also breed in these plantations, as might Common Crossbills after irruption years, whilst Turtle Doves are still maintaining a slender foothold in the area. The Beaudesert-Wandon Spur-Horsepasture Covert area is often the most rewarding for the coniferous specialists and indeed attracted a Two-barred Crossbill in the winter of 1979/80.

A new addition to the habitat range is the reclaimed opencast mining site at Bleak House-Cuckoo Bank. This area of trans-located heath, acid grassland, birch woodland, marshland, ponds and streams is already proving attractive to a range of nationally declining birds. In 2002, Sky Larks were particularly abundant with 173 territories, but the 27 Reed Bunting territories and five pairs of Northern Lapwing were also encouraging, while single pairs of Grey Partridge and Grasshopper Warbler were very welcome.

Similar habitats to those on the Chase can also be found in Sutton Park, but they are less extensive and prone to greater disturbance, so their birdlife is not as rich. Nevertheless, the blend of open heath, bog, marsh, woodland and freshwater still attracts a range of breeding and passage passerines, together with a few waterfowl. Covering 1,000 ha and completely encircled by residential development, the park is acknowledged to be one of the finest urban parks in Europe and was recently declared an NNR. The open heath is characterised by birch and bracken on the higher ground and heather, western gorse and acidic grassland on the slopes. In the valleys and hollows, such as Longmoor, the peaty, waterlogged soils support cross-leaved heath, purple moor-grass and cotton-grass, with *Sphagnum* moss in the boggier parts. The older woods are dominated by oaks, but there is also plenty of birch and rowan, while holly is notable in the understorey. Alder woodland is frequent along the streams and around the pools, such as Bracebridge, Blackroot and Wyndley.

Recent years have seen fewer records from the park, but Common Redstart and Tree Pipit may have disappeared as breeding species, though Lesser Redpoll and perhaps Common Stonechat are still hanging on. Sky Larks, Meadow Pipits and Yellowhammers also breed across the heath and there is usually a Grasshopper Warbler reeling in one of the damper areas. A superb Woodchat Shrike in 1999 shows that good birds can still be found here. Today the greatest threats are the ever increasing recreational pressures that damage the fragile vegetation and disturb some of the shyer species.

Relict broad-leaved woodland also occurs widely, even within the heavily urbanised Black Country, with Saltwells Wood one of the best examples. The WMBC carried out a survey of this wood and the adjacent Doulton's Claypit for the then Nature Conservancy Council in 1983 (Harrison and Normand 1984). Although this showed both the density and diversity of birds to be slightly below the national average for its size (25 ha), there were some unexpected finds such as Eurasian Sparrowhawk (then scarce), Common Kestrel, Woodcock, Stock Dove and Linnet. Most surprising of all were three pairs of Wood Warblers, which were totally unexpected in an urban oasis. Common Starling was the most numerous species and this, along with Bullfinch, Mistle Thrush and Eurasian Nuthatch all occurred at above average densities. Even without the Wood Warblers and Woodcock, which sadly no longer nest, the wood and claypit give local people a valuable introduction to wildlife.

Wetlands are the third most important habitat. Rivers and canals provide vital corridors, enabling a whole range of species to penetrate deep into the heart of the Black Country towns, where Grey Wagtails, for example, have been noted around shopping centres. Mallards, Moorhens, Common Coots and the occasional pair of Mute Swans and Canada Geese can all be found along the urban waterways, but a much greater variety of birds occurs at the larger areas of open water. Some very productive birdwatching can be enjoyed at places such as Chasewater, Fens Pools, Sandwell Valley and Sheepwash Urban Park. Whilst a single visit may not produce anything out of the ordinary, regular watching at these readily accessible sites not only provides much valuable data, but always carries the prospect of an exciting find.

The Chasewater complex, now a Country Park, comprises the 100 ha canal feeder reservoir and a surrounding mosaic of wet and dry heath, marsh, bog and developing woodland. The open water is divided into two parts by the causeway carrying the Chasewater Light Railway. With the larger area to the south used for a variety of recreational activities, including water skiing and powerboat racing, the northern part, known as Jeffery's Swag, is often preferred by wildfowl. Despite the disturbance from recreational activities and the proximity of the new M6 Toll Road, the southern shore is still often the one that waders, pipits and wagtails favour. However, most other passerines tend to prefer the areas east and north of the reservoir. Prior to the land reclamation, a flock of Twite regularly wintered in this area and, although they have long since gone, other species can still be found as evidenced by a huge flock of 800-1,000 Lesser Redpoll in December 2000.

Wintering waterfowl and roosting gulls are the main interest, though wader and tern passage can be exciting at times. Chasewater is unexpectedly the best site in the region for Sanderlings and has a justifiable reputation for turning up the unusual. Indeed, Britain's first Lesser Scaup was recorded here in 1987. The deep water attracts mainly diving species, espe-

Chasewater is an excellent place to study a variety of gulls.

cially Common Goldeneye and Common Coot, while one of the divers, scarcer grebes or sea-duck is likely to occur at some time during the year.

The second half of winter is usually the best time for gulls, with over 12,000 roosting on the colder nights. Most are Black-headed Gulls, but Lesser Black-backed and Herring Gulls regularly exceed 1,000 and there is often a rarity in the roost like a Mediterranean or Yellow-legged Gull. More than anywhere, however, Chasewater is *the* place for Iceland and Glaucous Gulls, although recently neither has been as regular as in the past.

Sandwell Valley is now arguably the best site within the West Midlands conurbation. The focal point is what was referred to as the balancing lake in *BWM*, but is now known as Forge Mill Lake. This was formed in the early 1980s and the eastern end has since become an RSPB reserve, together with an area of wet, marshy grassland. Between them these habitats attract a wide range of birds. Goosander, and to a lesser extent Eurasian Wigeon and Shoveler are the main feature of the lake in winter. The marsh also holds breeding Sedge and Reed Warblers, Reed Buntings and the occasional pair of Grasshopper Warblers, while winter visitors include Water Rails, Common and Jack Snipe and good numbers of Eurasian Teal. Since the formation of the reserve, this has been the best site in the region for Spotted Crakes and it has attracted three Pectoral Sandpipers. The most exciting find, though, was a Great Snipe in 1995.

Forbes *et al.* (2000) have provided an excellent account of the valley and its birds, which is much more extensive than the RSPB reserve alone. Other areas of open water, most notably Swan Pool and the River Tame itself, also hold waterfowl, though increased recreational activity has diminished the attraction of the former, with waders in particular pausing only briefly. Since 1996 there has been a small heronry on the island in Ice House Lake. The river—once one of the most polluted in Europe—is now much cleaner, but its heavily engineered banks deter most species, except Eurasian Teal and Goosander. It also comes into its own as a refuge when the enclosed pools are frozen over, but its main attribute is as a navigational aid for migrating wildfowl, waders and terns.

Several small blocks of woodland, both broad-leaved and coniferous, along with shelter-belts, free-standing trees, scrub, hedges, farmland and the grasslands on four golf courses also contribute to a very diverse range of habitats. The woods hold breeding Stock Doves and act as winter roosts for thrushes, and occasionally Bramblings; Long-eared Owls sometimes roost in the scrub; and Northern Lapwings, Sky Larks and Linnets occur on the farmland, but Tree Sparrows are now very scarce. Northern Wheatears regularly visit the closely cut turf of the golf courses.

From 1993-2000 a CBC was undertaken on 49 ha of Sandwell Valley, during which time 48 species were recorded and the average density was 119 territories per year, which was equivalent to 244 territories per km². Wrens (with 15 territories a year) were most numerous, followed by Willow Warbler (11), Robin and Common Whitethroat (10 each) and Blackbird (8). The most significant event was an apparent collapse in House Sparrows in 1994, when numbers fell from 15 to two pairs.

The Buckpool and Fens Pools Nature Reserve represents a remarkable transformation from old brick-pits, collieries, iron and steel works and railway sidings into a flourishing wildlife haven. The main habitat for birds are the canal feeder reservoirs, but there are also other pools, a canal, streams, marshland, grassland, scrub and even a remarkable remnant of ridge-and-furrow. Buckpool Dingle harbours a few woodland birds, including Great Spotted Woodpecker, Eurasian Treecreeper and Eurasian Jay. The three main pools have a wealth of fish, invertebrate and plant life that support many waterfowl such as Great Crested Grebes and, in winter, Eurasian Wigeon, Gadwall and Shoveler too. Common Kingfishers nest around the pools, while warblers, finches and Willow Tits frequent the patches of scrub. Later in autumn, Fieldfares and Redwings come to feed on the hawthorn berries. Amongst the unexpected was a superb Night Heron at Foot's Hole in 1994.

Another derelict land reclamation project is Sheepwash Urban Park. Bisected by the canalised and rather sterile River Tame, the park contains pools with margins of reed and reedmace and rough grassland broken up by new plantations of native hardwoods, including oak, birch, alder and willow. There are also a few old pastures with thick hawthorn hedges and some mature pools. For its size and location, the park boasts an impressive list of breeding birds, including occasional pairs of Little Ringed Plovers and Northern Lapwings, Common Terns, Sedge and Reed Warblers, Willow Tits and Reed Buntings. Winter brings small numbers of wildfowl and one or two Water Rails, Common and Jack Snipe and Woodcock. Almost anything might turn up on passage, as evidenced by a Dusky Warbler in 1996.

Two CBCs are of interest. One, conducted in 13 ha of woodland on Mons Hill between 1992-2002 recorded 38 species and an average of 261 territories per annum. Wren (with an average of 53 territories a year) was the commonest species, followed by Blackbird (37), Great Tit (23), Blue Tit and Wood Pigeon (19 each) and Dunnock (14). Other notable counts were Stock Dove and Song Thrush (five each), but Common Chaffinch only averaged six territories which reflects its generally lower densities in urban areas (Gibbons *et al.* 1993). Among the scarcer species, both Willow Tit and Bullfinch were recorded. The other, carried out on 22 ha at an urban fringe location at Rushall during 1997-2000, revealed 37 species with common birds at high densities. The average number of territories per year were Wren (28), Blackbird (17), Robin (15), Blue Tit (13), Great Tit (12), Dunnock (12) and Common Whitethroat (11). Other notable species were Lesser Whitethroat, Garden Warbler, Tree Sparrow, Bullfinch, Reed Bunting and Yellowhammer. This list would seem to indicate the low intensity farming that typifies many urban fringe locations.

The Mid-Severn Sandstone Plateau

Physical Features
This area embraces those parts of south Staffordshire and north Worcestershire, along with the western extremity of the former West Midlands county, that lie between the Stour and Severn valleys and extend westwards to the Shropshire border. Overall it covers 407 km², or 6% of the regional area.

Broadly speaking, it comprises an undulating plateau that extends from Stourbridge in the east to the Shropshire border in the west and from Wolverhampton in the north to Kidderminster, Bewdley and Stourport-on-Severn in the south. The borders of this area generally consist of imperceptible transitions, northwards into the clays of Staffordshire, south-eastwards into Arden and southwards into the Severn and Teme Valleys. To the east, the heavily urbanised fringe, which includes the western half of Wolverhampton, the greatly expanded villages of Wombourne and Kingswinford and the town of Stourbridge, runs into the neighbouring parts of the Black Country with no clearly visible definition on the ground.

The core of the area consists of an undulating plateau of Permo-Triassic sandstones that yield brown sandy soils with brown earths and podzols. However, the extreme south-west of the area is underlain by Coal Measure mudstones, sandstones and the thin seams of coal that were the basis of the former Forest of Wyre Coalfield.

The area is drained by the valleys of the Severn and Stour, which meet at Stourport-on-Severn, and the bedrock is overlain by the terraces of sands and gravels deposited in former times by these rivers. In the south, towards Bewdley, the valleys become narrow and more gorge-like, with steep sides, whilst the tributary streams, such as Dowles Brook, are characteristically fast-flowing.

Landscape Character

The core of the area is predominantly a rolling, rural landscape, which was once dominated by heathland and woodland. Indeed, this area still contains the region's largest woodland, Wyre Forest, and, with the exception of Cannock Chase and Sutton Park, most of its remaining heathland—remnants of which occur at Highgate Common, Kinver, Devil's Spittleful and Hartlebury Common, where they stand out as characteristic features.

Although much semi-natural, ancient woodland still survives, large areas have been converted into conifer plantations and this, combined with parklands such as those at Enville and Himley, creates the appearance of a tidy, well-managed landscape in a few places. The abiding impression, though, is of an open, intensively farmed, arable landscape with regularly-shaped fields. Even the enclosing hedges are low and closely trimmed, with few trees to diminish the feeling of vastness. Towards the Severn Valley, the light, sandy soils and rolling topography give way to heavier soils and a more irregular landform. Here the land is in mixed arable and pasture use with smaller fields and a well-wooded character derived not least from the plentiful hedgerow oaks. It is a landscape of isolated farms, hamlets and the occasional village connected by narrow country lanes.

Both the Severn and Stour are important wildlife corridors with one or two valuable marshlands that harbour some significant plants. Along the valley bottoms there is also more cover from wet alder and willow woods and lines of trees such as poplars. Millponds, constructed to power the cloth mills of Kidderminster, are another feature of the lower Stour valley.

The steep-sided Severn Valley is mostly clothed with fine woods, but in places there are both arable fields and pastures in the narrow floodplain. Above the historic town of Bewdley, with its core of fine Georgian buildings in mellow brick and local sandstone, there are shallows and rapids on the river. Kidderminster occupies a substantial area above the confluence of the Severn and Stour, with industrial development largely confined to the flood plain while post-war housing has spread onto the higher ground. Along with Bewdley and Stourport-on-Severn it forms a substantial urban area, but the towns have quite restricted urban fringes. At the opposite extremity of the sub-region, green belt restrictions have largely contained the westwards spread of Wolverhampton, Wombourne, Kingswinford and Stourbridge. Within this sector of the conurbation are a few precious open lungs, such as the Smestow Valley through Wolverhampton.

The former Royal Forest of Wyre sits on the impoverished soils of a wide, shallow bowl centred around the Dowles Brook. Large areas of the original semi-natural woodland core have survived along this valley and on steeper slopes elsewhere, but much of the plateau woodland has been clear-felled and replanted with conifers. The brook itself has carved a deeply-incised valley typical of a rejuvenated stream. Around the periphery of the forest, isolated hamlets and remote cottages, built in the distinctive local, yellow-grey sandstone, are reached along the narrow lanes that thread their way through the forest clearings. In early times the forest served as wood pasture, providing foraging for animals, but later it supported small industries such as charcoal burning, while the timber was used in the leather and boat building trades of Bewdley. Later still, there was small-scale exploitation of coal, though any vestiges of this have long since disappeared beneath a cover of vegetation.

The heathland is particularly conspicuous as hill and ridge top features, notably around Kinver. Here the underlying fine-grained sandstones and coarser pebbles produce freely draining, acidic soils that are very susceptible to leaching. Because of this they are agriculturally poor and many areas have consequently remained as heath or woodland. Unusual and fascinating former rock dwellings are found in the sandstone caves at Kinver and Wolverley. The sandstone, which produces the characteristically red soils, was also used for building stone.

Key Habitats

Dry, lowland heath and broad-leaved woodland are the two most important habitats—the former because it is one of Britain's most threatened habitats and the latter because it represents the largest single resource in the region. Though much fragmented, significant amounts of each still survive around Kidderminster, making this a particularly important area for wildlife.

The heaths stretch discontinuously along the ridge from Highgate Common, through Enville to Kinver Edge and then reappear at lower altitude at Devil's Spittleful and Hartlebury Common. However, the character of one area often differs markedly from that of its neighbours. For example, at Enville, most of the heathy vegetation has disappeared beneath a blanket of conifers in the Million Plantation. In contrast, Highgate Common, to the north, presents a mosaic of heather and bracken interspersed with grassy glades, scattered woods and a small conifer plantation. Kinver Edge, to the south, differs in having heather on the higher ground, great sweeps of bracken on the slopes and areas of oak, birch and pine woodland. Snakes and lizards can sometimes be seen here, sunning themselves on the sandstone rocks. At the southern end of the Edge, slender birches and aspen clad the sandy hillsides of Kingsford Country Park, with stands of larch and pine on the better soils.

The lower heaths at Devil's Spittleful and Hartlebury Common are different again. The former is a WoWT reserve that contains some of the best heathland in the county, while the latter is an important LNR. The dominant plants at both are heather, broom, bracken and gorse, along with hawthorn scrub and birch and oak woodland. Parts are also covered by acidic grassland with wavy hair-grass, whilst bird's-foot, moonwort and the rare grey hair-grass might be found. Hartlebury also has round-leaved sundew, the rare sand catchfly and an inland blown dune system—one of very few examples in the country—whilst both heaths are also good for insects. Grazing is necessary to keep down growth and prevent scrub encroachment and the eventual reversion to woodland.

Most of the specialist heathland birds have now been lost, but Green Woodpeckers, Meadow Pipits, Common Whitethroats, Linnets and Yellowhammers still nest, while roding Woodcock or even Turtle Dove may still be hanging on and a Dartford Warbler was an unexpected visitor to Devil's Spittleful in 1998. In winter foraging parties of tits roam the area, while Lesser Redpolls visit the birches and an Arctic Redpoll was recorded in Habberley Valley in 2001/2.

The focus of the woodland interest is the Wyre Forest—a major area of coniferous and broad-leaved woodland, with a fascinating flora and a wide range of insects and birds within its 26 km^2 (see Yapp 1962 and 1969). The whole forest has a high landscape, amenity and timber value, but its importance to wildlife is recognised by a third being an SSSI and a fifth an NNR, so that, between them, English Nature and the WoWT manage some 600 ha. These designated areas represent one of the largest and most diverse concentrations of semi-natural woodland in England, ranking in importance alongside the New Forest, the Wye Valley Woods and Blean Woods in Kent.

High oak forest is dominant, but there are three types. On the shallower, acidic soils of the plateau, sessile oaks thrive along with birch and rowan above a field layer that contains heather, bilberry, wavy hair-grass and great wood-rush. In the valleys, the deeper, basic soils support pedunculate oakwoods, with ash, small-leaved lime and wild service trees above a field layer of bracken and bramble, whilst yet other areas have stands of pedunculate oak above holly, coppiced hazel and the occasional yew. The undesignated parts of the Forest are mostly managed by Forest Enterprise and contain stands of Douglas fir, Corsican pine and larch. Within the forest there are also small meadows of species-rich, neutral grasslands; old orchards; an abandoned railway line; and flushes and streams, of which the Dowles Brook is most important.

This exceptional habitat diversity supports an excellent range of insects and birds, with records of over forty-five species of butterfly. Much of the Forest's remarkable range of wildlife can be enjoyed from a walk along the beautiful Dowles Brook. The unpolluted, fast-flowing stream contains a variety of fish, native crayfish and many invertebrates, which provide food for several species of birds, including Common Kingfishers, Dippers and Grey Wagtails. Along the valley floor, the open woodland, with tiny flower meadows and gnarled, old orchard trees, provides the perfect habitat for Lesser Spotted Woodpeckers, Common Redstarts, Wood Warblers and Pied Flycatchers. The latter, especially, takes advantage of the nest-boxes at the WoWT's Betts and Knowles Coppice reserves. Tree Pipits are plentiful, too, favouring forest clearings or the old railway line, while the elusive Hawfinch, although seldom seen, maintains a small population. Winter sometimes brings Brambling, too, but their appearances are erratic.

Just over half of the forest belongs to the Forestry Commission (Forest Enterprise), which since 1927 has progressively converted it into conifer plantations. These are generally of less interest, but Siskins now breed regularly and flocks of Common Crossbills invariably appear in irruption years, with perhaps a few staying on to breed the following spring. Woodcock can be seen roding above the treetops on summer evenings and Northern Goshawks, Common Buzzards and Common Ravens are all resident. At night-time the calls of Tawny Owls echo through the woods, while a churring European Nightjar was heard briefly in 1998. A careful search of the flocks of Siskins and Lesser Redpolls in the winter sometimes reveals an occasional Common Redpoll and the 1996 invasion brought 150 of the latter along with four Arctic Redpolls.

Several satellite woodlands, such as Ribbesford, Rock, Eymore and Coldridge Woods, surround the forest and between them share many of its characteristics, especially the deciduous dingle woods that clothe the steep sides of some tributary valleys. Most of the special birds in the forest proper also occur in these woods, though generally in smaller numbers or less often. However, in March 1993 an exceptional flock of 1,300-1,700 Siskin descended on Coldridge Wood.

Parkland, though not extensive, also makes a significant contribution to the birdlife of the open countryside. This is especially true of the Sheepwalks at Enville, which have long been known as a good spot for Common Ravens and raptors, and which have a happy knack of turning up the unusual, with records of Red Kite, Wood Lark and Snow Bunting.

Wetlands are very much subordinate to the heaths and woods, but they do add considerably to the overall diversity of the area. The two main rivers, Severn and Stour, contribute particularly to the range of birdlife, with the former being used as a migration route by many species, whilst the latter has one or two marshes, such as that at Wilden, which are fed by springs that issue from the underlying sandstone aquifers and spread out across the narrow, alluvial plain. Here an early re-profiling of the river actually raised its bed, helping to keep the marsh wet even in summer, and this is how it was when the WoWT acquired part of it in 1976. Just three years later, the then Water Authority completed a further flood alleviation scheme, which lowered the river bed. Despite assurances from the authority that this would not damage the marsh, it left much of it high and dry with the consequent loss of the marshland flora—a salutary lesson for anyone involved with mitigation measures to alleviate the adverse effects of development.

The bird life quickly deteriorated, with Common Snipe declining from around 15 pairs to just two within five years, by which time Common Redshanks and Yellow Wagtails had already ceased to breed. Sedge Warbler and Reed Bunting did remain, with the former maintaining its numbers at a dozen or so pairs, but the latter much reduced. Wintering populations were also affected, with Common Snipe dwindling from around 70 to about 20. Finally, the adjacent sugar beet factory closed. Without the washings from the plant, the settling beds silted up, or were filled and levelled. In their heyday they had been the haunt of breeding Little Ringed Plovers, passage waders and terns, and wintering wildfowl and Jack Snipe. There used to be a dozen or so of the latter, but the norm now is just two or three. The shorelines were also renowned as the best place in the region for wintering Water Pipits, with up to half-a-dozen every winter from 1974-91, but the only one since was in 1995. Sadly it has to be said that Wilden today is only a poor shadow of what it used to be.

Many of the above sites are within easy reach of Kidderminster, which is surrounded by some very good birding areas. In contrast, the western fringe of the conurbation is less fortunate. Here two of the better sites are the Himley Hall and Baggeridge Country Park complex and the Smestow Valley. The former, on the edge of Dudley, incorporates a lake, four small pools that used to provide power for an ironworks and areas of woodland and grassland. Between them these habitats hold a range of wetland and woodland species. The latter runs through the western suburbs of Wolverhampton, forming the largest green lung in the city. The main features are the Smestow Brook, Staffordshire and Worcestershire Canal and Valley Park Railway Walk, which run in parallel through areas of grassland, woodland and scrub. The variety of habitats supports good numbers of several species, including some six pairs of Willow Tit (one of the highest concentrations across the region) and above average numbers of Song Thrush, Common Whitethroat and Bullfinch. The unusual has occurred, with the West Midlands County's only Yellow-browed Warbler in 1998 and an adult male Red-backed Shrike in 2003. Within the valley stands Dunstall Park racecourse, redeveloped in 1993 into Europe's first floodlight all-weather track. The brook flows through a culvert beneath the site and a balancing lake was constructed to help alleviate flooding concerns. The security offered by this private site has since resulted in a total of 19 wader species being recorded, including high numbers of wintering Common Snipe, up to 700 Northern Lapwings and up to 2,000 European Golden Plovers. Flocks of about 1,000 passage gulls during late summer have included up to five Mediterranean Gulls in each year since 2001, whilst a Hoopoe foraged along the lake shoreline in 1997.

Birmingham, Coventry and Arden

Physical Features
This is the largest of the three sub-divisions, covering 1,354 km^2 and making up slightly more than half of the Midland Plateau and 19% of the regional area. It is closely associated with the medieval Forest of Arden, which broadly covered the north-western half of Warwickshire and much of north-east Worcestershire, reaching as far as Tamworth in the north, Nuneaton, Coventry and Warwick in the east, Stratford-upon-Avon, Redditch and Bromsgrove in the south and the Lickey and Clent Hills in the west.

Much of this area now lies beneath Birmingham, Solihull and Coventry, but it was previously covered by woods and heaths. Shakespeare set several scenes of *As You Like It* in the

Forest of Arden, thus securing its place in English folklore. It probably never was a real forest, though, as its name means either well-wooded district, or high land depending on its derivation. Nevertheless, beyond the confines of the conurbation, Arden still retains a wooded character.

To the north the area merges imperceptibly with the Black Country and Cannock Chase, the northern suburbs of Birmingham spilling across and masking any physical boundary. Between Solihull and Coventry, however, the plateau falls gradually into the valleys of the Rivers Cole and Blythe, while to the north-east its edge is marked by a steep escarpment that falls away into the Tame and Anker valleys. East of Coventry, the plateau then fades gradually into the Dunsmore and Feldon area, but southwards it is again more sharply defined by the steep drops into the valleys of the Alne, Arrow and Avon.

The former forest, if such it was, stood on two uplifted blocks of Palaeozoic rocks, namely the Birmingham Plateau in the west and the East Warwickshire Plateau in the east, though their underlying geology is locally masked by a covering of glacial drift. Linking the two is the lower ground of the Knowle basin—an area of Mercian mudstones again overlain by glacial drift. Here the gently undulating landform is cut by the valleys of the River Blythe and its tributaries, which have been extensively worked for sand and gravel around Meriden.

The highest land is in the west, where older rocks rise above the plateau to form a broken line of hills that reach around 300m at Clent and Lickey. In contrast, the eastern plateau rises no higher than 180m and consists of uplifted Carboniferous and Precambrian rocks. Red mudstones and sandstones from the Upper Carboniferous period cover most of it, but the productive Coal Measures outcrop in an arc stretching from Kingsbury, through Tamworth, Atherstone, Nuneaton and Bedworth, to Coventry. These outcrops were the basis of the Warwickshire coalfield, which later expanded into deep mining of the seams beneath the centre of the plateau, where Daw Mill Colliery is now the region's sole surviving pit. Along the same arc, vertical folding has brought Precambrian and Cambrian rocks to the surface and in the Nuneaton area these are still quarried for roadstone.

The two plateaux mark the watershed between the Severn and Trent catchments, with the Blythe and Cole flowing northwards into the Tame and then the Trent, while the Alne and Arrow flow southwards into the Avon and thence the Severn. The upper valley of the Arrow basin is also underlain by Triassic mudstones, but in places outcrops of Arden sandstone produce steep hills and escarpments.

Landscape Character

Arden is a very densely populated and urbanised area, with Birmingham and Solihull in the north-west, Coventry in the east and a number of smaller towns including Bromsgrove, Redditch, Warwick, Kenilworth, Bedworth and Nuneaton around its periphery. Between them, these towns and cities have transformed the landscape, superimposing upon it industrial townscapes, business and retail parks and housing estates. The result is many incongruous intrusions even in the open countryside, with huge stone quarries at Hartshill, red-brick terraces and colliery spoil heaps at Baddesley and Kingsbury, and the comparatively new mine at Daw Mill. Even the farmland around some of the urban fringes has a forlorn, impoverished look.

Evidence of human occupation goes back many thousands of years, but woodland clearance was slow because this was part of the vast Royal hunting forests that once swept across the West Midlands. So woodland persisted into Anglo-Saxon times and it may have been as late as the eleventh century before the land was gradually cleared to graze stock or grow crops. Enclosure for deer parks continued into the fifteenth century, however, and many of the woods, commons and heaths that we see today are the surviving fragments of this. More concerted enclosure began during the seventeenth century and by the time it was completed two hundred years later little of Arden's formerly extensive woodland remained. A few commons lasted longer, either as wood pasture with grazing beneath scattered trees, or as open heaths.

At the same time the canals arrived and exploitation of the coalfield began.

The influence of early settlers was totally eclipsed by that of the Industrial Revolution, which brought the rapid growth of towns and cities. In more recent times, Redditch has expanded still further as a New Town, whilst Tamworth, too, has experienced considerable growth. Within Birmingham and Coventry, the concentric pattern of outward growth from the central core through the inner city and Victorian suburbs to the twentieth century estates is very evident. The collapse of so many manufacturing industries in the 1980s left much vacant land—the so called 'brownfield sites' that created suitable habitat for Black Redstarts, whose numbers peaked around that time. Now the focus for urban development has switched to reusing these previously developed 'brownfield' sites rather than building on greenfield sites. The M42, M40 and M6 Toll motorways have all consumed land, however, and brought considerable pressure for new development to the east of Birmingham and Solihull, not least from the threat of the M42 widening and expansion of Birmingham Airport. One positive benefit to come from the new motorways has been the erection of nest-boxes for Common Kestrels along the M40, several of which have been used to good effect.

Despite the massive incursions imposed by urban pressures, there are many pleasant, remote rural parts. Arden's unique character derives from the intimate mixture of small woods, irregularly shaped fields, winding sunken lanes and spreading hedgerow oaks. Within this framework, timber-framed and red-brick farms and villages blend harmoniously into their settings. Apart from the Bentley Park and Monks Park area of north Warwickshire and the Clent-Lickey-Chaddesley area of north-east Worcestershire, there are few large woods. Instead, it is the many hedgerow oaks and remnants of ancient woodlands and parklands that ensure it remains one of the region's most wooded districts. This is true even of the area south of Birmingham, where the rectilinear fields and straight roads are evidence of Parliamentary enclosure.

This wooded appearance is complemented by the surviving relics of heaths and commons, which were once extensive, particularly across areas of glacial drift. The larger ones have now mostly been enclosed and divided into large fields by straight hedges, but some of the smaller commons, such as Yarningale, still have small irregular fields, thick hedges and winding lanes around them. Another legacy of Arden's days as a Royal hunting forest, is the number of deer parks, of which those at Packington and Stoneleigh are notable for their many venerable oaks and sweet chestnuts. Sadly, these parklands are increasingly being converted into golf courses, much to the detriment of their character and the indigenous wildlife.

Within this rural landscape, there are numerous subtle variations that add so much more to the appearance of the area. Of particular note are the low, rounded hills, steep slopes, tiny valleys and small, compact villages, though some of the latter closest to Birmingham and Coventry have expanded into commuter settlements, losing much of their character in the process. The best way to appreciate Arden's stark contrasts is to climb to the top of the Clent Hills. The views from here are stunning. Looking south-westwards on a clear day, the rural panorama stretches right across Worcestershire to the Malvern Hills and away to the Clee Hills in Shropshire. But turn around and the amorphous urban sprawl of Birmingham and the Black Country spreads like a carpet at your feet.

Key Habitats

No single habitat in this area is outstanding. Rather it is the intricate mosaic of woods, fields, grasslands and wetlands and the interaction between them that is its most precious feature. Trees are the common strand throughout, whether in woods, parklands or hedgerows. Farmland apart, the remaining stands of semi-natural broad-leaved woodland, numerous small copses and conifer plantations make woodland the commonest habitat.

Oakwoods are most frequent, with sessile oaks above bilberry and heather on the acidic soils, but pedunculate oaks, frequently with an understorey of coppiced hazel, on the more neutral soils. Examples of the former can be found in the Bentley Park-Monk's Park complex and at Clowes Wood, where one or two pairs of Wood Warblers once used to breed. Woodcock and Marsh Tits also nest in Bentley Park, which is generally the better part of the complex for birds. Common Redstarts and Pied Flycatchers have also been recorded in the past, but not recently.

The pedunculate oakwoods are more widespread, with the better examples, such as New Fallings Coppice and Chaddesley and Randan Woods, generally holding a good range of woodland birds, including Woodcock and sparingly Lesser Spotted Woodpecker. Chaddesley—the second largest woodland in Worcestershire—also has stands of poplar, planted for the match making industry, and some conifers. Birch commonly occurs in association with the oaks and its seed provides a main source of food for wandering parties of tits and other species such as Lesser Redpoll during the winter. Beechwoods are not common in the region, but there are some notable stands on the Lickey Hills that are regularly visited in autumn by a wide range of birds seeking beechmast, notably Common Chaffinches and less regularly Bramblings.

Conifer plantations, such as those at Hay Wood and Monk's Park, held Turtle Doves and Tree Pipits when the trees were small, but now Goldcrests and Coal Tits are more typically found in the mature trees. In irruption years, though, some plantations are regularly visited by parties of Common Crossbills. Nowadays, Common Buzzards seem to have colonised virtually every wood, Eurasian Sparrowhawks are widespread and even Northern Goshawks are sparsely distributed and increasing. Several new plantations have also been established and these currently sustain high populations of Song Thrushes, Common Whitethroats and Willow Warblers.

The area also has some fine parklands, notably at Arbury, Merevale, Packington and Stoneleigh. Packington and Stoneleigh, in particular, have several veteran trees that harbour a good range of invertebrates, making them attractive to woodpeckers and Eurasian Nuthatch. The holes in these gnarled old trees also provide nest sites for Western Jackdaws and owls, including Barn Owls. The WMBC has been carrying out surveys for the National Trust at two parklands in this area, namely Packwood House and Baddesley Clinton. These have shown that the commonest birds were all woodland species—Western Jackdaw, Rook, Blue Tit, Wren, Wood Pigeon, Blackbird, Great Tit, Robin and Common Chaffinch. Other characteristic

Arden's many woods and hedgerow trees provide nest sites for Stock Doves.

species included Stock Dove, Green Woodpecker, Mistle Thrush, Spotted Flycatcher and Eurasian Nuthatch, with the commoner waterfowl on the lakes.

Farming remains the predominant land use and its characteristic birds are under just as much threat here as anywhere. However, the multitude of hedgerows and hedgerow trees enable birds to move easily between sites, and woodpeckers, Eurasian Jays and Eurasian Nuthatches are frequently seen in hedgerow trees. Even the trend for low, neatly-trimmed hedges around arable fields seems to suit Common Whitethroats, if not Turtle Doves and Lesser Whitethroats which were much commoner when the hedges were taller and thicker. Despite the importance of the arboreal habitats, birders still devote most attention to the wetlands. These embrace a whole range of features, from the natural rivers and streams to the man-made canals, lakes, reservoirs, gravel pits and subsidence flashes, which between them support a wide range of birds.

Rising on the plateau, the rivers and streams are still in their headwater stage and so are mostly small, the largest being the Blythe, Cole, Alne and Arrow. Together with the canals, they nevertheless support modest numbers of the commoner waterfowl, along with Grey Wagtails around the locks and weirs. They are also sufficiently clean to have a healthy population of Common Kingfishers, even on the urbanised Cole, but neither the Alne nor the Arrow has been visited by Dippers for many years.

The Blythe—a scheduled SSSI—is perhaps the most important river. Here an interesting new development illustrates how business can contribute to wildlife conservation. The Blythe Valley Business Park is a complex of high-technology industries that has been landscaped to a very high standard. Several new habitats have been created and these have already attracted a few breeding pairs of Northern Lapwings, while both Common Quail and Grasshopper Warbler have been recorded on passage. The valley also contains several sand and gravel workings, many of them on land owned by the Packington Estate. At Marsh Lane, some of these have been developed into a private nature reserve, with access by permit from the estate. This truly excellent example of the growing trend for privately-owned reserves consists of two or three shallow pools, with gently shelving shores and substantial islands that are overlooked by four hides. Some of the adjacent land is cultivated and planted with crops especially designed to sustain declining farmland birds through the winter. Common Terns and several species of wader nest, while winter brings a good variety of wildfowl, along with Common and Jack Snipe. Amongst a whole range of other species that have occurred, mention might be made of a party of seven Little Egrets in 1998—the most recorded in the region—and, in 2002, a surprising Hoopoe followed by an Eurasian Spoonbill. A good range of passage waders has also been noted, including Avocet and Temminck's Stint.

Reservoirs are also major features in today's Arden landscape. Those at Earlswood and Bittell were constructed to feed the canal network, whilst Bartley supplies water to Birmingham. Earlswood Lakes typically hold Great Crested Grebes, a few wintering waterfowl and occasionally one or two passage terns. Common Swifts and hirundines also regularly gather here to feed and evening flocks sometimes attract the attention of a hungry Hobby.

Bittell Reservoir, neatly tucked away in the folds of some pleasant open countryside barely eight miles (13 km) from the centre of Birmingham, is usually more productive. There are actually two reservoirs here, of which Upper Bittell, at 40 ha, is the largest open water in Worcestershire. It is also deeper than Lower Bittell. Although more exposed and often disturbed by sailing, the upper reservoir is usually favoured by Great Crested Grebes and is the more likely of the two to attract any scarcer waterfowl that might be passing. Gulls also occur, but in much reduced numbers and apparently they no longer roost. However, Mediterranean and Yellow-legged Gulls are occasionally seen. There has always been some interchange of birds between here and Bartley Reservoir and this is often most evident amongst the gulls. Given the right conditions, wader and tern passage can also be good, especially in autumn when low water levels after the summer draw-down expose muddy shorelines. Lower Bittell is smaller, shallower, quieter and more secluded, with a fringe of emergent vegetation that is particularly attractive to dabbling duck. Amongst the more interesting wintering species are Eurasian Teal and a few Eurasian Wigeon and Shoveler. Linking the two reservoirs is a small, fast-flowing stream flanked by alder woodland, and known as Mill Shrub. Common Kingfishers are sometimes seen here, whilst winter regularly brings flocks of Siskins and Lesser Redpolls to the alders and often Grey Wagtails to the stream.

Just a few miles north of Bittell, Bartley lies right on the outskirts of Birmingham, where it forms a buffer between the tower blocks of the city on the east and the open countryside to the west. The reservoir aptly reflects its urban fringe setting, with solid concrete banks and short grass surrounds. Sadly, this unwelcoming appearance seems to deter the birds—the WMBCs President, Bill Oddie, having pointed out in *Gone Birding* that "it was possible to scan the water … and within about one minute be fairly confident that it was absolutely devoid of birds"! (Oddie 1983). Frustrating as this is, regular watching does produce some good birds, despite the introduction of sailing and windsurfing. Winter waterfowl and roosting gulls are the main interest. During the day a few Great Crested Grebes and Common Goldeneye may be the only birds present and even the gull roost is erratic, with perhaps 3,000 birds one night and none the next. Perseverance can be rewarding, however, with Yellow-legged Gulls regularly present; Mediterranean, Glaucous and Iceland Gulls recorded on occasions; and once a Laughing Gull. Hard weather is usually the most productive time, as the deep water remains open when shallower ones nearby are frozen solid. Such conditions might well produce a diver, scarcer grebe, Shag or sea-duck, with Common Scoter not unusual on passage. A few passage terns are also noted most years and waders drop in from time-to-time despite the inhospitable shoreline.

There are also valuable wetlands well within the urban areas. One good example is in Coventry, where the River Sowe creates an important wildlife corridor for the inhabitants of the city as it meanders through the eastern suburbs. Along its valley are rough, pony-grazed pastures, flood meadows, remnants of overgrown hawthorn hedges and patches of scrub, willow and alder woodland and a few mature oaks. The two main features are the colliery subsidence pools at Stoke Floods and Wyken Slough, both of which are LNRs. The former, along with a separate marsh at the latter (mentioned below), are also Warwickshire Wildlife Trust (WaWT) reserves. Each is fringed by stands of reedmace, whilst at Stoke Floods reed canary-grass, yellow iris and patches of rush add further variety. Most of the commoner waterfowl, including both Great Crested and Little Grebes, take advantage of the cover afforded by this emergent vegetation at some time of the year, as might Water Rail and Common Snipe in winter. Wyken Slough, which is the largest area of water in Coventry, also has a small, separate marsh with reed sweet-grass and reedmace, while two new islands have been created in the lake to provide a safe sanctuary for birds. In winter the marsh is favoured by Common Snipe, Water Rail and one or two Jack Snipe. Reed Buntings also breed still, but there is no longer the large roost there used to be. Common Kestrels often hunt the area and Common Kingfishers are regularly seen and in late summer they sometimes take their young to feed around the pools. Common Terns have also been seen fishing in summer, whilst Common Gulls are always present in winter. The pool also acts as a staging post for gulls going to roost at Draycote Water. Flocks of winter thrushes feed along the hedgerows in autumn, whilst regular watching has also revealed a surprising range of migrant passerines moving through the area, especially chats, warblers and sometimes Ring Ouzel.

In Birmingham, even the city's public parks often hold a variety of common waterfowl, many of which breed, including Great Crested Grebes. Just two miles from the city centre, at Edgbaston Park, is a very special urban sanctuary. Part is a golf course, but the private pool and its surrounds are an SSSI. For many years the birdlife was monitored by boys from King Edwards's School and a CBC was carried out annually from 1966-84. As well as the usual range of waterfowl and woodland birds, this revealed some unexpected surprises for an urban area, including Little Grebe, Reed Bunting and Willow Warbler. The region's first Cetti's

Warbler was also recorded here, back in 1975. Although little is known about its birdlife to-day, it is probably just as varied.

Nearby is the canal-feeder Edgbaston Reservoir. Hemmed in on all sides by urban development, this is nonetheless another site that repays regular watching. The open water, gently shelving and gravelly shorelines, marshy inlets along two streams and a small patch of mixed woodland attract a surprising variety of birds. Winter wildfowl may include Eurasian Wigeon, Eurasian Teal, Gadwall, Shoveler or Common Goldeneye and the sporadic gull roost has reached 6,000 birds. Rarities sometimes join the roost and the region's first-ever Laughing Gull was discovered here in 1985. Spring passage usually brings a few terns, while the occasional wader sometimes takes advantage of the low water level in autumn. Grey Wagtails are also regular visitors, while the small wood and adjacent gardens hold Tawny Owl, Great Spotted Woodpecker, Eurasian Nuthatch and Eurasian Treecreeper. Common Swifts often feed overhead and a variety of migrants pass through in spring and autumn.

The reservoir also links into the Harborne Walkway, which leads through a wooded cutting to the Harborne Nature Reserve. This small reserve consists of disused allotments that the WMBC manages under an agreement with Birmingham City Council. Many native trees, shrubs and herbaceous plants have been planted to enrich the habitat, which is principally a steep hillside of grassland, scrub and naturally developing oak woodland dropping into the valley of the Chad Brook. Here there is a small wetland area and a group of alders that attracts feeding parties of Siskins and Lesser Redpolls in winter. The range of habitats is further enriched by a small conifer plantation, with Goldcrests and Coal Tits, and a wildflower meadow, where Goldfinches feed on the teasel heads. Both Blue and Great Tits use the many nest-boxes and Tawny Owls have bred successfully in one of the tunnel boxes. Many birds also visit the regularly stocked feeding station. Though probably nesting in the more mature trees of surrounding gardens, all three woodpeckers also visit the reserve, but the Lesser Spotted Woodpecker is rather erratic.

Moving into the centre of Birmingham itself, feral pigeons, Common Starlings and House Sparrows no longer rule supreme here. In an effort to reduce their numbers, people have been asked not to feed the pigeons, while the demolition of traditional, red-brick buildings has deprived House Sparrows and Common Starlings of the nooks and crannies in which they used to nest. Many buildings have also been netted over, or chemically treated, to dissuade Common Starlings from roosting. Today the pigeons seem as plentiful as ever, but House Sparrows have vanished from many areas and Common Starlings are nowhere near as numerous. Indeed, the city centre roost collapsed from a peak of 56,000 birds in 1985 to just one in 1992—leaving the spectacle of huge flocks wheeling against the night sky as nothing but a distant memory. However, the protection measures alone were not responsible, as the trees in St Philip's churchyard, which used to hold many hundreds of birds, were also abandoned. In recompense, Lesser Black-backed and Herring Gulls are now nesting on many of the flat-roofed buildings in the city, just about as far from the coast as they could possibly be. Also, Peregrine Falcons now nest on the British Telecom tower. Further out, the birdlife of many leafy, suburban gardens, such as those of Solihull, is probably richer now than in many country districts.

Lastly, the Clent and Lickey Hills are good examples of the habitat mosaics to be found in Arden. Being so close to so many people, the Clent Hills—of which there are three—are inevitably a popular place for recreation, which puts tremendous pressure on the wildlife. This is the dilemma with which the National Trust, which owns most of the area, and Worcestershire County Council, which manages part as a Country Park, have to wrestle.

The acidic soils support only a limited flora. On the open hills, such as Walton, bracken now cascades down the hillsides, threatening to swamp the last remnants of acid grassland. Sky Larks and Meadow Pipits used to nest commonly amongst the wavy hair-grass, with up to 20 pairs of the latter (*BWM*). Recent surveys, carried out for the National Trust by the WMBC, showed just two singing Sky Larks in 2000 and none in 2002, whilst Meadow Pipits had dropped to three and two singing birds respectively. Worse still, there were half a dozen pairs of Tree Pipits twenty years ago, but only three in 2000 and none in 2002. In contrast, Common Redstart and Linnet numbers have remained stable over the past twenty years and migrant Ring Ouzels are still fairly regular visitors to the surrounding fields and paddocks in spring. The open hillsides are also dotted with oak, birch, hawthorn and rowan, whose berries prove irresistible to migrant thrushes in autumn. Otherwise mature native trees are confined to the semi-natural woodland along the valleys, and to Adams Hill, which is surmounted by a group of planted beech that sometimes attract Bramblings. There are also plantations of larch and Scots pine that once held breeding Willow Warblers and Lesser Redpolls. For Willow Warblers, the hills still remain something of a stronghold, with at least 20 singing males, but Lesser Redpolls have all but disappeared. Also lost are the Wood Warblers that used to nest in the clumps of sycamore on Walton Hill, but Common Ravens are new arrivals. Not far north of Clent is the Lutley Wedge, a tongue of open countryside on the outskirts of Halesowen which regular watching has shown to be something of a migration hotspot. Many of the birds that visit the Clent Hills, such as Ring Ouzel, also occasionally occur here and Wryneck and Wood Lark have been amongst some unexpected discoveries.

Standing hard against Birmingham's boundary, the Lickey Hills are also popular for recreation. Fortunately they differ from the hills at Clent in that the harder Cambrian rocks are less easily eroded by trampling feet. Wildlife is still affected, however, with vegetation trampled and shy species often forced to seek sanctuary elsewhere. For example, Common Redstarts were recorded until the mid 1990s and Pied Flycatchers until 1997, while scarcely any Wood Warblers—of which there were once 20 pairs—remain. The steeper slopes are frequently clothed by Scots pines over an understorey of bilberry, while the more gentle ones support stands of beech, larch and fir as well as native oak-birch woodland. This diversity sustains a good population of resident woodland birds, with limited CBC data showing Robin, Blue Tit, Wren, Great Tit and Blackbird as the commonest breeding species, in descending order. In winter they are augmented by Siskins, Lesser Redpolls and occasionally a few Bramblings. The conifer plantations are of limited interest, except when Common Crossbills arrive in irruption years. Acidic grassland or heather covers the open hillsides, with bracken on the lower slopes. Here again, disturbance is too great for larks and pipits to nest, though up to four pairs of Tree Pipits did struggle through until the early 1990s. On the positive side, however, a Dartford Warbler on the hills in December 1995 was the first in the region for eighty years.

The Meres and Mosses

Physical Features

The Meres and Mosses form the fourth largest sub-region, covering 684 km^2, or almost 10% of the region's area. They comprise the Staffordshire components of the hugely extensive *Meres and Mosses Natural Area* and the *Shropshire, Cheshire and Staffordshire Plain Character Area.*

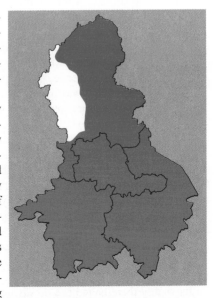

Essentially the area covers that part of the county lying north of the M54 and west of the M6 motorways. It consists mostly of a low-lying, flat or gently undulating plain, crossed by meandering, slow-flowing streams and small rivers. Much of the land lies between 60-100m above sea level and is deeply rural, except to the east, where it includes the towns of Stafford and Stone and comes up to the edge of Newcastle-under-Lyme and the Potteries. To the west and north, there is no visible definition to the boundary as the plain extends across into Shropshire and Cheshire respectively, but to the east, as well as the encroaching urban influence mentioned above, the rising ground of Cannock Chase provides a clear demarcation. Southwards there is a gradual transition into the Mid-Severn Sandstone Plateau.

Without doubt, glacial activity has had the greatest influence on the area. The bedrock consists of Triassic sandstones, silts and muds, but the landform, soils and vegetation have been largely shaped by the thick covering of boulder clay, silts and sands left by the retreating ice sheets. A broken line of Triassic sandstone, softened by glacial deposits, provides some relief from the flatness of the plain as it forms a low backbone that extends from Ashley Heath in the north, through Gnosall to Codsall in the south. Cutting at right-angles across this is another line of hills, this time comprising Carboniferous sandstone, that extends from Newcastle-under-Lyme in the east to Shrewsbury (Shropshire) in the west, forming small, hummocky ridges and valleys around Hanchurch and Maer, where the hills rise above 200m.

North of Stafford, drainage is south-eastwards, along the River Sow and its numerous small tributary streams, whilst south of Stafford the general direction of flow in the tributary streams is eastwards into the River Penk, which itself flows northwards.

Landscape Character

The meres and mosses are undeniably the most important characteristic feature of this area, even though there are actually few examples within Staffordshire. The best are the NNR at Aqualate Mere, close to the Shropshire border near Newport, and the Staffordshire Wildlife Trust (SWT) reserve at Black Firs and Cranberry Bog. These, together with Betley Mere and Copmere, are designated sites under the Ramsar Convention on the Conservation of Wetlands of International Importance. There are also other examples at Doley Common, Loynton Moss and Maer Pool. These are small features in a vast area, however, and the general impression of the area as a whole is one of an expansive agricultural plain dotted, with small villages and criss-crossed by narrow lanes that wind between high hedge banks. Red-brick is the predominant building material, though there are also some fine half-timbered houses and stone churches.

The clay soils retain the winter rains well into summer, supporting lush pastures that are primarily used to produce silage or hay for dairy cattle. These irregularly-shaped pastures are enclosed by thick hedges lined by mature trees, principally oaks, but with some ash and sycamore, which create the illusion of a landscape more wooded than it actually is. In fact woods are few and small, except for the plantations on the more thirsty sandstone ridges of the Hanchurch and Maer Hills and at Burnt Wood and Bishops Wood. Further south, the extensive parklands at Aqualate, Chillington and Weston Park add diversity to the pastoral scene, whilst farming in this area is more mixed, with some beef cattle and arable production. Willows and alders identify the courses of the many small streams that drain the area, while rushy pastures and scrub signify the presence of farm ponds or shallow, peaty depressions.

Oak-birch woodland was once characteristic of the thin, sandy soils on the higher ground, but during the last century much of this was felled and replanted with alien conifers, forming strong visual features. Today the main clues to the more natural vegetation of former times are the patches of bracken and gorse, which introduce a heathy touch to the landscape.

The sub-region exhibits traces of a long history of human occupation, with evidence of extensive cultivation in late prehistoric, Roman and medieval times. In general, though, it has largely escaped the worst of human influence. Indeed, by excavating marl pits to fertilise the soil—at times it seems in almost every field—man has inadvertently created a multitude of small ponds, or mini-meres, that reinforce the character of the area. Another by-product, this time of salt extraction, has been the formation of saline flash pools, such as those along the River Sow at Doxey Marshes on the edge of Stafford. The coming of the Shropshire Union Canal also necessitated the construction of Belvide Reservoir, which is one of the foremost sites for birds in the region.

Inevitably there have been disadvantages, particularly with the quickening pace of change since the Second World War. The coming of the M6 and M54 motorways has brought increased pressure for housing, commercial development and recreational opportunities, whilst modern farming practices have brought about subtle changes to the countryside. These have not always been evident to the human eye, but they have profoundly affected the wildlife. As a result, habitats have become more fragmented and the links between them have often been severed, threatening the survival of some characteristic, but rare, species.

Key Habitats

The meres and mosses are internationally important, not only as examples of glacial retreat, but also because the pollen obtained from peat samples provides evidence of the post-glacial colonisation by plants.

They consist of hollows, some with steep sides—known as kettle holes—that were formed some 10,000 years ago by the retreating ice sheets. As the ice melted these hollows filled with water and became vast meres, but with no inflow or outflow, they gradually filled with falling leaves and other plant debris which fell to the bottom and formed peat. Today the best examples exhibit a complete transition from open water, through swamp and fen to willow and alder carr, and eventually dry oak-birch woodland. Such a transition can clearly be seen at the Aqualate Mere NNR. Here there is a thriving heronry and the undisturbed mere supports several species of waterfowl, with Mallard reaching 2,539 in January 1982—a record for the period 1979-2001. Water Rails, Sedge and Reed Warblers and Reed Buntings shelter and nest in the fringing reeds. The alder and willow carr is a favourite haunt of wintering Siskins and Lesser Redpolls and also the elusive Lesser Spotted Woodpecker. The unimproved pastures, east and west of the Mere, still support a few pairs of Northern Lapwing, Common Snipe and Common Redshank. The blend of habitats is also especially rich in insect life.

Many of the shallower meres have lost all trace of open water and have completed the transition into mosses. One such example is the SSSI at Loynton Moss, three-quarters of which was cleared for agriculture in 1969 before the SWT was able to step in and rescue the remaining 13 ha. At one time there were over 40 ha of open water here, but by the eighteenth century this had shrunk by two-thirds and the last appreciable area of open water finally vanished in the 1950s. The reedbeds, however, remained wet throughout the year until the 1970s, when the surrounding agricultural land was drained. The original lake is now covered by a mat of vegetation that flourishes on the nutrient-rich peat, providing a niche for birds as diverse as Woodcock and Common Buzzard. In conjunction with English Nature, the SWT aims eventually to restore the pre-1970 water level.

Yet a further stage in the development of a mere can be seen at the SWT reserve at Black Firs and Cranberry Bog. The latter is an outstanding example of a quaking bog—or Schwingmoor basin mire—similar to that at Chartley Moss and described in the Chapter on Needwood. The gradual build-up of peat in the meres and mosses creates very acidic conditions, especially suited to ericaceous plants, such as heather, and to a few other rare and specialised plants and animals. In addition to the conifers at Black Firs, which were planted in the nineteenth century, alder, oak, birch and sycamore have all increased through natural succession, so that the resultant mixed woodland supports a good range of common woodland birds.

Unimproved grassland is now very rare, but some small fragments still survive, often in wet places, such as the Mottey Meadows SSSI. Marsh marigolds and fritillaries are among the more interesting plants to occur here and Eurasian Curlews still breed in the area. Nearby, the SWT manages a small, but floristically rich, area of wet grassland along the Whiston Brook at Bickford Meadows. It also has another fine example of a wet pasture at Allimore Green Common, which despite its tiny size sports half-a-dozen plants not found elsewhere in the county as well as five species of orchid and some rare invertebrates. Elsewhere, some areas of flood plain also retain patches of semi-natural vegetation, such as rushy pastures, which can attract breeding or wintering waterfowl or even hunting owls, while the unpolluted streams and rivers are home to Common Kingfishers, dragonflies, crayfish and otters. The agricultural land around High Offley is also well known for its population of Corn Buntings and, although not so good in the 1990s, remains one of the more regular haunts in the region for Common Quail.

Semi-natural woodland and heathland once spread along the sandstone ridges and the area around Ashley Heath used to be known as the Woodland Quarter of Staffordshire. Unfortunately, most has now been felled, particularly on the Hanchurch and Maer Hills, and either cleared for agriculture or replanted with conifers, attractive only as a roost or to a few conifer specialists such as Goldcrest, Coal Tit, Siskin and Common Crossbill. However, a huge flock of 500 Goldfinches was at Hanchurch in 1985. Four small parts of Burnt Wood, amounting to 12 ha, represent some of the last remaining fragments of ancient oakwood. Managed as oak coppice until the 1920s, it was saved from clear felling in 1933, designated an SSSI in 1951, purchased by the Forestry Commission ten years later and leased to SWT in 1979. It is a characteristic oak-birch wood, with an understorey of rowan and holly and a diverse field layer. It is also well-known for its invertebrates, and especially its range of butterflies and moths. A good range of the commoner woodland birds also occurs, including Woodcock, all three woodpeckers and Common Raven.

All in all, this sub-region gives the impression of a quiet, peaceful and largely unspoilt tract of countryside. Despite its predominately rural character it is therefore ironic that three sites have been created by man's past activities.

The first of these is the SWT reserve at Jackson's Coppice and Marsh, which originated when a river was dammed to provide water for a nearby mill. This created a boggy area upstream, which was subsequently managed as water meadows until the middle of the last century. The western end has ragged robin, bogbean, marsh marigold and yellow iris, plus some notable roadside bird cherries. The wetter middle comprises dense willow and alder scrub with clumps of greater tussock sedge, while at the eastern end the braided river channels fan out through an area of alder carr. The birdlife is good, with Common Kingfishers, Sedge and Willow Warblers, Willow Tit and Reed Bunting all having bred, whilst Woodcock are often seen.

Woodland birds in the coppice have included occasional Pied Flycatchers.

However, the two prime birdwatching sites are the canal-feeder reservoir at Belvide and the subsidence flashes at Doxey Marshes.

The history of Belvide and its habitats and birds were well described by Smallshire (1987). The water covers 74 ha, but the shoreline is less than three miles long, so it is easily watched. It is a WMBC reserve with several hides, one with a feeding station in front of it. There is a brick dam at the eastern end, but otherwise the gently shelving shoreline is natural, with stands of common reed in the shallower parts. The water quality is generally good, though it suffers nutrient enrichment from agricultural run-off into the three small feeder streams and this periodically causes algal blooms. Birds are most affected by the water levels, with wildfowl at their most numerous when they are high and waders when they are low.

At the western end of the reservoir, a physically detached marsh is steadily being invaded by scrub as it progressively dries out. Also integral to the reserve is a small 3 ha broad-leaved copse with an open canopy and well-developed shrub layer. A feeding station is also maintained here and this attracts a good range of woodland birds. Great Spotted Woodpeckers are regularly about, Lesser Spotted Woodpecker has been seen and Pied Flycatchers have bred.

The real bird interest centres around a good range of breeding species in summer; the flocks of waterfowl and gulls in the winter; and passage waders, terns and migrant passerines in spring and autumn. Notable among the breeding waterfowl are several pairs of Gadwall, whilst the reedbeds hold nesting Sedge and Reed Warblers and at times a good roost of Reed Buntings. Up to 5,000 wintering waterfowl have been recorded in the past, though numbers in recent years have been more modest. Nevertheless, some commendable counts have been made, such as up to 100 Common Goldeneye in the 1980s and a peak of 190 Goosander in 1996, although the size and depth of the reservoir are generally more suited to dabbling rather than diving duck. The gull roost is also substantial for the size of water, reaching 6,000 on occasions and often containing a rarity such as Yellow-legged or Mediterranean Gull in autumn and Iceland or Glaucous Gull in winter. Black-winged Stilt, Marsh Sandpiper and both Caspian and Whiskered Terns are amongst the variety of passage waders and terns that have been recorded. Large numbers of waders are unusual, but the count of 172 Black-tailed Godwits in 1999 was certainly impressive for an inland site. Ospreys and Marsh Harriers appear on passage most years, usually in spring, whilst less usual was a Little Bunting in 1995.

Doxey Marshes is a SWT reserve within the flood plain of the Sow Valley on the very outskirts of Stafford. It is bordered by the West Coast mainline railway, the M6 motorway and a mixture of housing estates, distribution depots and out-of-town retail stores. Brine pumping has resulted in a series of shallow pools, or flashes, set within a framework of reed-fringed ditches and damp meadows grazed by cattle. The marshes contain an especially diverse flora of over 250 flowering plants, the largest expanse of reed sweet-grass in the region and myriad insects—all of which provide an abundance of food for birds.

The most important species are the breeding waders, which usually include Little Ringed Plovers, Northern Lapwings, Common Snipe and Common Redshanks. Eurasian Teal also attempted to breed in 2001. Other breeding birds include Reed and Sedge Warblers and Reed Bunting, whilst the vast majority of the region's nesting Water Rails appear to reside at Doxey. There are also several pairs of Sky Larks and the reserve provides a source of mud for nests and plenty of food for the local House Martins.

In autumn and winter snipe are the main interest. With recent counts of over 500, this is easily the most important site in the region for Common Snipe, while Jack Snipe also appear in good numbers. Migrant thrushes arrive to strip the berry-laden hedges before resorting to the damp pastures. Spring and autumn can bring a wide variety of passage birds, though interesting ones have occurred at other times. The region's first Cattle Egret appeared here in January 1987, but it may well be some time before the excitement of the 1996 River Warbler is repeated.

The Potteries and Churnet Valley

Physical Features

This sub-region covers 509 km², or 7% of the region, and falls within the *Natural* and *Character Areas* of the same name. It measures almost 20 miles (30 km) from north to south and 25 miles (40 km) from east to west. To the south-west, it is dominated by the North Staffordshire conurbation, which comprises the six towns of the Potteries, namely Tunstall, Burslem, Hanley, Stoke, Longton and Fenton, and the older town of Newcastle-under-Lyme. To the west the urban area extends to the Shropshire and Cheshire borders, but southwards there is a gentle transition down into the Trent valley, whilst to the north-west the land rises abruptly to the ridge of Mow Cop and more gradually onto Biddulph Moor. To the north-east it rises to meet the Millstone Grit of the Moors and the Carboniferous limestone of the Dales, which rise abruptly along the Weaver Hills and Ipstones Edge.

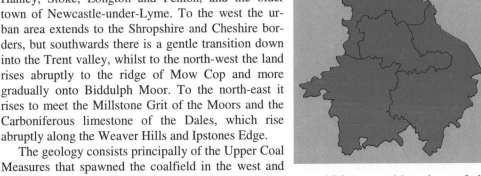

The geology consists principally of the Upper Coal Measures that spawned the coalfield in the west and Permo-Triassic sandstones in the east, though the latter are widely covered by a layer of glacial drift. The resultant landform is basically one of rising ground with flat-topped ridges between a series of steep, deeply incised valleys. The latter were mostly created by the melt waters of the last Ice Age.

Outcrops of Millstone grits and shales form a broken line of high ground that stretches from near Cheadle in the south to Biddulph Moor in the north and this forms a strong physical barrier between the industrialised Potteries to the west and the deeply rural Churnet Valley to the east.

Landscape Character

Visually, the difference between these two parts could hardly be more dramatic. To the west, the sprawling urban complex of the Potteries, with its attendant roads, railways and power stations, presents a dreary aspect, while to the east, in stark contrast, the remote and beautiful Churnet Valley must surely be one of the most picturesque parts of the whole region. Indeed, along with the Dales, it is the scenic beauty of this area that belies the more popular image of Staffordshire based on the Potteries and the Black Country.

Man's greatest influence on the landscape has to be the amorphous sprawl of the Potteries. The serried ranks of red-brick houses, important sandstone buildings and an occasional surviving bottle kiln are all part of the city's industrial heritage. So too is the considerable amount of open land—much of it polluted by past industrial activity—that became entrapped between these settlements as they expanded outwards. With the decline of the traditional coal, steel and ceramics industries towards the end of the last century, Stoke worked extremely hard to rid itself of the unenviable image that so much derelict land was creating. A major boost to this effort came in 1986, when the city hosted the National Garden Festival on the site of the old Wedgwood factory. Much land has now been reclaimed for new housing, distribution depots (where gulls sometimes roost on roofs), retail parks and amenity use. Examples of the latter can be found at Hanley Forest Park and more especially at Ford Green, where the marsh continues to be a valuable site for birds.

Even so, the urban fringes still contain very many abandoned or derelict post-industrial sites intermixed with pockets of genuine countryside and small, unkempt and over-grazed pastures—the latter frequently used as horse paddocks. Leaving the urban fringe and moving southwards, the landscape becomes more pastoral and lush, with medium sized fields enclosed by strong hedges dotted with oaks.

The Churnet Valley, with its beautiful woods and Germanesque architecture, is reminiscent of the Rhine. The river flows south-eastwards from Leek, across undulating upland pastures. As it does so, it picks up faster-flowing tributaries from the steep-sided side valleys, known locally as cloughs. Towards its lower end, the parkland settings of the Wootton estate and the theme park at Alton Towers are notable features. Otherwise the character of the valley is that of pleasant small villages, fields enclosed by strong, well-timbered hedgerows and an abundance of mixed woodland. Throughout its length, the number of tiny villages, old mills and lime kilns provide evidence of past industrial activity on a small scale. North-eastwards, towards the higher ground, the character changes as drystone walls replace the hedges and the larger fields take on the regular shape of an enclosure landscape. Gritstone also replaces brick as the vernacular building material in the tiny hamlets that are linked by narrow, twisting lanes.

Key Habitats

The most important habitats are to be found along the Churnet Valley, where the unique blend of ancient, semi-natural woodland, unimproved grassland and fast-flowing streams is of high conservation value.

Of these, the woodland is most important for birds—the cover along the Churnet and its tributaries being second only in extent to that of the Wyre Forest. Moreover the linear shape creates a longer woodland edge, which is where birds so often prefer to be. Their importance has been recognised by the creation of the Churnet Valley Woodlands SSSI.

The steep-sided valley slopes are frequently clothed by ancient broad-leaved woodland, though in several places this has been replaced by plantations of conifers, especially Corsican pine. Sessile oak is usually dominant in these extremely varied woods, but it occurs in association with a string of other species including ash, birch, holly, rowan, hazel and, less often, field maple and guelder-rose. There are also some stands of beech, whilst alders frequently line the stream sides and river valley. The ground flora is equally varied and includes some local rarities, such as great wood-rush. The woods are also rich in bryophytes and have plenty of decaying and dead timber upon which deadwood beetles feed. Their birdlife too is very diverse, with top predators such as Northern Goshawk, Eurasian Sparrowhawk and Common Buzzard, all three native woodpeckers, Tree Pipit and that familiar trio of upland oakwoods, Common Redstart, Wood Warbler and Pied Flycatcher.

The river and its fast-flowing, crystal-clear tributaries are noted for their brown trout, crayfish and caddis-flies as well as for their Common Kingfishers, Dippers, Grey Wagtails and, more recently, breeding Goosanders. Small pockets of unimproved grassland have also survived along the valley floor and the lower slopes. The drier meadows of the slopes often support a rich flora containing species such as common knapweed, yellow rattle and orchids, whereas the wetter meadows tend to be dominated by meadowsweet.

The RSPB's reserve at Coombes Valley is perhaps the easiest place to experience the Churnet woods. This 100 ha reserve comprises ancient sessile oakwoods lying either side of the fast-flowing Coombes Brook, together with areas of both neutral and acidic grassland that provide valuable feeding areas for birds. As well as oaks, the tree cover comprises birch, rowan and ash, with holly and hazel in the shrub layer and a diverse ground flora. Alders also occur in the wetter parts, while hawthorn scrub is scattered on the open hillsides. Common Redstarts, Wood Warblers and Pied Flycatchers are all present in good numbers, supported by all three British woodpeckers, Tree Pipit, Eurasian Nuthatch and Eurasian Treecreeper. Both Tawny and Long-eared Owls also occur, as do Eurasian Sparrowhawks, whilst Common Kingfishers come to the pool to fish and Dippers and Grey Wagtails search for food along the brook. In autumn, flocks of Fieldfares and Redwings arrive, sometimes in their thousands. The unusual moonwort also grows in the meadows to the north.

Much of the valley's wildlife can also be enjoyed by using Staffordshire County Council's Consall Nature Park and the Caldon Canal as a base from which to explore, or by visiting the SWT's reserves at Cotton Dell and Harston Wood.

Nestling between the enclosing hills at the head of the Churnet Valley is the long, narrow reservoir at Rudyard. At the northern end is a marshy wetland, whilst the western flank is backed by mixed woodland. When the water level is high, waders tend to congregate along the northern end of this shore, which is the least disturbed area. However, being a feeder reservoir, the draw down caused by the summer holiday canal traffic is often quite substantial and the shoreline can retreat by several hundred metres. This exposes large areas of mud that attract passage waders and dabbling duck. Over the years the former have included a few rarities, such as Pectoral Sandpiper. Generally there is a good range of the commoner wildfowl, though only in small numbers, whilst Common Redstarts and Wood Warblers are amongst the summer visitors to the adjoining woods. In winter, wild swans or Pink-footed Geese pay occasional visits, while the beech trees at the southern end have been known to attract large flocks of wintering Bramblings, with 1,000 in 1992 being one of the largest concentrations to occur during the period covered by this book. Although not an outstanding site, Rudyard does repay regular visits with some good birds.

A few miles south of Rudyard, Deep Hayes Country Park is another example of the steep sided, secluded cloughs that are so typical of the Churnet tributaries. There are woods, meadows and a ridge that gives good views across the surrounding countryside. The birds here are similar to those at Coombes Valley, but fewer in number. Woodpeckers are frequently noted and amongst the warblers that visit in summer are a few Wood Warblers. There are also three pools that attract Mallard, Tufted Duck, Common Coot and, on occasions Common Kingfisher. At the opposite end of the valley, the parklands at Alton and Wootton also enrich the habitat diversity, even if their birdlife is much the same as that of the other woodlands. Regular watching at Brookleys Lake has also revealed good numbers of Goosanders, as well as the rarer Greater Scaup and Smew, joining the commoner waterfowl in winter.

North-east of the Churnet Valley, acidic grasslands and patches of lowland heath occur in the area leading up to the moorland fringe. For the most part drainage is good, but where it is impeded characteristic rushy pastures occur and these might hold Northern Lapwings. The drier heaths are dominated by ling and wavy hair-grass, whilst purple moor-grass, cross-leaved heath and rushes again denote the wetter areas. At the SWT's Rod Wood reserve there is a gradation of habitats from unimproved acid grassland to heath, scrub and woodland. Yellow rattle—a characteristic plant of such grasslands—is abundant in the old meadows, but there are also many plants that are rare in Staffordshire including adderstongue.

Compared to the Churnet Valley, the wildlife of the Potteries inevitably appears rather mundane. There are, nevertheless, some very valuable sites, both around the urban fringe and within the built-up areas. This time, though, it is the wetlands that arouse most interest amongst birders.

To the north of the conurbation, open water combines with a fast-flowing river and both oak and beech woodland to provide a wide range of habitats at Knypersley Reservoir and Greenway Bank Country Park. The range of birds is equally varied, with most of the commoner waterfowl breeding and other species joining them in small numbers during the winter. The occasional wader or tern has also been noted on passage. Amongst the resident woodland birds, Eurasian Sparrowhawks, Stock Doves and Tawny Owls breed, whilst summer visitors include several species of warbler. Indeed, Wood Warblers, Common Redstarts and Pied Flycatchers have bred on occasions, whilst Dippers and Grey Wagtails occur along the headwaters of the Trent. In years with a heavy crop of beech mast, a few Bramblings may join the flocks of finches and tits that gather to feed on the seed. The area is not known for rare birds, but a European Serin in March 1995 was an unusual visitor.

East of the conurbation, Park Hall Country Park provides a very different habitat. Subjected to coal mining, then sand and gravel extraction and finally waste disposal, the area became a desolate and dangerous assortment of old pit shafts, spoil mounds, sludge lagoons and unfenced canyons. Now these have been reclaimed into a developing area of heath, woodland and secluded pools. The park sits astride a sandstone ridge and there is an exposed cliff face of geological interest. However, for birdwatchers the most important feature is an old pinewood, which is widely regarded as the most reliable place in the region for Long-eared Owls. The grassy heaths support Sky Larks, Meadow Pipits and perhaps Grey Partridge, whilst Linnets and Yellowhammers inhabit the patches of gorse. Raptors frequently hunt over the area, mostly Common Kestrel and Eurasian Sparrowhawk, but both Northern Goshawk and Rough-legged Buzzard have been seen. There are also one or two reedy pools that hold a few of the commoner waterfowl and, in winter, perhaps a Common Snipe or Water Rail, while the adjacent fields are the traditional site for a flock of up to 300 wintering European Golden Plovers. Being the highest point east of the Potteries, the area also has the potential to attract migrants, with records of Ring Ouzel, Northern Wheatear and Firecrest.

To the north, the little known Wetley Moor SSSI is also worth exploring. Jointly owned by the City of Stoke-on-Trent and Staffordshire Moorlands District Council, this 120 ha site possibly contains the largest expanse of lowland wet heath in the region. Northern Lapwing and Eurasian Curlew can be found in the surrounding fields, whilst the moor itself holds Reed Bunting and, in summer, Meadow Pipit and Grasshopper Warbler. Winter brings both Common and Jack Snipe, plus the occasional Common Stonechat, while Long-eared Owls, probably from Park Hall, have also been noted. The site's altitude also makes it attractive to passage Northern Wheatears.

Another site for which there have been few records in recent years is Trentham Gardens. The main feature here is the lake, which forms one of the largest areas of open water in the Potteries. Although visitor pressure tends to drive away any shy species, there is still a heronry with 20-30 nests and the more tolerant wildfowl are present in good numbers, including a few pairs of Mandarin Ducks. The adjacent King's Wood SSSI is an ancient oakwood that has been under-watched recently, but doubtless still supports a good range of woodland birds. Surprises can occur, as evidenced by a Little Bunting in 1992, which was seen on the nearby Kingswood Bank.

Within the built-up area, a few valuable fragments of the former semi-natural vegetation have miraculously survived amidst the plethora of old mines, clay pits, spoil banks and subsidence pools. Perhaps the best example is the Whitfield Valley, which was Stoke-on-Trent's first designated LNR. This includes dry acid grassland, boggy areas, old hawthorn hedges and willow, birch and hawthorn scrub. There are also one or two small pools, but the main feature is Ford Green Marsh—a small pool fringed by emergent stands of reedmace and sweet-grass. This marsh became the city's first scheduled SSSI because of its ornithological interest. This was largely on the strength of the huge autumn roost of Barn Swallows, which due to the species' decline in numbers and change of habits, unfortunately no longer exists. Nevertheless, a good variety of birds are still present, including Water Rails, both Common and Jack Snipe and perhaps a roost of Pied Wagtails during the winter. The surrounding grasslands also hold a few pairs of open-ground species such as Meadow Pipits and the declining Sky Lark, whilst Reed Buntings can be found in the wetter areas of rank grass and scrub. Overhead, Common Swifts and House Martins hawk for insects during the summer months and Common Kestrels hover in their search for small mammals.

The premier site in the Potteries for wintering wildfowl and gulls, and for passage waders and terns, is Westport Lake. This former subsidence pool, along with some smaller, reed-fringed pools, a stream, patches of scrub, willows and both alder and birch woodland, is a real urban gem, which is more fully described by Emley and Low (1982). The site suffers from the presence of a large flock of feral geese, but many of the commoner waterfowl still attempt to breed here, including Great Crested Grebes and sometimes Tufted Duck. Later they are joined for the winter by small numbers of other species, mainly diving duck such as Common Pochard and Common Goldeneye. Occasionally a diver, or one of the scarcer grebes or sea-duck, also makes an appearance. Most of the Potteries' gulls roost in Cheshire, so numbers here have never been high and in recent times they have declined with the closure of nearby landfill sites. Nonetheless, passage Little Gulls occur most years and a scarcer species such as Mediterranean, Yellow-legged, Iceland or Glaucous Gull might still be encountered, whilst a Sabine's Gull appeared in 2001. One sharp-eyed observer has discovered several colour-ringed Black-headed Gulls here, including birds from as far away as Sweden and Finland and another from Essex that returned for three consecutive years. Waders and terns are seldom numerous, but almost any species might occur and the same is true of migrant passerines. A movement of Meadow Pipits often heralds the arrival of spring and not long afterwards flocks of Common Swifts and hirundines can be seen feeding across the water. Several warblers and a few pairs of Willow Tits and Reed Buntings breed amongst the emergent vegetation and scrub. Late summer then sees chats and hirundines moving south, to be followed by larks, pipits and thrushes arriving for the winter. The lake is situated in a valley and this may account for the many rare and scarce species to have been seen here. Amongst these, a Purple Heron occurred in 1994, but pride of place must go to the Hume's Warbler that was discovered later that year.

In recent years land reclamation projects to the west of Newcastle-under-Lyme have created several new sites which have produced some exciting birds. A major opencast coal working has been restored at Bateswood. When mining ceased in 1990, British Coal Opencast gifted the site to the SWT as a nature reserve. The range of habitats includes some scrub, mature woodland and open water, but it is the grasslands that are most important. Indeed, the site has become a stronghold for Sky Larks, while the wet grassland and shallow scrapes also attract Northern Lapwings and occasionally Common Snipe. Linnets and Grey Partridges also find sanctity amongst the scrub and surrounding fields of an otherwise hostile environment. It is comforting to see attention being paid to these once familiar species that are now in serious decline.

Just to the north-east is the new Apedale Country Park. Here the once heavily industrialised valley now supports a considerable growth of scrub and young woodland that attracts a variety of warblers. It also contains a string of old pits, many now covered by stands of common reed that host what is probably the largest colony of Reed Warblers in the sub-region. There is also a steep broad-leaved wood that holds a good range of commoner woodland birds. However, it is the hillside north of Silverdale that has proved of most interest. This too was stripped by opencast mining and then reinstated as grassland, but as at Bateswood, the ground was nutrient deficient and the growth rate poor. Northern Lapwings and Sky Larks took to nesting amongst the sparse vegetation and the area also attracted passage Whinchats, Common Stonechats and Northern Wheatears. However, the real excitement was the appearance of open-ground rarities such as Richard's Pipit and Lapland and Snow Buntings. The alders that were also planted following reinstatement are now large enough to attract wintering Siskin and Lesser Redpoll, but as they mature so the grassland is becoming more enclosed. There is also more disturbance, particularly from dog-walkers. To the south of Apedale, on the opposite side of the B5367 road, is Black Bank and the former Silverdale colliery. In winter, the large, open fields here have been holding Common Snipe and regular flocks of European Golden Plovers, as well as nesting Northern Lapwings. Little Ringed Plovers have also bred at a lake on the colliery site and a few passage waders have been noted here too. However, many of these habitats are likely to prove transitory. Already Northern Lapwing numbers are falling as grass covers the patches of bare earth and the colliery lake could be filled in the future.

Further stands of reedmace can be found in a few old marl pits along the Lyme Valley and in recent years these have been used by roosting Barn Swallows, following the demise of the once regular Ford Green roost. Similar roosts have also occurred at Pool Dam Marsh and at Trent Vale.

To see two of the star birds of the Potteries, however, you need to search the old factories for Black Redstarts or listen for the calls of Pink-footed Geese as they pass overhead in late January and early February *en route* from Norfolk to the Lancashire mosses. Some skeins follow the Trent, others take a direct route across the moors, but they all converge on the Potteries, where some spectacular movements have been noted, though none better than the 2,500 on January 31st 1996.

The Moors

Physical Features

The moors of North Staffordshire occupy the further-most tip of the county. Extending across 200 km², or 3% of the region, they measure 12 miles (20 km) from north to south and about the same from east to west. For the most part they consist of an upland area, indented by the deep valleys of fast-flowing streams, but largely above 250m and rising to almost 500m on Oliver Hill, near Flash. To the south-west, however, they include a substantial fringe of lower farmland around the foothills, within which Gun Hill stands up as a moorland outlier. These foothills have an irregular topography with rounded, hump-backed hills separated by the narrow valley of the Dane and the somewhat broader ones of the Manifold and Hamps.

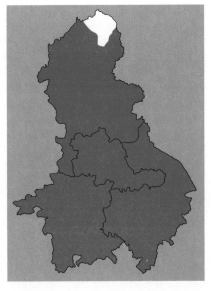

The Moors are at the southern end of the Pennines and fall within the Dark Peak section of the Peak District National Park. They also lie within the *South West Peak Natural Area* and *Character Area*. To the north the moorland landscape continues into Cheshire and Derbyshire, but to the south it ends quite abruptly, either where the sombre gritstone abuts the sparkling white limestone of the dales, or where the land falls sharply away into the Churnet Valley.

The geology consists of inter-bedded and folded shales and Millstone Grit, with some limestone outcrops to the south-east. Within the overall upland area, a series of gritstone edges—exposed by a combination of glacial and fluvial action—give rise to the dramatic crags of The Roaches and Ramshaw Rocks. Exposures of Coal Measures also form basins, such as Goldsitch Moss, while softer shales occur along the upland fringe east of Flash and south-east of Morridge.

The A53 Leek-Buxton road bisects the area, more or less following the watershed between the Dane and its tributaries, which flow westwards, and the Dove, Manifold and Hamps, which flow eastwards. In the extreme south, however, the headwaters of the Churnet flow south-eastwards.

Climate is also crucial to the birdlife of this area. Temperatures are around 3-4°C lower than across most of the region and rainfall can be as high as 1,300 mm a year. Winters especially can be harsh, with snow twice as likely as further south and sometimes lying for several days. As a consequence, most species forsake the area for the lower ground of the moorland fringe during the winter months.

Landscape Character

Although archaeological evidence points to human occupation of the lower hills since prehistoric times, it was the enclosures of the eighteen and nineteenth centuries that established today's intricate pattern of fields enclosed on the higher ground by drystone walls and at lower altitude by hedges.

The area is served by a network of narrow, twisting roads that make these moors more accessible than those of most upland regions. This serves to increase their popularity for various recreational pursuits, including rock climbing and para-gliding, which in turn has an adverse effect on wildlife. Past industrial activity has left a small legacy of quarries, pits and shafts, notably around Flash, as well as numerous small watermills along the fast-flowing streams.

The backbone of the area is a bleak, windswept expanse of exposed, rolling moorland. Across it, settlement is sparse, save for a few isolated farmsteads that stand within small areas of in-bye fields. Occasionally these farmsteads are clustered together into small hamlets, whilst Flash is reputedly the highest village in England.

Around the moorland fringe, the squat gritstone farmsteads nestle into the sheltered folds of the hills, away from the biting winds. Hamlets and villages are more widely scattered here, notably around the valley mills. In the south-west of the area, brick replaces gritstone as the vernacular building material. Hedges also replace drystone walls in a mosaic of permanent pastures, marshy corners, scattered trees, patches of scrub and the occasional cereal field.

Key Habitats

The Moors are arguably the most important area for birds in the whole region. Indeed, a large part has been designated as a Special Protection Area (SPA) under the European Birds Directive because of its assemblage of upland birds, in particular breeding Merlin, European Golden Plover and Short-eared Owl. Just over a third of the area also falls within the Leek Moors SSSI. For birds, the real value of the moorland mosaic lies in the combination of rocky outcrops and broad sweeps of heather on the exposed summits, rushy pastures and wet flushes in the hollows, and hay meadows on the lower ground.

Heather moor is an internationally important habitat. Most of that in North Staffordshire is dry heath and occurs on thinner layers of peat than other areas further north in the Dark Peak. Much used to be managed as grouse moor, with rotational burning to keep it in prime condition for the birds, but the impression today is that there is less management. However, accidental fires, such as that recently on the Roaches, can cause considerable damage, putting yet more pressure on the Red Grouse and other species associated with this habitat. Botanically, this is a species-poor habitat, with little other than ling, cotton-grass, wavy hair-grass and the occasional patch of bilberry. However, it is very important for birds and the RSPB has carried out three comprehensive surveys of the area (Waterhouse 1985, Brindley *et al*. 1992 and McKnight *et al*. 1996). Meadow Pipits and Red Grouse are the commonest and most widespread species breeding on the moors. Eurasian Curlew and a few Twite also nest, Merlins and Short-eared Owls do so most years and Hen Harriers very occasionally, but European Golden Plover has probably now disappeared as a breeding species.

The RSPB surveys showed the Red Grouse population to be stable between 1985 and 1996, particularly at Swallow Moss and the Roaches where management was clearly beneficial. However, it was noted that some moors were in need of corrective management and the numbers of grouse reported from elsewhere since then indicate some declines. The Twite population of the area is especially important and vulnerable, since it is the most southerly in England and is geographically isolated. McKnight (*op. cit.*) stated that the 27% fall in numbers of this moorland finch to just 64 pairs in 1996 was cause for concern, but numbers may now be as low as 5-10 pairs (Gribble 2000). Similarly, Eurasian Curlew numbers fell by 57% during 1985-96 and this was coupled with some contraction in range to the north and west. European Golden Plovers also declined in this latter period, from 12 pairs to one. However, Merlins increased from just one pair in 1985 to three in 1992 and 1996, whilst two pairs of Short-eared Owls were also noted in the latter two years, whereas there were none in 1985.

Wet flushes and the rocky outcrops along the Gritstone edges are also important for several species. The former, in particular, are an essential ingredient of the habitat mosaic needed to sustain birds such as Black Grouse, Northern Lapwing and Common Snipe, whilst Eurasian Teal occasionally nest in such situations. The rocky outcrops form equally important components in the territories of Ring Ouzels and Common Ravens.

Again most of these species are in decline. Whilst noting that the Black Grouse population

70

had been relatively stable during 1992-96, McKnight (*op. cit.*) observed that, with only six males at the one and only lek, it was perilously low. Sadly, it has since been lost to the region as a breeding species and is believed to be extinct altogether. The last definite breeding was in 1996 (McKnight *op. cit.*). Thereafter, four males and three females were seen in 1998, just two males the next year and a single female was at the former Swallow Moss lek site in 2000. However, it is understood that birds are being reintroduced into the South West Peak and at least one female has reportedly since wandered onto the Staffordshire moors (*per* F.C. Gribble). Ring Ouzel numbers have plummeted, too, from a healthy 61 pairs in 1985, which was perhaps a better year than most, to an estimated 5-10 pairs in 2000 (Gribble 2000)—a fall of nearly 90%.

The grasslands are vital to the breeding waders. Most comprise either a mixture of sheep's fescue and common bent, or are dominated by purple moor-grass, with swathes of bracken on the deeper soils of the lower slopes. The wetter areas, with tussocks of rush, are used for feeding and nesting by Eurasian Curlew, which is one of the internationally important species, and Common Snipe, though sadly no longer by Common Redshank. Short-eared Owls also hunt across these areas. In recent years, grassland management regimes have changed, much to the detriment of the breeding waders such as Northern Lapwing, Common Snipe and Eurasian Curlew. Nor have these birds been helped by recent dry summers and all are in serious decline. Northern Lapwing and Common Snipe have suffered most, the numbers of both having fallen by 82% during 1985-96 compared with the 57% decline in Eurasian Curlew already mentioned. Common Redshank was lost as a breeding species between 1985 and 1992.

McKnight (*op. cit.*) considered the main factors leading to these alarming declines were drainage, increased grazing and the conversion of herb-rich hay meadows into silage fields, with the species most dependent on wet ground and hay meadows for feeding and nesting declining most.

Tussocks of grass are also used by nesting Sky Larks and Twite, while Whinchat have a strong affinity with stands of bracken. The latter is one of very few species not in decline, its numbers having been stable over the period 1985-96. Ring Ouzels and Northern Wheatears, on the other hand, prefer the short swards around rocky outcrops. The latter has benefited from the recent spread of rabbits after myxomatosis and its population actually grew by 20% during 1985-96. Other key species include Reed Bunting, whose numbers halved during 1992-96, Common Cuckoo, which was stable, and Grey Partridge, 14 pairs of which were recorded in 1996. Long-eared Owls also bred in 1996 and hunting Hobbies have become a much more regular sight in recent summers.

Although the breeding birds command most attention, the moors are not entirely devoid of interest at other times. In autumn migrant thrushes sometimes arrive in large numbers to feed on berries, while winter usually brings one or two Hen Harriers, perhaps a Peregrine Falcon and even the occasional Snow Bunting.

The SWT owns 120 ha of this priceless moorland habitat at its Black Brook reserve. This includes some 45 ha of conifers planted in 1972 at Brund Hill and Gib Torr, which the Trust intends to restore as moorland. The rest of the reserve comprises a blend of heather and acid grassland, with cowberry, crowberry and, in the wetter areas, cotton-grass. The Trust also has reserves at Swineholes Wood and at Black Heath/Casey Bank—both close to each other along Ipstones Edge, at the southernmost edge of the moors. Swineholes Wood has been scheduled as an SSSI because of its large expanse of heath, which is a fine example of the transition from lowland heath to upland moor, but it also contains open secondary woodland that has developed naturally and a few larch and Scots pines that stand as relics of former planting. Amongst its interesting flora, mention might be made of cow-wheat, which is uncommon in the county, though of more significance are the moorland bumblebee and a few nationally notable moths. Woodcock can be seen roding across the reserve at dusk. Black Heath, too, is an SSSI important for its remnant heath, while Casey Bank contains largely unimproved, marshy grassland that is much beloved by Common Snipe, Eurasian Curlew and Northern Lapwing.

Although in the past there were other favoured spots for certain species, notably the Roaches and Swallow Moss, the fragile bird community of the moorland has become so depleted that few, if any, of these places can still be considered wholly reliable for any species. Apparently English Nature has negotiated an agreement to remove livestock from a formerly good site at Gradbach Hill. As a result, the vegetation is slowly beginning to recover and it will be interesting to see which birds return. Perhaps it is in the interests of the birds not to focus on particular sites, but rather it is better to explore the moorland generally.

There are a few patches of wet alder, birch or willow woodland along some of the streamlines, but the beautiful semi-natural oakwoods are the most important for birds. These are concentrated along the deeply incised, narrow valleys of the River Dane and its tributaries. Sessile oak is normally dominant, but pedunculate oak, birch and rowan also occur—the fruits of the latter being avidly sought by migrant thrushes when they arrive in autumn. The ground cover comprises wavy hair-grass and bilberry. The breeding bird community in these woods is typical of upland oakwoods, with Tree Pipit, Common Redstart, Wood Warbler and Pied Flycatcher. Some areas of heather moor and grass have been planted with conifers, mainly pines and spruce. In their early stages of growth, these plantations attracted Black Grouse, Short-eared Owls and even Hen Harriers. As they have matured so they have become less hospitable, except along rides and around clearings and edges, where they attract Long-eared Owl, Eurasian Sparrowhawk and Common Crossbill.

The rivers and streams, though less important than those of the nearby Dales, still hold Dippers and Grey Wagtails and are occasionally visited by Common Sandpipers, though it is doubtful whether any still breed along them as they used to. However, as mentioned below, they do maintain a foothold at Tittesworth Reservoir.

Situated in the moorland fringe, Tittesworth, and particularly the pools and islands in the conservation area north of the causeway, acts as a focal point for some of the less sensitive birds. In a regional context, the reservoir's prime importance is as the sole surviving breeding site for Common Sandpipers, with up to half-a-dozen pairs having bred here now for several years. Indeed, the Peak District population is the most southerly in England that is viable. Locally the reservoir is important for its wintering swans, geese and ducks, while the fluctuating summer water level can expose a considerable area of mud for passage and summering waders. The latter include both Little Ringed Plovers and Northern Lapwings, but regrettably their breeding attempts are often flooded out. Eurasian Curlews also nest on the nearby fields and in spring a hundred or more may gather to the north of the reservoir before dispersing to breed on the moors and in-bye pastures. Among the passage migrants and vagrants, Ospreys are more or less annual visitors, whilst Temminck's Stints have occurred three times, a White-rumped Sandpiper appeared in 1984 and a Bluethroat in 1994. On occasions, the reservoir also serves as a sanctuary for a few Pink-footed Geese, which are presumably sick or tired birds dropping out of the passing skeins that over-fly the area in autumn and winter. The River Churnet, which flows into the reservoir, is a favourite spot for Dippers and the surrounding mixed woodlands attract Common Redstarts and the occasional Pied Flycatcher.

The moors are not noted for rare birds, but another Bluethroat occurred at Knotbury in 1988 and Swallow Moss was visited by Rough-legged Buzzards in the 1994/95 winter and a European Serin in 2001. Dotterel were also noted annually in spring during the early 1990s.

Our moorland birds are certainly very special. Yet the apparent fate of the Black Grouse has shown just how vulnerable they are. Fortunately their future prospects look brighter as increasingly more land comes under sympathetic management, either by conservation bodies or through payments under the Environmentally Sensitive Areas scheme and its imminent successor the new Environmental Stewardship Scheme. For the birds' sake, it is to be hoped that these changes will not be too late.

The Dales

Physical Features

The Dales occupy 94 km^2 of north-east Staffordshire (just over 1% of the region), where they form a compact, elliptical area some 9 miles (15 km) from north to south and 5 miles (8 km) from east to west. They are part of the Peak District National Park and lie within the *White Peak Natural Area* and *Character Area*, which extends north-eastwards into Derbyshire. To the south they fall away sharply from the Weaver Hills into the Churnet Valley, whilst to the west the sparkling white limestone contrasts sharply with the sombre grey gritstone of the Moors.

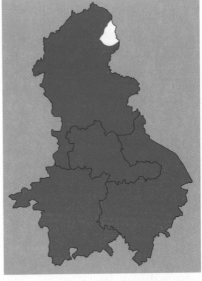

Although the dales are the most distinctive feature, the area consists primarily of a gently undulating, elevated plateau of white limestone, some 300-420m high, which is dissected by the deeply entrenched valleys of the Rivers Dove, Manifold and Hamps, along with their tributaries. It is these valleys which provide the widely renowned, spectacular dales scenery.

The nature of the limestone was determined by the environmental conditions prevailing at the time of deposition. Gently dipping, thick beds of pale-grey shelf-limestone are most widespread, but heavily folded, thinner beds of the slightly darker basin-limestone occur particularly in the Manifold Valley. Within these basin-limestones are outcrops of finely-grained hard reef-limestone that are very weather resistant and stand up as conical hills, such as Thorpe Cloud and Wetton Hill. The geological picture is completed by a covering of fine glacial silt, or loess, across the plateau, which produces the rich, loamy soils that support such fine pastures.

Geology, climate and drainage have all combined to create the dramatic scenery. The high rainfall on the impervious gritstone moors, where the Dove and Manifold have their sources, produces sufficient run-off to maintain their flow across the porous limestone in all but the driest weather. Incision by these two rivers has lowered the water table, leaving some of the tributary valleys high and dry. Indeed, even sections of the Hamps and Manifold disappear underground except in the wettest winter weather. There is, however, a noticeable scenic contrast between Dovedale, with its narrow, vertical-sided valley produced by the joints and fissures in the limestone, and the Manifold valley, where erosion of the basin limestones has resulted in a more open dale.

Landscape Character

Evidence of human occupation goes back well over 10,000 years and the land has been farmed for about half that time. Initially this produced a pattern of common grazing in open fields that persisted until the enclosure era. Then the land was divided into large rectangular fields by the characteristic white limestone walls we see today, often with smaller, narrower enclosures around the villages.

Lead mining from the seventeenth to the nineteenth centuries left many scars on the surface, but unfortunately pumping out the mines lowered the water table. More noticeable today are the scars of the limestone quarries. One or two of these are within Staffordshire, whilst several others are clearly visible on the Derbyshire side of the border. Limestone has been

73

used as a building material for centuries, contributing much to the character of the villages, farmsteads and drystone walls, but today it is often used for roadstone.

The large plateau fields have mostly been agriculturally improved to support intensive stocking with dairy herds. More recently, though, this traditional type of farming has been replaced by the specialised production of grass leys. This has all been at the expense of the permanent pastures and species-rich hay meadows that were once so typical of the area, but which have now largely been consigned to history. Those that survive are generally on the more gently sloping dale sides, but even these are suffering through lack of management and consequent scrub encroachment. The steeper dale sides are either carpeted with grasslands grazed by sheep or clothed with ash woodland. The upper slopes are also dotted with invasive hawthorn and gorse scrub, whilst higher still there are caves in the dramatic, towering cliffs that rise to a craggy skyline.

Today there is little tree cover on the plateau, save for a few isolated copses of sycamore planted to provide some shelter to the farmsteads. But it hasn't always been so. Once there was a covering of oak-birch woodland, but very few fragments still survive.

Key Habitats

With their crystal clear streams, rocky outcrops, calcareous grasslands, areas of scrub and ashwoods, the dales are of outstanding wildlife value. Indeed, they have recently been nominated as a Candidate Special Area of Conservation (SAC), in recognition of their European importance. The Hamps and Manifold Valleys are also scheduled as an SSSI. All of these are important habitats for birds.

The clean waters of the Dales streams are rich in plants and invertebrates and have been renowned since Isaac Walton's time, at least, as superb trout fisheries. Some of them are winterbournes that run dry during the summer months, when they may disappear down swallow holes. The propensity to run dry increased when the drainage system for the lead mines lowered the water table, but in recent years it has been compounded by the run of dry summers. Large beds of butterbur, such as those at Ilam, are a characteristic feature and provide bankside cover for Moorhens and Common Coots. Common Kingfishers, too, can often be seen, especially where fish have been trapped in the pools left behind after a stream has ceased to flow. On the faster-flowing stretches, the wealth of invertebrate food sustains good populations of Dippers and Grey Wagtails, while Goosanders are regularly seen even in summer and breeding was proved in 1991.

The commonest woods are the semi-natural ashwoods that cling to the sides of the dales. The ash is one of the last trees to come into leaf and it has a fairly open canopy, which allows light into the woodland floor, so these ancient, semi-natural woods are floristically very rich. They are also good for mosses, lichens, liverworts and ferns. Amongst the birds, Common Chaffinch and Willow Warbler are probably still the commonest species, though the fortunes of the latter have been very variable of late. The supporting cast includes a wide range of warblers and a few Common Redstarts and Green Woodpeckers. Two new species to have recently colonised the dales woods are Common Buzzard and Common Raven.

The SWT has two reserves with woodland in the Dales. Of these, Castern Wood has been described as arguably the finest and most scenic of the Trust's reserves. Situated on the steep slopes leading down to a meander in the River Manifold, it comprises ancient ash woodland, scrub, species-rich limestone grassland and some superb views. The reserve is also known for its five species of bats that winter in the adit to an old lead mine and for its wide variety of insects, which in turn attract many birds to the area. The other reserve is the nearby Weag's Barn. This too contains grassland and scrub as well as woodland, whilst its flora includes some uncommon plants including mountain currant, maidenhair fern and toothwort. The only other woods are the remnant oak-birch woods on the plateau itself. These are few and far between, but they might hold a wider range of birds than the ashwoods.

The dales are famous for their especially rich, limestone grassland flora. Indeed, some sites are of international importance, but all depend on being grazed by sheep, which are fast disappearing as farming changes. The earlier cutting for silage has had a significant effect on the birds, with a dramatic decline in ground nesting species, such as the Sky Lark and Meadow Pipit. Northern Lapwing and Eurasian Curlew, both once reasonably common, have also virtually disappeared, even from the acidic grasslands that once provided suitable nest sites as well as rough grazing for sheep.

Above the woods, towards the top of the dales, there are often extensive patches of scrub—a much under-valued habitat of particular importance to some scarce or declining birds. Hawthorn scrub is commonest, but there are also large areas of gorse and in some places hazel, the latter probably a remnant of the former woodland cover. These scrub habitats are often preferred for nesting by species such as Common Whitethroat, Linnet and Yellowhammer, while Bullfinches also nest in some of the denser patches. Sometimes Common Redstarts occur in these areas too. The sheer limestone cliffs, with their fissures and caves, and the quarry faces provide safe nest sites for many Western Jackdaws, plus a few pairs of Stock Doves, Common Kestrels and sparingly Common Raven and Peregrine Falcon.

Two CBC census plots provide an insight into the farmland bird communities. On 68 ha at Calton, there were on average of 83 territories per year during 1981-97—a density of 122 per km^2. The commonest birds, with their respective average number of territories a year were Common Chaffinch (15), Blackbird (10), Blue Tit (7), Wren (6), Common Redstart (5), Sky Lark (5), Meadow Pipit (5), Willow Warbler (3) and Great Tit (3)—a community which shows some differences to those of lowland farms. Whilst numbers fluctuated from year-to-year, most of these species were fairly stable over the period as a whole, though Common Redstarts appeared to crash at the end of the period. Small colonies of Linnets and Tree Sparrows were also noteworthy, not least because they too appeared to be relatively stable. Of the waders, Northern Lapwings nested on average every other year, with up to five pairs on occasions, but there was only one nesting attempt by Eurasian Curlew. A pair of Little Owls nested most years and other species of interest that sporadically held territories were Stock Dove, Great Spotted Woodpecker, Northern Wheatear, Spotted and Pied Flycatchers, Eurasian Nuthatch and Bullfinch.

The ashwoods in the Dales resound to the song of Common Chaffinches.

The second plot, on a steep-sided dale at Wetton Mill, was only surveyed from 1992-95, during which time the average number of territories on 91 ha was 43 a year, which represents a density of 47 territories per km^2. The three commonest species, again with their respective average number of territories a year, were Meadow Pipit (10), Sky Lark (7) and Northern Wheatear (7). These characteristic upland species were then followed in order by Pied Wagtail (4), Common Chaffinch (4), Wren (3) and Goldfinch (2). Significantly, during this relatively short period Northern Wheatears declined by 70%, whilst the number of Meadow Pipit, Sky Lark and Pied Wagtail territories halved. However, since these declines were contrary to the stable situation found for the same species at Calton, it is impossible to know which of the two reflects the general trend for the area.

Indeed, it would be interesting to have more comparative data from this little watched sub-region. Back in 1977, 300 singing Willow Warblers were counted along a nine mile (14 km) stretch of the Manifold Valley between Hulme End and Waterhouses, but how many would there be today? Whilst there are no special sites for birds, Dovedale and the Manifold and Hamps Valleys are all easy to explore and most of the characteristic species can be found along them. Above all else, the Dales offer excellent bird-watching amidst some of the finest scenery in England.

Needwood

Physical Features

Needwood consists of a rolling plateau that lies generally between Stoke-on-Trent, Uttoxeter, Burton-on-Trent and Stafford. From east to west it stretches just over 20 miles (32 km) and from north to south 10 miles (16 km) and covers 484 km², or 7% of the region. Much of its boundary is clearly defined, with the River Dove separating it from the South Derbyshire Claylands to the north-east, an abrupt drop into the Trent Valley along the south-east and the escarpment of Cannock Chase to the south-west. To the north-west, however, the land grades into the Potteries and Churnet Valley sub-region. The whole area forms the south-western section of both English Nature's and the Countryside Agency's *Needwood and South Derbyshire Claylands Area.*

At one time the eastern part of this area, between the rivers Blithe, Trent and Dove, formed the core area of the former Needwood Forest. Here strata of the Mercia mudstones are covered with a substantial layer of glacial till, which creates heavy, poorly-drained soils. North-west of the Blithe, the mudstones are replaced by the Triassic sandstones of the Churnet Valley area, which yield sandy soils in places where they are not covered by till.

Drainage is generally by small streams which flow from the backbone of higher ground that stretches through the area from north-west to south-east. Those to the south-west of this line, of which the Blithe is the largest, flow into the Trent, while those to the north-east flow down the steeper slopes into the Dove. The Dove itself prescribes a sweeping arc as it meanders firstly south-westwards and then south-eastwards across a wide flood plain to its confluence with the Trent downstream of Burton-on-Trent.

Landscape Character

Because of its Forest origin, the land to the east of the River Blithe remained unenclosed until the nineteenth century, but it now exhibits the neat, orderly appearance of an enclosed landscape, with straight roads running between rectilinear fields and blocks of coniferous and broad-leaved woodland. This reflects the presence of several large estates, notably those of the Duchy of Lancaster. Many of the deciduous woodlands are ancient, while some of the conifer plantations are on these old woodland sites. Much of the former forest now falls within the boundary of the new National Forest, which hopefully will recreate many of the earlier habitats of benefit to birds.

The land rises to a prominent wooded scarp above the Dove, with a hilly but less wooded and dramatic landscape above the Trent. Attractive red-brick villages with sandstone churches and occasional half-timbered buildings lie towards the edge of the Forest, where they are sheltered within the fertile valleys. On the higher plateau there are more recent settlements at crossroads and a scattering of nineteenth century farms. Oak dominated landscaped parklands are also significant features, whilst hedgerow tree cover is variable. Even within the heart of the former Forest, most of the land is in agricultural use. Pasture predominates, but the more fertile ground is often under arable cultivation.

To the north-west of the River Blithe lies a large area with smaller fields that are mostly under pasture and bordered by well-timbered hedgerows. Locally some of the hedges have deteriorated, but the small woodlands, spinneys and copses still give a predominately wooded character. As well as valley villages, there are scattered farmsteads standing within an irregular field pattern that is much older than that of the former Forest area. On the higher ground there are occasional patches of heathland. Hamlets, developed amidst commons and wastes like Loxley Green and Scounslow Green, straggle along winding roads which, in the valleys, are often sunk between high, overgrown hedges.

Remnants of ridge-and-furrow and the earthworks of deserted settlements show that the whole area was once more densely populated, but today the overall impression is of a sparsely populated, rural sub-region, with Uttoxeter the only town.

Key Habitats

The wetlands and woodlands are of most value to birds.

The Rivers Dove, Trent, Blithe, Swarbourn and Tean all provide important habitats for wildfowl and wading birds. The Dove flows across a broad, flat floodplain of low-lying, wet meadows that contain a large population of the nationally important black poplar. Many of the meadows have been agriculturally improved so Yellow Wagtails and waders are in decline, but there are still a few pairs of breeding Northern Lapwings and an occasional pair of Eurasian Curlew. Oystercatchers, too, have been seen in recent years, but the only breeding record came from a nearby gravel pit. Though narrower, the floodplain of the Trent also supports a few breeding pairs of Northern Lapwings, Common Snipe and Common Redshank, together with a few pairs of Yellow Wagtails (F.C. Gribble *pers. comm.*)

Indeed, the Trent valley contains one very special habitat at the SWT's reserve of Pasturefields Saltmarsh. Saltmarshes were once a feature of the valley, but this remarkable remnant is now the last known natural example still surviving in inland Britain—as opposed to those at Doxey Marshes and Upton Warren, which are the result of man's activities. Because of its unique importance, English Nature has scheduled it as an SSSI and advanced it as a candidate SAC under European legislation. Clearly, its importance and sensitivity require access to be strictly controlled. Fed by a natural brine spring, the flora contains several salt-tolerant plants more typically found around the coasts. Its value to birds, though, lies principally in its waders, with Northern Lapwing and Common Redshank both breeding and Common Snipe winter visitors.

This sub-region also has one of the region's best sites for bird-watching, namely Blithfield Reservoir. There is something of interest at every season, with a broad range of breeding species, a whole variety of passage birds in spring and autumn and large flocks of waterfowl in winter. However, it is probably best known for its passage waders, being one of the top sites for virtually every species.

The reservoir is crossed by a causeway carrying the B5013. To the north-west it then splits into two arms. Views can be obtained from the road, but the WMBC has access arrangements with South Staffordshire Water plc and there are several hides from which to view the birds. The most productive areas are usually the two arms of Tad Bay and Blithe Bay, with the former being designated a reserve area. Between these two arms is Stansley Wood, a small oakwood that holds Garden Warbler, Common Chiffchaff and Willow Tit. Spotted Flycatcher also occurs erratically, while Marsh Tit is unusual, but has been recorded from time-to-time. On the opposite side of the reservoir, the north-eastern shore is clothed by a large block of coniferous woodland, but little information is received from here.

Much depends on water levels, especially for wader passage. The spring level is governed by the amount of winter rain and after a wet winter there is little mud to attract waders. Time was when low water levels could be anticipated in autumn after a summer of low rainfall and high water consumption, but the Water Company has now installed a pump back facility from downstream on the River Blithe that helps keep water storage at a higher level. Flocks of waders, such as Ringed Plovers, Dunlin and Ruff, used to be virtually guaranteed and often appeared in impressive numbers for an inland locality, but the real specialties were Little Stints and Curlew Sandpipers, which were more regular here than anywhere else in the region. Amongst them might well have been a national rarity, perhaps even one from America such as a Baird's Sandpiper, White-rumped Sandpiper or Lesser Yellowlegs—all of which have been seen in the past. How the higher water levels resulting from pumping will affect the number and variety of waders in the future remains to be seen. Tern passage is reliable, although numbers, especially of Black Terns, depend very much on the right weather conditions. Since 1979 Blithfield has had nearly twice as many passage Ospreys as anywhere else.

Some of the wintering waterfowl appear in relatively impressive numbers, with at times large concentrations of Great Crested Grebes, Eurasian Wigeon and Eurasian Teal—the latter having reached a regional record of 3,410 in January 1991. Shoveler and Goosander have both reached numbers of national importance on occasions too. This is also the most consistent site in the region for Pintail, although much greater numbers may appear on the flood meadows of the region's main rivers after periods of inundation. Another winter spectacle is the gull roost, but searching through thousands of birds in the hope of spotting the Iceland or Glaucous Gull can be frustrating.

A whole range of passerines also pass through during the course of a year, but few will ever engender as much excitement as the Arctic Warbler of 1993, which was the first to ever occur inland in Britain.

In and around the former Forest, woodland remains a major feature, with both ancient and semi-natural woodland and commercial plantations. Spinneys and copses are also frequent. Oak and larch are regarded as being of particularly good quality and the wild service tree and small-leaved lime are notable species. The greatest concentration of woodland lies within the triangle formed by Bagots Wood, Hanbury and Yoxall. These woods provide an important habitat for invertebrates, woodland birds and a number of scarce plants. For many years, the Bagots Wood heronry, with over 80 nests, was the largest in the region, the birds doubtless attracted by the rich feeding at nearby Blithfield Reservoir. However, a recent decline in numbers has relegated it to second place behind a heronry near Tamworth. This may be because

The gnarled, old trees of Needwood provide holes for Little Owls.

algal blooms and a higher water level at the reservoir have made feeding more difficult.

Parklands, with their veteran trees, are also of considerable value to deadwood invertebrates, fungi, bats and birds. Within the old Yoxall Park, the SWT has managed to secure a remnant of the former forest in its Oakwood Pasture reserve. The outstanding features of this area of wood pasture and woodland are the ancient oaks, hollies and crab apples that stand above acid grassland. The birdlife is good, too, with Common Buzzards, Little and Tawny Owls, all three woodpeckers and Pied Flycatcher. The National Forest has also been active in the Yoxall and Wychnor areas, further enhancing the habitat.

A wide range of wildlife habitats occurs in the farmland across the sub-region, ranging from damp lowland grassland and marshland to drier neutral grassland. Arable weeds such as field pansy, field forget-me-not and scarlet pimpernel are characteristic of the drier soils, where the land supports Grey Partridge, Common Quail and brown hare. Open ground species are also attracted to the former airfield at Needwood and three Lapland Buntings were discovered there in 1986.

Finally, another very unusual habitat is the quaking bog—or schwingmoor—found at the Chartley Moss NNR. This was formed when vegetation created a skin over a lake left as a kettle hole during the ice ages. Peat then built up on this skin and eventually became thick enough to support large trees. Even a single person jumping on the surface will set the peat quaking and the trees swaying. Because of its international importance, this site, too, has been chosen as a candidate SAC under the European Habitats and Species Directive.

The Trent and Tame Valleys

General Introduction

The boundaries of this sub-region correspond to those of English Nature's *Trent Valley and Rises Natural Area*—a much larger area that extends into the East Midlands. This sub-region thus covers an amorphous area embracing those parts of south-east Staffordshire and north-east Warwickshire that are bounded roughly by Burton-on-Trent, Kings Bromley, Tamworth, Nuneaton, Coventry, Rugby and the Derbyshire and Leicestershire borders. This whole area measures only 433 km², or less than 6% of the region, but its ornithological interest is outstanding, with some species occurring in nationally or locally important numbers.

To describe this long, narrow sub-region, we have divided it into three roughly equal parts that correspond to the Countryside Agency's *Character Areas* (shown below in brackets). However, we have chosen the following names, which are more relevant to the parts within this region.

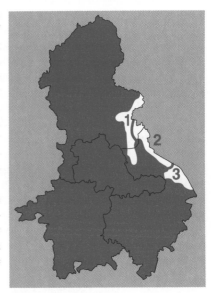

1. The Trent and Tame Washlands   (*Trent Valley Washlands*)
2. Mease and Anker Lowlands   (*Mease/Sense Lowlands*)
3. High Cross Plateau   (*Leicestershire Vales*)

The Trent and Tame Washlands

Physical Features

The Trent and Tame Washlands comprise a linear tract of low-lying land, 154 km² in extent, that includes the middle and lower reaches of the Tame Valley, from its confluence with the Blythe and Cole near Coleshill down to the Trent; the Trent Valley itself from the confluence with the Blithe at Kings Bromley downstream to the confluence with the Dove below Burton-on-Trent; and the Dove downstream of Tutbury. The valleys form part of an important migratory route for birds crossing the country between the Humber and Severn estuaries.

To the west, the washlands are clearly defined by the sandstone escarpments that rise up to Cannock Chase and the Needwood Forest. To the east, the Middle Tame Valley south of Tamworth is equally well defined by the edge of the Arden plateau, but north of this the countryside rises more gently onto the Mease and Anker lowlands.

The underlying geology consists of red Mercian mudstones and siltstones from the Triassic period. Overlying these are glacial, inter-glacial and alluvial deposits, which have formed terraces of sand and gravel alongside the rivers and these have been extensively quarried.

Landscape Character

The soils across the floodplain consist of heavy clays, flanked on either side by coarsely textured, sandy loams and these have determined both the farming and settlement patterns. Early settlements were on the terraces, above the flood level, and it was not until the last century that

81

the two major towns of Tamworth and Burton-on-Trent spilt over onto the floodplain.

The landscape is a fragmented mosaic of pasture and arable land, inter-mixed with numerous gravel pits and urban development. Except at times of flood, the rivers themselves are scarcely visible as they meander between vertical banks, but their courses can be clearly traced by the sinuous lines of pollarded willows, poplars and alders. In a landscape where woodland is scarce, these riverside trees and scrub give the illusion of a wooded appearance. Low-lying, fields border the rivers, forming stretches of permanent pastures that are grazed by cattle. They are generally enclosed by full hedges, but have few hedgerow trees.

So it is left to the riparian vegetation to screen the scars of the gravel pits and give the landscape its sense of lushness and enclosure. Flooding across these low-lying areas is a regular occurrence that temporarily transforms the landscape. On the better drained soils of the river terraces are large, open arable fields, separated by low, heavily cut hedges with just a few trees. Even those hedgerows trees that have survived are often over-mature, stag-headed oaks. Just occasionally a pond or copse provides some relief to what is otherwise rather monotonous countryside.

The tranquility of this rural landscape is frequently disrupted by urban influences, with the Middle Tame Valley between Coleshill and Tamworth particularly vulnerable. Ironically, this area contains the core of a wetland chain that is so important for birds. Being so close to the West Midlands Conurbation, few parts are far from the incursion of housing estates, superstores, distribution parks and main roads. But it is perhaps the power stations and gravel pits that have had the greatest impact on the landscape. With rivers to supply cooling water and coal from nearby collieries, maybe it was inevitable that power stations would become a feature of the washlands. The cooling towers of Hams Hall power station—once so dominant in views of the valley—have now been demolished to make way for a much smaller gas-fired power station and the giant sheds of the new Hams Hall Distribution Park, but those at Drakelow, on the Derbyshire side of the Trent near Burton, remain and lines of pylons stride out across the countryside from both sites. Incongruous as these structures are, they do provide perches and even nesting sites for birds, including Peregrine Falcons.

The sands and gravels of the river terraces have long been a source of building materials, with excavations, pits, conveyor belts, hoppers, mounds of gravel and such paraphernalia all creating blots on the landscape. While working is still in progress, the open pits, with their undulations and shallow pools, attract waders, such as breeding Little Ringed Plovers and Common Redshanks and passage Common and Green Sandpipers. This is only a transient stage, however, and it is the after use that is most important. Extraction of the earliest pits in the Tame Valley began before there were any planning controls to impose restoration conditions. As a consequence, most were abandoned once they were exhausted and, without pumping, soon flooded to form lakes, with willow scrub on the old silt beds. Planning conditions later required many to be filled and restored to agriculture, a process which met with very variable success. Fly-ash from the power stations was frequently used as a fill material, which in some case led to the appearance of an unexpected flora.

Of the settlements, Burton-on-Trent and Tamworth are the largest. Burton is well known as a brewery town. Some riverside meadows have benefited from this, as wells in the washlands provide the water used in the breweries so the use of chemical fertilisers and herbicides is forbidden. Tamworth, situated at the confluence of the Tame and Anker, has a history dating back at least to Saxon times. However, much of the town dates from the twentieth century, when it was substantially expanded under a town development agreement with Birmingham. Villages are mixed, ranging from small rural settlements to old mining villages and those that have experienced significant suburban expansion. Other notable changes since the publication of *BWM* have been the arrival of the M42 and M6 Toll motorways, the development of a major golf complex at the Belfry and the National Memorial Arboretum—all of which have significantly altered the appearance of parts of the countryside.

Key Habitats

For birders, the wetlands are undeniably the most important habitat, especially the chain along the Middle Tame Valley between Coleshill and Tamworth. Indeed, this has now become one of the premier sites for birds in the region. Created largely from disused gravel workings, this chain is certainly of regional, if not national, importance for its wintering waterfowl, having held over 1% of the UK's wintering populations of Little Grebe, Gadwall, Shoveler, Common Pochard, Tufted Duck and Common Coot as well as regular wintering Eurasian Bitterns—a priority species in the national BAP. As if this were not enough, it contains one of the largest inland colonies of Common Terns in the country and several species of breeding waders, while a wide variety of species stop-over on passage. Nor are birds the only important wildlife. The flora includes several rare or unusual plants, while otters—another priority species of the national BAP—are beginning to return after an absence of many years.

Strangely, none of this is recognised in English Nature's *Natural Area* profile, which simply describes gravel pits as "open bodies of water with little fringing vegetation owing to steep banks, and so have little nature conservation interest" (English Nature 1998). It also mentions Eurasian Bitterns at Attenborough Gravel Pits (Nottingham), but not their regular presence in the Tame Valley, where they have now been recorded for ten consecutive winters. Nevertheless, the valley has at long last gained high level recognition as it is identified as "an Area for Concentrated Biodiversity Enhancement" in the latest Regional Planning Guidance (ODPM 2004). Notwithstanding English Nature's comments, some of the disused gravel pits have developed transition zones from open water, through reedbeds to damp woodland and rough grassland, providing a rich mosaic of habitats for a whole range of wildlife to exploit.

Whilst it is the wetlands of the Middle Tame that are of prime importance, the string of flooded gravel pits resumes downstream of Tamworth and continues to Burton-on-Trent and also back upstream along the Trent to Kings Bromley. Several of these are newer pits—indeed some are still active—so their habitats are perhaps more transient than most of those along the Middle Tame. Nevertheless, they, too, have important populations of wintering wildfowl, breeding waders and passage birds.

There are several key sites within the general complex of the Middle Tame Valley. Beginning in the south and working downstream, the first site is Shustoke Reservoir—a small water-supply reservoir in the valley of a tributary stream, the River Bourne. Since *BWM* was published it has been opened up to public access. With steeply-shelving banks, many of them artificial, Shustoke is primarily a place for diving birds. It comes most into its own during hard weather, when it freezes less readily than other sites because of its deeper water.

Just across the Tame from Shustoke is the WMBC's Ladywalk reserve. Situated in a loop of the river behind the Hams Hall Distribution Park, this reserve has been managed by the WMBC since its inception in 1970, firstly under agreement with the then Central Electricity Generating Board and now under lease from its successors Powergen. Kington (1989) has provided an excellent account of the site's early history and birdlife. Today five hides, including one for public use, overlook the reserve, which consists of two large and several smaller flooded gravel pits, a large reedbed and a tract of wet birch and alder wood. There are also some old lagoons, which have been filled with power station flyash and the marsh now supports thriving colonies of southern marsh orchids, marsh helleborines and yellow birdsnest. Ladywalk is widely known as *the* place to see Eurasian Bitterns. Indeed, with up to four each winter for the past ten years, it is one of the foremost wintering sites in the country for this nationally scarce and threatened species. It is also an excellent place for Water Rails and Common Snipe, whilst another of its specialties is the winter roost of Eurasian Curlew. Grey Wagtails are often present, as are Goosanders in winter, though the latter often prefer the deeper Whitacre Pool just across the river. Also in winter, Siskins and Lesser Redpolls visit the alders and flocks of Fieldfares and Redwings are regularly present. In summer, the surrounding reedbeds and scrub are alive with warblers, especially Reed and Sedge Warblers, while declining birds regularly seen in these habitats include Willow Tits and Reed Buntings.

Back on the opposite bank, the WaWT's reserve at Whitacre Heath comprises small pools, a scrape and a succession from sedges, common reed and reedmace, through willow carr to birch scrub and alder woodland. There are also rough grazing pastures at each end of the reserve. Hides and a feeding station provide excellent views of the birds and the reserve is also good for butterflies and dragonflies. The reedbeds and thickets provide a secluded refuge for waterfowl and safe nest sites for Water Rails and a small colony of Reed Warblers. The open grasslands hold nesting Sky Larks and, even more pleasingly, Northern Lapwings, Common Redshanks and possibly Eurasian Curlew. In winter the marshy vegetation provides cover for Common Snipe and up to a dozen Jack Snipe.

Continuing downstream, the next sites are the complex of three main lakes at Lea Marston and Coton. These were originally created by gravel extraction, but were then incorporated into a river purification scheme that is now managed by the Environment Agency, which has provided a hide at Coton. Lea Marston, the southernmost lake, was engineered specifically to encourage sedimentation, with a long central island to facilitate dredging. Of the two northern lakes, known as Coton Pools, the river flows through the larger one—again to encourage sedimentation—but the smaller one is off-river. These lakes have proved ideal for diving birds, with the average counts of 1,200 Common Pochard and 1,800 Tufted Duck being of national significance. Great Crested Grebes and Common Coot are also numerous and this has proved to be the best site in the region for the scarce Greater Scaup and rare Ferruginous Duck. Birds naturally move between all three lakes, but in recent winters Smew seem to have favoured the Coton Pools.

Adjoining Coton Pools to the north is Kingsbury Water Park. Here Warwickshire County Council has incorporated some thirty pools created by sand and gravel extraction into a carefully managed recreational asset of 250 ha that maintains a fine balance between the needs of water sports, informal recreation and nature conservation. The WMBC has a visitor base in a cabin here. It has also recently designed and supervised the revamp of the Cliff Pool Nature Reserve funded by SITA (Societe Industrielle de Transport Automobiles) as part of its landfill tax obligations. The outstanding feature of the reserve is its colony of Common Terns, which is one of the largest inland terneries in the country. Common Shelduck, Oystercatcher, Little Ringed Plover, an occasional pair of Common Redshank, Turtle Dove, Barn Owl and eight species of warbler also breed. In winter the shoreline is a favourite feeding ground for Eurasian Wigeon and a small flock of feral Greylag Geese, while the pools attract Shoveler, a few Common Goldeneye and occasionally one or two Smew. A good variety of waders and terns also move through on passage. Indeed, both Roseate and White-winged Black Terns occurred in the same year.

North of Cliff Pool, further active gravel pits straddle the Staffordshire/Warwickshire boundary at Drayton Bassett and stretch to the very outskirts of Tamworth, while on the opposite bank is Dosthill Lake and some other former gravel workings. Dosthill Lake, with its substantial island, was once the largest body of water in the entire valley, attracting a wide range of birds. Black-headed Gulls set up a colony, the Common Terns temporarily moved here from Kingsbury Water Park and both Little Ringed Plover and Common Redshank bred. Winter brought large flocks of Eurasian Wigeon and good numbers of Common Snipe, whilst both Barn and Short-eared Owls hunted the adjoining rough grasslands. Following a Public Inquiry, planning permission was granted for summer water skiing and the lake has since become the Midlands Water Ski Centre. It is now virtually divided into two by a bund and planning permission is being sought for winter skiing. Due to disturbance few birds now breed, but waterfowl continue to use the pool during the winter and a gull roost has recently become established.

At the same time the birdlife of the gravel pits west of the river, known respectively as Fisher's Mill (Warwickshire) and Drayton Bassett (Staffordshire), is becoming ever more interesting, but the pits are still active and access is therefore restricted. Oystercatchers, Little Ringed Plovers, Ringed Plovers and Common Redshanks all nest here, while winter regularly brings Common Stonechat, usually a Water Pipit or two and occasionally hunting Barn and Short-eared Owls. A succession of rarities has also appeared, including the simultaneous appearance of a Pectoral Sandpiper and a Least Sandpiper. The pits both here and across the river at Dosthill North have also attracted Smew in recent winters.

Downstream of Tamworth, gravel pits resume at Elford and continue intermittently to Branston, on the southern outskirts of Burton-on-Trent. Within this stretch there are pits that are now exhausted and overgrown, such as Elford, but others in various stages of working. There are also extensive flooded pits of former workings upstream on the Trent at Kings Bromley. All of these hold similar birds to the pits of the Middle Tame Valley, but numbers tend to be smaller because the sites are separated rather than forming a continuous chain. Even so, they still produce the occasional unexpected find like a Desert Wheatear in 1996. The focal points within this area are Branston Water Park and its adjoining gravel pits and Croxall Pool. The former comprises a lake with a reedbed along one side, a small meadow and an area of woodland, whilst on the opposite side of the canal a series of gravel pits extends southwards to Newbold Quarry. Among the more interesting birds, Common Shelducks, Willow Tits and both Reed and Sedge Warblers breed and the Park is a regular location for Lesser Whitethroats. On one occasion in 1993 a Purple Heron flew over—the first in Staffordshire since 1856! Croxall Lake, now a SWT reserve, holds a variety of waterfowl and has been a fairly regular haunt of Smew in recent winters. It has also been regularly visited by the small herd of Whooper Swans that has recently been wintering in the valley.

The rivers themselves, along with their tributary streams, complete the aquatic habitats. The Tame was once one of Britain's dirtiest rivers, but it is now much cleaner thanks largely to the Lea Marston purification lakes. The riverbanks are used by nesting Common Kingfishers and, in a few places, by small colonies of Sand Martins, while water voles still survive along certain stretches. At Burton, the concentration of Mute Swans on the Trent is one of the largest in the region, with rarely less than a hundred birds throughout the year.

The adjoining washlands are also of great value to birds, especially where they contain permanent pastures. Although very few show much floristic diversity or traces of ridge-and-furrow, even the species-poor fields, dotted with rushes and other tussocky vegetation, provide winter feeding grounds for wildfowl, plovers and thrushes, especially as the floodwaters recede. If they remain wet enough through the summer as well, they sometimes attract breeding waders, such as Northern Lapwing and Common Redshank though these species mostly resort to the gravel pits. Surveys undertaken in 1998 and 2003 for the BTO Waders of Wet Meadows inquiry show drastic declines in all species, with Little Ringed Plovers down by 80%, Northern Lapwings 70%, Common Redshanks 60% and Oystercatchers 50% (F.C. Gribble *pers. comm.*). The most productive area for birds is usually the flood plain around the confluence of the Trent and Tame near Alrewas. Here in winter, the meadows and adjacent gravel pits are fairly regularly visited by swans, geese and ducks, including Eurasian Wigeon, the small herd of Whooper Swans mentioned above and perhaps Bewick's Swans, White-fronted Geese and Pintail as well.

The open arable fields attract Sky Larks, wintering flocks of Northern Lapwings and European Golden Plovers plus a few surviving Linnets, Tree Sparrows and Grey Partridges. Even Corn Buntings can still be found in a few favoured spots, notably around Whitemoor Haye, while Yellow Wagtails are noted on passage and Common Quail—always an irregular migrant—appear occasionally. The concentration of prey also attracts raptors, such as Merlin and Peregrine Falcon, and owls, notably Barn Owls and, in winter especially, Short-eared Owls.

The valleys have many small copses, both broad-leaved and coniferous, that have been planted as game coverts. These apart, woodland is scarce, though in years to come the National Forest and the newly planted National Memorial Arboretum should help to redress this a little. Past clearance has virtually eliminated the ancient semi-natural woodland that once thrived on the Mercia mudstones, but a few remnants can still be found along the river escarpments, most noticeably at Hopwas Wood. Willow Tits were often found in these woods, but the small populations that still survive in the Tame Valley now mostly inhabit the scrub and wet woodland on the silt beds. With so little woodland, hedges become more important as a substitute habitat for many species, yet these too have been decimated in the more intensively farmed areas, to the detriment of Tree Sparrows, Linnets and Yellowhammers. There is one intensive arable area around Minworth and Curdworth, however, that still seems to attract good flocks of passerines, providing prey for regular wintering Merlins.

The Mease and Anker Lowlands

Physical Features

This area covers the claylands that surround the River Mease in south-east Staffordshire and the tributaries of the River Anker in north Warwickshire, together with the Anker valley itself above Tamworth, where it eventually merges into the High Cross Plateau. It is bounded to the south-west by the scarp slope of the Midland Plateau. The area is covered by Mercian mudstones, which yield productive, reddish clay soils. The main rivers are the Sence, Mease and Anker, all of which eventually drain into the Tame. The geology and drainage pattern have produced gently rolling clay ridges interspersed with shallow valleys that become virtually flat around the rivers.

Landscape Character

This is a thinly populated area of arable farms with low, sparse hedges and few hedgerow trees. Enclosure of the open landscape during the eighteenth and nineteenth centuries imposed the strongly rectilinear field pattern of today. The landform, however, is still emphasised by copses and spinneys on the ridges and by occasional groups of streamside trees. The removal of many hedgerows, and the ash and oak trees that grew within them, has created an open, impoverished landscape, which in places is little more than an arable prairie. The isolated red brick farmhouses, standing four-square within the rectangular field pattern, add to the remote, rural character.

Small villages—their red-brick cottages clustered around spired churches on the crests of hills—are very prominent features in the landscape. So, too, are the badly-sited lines of pylons and the M42 motorway, which cuts a swathe right through the area. Otherwise urban influence is mainly confined to the periphery. Here, the villages near to Burton-on-Trent have acquired significant amounts of post-war development, while the Anker valley has been affected by past industrial and mining activity in the adjacent towns of Nuneaton, Atherstone, Polesworth and Tamworth. The most evident legacy of this are the colliery subsidence pools at Alvecote.

Key Habitats

The prime habitat is again the wetlands, and especially the complex of pools at Alvecote, in the Anker valley. Designated as an SSSI in 1955, this was the first Nature Reserve to be managed by the WaWT. The pools are a result of mining subsidence in the 1940s and an impressive list of birds has built up since then. A good range of waterfowl has included breeding Great Crested Grebe, Common Shelduck and Tufted Duck, with Garganey present during the breeding season on occasions. Many passage waders have been recorded and Little Ringed Plovers and Northern Lapwings have bred. Perhaps one of the more exciting finds was in May 1987 when a pair of Black-winged Stilts arrived and were observed copulating. Unfortunately they did not breed and it was thought they were immature birds. At one time the pools were *the* place for moulting Mute Swans in late summer, with up to 200, but nowadays the flocks are more dispersed with Alvecote holding less than 100. The rich flora includes bladderwort and southern marsh orchids, while an interesting example of a species adapting to its habitat are the wolf spiders living on the coal tip, which are black.

Across the area as a whole, the open arable fields hold few birds, especially where grubbing up of hedges has removed any cover for feeding, roosting and nesting. Some of the marshy areas along the rivers have marsh marigold and yellow iris, along with alders and hawthorn scrub, which might provide a niche for the occasional riverside species, such as Reed Bunting, but these are few and far between. There are also some low-lying meadows at Austrey.

Converting barns into residential accommodation has deprived Barn Swallows and Barn Owls of nest sites, so the WMBC was pleased, when in 2000, it was asked to join with the Hawk and Owl Trust and the Environment Agency in a scheme to erect nest-boxes to encourage Barn Owls to return (Coleman J. 2002, Coleman A.E. 2002 and 2004). Just over half of the boxes erected within the WMBC's area are along the Mease and Anker valleys, where they link up with existing schemes in neighbouring counties in the East Midlands. To start with, occupancy by Barn Owls was low, but there are now encouraging signs of some increase. Meanwhile, Common Kestrels, Stock Doves, Little Owls and possibly Tawny Owls have all put them to good use.

The High Cross Plateau

Physical Features
This upland plateau consists of Mercia mudstones and Lias clays beneath a thick covering of glacial drift. The plateau forms the watershed between the Avon and Soar catchment areas and is dissected by their small feeder streams, the largest of which is the River Swift. The result is an undulating countryside of rolling ridges and broad valleys, with light, well drained soils on the summits, but heavy clays in the valleys.

Landscape Character
This is essentially open, remote countryside. Despite some new development, the villages are mostly small and compact, while evidence of past enclosures can be seen in the large, rectangular fields. Hedges enclose the fields, but on the plateau summits there are few trees and, apart from the occasional planted shelterbelt, very little woodland. Most of the villages nestle into the south-facing valleys and here the landscape is more intimate, with smaller fields enclosed by thorn hedges and lined with ash trees. Despite the closeness of Coventry, Nuneaton and Rugby, urban influence has, for the most part, been kept to the periphery and this is very much an agricultural area.

Key Habitats
Farmland is the principal habitat of the High Cross Plateau and the neutral grasslands, hedges and streams of the area do support a reasonable range of wildlife, but with little that is really outstanding. However, there are several small, private estates which could be good for birds because of their seclusion, but little is known about them.

Most of the grassland has at some time or another been fertilised, or ploughed and reseeded, but one or two meadows still have flowers such as great burnet and yellow rattle, while lady's mantle or an occasional orchid might be found in some of the unimproved pastures. The thorn hedges and pastures with remnants of ridge-and-furrow attract good numbers of wintering thrushes and sometimes small flocks of Northern Lapwings, though the latter are nowhere near as numerous as they once were. The alders and willows that line the streams may also be visited by flocks of finches in winter. The shelterbelts, being secondary woodland, have limited value, but are used as roost sites by flocks of Wood Pigeons and corvids. A colony of Sand Martins also nested in a small sand and gravel quarry at Copston Magna in 1997, when 30 holes were counted. Other notable breeding species include Hobby and Corn Bunting.

A farmland CBC survey carried out at Willey during 1980-89 showed the three commonest species to be Blackbird, Robin and Dunnock. Of more significance were the changes during that time, which tell an all too familiar story. The number of Sky Lark territories, for example, dropped from 15 to one, while Spotted Flycatchers were lost after 1983, Linnets after 1984, Grey Partridges 1986 and Tree Sparrows 1987. At the same time Yellowhammers were beginning to decline, while Turtle Doves and Willow Tits were petering out.

Dunsmore and Feldon

Physical Features

This broadly rectangular sub-region, aligned along a north-east to south-west axis, is roughly 30 miles (48 km) long and on average 10 miles (16 km) across and covers 705 km², or 10% of the region. It is broadly bounded to the north by the M6 motorway, to the north-west by the Avon valley and to the south and south-east by the Cotswolds and the Northamptonshire Uplands respectively. It forms part of the *Midlands Clay Pastures Natural Area,* is the same as the *Dunsmore and Feldon Character Area* and includes the towns of Leamington Spa and Rugby. The Feldon sub-area covers the southern three-quarters, whilst Dunsmore comprises the northern quarter on the higher ground between Coventry and Rugby, with a ridge extending southwards to Leamington and outliers to the north of the Avon.

The whole area is underlain by calcareous Lias clays, although in the Dunsmore area these are covered by deposits of glacial gravels that produce acidic soils on an elevated plateau rising to 120m. Rivers and streams, notably the Avon and Leam, have dissected this plateau into a series of interlocking ridges and valleys. The gravels across the ridges produce light, sandy soils, which, as the place names indicate, were once covered with tracts of heathland, but the valleys are lined with heavy, neutral clay soils.

Drainage across the whole sub-region is westwards or north-westwards into the Avon via the Leam and other minor rivers and streams such as the Itchen, Dene and Stour. Both the Avon and the Leam have poorly-defined flood plains and indeed some stretches of the Avon valley are quite narrow. The Leam valley is generally the broader, with a wide expanse of terrace gravels. Both can attract waterfowl in small numbers at times of flood.

Landscape Character

Because of their geological differences, the two parts of this sub-region are subtly distinct in appearance. Dunsmore, in the north, has an affinity with all of the surrounding *Character Areas*, suggesting that it might indeed be part of any one of them. In particular, it is similar to *Arden* in that the acidic soils once supported tracts of heathland, evidence of which can still be found in the flora along roadside verges and in woodland clearings. Mature hedgerow oaks, ancient woodlands and parklands further heighten this similarity, creating a well-wooded character quite different to that of Feldon. Indeed, it is ironic that the greatest concentration of woodland in Warwickshire is not to be found in the former forest of Arden, but in the complex of small woods in the Dunsmore area around Princethorpe.

Even so, across this area as a whole, the overall impression is of a flat, open landscape in which large, rectangular arable fields have replaced the former heaths on the plateau summits and it is this feature that ties Dunsmore most closely to Feldon. Clusters of red-brick houses, some of them timber-framed, form villages that nestle into the valleys of this typical enclosure landscape. Boundary hedges of hawthorn and blackthorn, with their numerous hedgerow oaks, are visually very significant, while in the extreme north the influence of large estates can be seen in the parkland settings of a few country houses.

Development pressures are very strong around the peripheries of Coventry, Rugby and Leamington Spa, with new housing, retail and business parks all evident. The urban influence has also spread into the countryside as most villages are now commuter settlements, roads have been improved and yet more golf courses have appeared. Sand and gravel workings still scar the landscape as quarrying for building and construction works continues. On the other hand several former workings are now extremely valuable sites for wildlife.

Feldon mostly comprises an open, clay vale with a traditional rural feel. Its many compact villages are set in a typical enclosure landscape of regularly-shaped fields. Prior to farm mechanisation after the second world war, the heavy clay soils were too difficult to plough and much of the area was permanently under pasture, with many of the meadows containing remnants of ridge-and-furrow. However, farming here has changed dramatically in the last fifty years and virtually all of the once common flower-rich meadows have disappeared as ever increasing areas of land have been brought into arable cultivation. Apart from the two areas mentioned below, there is little woodland cover and the tidy hawthorn hedges were denuded of their lofty elms by the virulent outbreak of Dutch elm disease in the 1970s. As a consequence, today's landscape is much more open, with red brick or limestone villages creating focal points in views that extend to the wooded escarpments of Edge Hill and the Cotswolds. Deserted settlements, some depopulated as a result of the Black Death and others by landowners repossessing their land for sheep grazing, are another feature that add to the feeling of remoteness and tranquillity.

An undulating low ridge of limestone runs along the backbone of Feldon, introducing some relief to the otherwise flat plain. Here the landscape is more intimate in character, with smaller fields and some woodland in the Harbury area to instil a greater feel of enclosure. In the past the limestone was quite extensively quarried for the cement industry and there are several abandoned quarries of considerable nature conservation interest. To the west of this ridge, woodland is more frequently encountered, especially along the gentle scarps that drop down into the Avon Valley, and several landscaped parklands, such as Compton Verney and Walton Hall, enrich the landscape.

The river valleys, particularly that of the Leam, tend to be broad and shallow, with cultivation extending to the very edge of the banks, leaving just the riparian willow pollards, lines of alders and patches of reed to mark the watercourses. The Stour, however, is different as it has a steeper gradient, with riffles and the occasional waterfall. Indeed, it once supported one or two pairs of Dippers, but these have long since gone, though Grey Wagtails are still present.

Key Habitats

The most important habitat in Dunsmore is the concentration of ancient, semi-natural woods in the Princethorpe area. These are mostly oak-birch woods with a field layer dominated by bracken on the sandier soils and bluebells on more neutral ground. The latter also support more diversity, with ash, holly and hazel all frequent and small-leaved lime and wild service tree occasionally encountered. Alders thrive in the wetter areas, lining many streams and providing food for Goldfinches, Siskins and Lesser Redpolls in winter.

Further south, in Feldon, other ancient woods are dotted along the Lias ridge between Long Itchington and Walton. These are dominated by ash with field maple and some oak. Hazel and hawthorn understoreys are diversified by a range of calcicole shrubs, including dogwood and wayfaring-tree.

The WaWT has three woodland reserves in the Princethorpe complex. All three used to be coppiced and exhibit the classical coppice-with-standards structure, but the subtle differences between them broaden their overall diversity. Ryton Wood has changed little over the years and retains many characteristics of a traditional pedunculate oakwood, with birch and ash above a shrub layer of field maple, hazel, hawthorn, holly, rowan and blackthorn. Honeysuckle is also widespread and this is an important site for the dormouse. Wappenbury Wood comprises oak and ash above birch and hazel, which again provides plenty of food for birds. Aspen also occurs in the older woodland and small-leaved lime has been recorded. This wood is rich in *Lepidoptera*, particularly moths, and a good range of birds have been recorded, including Lesser Spotted Woodpecker. Oak and hazel are again dominant in Old Nun Wood, which is the smallest of the three. Sallow and sweet chestnut also occur here and there is a diverse ground flora with primroses, bluebells, wood anemone and yellow archangel. The range of trees and shrubs meets the exacting requirements of many birds, an excellent range of which have been recorded. Wappenbury Wood used to be the regional stronghold of the Common Nightingale, but sadly this species and the Tree Pipit have been lost as their range has contracted nationally. Others, such as Woodcock and Lesser Spotted Woodpecker, still maintain a presence, although their respective habits of lying camouflaged amongst the bracken and feeding high in the canopy mean neither is easy to locate.

Unimproved grassland is rare, but one or two important examples survive, again most notably the floristically rich WaWT reserve at Draycote Meadows, which is acknowledged to have the finest meadows in Warwickshire. There are also some old flood meadows along the narrow river valleys, with ancient pollards and even reedbeds in places. Surviving ridge-and-furrow pastures are frequently used by feeding birds, particularly in winter. Huge flocks of Northern Lapwings, sometimes several thousand strong, used to be a regular feature, but numbers these days are much smaller. A few European Golden Plovers also occur, as do large numbers of Black-headed Gulls. The south of Feldon is also one of the best places in the region for Common Gulls. The haws along the hedgerows attract large numbers of Fieldfares and Redwings in autumn, which later turn to feeding on the pastures as the rising winter water-table brings earthworms nearer the surface. Joining them are Common Starlings, but in much reduced numbers, and Rooks, which are plentiful in places. Apparently the Feldon area is now the regional stronghold of the Tree Sparrow, too, with an estimated population of 350 pairs, which might be one of the best populations in the UK (J.J. Bowley *pers. comm.*). Cavities in the mature hedgerow ash trees provide nest sites for the Tree Sparrows and a range of other hole-nesting species. The area is also a regional stronghold for Yellow Wagtails, small

The arable crops and field margins of Feldon are increasingly used by Yellow Wagtails.

colonies of which breed in wheat and bean crops where there are good field margins. Other scarce farmland species such as Grey Partridge can still be found sparingly as well.

A CBC carried out on 185 ha of farmland at Moreton Morrell during 1980-96 revealed an average of 356 territories a year, which is equivalent to almost 200 territories per km^2. During this time 59 species were recorded, of which the commonest, with their average number of territories per year, were Blackbird (47), Common Chaffinch (43), Blue Tit (31) and Wren and Robin (30 each). Between them these five species made up a half of all territories. It is instructive to look at some examples of the changes that occurred over the seventeen years of this survey, which covered both farmland and woodland. Perhaps the most noticeable feature was that, despite marked annual fluctuations in numbers, resident species such as Wren, Dunnock, Robin, House Sparrow, Common Starling and Goldfinch remained stable overall. A few species showed increasing numbers, mostly during the 1990s. These included Blackcap, Long-tailed Tit, Greenfinch and most of all Common Chaffinch, which almost doubled its population. Some others exhibited conflicting trends. Song Thrushes, for example, declined from the mid-1980s, but were recovering by the end of the survey period, whilst Common Chiffchaffs showed a threefold increase in the late 1980s and early 1990s, only to decline again thereafter. In the early years one or two pairs of Northern Lapwing were also present, but they then disappeared for twelve years, only for two pairs to return again in the last year of the survey. Inevitably there were some significant losses. Willow Warblers and Yellowhammers both declined by more than half from the mid– to late 1980s onwards, Sky Lark numbers fell from five or six pairs in the early 1980s to just one or two by the 1990s and Grey Partridge numbers halved in the early 1990s. No Tree Sparrows were recorded after 1990.

A little to the north-east, the area around Chesterton holds many of the birds that are typical of the Feldon countryside. Large numbers of Wood Pigeons, Western Jackdaws and Rooks are always in evidence, Common Starlings and House Sparrows are still quite numerous, Tree Sparrows can also be found around the village and Common Kestrels regularly hunt the area. The higher fields towards the ornate windmill are favoured by a few Sky Larks and Meadow Pipits, while in winter the lower ones attract flocks of European Golden Plovers, Fieldfares and Redwings A chain of small pools has been created along the valley beyond the church and these, together with the secluded mill pool, hold small numbers of waterfowl, including Great Crested Grebes, Mute Swans and Tufted Ducks.

Abandoned limestone workings in the Harbury area have developed plant and insect communities of high diversity, especially at Bishop's Hill, and these partly compensate for the loss of unimproved grasslands. Invasion by hawthorn, bramble and coarse grasses is a constant threat to the more delicate limestone flora, but at the WaWT's Ufton Fields reserve some areas are kept free from encroaching scrub to enable rare orchids to flourish. The scrub that has developed on some of these sites is particularly good for Turtle Doves. Ufton Fields also has wetland habitats, as does nearby Lighthorne. Overall, these sites support a wide range of birds including breeding Little Grebes, Tawny Owls, Green Woodpeckers, Grasshopper Warblers, Lesser Whitethroats and Willow Tits, whilst Hobbies regularly come to hunt the dragonflies in summer. Lighthorne, with its areas of rough grazing, also supports large populations of Sky Larks, Meadow Pipits and Linnets. Notable among the winter visitors are Eurasian Teal, Water Rail and both Common and Jack Snipe, again mostly at Lighthorne. Many chats, warblers and passing raptors have also been noted on migration, while amongst the scarce or rare species, Little Egret, Green-winged Teal, Spotted Crake, Golden Oriole, Great Grey Shrike and Common Crossbill are indicative of the habitat diversity of these sites.

If the limestone quarries have enriched the flora, then the sand and gravel quarries have certainly enriched the birdlife. While they were active quarries, Sand Martins excavated nest holes in the exposed faces and the opportunistic Little Ringed Plover also bred. Once they were exhausted, some were returned to agricultural use, but others were abandoned and allowed to fill with water. One group was used as a landfill site and then reclaimed to create the

Ryton Pools Country Park. As well as a few of the commoner wildfowl and gulls on the pools, Sky Larks frequent the seeded grasslands and several woodland species come and go from the adjacent Ryton Wood.

Fine parklands are also a feature of the sub-region, though for birds there is none better than Coombe Abbey, where the grounds of a former Cistercian abbey make up Coventry's only Country Park. There is a large lake, two smaller pools, reedbeds, woodlands, some grassland with a small wildflower meadow and formal gardens. The range of woodland birds includes good numbers of Stock Doves as well as the less common Willow and Marsh Tits and Lesser Spotted Woodpeckers. In winter, small passerine flocks can be seen, which include Lesser Redpolls and Bramblings. The lake holds a range of waterfowl, with a notable flock of 50 to over 100 Shoveler in autumn and occasionally something more unusual such as a Ferruginous Duck in 2001. One or two pairs of Water Rails and a good colony of Reed Warblers nest in the reedbeds, while in 2001 there were 19 nests in the Great Cormorant colony and at least 12 pairs were though to have reared young. However, the real importance of Coombe is its heronry, first mentioned in 1872 and now the largest in Warwickshire, with around 50-60 nests.

This sub-region contains two outstanding sites for birds, both of them man-made, namely Draycote Water and Brandon Marsh. Draycote Water, constructed in 1969 as a major water supply reservoir, has, along with Blithfield Reservoir, become one of the two foremost sites for birds in the region. Draycote tends to attract more diving duck and roosting gulls, but fewer dabbling duck and waders. Already in its comparatively short history it has established several regional records, both in terms of new species and the sheer numbers of some of the commoner ones.

It has become *the* place in the region to see Great Northern Divers, which visit almost annually. Scarcer grebes, Smew or an occasional sea-duck are also noted amongst the rafts of winter waterfowl. Numbers of the latter can be quite impressive, with recent counts of almost 200 Common Goldeneye and Goosanders, around 250 Great Crested Grebes, over 1,000 Common Pochards and Tufted Ducks and up to 2,000 Eurasian Wigeon. The gull roost eclipses all of these, being one of the largest inland roosts in the country, with 40,000 birds at times. Size apart, it is well known for the number of Common Gulls, for the frequency with which scarcer species such as Mediterranean and Iceland Gulls appear and for producing real rarities such as the region's first Franklin's Gull. A variety of terns, including a few Black Terns, pass through most years, sometimes in spectacular numbers if the weather conditions are just right at the critical time. Weather conditions are also critical to the strength of the wader passage, but very much also depends on the water level being low enough to expose a muddy shore. If it is, then regular migrants, such as Greenshank, can appear in moderate numbers and might bring a rarity with them. Buff-breasted Sandpipers occurred in three consecutive Septembers and a Baird's Sandpiper in 1996 was the first to be recorded in the region. There are several embankments around the reservoir and their short grass swards, low walls and stone pitching provide perches and rich feeding areas for open ground species such as larks, pipits, wagtails and chats. Among the more numerous are Meadow Pipits, Pied and Yellow Wagtails and Northern Wheatears, but White Wagtails, Black Redstarts, Whinchats and Common Stonechats are not infrequently noted.

As a breeding site, Draycote is rather disappointing, although the waders and terns that nested when the dams were being reinforced show how good it could be if only the water level could be dropped sufficiently to expose islands. For many years birds have had to compete with sailors and fishermen for water-space, but STW has recently created a sanctuary in Toft shallows, provided a new observation hide and is constructing a new wader scrape. These improvements are welcome, but the size and configuration of the reservoir is such that many birds will still be dispersed around the entire water.

Brandon Marsh owes its existence to a mixture of colliery subsidence and gravel extraction, although today it is the headquarters of the Warwickshire Wildlife Trust. Past mineral workings have resulted in a succession of habitats from open water, through stands of reed sweet-grass and reedmace to alder and willow carr. It also has the largest reedbed in Warwickshire, while areas of rough grassland and two small woods complete the range of habitats. A second extensive area of common reeds has recently been planted, too, and this has already been visited by wintering Eurasian Bitterns.

The range of birds seen at Brandon is excellent and includes a notable list of warblers together with a few first records for the region. Wildfowl and waders are also of interest.

Both Little and Great Crested Grebes breed, while winter brings good numbers of Eurasian Teal and a few Eurasian Wigeon along with a variety of other, commoner duck. This is also one of the more consistent sites for passage Garganey. Diving duck are seldom numerous, but the regular Tufted Ducks are usually joined in winter by a few Common Pochards and perhaps one or two Common Goldeneye, whilst Smew has been recorded. Oystercatchers, Little Ringed Plovers, Ringed Plovers, Northern Lapwings and Common Redshanks have all attempted to breed recently and a small colony of Common Terns is thriving on the tern-rafts provided. Cetti's Warblers are recent arrivals that now seem to be well established, while the declining Grasshopper Warbler can still be heard 'reeling'. Hobbies are another highlight of summer, often coming to the reserve to hunt dragonflies, while Common Kingfishers are frequent visitors at all seasons.

Small numbers of waders and a few terns pass through on passage, with this being one of the two best sites in the region for Green Sandpipers in late summer when up to 20 may be present. Sedge Warblers and Reed Buntings have both declined, but the colonies of Reed Warblers in the reedbeds remain strong and there are between four and six Water Rail territories each year. The latter species is more numerous in winter, however, when it is joined by Common and Jack Snipe. This is also the time when Woodcock are sometimes seen at dusk as they leave the cover of the woodland floor to feed and flocks of Siskins and Lesser Redpolls gather in the alders. Long-eared Owl roosts have also been discovered here on more than one occasion.

Over the years Brandon has been by far the best site in the region for Bearded Tits, although recent years have brought very few records from anywhere of this delightful little bird. More unexpectedly, a Melodious Warbler recently provided some lucky ringers with a surprise in their nets. Brandon can also lay claim to the region's first Great White Egret, Citrine Wagtail and Savi's, Great Reed and Barred Warblers.

The Cotswold Fringe

Physical Features

The great line of Jurassic hills that stretches across the country from Dorset in the south to Yorkshire in the north barely touches this region. Indeed it covers a mere 272 km², and makes up only 4% of the regional area.

The hills form an extensive upland plateau, with a gradual dip slope to the south-east and a characteristically steep scarp slope to the north-west that descends into the Feldon plain and the Avon and Severn valleys below. It is this escarpment—one of England's most distinctive physical features—that provides such a strong physical boundary to the south-east of the region, appearing as an almost continuous line of prominent hills that form a pleasing backdrop to innumerable views from the valleys and plains beneath.

The scarp consists of two distinct parts, separated by an area of dissected hills around Ilmington and Long Compton. To the south-west are the limestone hills that are the true Cotswolds, while to the north-  east are the ironstones of the Northamptonshire Uplands. We have linked the two together because they form a strong, unified feature that has a significant influence on bird migration, perhaps because their south-west to north-east alignment acts as a navigation aid to birds moving across the country between the Severn and the Wash. The Countryside Agency, however, treats them as separate *Character Areas*, while English Nature, taking a wider view, regards the Cotswolds as a separate *Natural Area*, but includes the Northamptonshire Uplands along with Dunsmore and Feldon in the much larger *Midland Clay Pastures Natural Area*. The only parts of the Cotswolds in Worcestershire are Bredon and Broadway Hills—with the latter, at 313m, being the highest point. A larger area lies within Warwickshire, but here the hills are lower. The same county also contains part of the Northamptonshire Uplands.

The true Cotswolds comprise beds of rock ranging from the oolitic limestone which lies at the top of the scarp and across the plateau top, down through various beds of Lias shales, silt stones and sandstones. In many places, notably the north side of Bredon Hill, there is evidence of mud slides and the softer, lower beds have slumped or eroded, leaving hummocky hills around the foot of the escarpment. Bredon Hill itself is an outlying hill, detached from the main scarp, and rising to 293m above the flat vale landscape. The slopes of the hill radiate in all directions from the limestone capped summit, but are steepest to the north and west.

The Northamptonshire Uplands are underlain by Lias clays that are locally capped with marlstones bearing iron ore, which give rise to rich brown soils. Evidence of former quarrying can be found, for example, on the Burton Dassett Hills. The outlying Napton Hill, at around 150m, is a significant feature in the landscape.

Landscape Character

The Cotswolds is one of the best known and best loved areas of Britain, largely because of the unique unity and character given to it by its honey-coloured stone walls and buildings. Although the hills reach no great altitude within this region, the dramatic scarp slopes around Broadway, Meon Hill and Long Compton, together with the outlying hills such as Bredon and

Brailes, are dominant landscape features that stand in sharp contrast to the flat plains below.

The underlying limestone yields shallow, calcareous soils with a generally low fertility and the steep scarp slopes consist mostly of rough pastures that are used for sheep grazing. Small woods, clumps of trees, patches of scrub and improved calcareous grasslands also clothe some of the slopes. On the plateau above the scarps much of the land is under arable cultivation, with occasional blocks of planted woodland, as on Bredon Hill. The Iron Age hill forts on Bredon Hill and Meon Hill provide evidence of early occupation, but today it is the small, compact villages that catch the eye. Those around the northern foot of Bredon Hill have half-timbered cottages that contrast with those on the southern edge, which have the typical Cotswold stone houses and walled gardens. Other villages are strung out along the spring line at the foot of the scarp like tiny pearls on a necklace, with Broadway, surely one of the best known Cotswold villages, the only settlement of any size.

The most prominent feature of the Northamptonshire Uplands is Edge Hill. With a mantle of woodland, its appearance is quite different to the outlying hills of Burton Dassett, Napton and Shuckburgh, which have open, undulating grassy slopes. Throughout much of the area, the clusters of richly-coloured, ironstone cottages create contrasting, but equally attractive, villages to those in the Cotswolds. Sheepwalks have long been a feature in the countryside and the area's prosperity was founded on sheep. Wealthy merchants later established large estates, such as at Compton Wynyates, and these strongly influenced the development and character of the villages we see today. The large estates at Compton Wynyates, Farnborough and Shuckburgh also had a strong influence on the appearance of the landscape, creating parklands and woodlands, of which those on the National Trust's property at Farnborough are especially fine. Perhaps the most significant change in the landscape occurred with the enclosure of the sheepwalks. This took place in the late-eighteenth and nineteenth centuries and created the regularly shaped fields we see on the plateau tops today.

Tourism is an important part of the local economy, but agriculture is still the major land use, with much of the land now under arable cultivation. The steeper scarp slopes, however, remain either under woodland or grass, though the latter has mostly been agriculturally improved.

Generally the hand of man has fallen gently on this area, moulding the landscape and using its natural materials in a very sympathetic way. The one exception is the M40 motorway, which has introduced a corridor of noisy, fast-moving traffic into a hitherto tranquil scene.

Key Habitats

Bredon Hill contains such a rich variety of features that it is an outstanding habitat in its own right. Above all else, it has been included as a candidate SAC for its old trees, especially ash, and the associated beetles that depend on dead wood, such as the nationally scarce violet click beetle. As well as ash, there are also ancient field maples and oaks, particularly in the old deer park above Elmley Castle. Here, above the village, the unstable silts and clays on the north side of the hill contain much hawthorn scrub and pockets of ancient woodland where a few pairs of Common Redstarts nest. Higher still, Sky Larks and Tree Pipits still sing above the summit grasslands and crops, while Common Ravens patrol the hillsides. Within the foothill villages the larger gardens support a good population of Spotted Flycatchers. This has been studied for four years by J. Clarke (*pers. comm.*), who has encouraged many villagers to put up half coconut shells as 'nest-boxes' in their gardens and to help protect the birds by not pruning vegetation during the nesting season. His infectious enthusiasm has inspired many villagers to take a real interest in this declining species. On the south side of the hill, the free-draining soils harbour arable weeds such as Venus's looking-glass, field madder, dwarf spurge and wild pansy. The old quarries are home to some unusual limestone plants and good numbers of several species of snails can be found, both in the quarries and on the drystone walls. There are also stands of conifers and sweet chestnuts on the hill.

Within this sub-region there is little floristically rich grassland as most has been agriculturally improved. Indeed, much of the flatter ground that occurs to the south of Shipston-on-Stour is now in arable cultivation and here Yellowhammers are characteristic birds of the hedgerows, whilst in a good year Common Quail might be heard calling. Corn Buntings have generally declined, but still survive in one or two areas, such as on Ilmington Downs. Sadly Dippers have now been lost from the tiny, fast-flowing streams that form the headwaters of the River Stour, as have the Tree Pipits that once nested on Broadway Hill. On the other hand, Common Buzzards are new colonists that can now be seen soaring above woods such as Whichford. Likewise, Common Ravens have spread eastwards, following the buzzards, and can now be seen from Bredon Hill right round to Shuckburgh Hill. They usually nest in old parkland trees on private estates. In recent years one or two Merlins have over-wintered and sightings of Red Kites have increased as birds spread northwards along the M40 motorway corridor from the Chiltern introduction scheme. Little information is received about the birds of the Broadway Hill area, which is a pity as there are some pleasant walks which might produce a reasonable variety of species.

The birdlife of the hanging woods at Edge Hill is typical of lowland beechwoods, even though much of the beech has given way to sycamore and other less favourable trees. Cavity nesting species are present at relatively high densities, including Stock Dove, Western Jackdaw, both Green and Great Spotted Woodpeckers, Eurasian Nuthatch, Eurasian Treecreeper and Marsh Tit. In the shrubbier parts, good numbers of Blackcaps, Common Chiffchaffs and Bullfinches may be found, with a few Spotted Flycatchers along the edges. Predators nesting in the woods include Common Buzzard, Eurasian Sparrowhawk and Tawny Owl. *BWM* noted that Wood Warblers appeared to be absent, but they probably bred regularly until the 1930s, and then again from 1965-68. Subsequently they were seen on a few occasions up to 1990, but only possibly nested in 1988 (J.J. Bowley *pers. comm.*).

Recent surveys carried out by the WMBC for the National Trust at Farnborough Park have revealed a good array of breeding birds in the woods and parkland. Among the usual species, Common Chaffinches are at a high density, while scarcer birds include both Marsh and Willow Tits, Spotted Flycatcher, all three woodpeckers and Bullfinch. Lakes are generally scarce in this hilly sub-region, so those at Farnborough enrich the habitat diversity and provide a sanctuary for Common Kingfishers and waterfowl such as Great Crested Grebes, Mute Swans, Mallard, Tufted Ducks and Common Coots. Nearby the small canal-feeder reservoir at Wormleighton attracts similar species. In addition, after a summer of heavy boat traffic, the autumn water level is often low, exposing patches of mud that attract a few waders. Water Rails have probably bred here and regular watching has found Spotted Crake, Grey Plover, Little Stint and Wood Sandpiper in recent years. An overflying family party of Whooper Swans was a good reward for a Christmas Day visit in 2000.

For many birders, the main interest of this small sub-region is to be found at migration times on the hill tops of Napton, Ilmington Downs (including Nebsworth Hill), Meon Hill, Broadway and Bredon. The theory that migrating birds might follow the line of the scarp face was advanced by Eric Simms (1949) and commented upon in *BWM*. Others questioned it, arguing that migrating birds were more likely to pass through on a much broader front and could turn up anywhere. As a result, interest in this area waned until recently, when a new generation of birders discovered its potential. It is now known that birds not only follow the line of the scarp, but use gaps within it, particularly when travelling south in autumn. As an example, one observer has reported counts of up to 200-300 Sky Larks and Meadow Pipits an hour passing through the Fenny Compton-Wormleighton gap.

Evidence of migration is generally most apparent in autumn, when it might be witnessed at any or all of the hills. At this season it seems that weather plays a crucial role, with birds often making a landfall on still mornings when the outlying hills rise like islands above the mist shrouded valleys below. Migrating raptors also use the thermals that rise along the scarp to gain height. Judging the right conditions can produce some rewarding observations, with substantial movements of departing summer visitors such as hirundines, wagtails and chats in August and September, followed in October by larks, pipits and the arrival of winter thrushes and finches. Associated with these movements there is always the chance of something more exciting, as recent records of Honey-buzzard, Rough-legged Buzzard, Richard's Pipit, Icterine Warbler, Yellow-browed Warbler and Snow Bunting testify.

Of all the hills, Bredon has emerged as the focus for migration watchers, presumably because it is the largest and therefore the one most likely to attract more birds. Moreover, a small, but significant, spring passage of species such as Northern Wheatear and Ring Ouzel has been observed here and it now seems this is a regular spring stop-over point for one or two Dotterel. A Stone-curlew discovered on the hill in 1995 has been followed by two other reports within or near to this Cotswold fringe, which is interesting as they formerly bred on the stony, barren parts of Broadway and Bredon Hills until around 1840 (Hastings 1834, Harthan 1946).

The Severn and Avon Vales

Physical Features

This large area is 25 miles (40 km) from north to south and 31 miles (50 km) from east to west, reaching northwards almost as far as Kidderminster and Bromsgrove, and eastwards to the edge of Warwick. Its northern boundary abuts the rising land of the Midland Plateau, whilst to the south-east and the west its boundaries are clearly defined by the strong outlines of the Cotswolds and Malvern Hills respectively. It is thus the second largest of the sub-regions, covering 1,206 km², or 16% of the region. It lies mostly in Worcestershire, but also covers south-west Warwickshire and includes the city of Worcester and the towns of Droitwich Spa, Evesham and Stratford-upon-Avon.

The whole area falls within the *Severn and Avon Vales Natural Area* and *Character Area*, but the geological structure creates two distinctive sub-areas. In the north and west, the underlying Mercia Mudstones yield heavy loams that once were covered by the former forests of mid-Worcestershire, while to the south and east the heavy Lias clays support the intensive market gardening area of the Vale of Evesham. Together, these soft rocks have produced a uniform, low lying plain, relieved only by thin bands of Rhaetic limestone that form low escarpments and the outlying hills of Jurassic limestones. The most noticeable example of the latter is Bredon Hill, which sits within the Vale of Evesham, but has such a strong affinity with the Cotswolds that we chose to include it within that sub-region as previously described.

The valleys of the Avon and Severn both contain deposits of sand and gravel that are commercially worked for aggregates, with abandoned workings forming valuable wetlands for wildlife. An important geological feature is the extensive salt deposits found in the Mercian mudstones in the Droitwich area.

Of the two main rivers, the Severn is the faster, flowing purposefully between high banks, whilst the Avon meanders more leisurely across a broader floodplain, where it has formed a series of terraces with light, well-drained soils. These terraces are eminently suited to arable cultivation, but the soft clays on the Lias, though inherently productive, are heavy and difficult to work. Around Evesham, a covering of fluvio-glacial drift yields freely draining soils that are ideal for growing horticultural crops. Both rivers are prone to winter flooding—indeed the more volatile weather patterns of recent years seem to have made flooding more prevalent.

The sub-region enjoys the mildest climate of any, with plants sometimes flowering up to a fortnight earlier than in the surrounding sub-regions, which can be a considerable advantage to the fruit growers in the Vale of Evesham.

Landscape Character

This has always been a productive farming area, noted as far back as medieval times for its cornfields, then later for its orchards and more recently for its market gardening.

By Medieval times most of the villages had developed into compact settlements of timber-framed or mellow Cotswold stone buildings, surrounded by strip farming that created the distinctive ridge-and-furrow pattern. These fields mostly remained open until the eighteenth century, when enclosure created the regular medium-sized fields that exist today. The compact settlement pattern contrasts with other parts of Worcestershire. Several small or medium-sized towns also developed over the centuries, including Worcester, Droitwich Spa, Pershore, Evesham and Stratford-upon-Avon. Although their origins are quite varied, they were often unified through their building materials, which frequently included timber-framing and red brick.

The low-lying terrain and undulating topography have created poorly drained basins. These used to flood periodically, allowing a thin layer of alluvium to develop, and many still remain wet despite past drainage attempts. Following some severe recent floods, interest has been reawakened in once again using the floodplain's tremendous capacity to store flood waters. As a result, attempts are now being made, most notably by the WoWT, to reverse past attempts at drainage and reinstate the largest of these areas, Longdon Marsh, as a major wetland.

At the other extreme, the limestone escarpments add some welcome relief to what would otherwise be very monotonous, flat countryside. At their greatest development, these bands form low, but scenically significant, winding escarpments in a broken line from near Upton-on-Severn to just south to Bromsgrove. Similar escarpments also occur further east in Warwickshire, between Alcester and Stratford-upon-Avon.

Away from the river terraces, soils are heavy across much of the sub-region and those on the mudstones tend to have a nutrient deficiency. This helps to explain why clearance of the Royal hunting forests that once spread from the Malverns and Wyre right across to Arden was so slow. Even though the forests have now virtually disappeared, their influence on the life and appearance of the countryside can still be seen in the wealth of timber-framed buildings, small relict woodlands and myriad hedgerow trees scattered across the area. Nowadays, the fertile land is used intensively for arable, livestock and mixed farming.

Along the foothills of the Malverns material washed down from the higher ground has spread out across the plain, producing poor, gravelly soils that support commons, such as that at Castlemorton. Here clearance of the forest, known as Malvern Chase, quickly followed enclosure in the early seventeenth century and today very little remains. However, there is some compensation in the species-rich grasslands of the south and south-west, some of which contain wild daffodils and green-winged orchids. North-west of Worcester hamlets and small villages are scattered throughout a landscape that is heavily wooded.

On the eastern flank of the river, between Worcester and Kidderminster, the light, sandy soils have been extensively farmed, with market gardening in recent times, and there are numerous scattered hamlets around Ombersley. The salt deposits around Droitwich made the town important even as far back as Roman times and it later became an elegant spa. Since the 1960s it has grown considerably through its role as a town expansion area for Birmingham.

There are more woodland remnants between Worcester and Pershore, in what was the ancient forest of Horewell, and on the neutral soils around Himbleton, at Goosehill, Trench and Grafton. Several of these were predominately oakwoods over hazel that were formerly coppiced. The sub-region also contains some precious grasslands and relict commons set amongst mixed farmland and several important parklands, often landscaped by Lancelot 'Capability' Brown, whose contribution to the appearance of this area as we know it today was immense. Many are registered by English Heritage as being of historic interest and that at Croome Park is being restored by the National Trust as a fine example of Brown's work.

Along the rivers, most of the former low-lying, wet meadows have now been agriculturally improved and their birdlife is consequently not so good. One exception is the floristically rich Upton Ham SSSI at Upton-on-Severn, which at times of flood attracts some large concentrations of wildfowl. Downstream of Evesham, the Avon prescribes broad, sweeping meanders across its floodplain and winter flooding is a frequent occurrence here as well. Riverside alders and pollarded willows are important landscape features that enable the courses of rivers, streams and even ditches to be identified from some distance. Wet pastures and extensive gravel workings also feature in the landscapes of the lower Avon and Severn valleys, producing a new range of wetland habitats.

Visually the Vale of Evesham is a very distinctive area, with orchards, glasshouses and all the paraphernalia of an intensive market gardening industry. To the south-east it extends to the foothills of the Cotswolds, but elsewhere its boundaries are not so easily defined as it merges into the surrounding areas. The Vale has an open, agricultural landscape with little woodland and few hedges or trees, apart from stream and riverside willows. What small plantations there are tend to be of ash or oak, while the hedgerows are predominantly hawthorn, which reflects their origin as enclosure plantings. Elm trees were once common in the hedgerows, but Dutch elm disease killed them in the 1970s and with them went the white-letter hairstreak butterfly – unable to survive without its food plant.

South of Bredon Hill is the Vale of Gloucester, where the appearance of the countryside is very similar to the Vale of Evesham. However, without a covering of fluvio-glacial drift to render the soils workable, cattle rearing replaces market gardening. The sole exception is at the base of the hill, where material has washed down and spread across the plain. The freely draining soils that have developed on this drift support a wide variety of arable crops.

Key Habitats

There are several key habitats in this extensive sub-region. To begin with, the geology and natural features are important not only for the way they have shaped the landform and contributed to the character of the area, but also for the fossil remains found at specific sites. For birds and birders, though, the wetlands and woodlands are most significant.

The wetlands can be divided into two groups, according to whether they are natural or man-made. Turning firstly to the natural habitats, there are three main rivers, namely the Severn and its two tributaries, the Avon and Teme. The Severn, rejuvenated upstream when it cut through the Ironbridge gorge, flows wide and deep between high banks as it makes its way towards the Bristol Channel. Its population of fish is very diverse, which makes it attractive to predator birds such as Great Cormorants, several of which can sometimes be seen standing around in trees. With up to 150 birds, the herd of Mute Swans at Worcester is also one of the largest in the region.

The Severn below Worcester, and the Avon downstream of Evesham, are bordered by a system of old meadows, known as hams. Traditionally these alluvial grasslands were managed as hay meadows on a strip system, known as Lammas, which created an open landscape of wet grassland. This was much beloved of breeding waders such as Northern Lapwing, Eurasian Curlew and Common Redshank, but regrettably the meadows are now too dry in spring and summer, so the birds have mostly gone. In winter, though, they are often flooded and this is when most birds visit them. The areas around Bredon, Longdon Marsh and Upton-on-Severn are often inundated and at such times they can attract very impressive numbers of wildfowl and waders for inland locations. For example, Bredon's Hardwick held 258 Bewick's Swans in 1986, 730 Dunlin in 1990 and 2,500 Eurasian Wigeon in 1996, while Longdon Marsh had 475 Pintail in 1998 and 2,000 Eurasian Teal in 2001—all of which were either the highest or second highest regional counts ever.

Compared with the Severn, the Avon winds its way slowly across the wide flood plain. Together with its adjoining wetlands and meadows, it forms a very important wildlife corridor. Beneath Bredon Hill, the especially lush bankside vegetation contains a national rarity in greater dodder as well as providing nest sites for birds such as Sedge and Reed Warblers. This area used to hold most of the British population of the rare Marsh Warbler, too, but sadly this has now become extinct. Nevertheless, the LBAP for Worcestershire contains a habitat action plan designed to protect the sites where the birds used to breed, so if they ever return there will be somewhere suitable for them to go. The crowns of willow pollards along the banks also provide unusual nest sites for Canada Geese and Mallard, whilst the Strensham area holds a few small colonies of Common Nightingales. At nearby Nafford, the WoWT is creating a major new wetland reserve—the Gwen Finch reserve—which will have the largest reedbed in Worcestershire, complemented by wet grassland and willow carr designed to entice breeding waders and otters. The network of ditches that drain the washlands, or hams, are also of considerable importance, though few can now maintain a sufficiently high water-level through spring and summer to enable waders such as Common Redshank to breed. In its lower reaches, below Knightwick, the Teme, too, is liable to flooding as it meanders across its gradually broadening valley.

There are also a variety of important standing waters, mostly man-made. The lakes such as those at Croome, Charlecote, Hewell and Pirton were created as focal points in the landscaped parklands. The most valuable of these ornamental lakes for birds is the pool at Westwood Park. Then there are the flooded pits of past industrial working. These include the old clay pits at Grimley, former sand and gravel quarries at places such as Holt and the brine subsidence pools at Oakley and Upton Warren. All support a good range of breeding and wintering waterfowl and waders, but Upton Warren is particularly outstanding, not only for the variety of birds that visit it, but also because it contains a small saltmarsh, which is an extremely rare habitat in inland Britain.

The Grimley and Holt area consists of old, flooded brick-pits and sand and gravel workings. The three brick-pits at Grimley sprang to prominence in 1977, when the first Worcestershire heronry was established. The WoWT secured a licence to count the herons, but persistent requests to become involved in managing the site were rebuffed. Meanwhile willow encroached into the open water and Himalayan balsam swamped the more fragile natural flora. Eventually, in 2002, the Trust secured a lease on this important SSSI with the aid of Heritage Lottery funding. The succession of habitats goes from pools, through marsh, swamp and tall herb communities, to scrub and willow woodland. The principal feature is the heronry, which began with two nests, but may now reach 30. Most commoner waterfowl nest too, including Tufted Duck, but a wider range occurs in winter. In freezing conditions, species such as Common Goldeneye move onto the River Severn, while flood waters occasionally attract wild geese or Bewick's Swans. Away from the water, the elusive Lesser Spotted Woodpecker can sometimes be seen feeding in the riverside trees. On the opposite bank the more open Northwick Marsh provides safe feeding and roosting areas for Common and Jack Snipe. Both Grimley and Holt have a long history of gravel extraction and there is a range of habitats from former workings that have been restored to agriculture, through to abandoned silt beds and active quarries, with Sand Martins nesting in the faces. Weed seeds on the disturbed ground around the pits provide food for finches and buntings, while Little Ringed Plovers nest at Grimley.

Another, much smaller gravel pit was recently excavated to create a lake on the Kemerton estate below Bredon Hill and this, too, has proved attractive to birds. Northern Lapwings and Common Redshank have bred and the newly planted reedbed already holds some 20 pairs of Reed Warblers, while Sedge Warblers nest in the surrounding vegetation. An even bigger triumph for nature conservation is the estate's farmland. Managed by a landowner keen to promote nature conservation, the tall, thick hedges, wide field margins and headlands support growing populations of birds that are generally in decline. Yellowhammers and Linnets, for example, are both doing well, with the former having leapt from six pairs to 30 in ten years. Common Whitethroats and Bullfinches have also increased, a few Tree Sparrows are present and Grey Partridges frequent the hedge bottoms. Also noteworthy are winter roosts of 20,000 Common Starlings and 300 Reed Buntings. Perhaps the greatest achievement of all is that the estate now acts as a model example of what can be achieved and is arousing considerable interest amongst other land owners.

The Severn and Avon valleys also contain several other sand and gravel quarries, such as those at Kinsham and Ryall. All attract a wide range of birds, particularly passage waders, and are liable to produce an unexpected surprise. For example, in 2002 the quarry at Salford Priors produced the first breeding record of Common Sandpipers in Warwickshire. The best site is

Good numbers of Yellowhammers and Linnets thrive where farming is sympathetic to wildlife.

Bredon's Hardwick. Although one of the pits has been restored as part of a leisure park, the southernmost pool, with its two or three islands and regenerating willow, holds most birds, but there is no public access, so watching is restricted to views from the roadside. Its situation on the River Avon very close to the confluence with the Severn, means the area is ideally placed to receive migrants moving up the Bristol Channel and a string of excellent records, including several rarities, has been amassed. The pools also provide a convenient sanctuary for any wildfowl or waders feeding on the flooded meadows. These include regular flocks of Northern Lapwings and European Golden Plovers, which are sometimes joined by a few Dunlin or Ruff. Eurasian Wigeon and Pintail can also gather in large numbers, while a small herd of Bewick's Swans, or perhaps a family party of White-fronted Geese, might wander up from nearby Slimbridge to graze the adjoining meadows. In winter, flocks of thrushes feed on the flood meadows, where they might attract the attentions of a passing Peregrine Falcon. Among the many rare visitors was the region's first Collared Pratincole in 1994.

Upton Warren—now officially known as the Christopher Cadbury Wetland Reserve after the benefactor who purchased it—is an SSSI and WoWT reserve. For wildfowl and waders it is the best site in Worcestershire and one of the foremost in the region. Almost anything might appear here, from an American wader to an Asiatic warbler, though amongst its many claims to fame, few can surpass the first breeding of Avocets in the region in 2003.

Vast underground salt reserves found at Stoke Prior in 1828 led to deep extraction over about 150 years. This caused subsidence and resulted in a series of pools which now form the two parts of the reserve. The Moors Pool to the north holds most of the wintering and breeding waterfowl, while the three shallow flash pools to the south, on the opposite side of the River Salwarpe, are superb for waders. The Moors Pool, and a smaller one north of it, have fringing reedbeds that provide breeding sites for Reed Warblers and occasionally a winter refuge for an Eurasian Bittern. Oystercatchers, and in most years Common Redshanks, also breed on this pool. A small, rushy marsh, known as Amy's Marsh, has been created in the south-eastern corner of the main pool and this is a favourite area for waders. Water Rail and both Common and Jack Snipe are also seen from the autumn through to spring, whilst Cetti's Warblers have recently established a small breeding population and Hobbies are frequent summer visitors.

The flash pools are affected by brine seepage from the underground salt workings, which inhibits plant growth and so provides waders with large areas of bare, muddy ground. Northern Lapwing and Little Ringed Plover both breed—the latter assisted by cages to keep predators at bay—while Common Redshank do so most years, though with variable success. In late summer the pools are especially good for passage Green Sandpipers, with twenty or more present on occasions. There is also a regular roost of Eurasian Curlews, which is sometimes joined by a passage Whimbrel or two. The saline run-off into the River Salwarpe has reduced in recent years, but some salt tolerant plants, notably dittander, can still be found here, whilst Siskins and Lesser Redpolls visit the bankside alders in winter. It is slightly invidious to single out anything from Upton Warren's long list of rarities, but mention might just be made of a Wilson's Phalarope in 1985, a Least Sandpiper in 1988 and the region's only Rustic Bunting in 1987.

A wide range of plants and birds also occur at nearby Westwood Pool, which floristically is among the best standing water sites in Britain. It is especially noted for the extremely scarce eight-stamened waterwort and the ribbon-leaved water-plantain—the latter occurring nowhere else in Britain. Being private, access is strictly controlled, but its seclusion means birds can feed, rest, roost and nest in relative peace. On cold nights especially, there is a sizeable gull roost which often contains a Mediterranean or Yellow-legged Gull. Otherwise, small numbers of wildfowl are present during winter and passage terns occur most years. The fringing reeds and scrub are used by breeding Great Crested Grebes, Reed and Sedge Warblers and Reed Buntings. Rarities have included Long-billed Dowitcher in 1990, Surf Scoter in 2000 and a splendid Pallas's Leaf Warbler in 1987.

A wetland with a difference is the WoWT reserve at Feckenham Wylde Moor. This is the last remnant of a marsh formerly noted for its rare species. Drained in the nineteenth century, it lost much of its interest until the outlet became blocked and the water table rose. Now the underground springs and peaty soils are once again creating a marsh with rushes, an extensive reedbed and damp grassland. The site is good for dragonflies and until recently held breeding Common Snipe, but nowadays its bird interest is confined to a good range of commoner species. Another changed wetland is the Droitwich Canal, where much of the extensive reedbed was cleared during restoration work. Nevertheless, Sedge and Reed Warblers and Reed Buntings are still breeding, albeit in reduced numbers.

Grasslands are the most precious habitat in the sub-region, with neutral, calcareous and acidic all represented. Nationally we have lost 95% of our neutral, unimproved grassland since the second world war and English Nature estimates that the *Severn and Avon Vales Natural Area* now holds 10% of what remains—most of it in Worcestershire. So the remaining flower-rich meadows, with their cowslips, green-winged orchids, wild daffodils, meadow saffron and adderstongue are of national importance. So much so, that Eades Meadow and Foster's Green Meadows have been declared an NNR. Many grasslands are also enclosed by ancient, species-rich hedgerows, which add to their diversity, and some still show signs of the ridge-and-furrow pattern produced by Medieval strip farming. It is to pastures such as these that flocks of Fieldfares and Redwings come to feed in winter along with Black-headed Gulls, Northern Lapwings and occasionally European Golden Plovers.

Generally, the Vale of Evesham is too intensively farmed to support much wildlife, but the open grassland on Windmill Hill, near the Littletons, supports a good limestone flora, with several species of orchid. Common Kestrels can often be seen hunting over the grasslands or along the roadside verges, some of which contain interesting species such as bee orchid.

In contrast, the commons around the foothills of the Malverns—of which Castlemorton is the most important—have acidic grasslands with extensive patches of scrub, notably gorse, and tussocks of rush in the damp hollows. An important feature of Castlemorton is its population of the rare black poplar, which is one of the largest in Britain. The Common is also excellent for birds, with good populations of Green Woodpeckers, Common Stonechats, Linnets and Yellowhammers, but Willow Warblers have declined dramatically with 18 pairs in 2003 being the second-lowest count ever recorded. In winter a few Common Snipe, and maybe one or two Jack Snipe, visit the wetter areas and there is always the possibility of a sentinel Great Grey Shrike.

Woodland is generally sparse in the sub-region and most woods are very small, usually less than 10 ha. They nevertheless make a significant contribution to the area, both visually and ecologically. Many are semi-natural remnants of the former Royal Forests and Chases that were centred around Feckenham, Malvern and Ombersley and fortunately most of these have escaped being replanted with conifers. Elsewhere, some afforestation has occurred, usually with pines, spruce and larch, but many of these have failed through lack of management and competition from the broad-leaved, native species. These conifer plantations have little conservation merit, but are favoured by a few specialist birds such as Goldcrests, Coal Tits and irruptive Common Crossbills. Eurasian Sparrowhawks and Common Buzzards also nest in the more secluded ones.

Today the remnants of ancient semi-natural woods are concentrated in two areas. Firstly, on the Mercia mudstones west of Ombersley are Monkwood, Ockeridge Wood and Shrawley Wood. The first two of these were formerly managed as coppiced oakwoods, but were later cleared and replanted with native species by L.G. Harris Brushworks to produce white-wood poles for brush handles. Between them these three woods hold a nationally important population of dormouse. Monkwood is also noted for its butterflies, especially wood white, while its birds include Tawny Owl, Lesser Spotted Woodpecker, Marsh Tit and a range of warblers. One, or possibly two, European Nightjars were surprise discoveries here in 1994. By far the best of the woods is Shrawley. Scheduled as an SSSI, it has some huge oaks that tower above the largest stand of small-leaved limes in Britain. Beneath that, carpets of bluebells and bracken cover the ground. Providing the limes are coppiced, warblers are plentiful, especially Garden Warblers, whilst Common Buzzards are also amongst the breeding birds. Dippers are sometimes seen along the Dick Brook, which flows through the wood creating a valley with base-rich soils that support a flora that is more diverse than that of adjacent areas.

Secondly, two of several woods occurring on the Lias clays south-west of Feckenham are Grafton and Trench Woods. These were oak-ashwoods above hazel coppice and Grafton Wood still has a rich ground flora and supports a strong colony of brown hairstreak butterflies and a good range of common woodland birds. Most of Trench Wood, however, was also acquired, cleared and replanted by Harris Brushworks. Unfortunately this often involved using non-native species, notably sycamore and Italian alder, or stock that was not of local provenance. By the time the WoWT acquired this part of the wood as a reserve in 1986 the conifer and beech plantations had more or less failed, but birch, oak and ash were regenerating into scrub. The rest of the wood, outside the reserve, was coppice-with-standards that through neglect has now developed into high forest, creating a niche for woodpeckers, Eurasian Nuthatches and Eurasian Treecreepers. The plantation trees were closely spaced to encourage straight growth and so resembled coppices. Along with the scrub, they were much favoured by warblers and used to be the regional stronghold of Common Nightingales, with 14 pairs in 1990. Sadly the latter have now all gone from here, but a few pairs do still survive elsewhere in the sub-region, notably at Langdale Wood.

Surveys carried out for the WoWT at Trench Wood in 1987 and 1990 revealed the total number of territories of all species of birds to be 305 and 332 respectively. However, numbers fell as the plantations matured and shaded out the understorey, so that a repeat survey in 2003 found only 121 pairs. Woodcock, Turtle Dove and Grasshopper Warbler were lost as well as the Common Nightingales, though none had been present in good numbers in the earlier years. The largest declines were amongst the scrub-loving species, with Willow Warblers down by 95%, Blackcaps 80%, Garden Warblers 74% and Bullfinches 67%.

The birdlife in many of these semi-natural woods has been closely monitored by the WoWT and Green and Westwood (1991) provided much valuable information too detailed to summarise here. Elsewhere, abandoned osier beds and areas of willow and alder carr along the river valleys have also matured into secondary woods, where they provide plenty of decaying timber for species such as Lesser Spotted Woodpecker and Willow Tit.

The innumerable parklands with their blend of copses, old freestanding trees, pastures and lakes also have considerable wildlife value. The holes in veteran trees provide nest sites for a range of species from Eurasian Nuthatch to Stock Dove and Little Owl. At Charlecote Park there is a thriving heronry and a spreading rookery, while surveys carried out for the National Trust by the WMBC have shown the six commonest species to be Western Jackdaw, Common Chaffinch, Blue Tit, Mallard, Wood Pigeon and Wren. Among the more typical parkland species to be recorded, Lesser Spotted and Green Woodpeckers, Mistle and Song Thrushes and Spotted Flycatcher are all listed as Species of Conservation Concern (Gregory *et al.* 2002).

Orchards of plums, apples and pears were once a feature of the Vale of Evesham, but in the last fifty years most of the older ones have been grubbed out to make way either for more horticultural cultivation or for newer, lower varieties of fruit trees that make picking easier. Soft fruit cultivation has also increased with the advent of pick-your-own. Modern, intensively managed orchards are of little value to wildlife, but any old surviving orchard might well have species-rich grassland underneath, while the trees themselves provide a niche for insects and birds such as Green Woodpeckers and Little Owls. Mistletoe is also abundant on the old orchard trees, with this sub-region being one of its national strongholds.

Finally, three CBC surveys reveal some interesting variations in farmland bird communities. A long running census at Naunton Beauchamp from 1980-96 showed an average of 179 territories a year on 73 ha, which is equal to 247 per km^2. The most numerous species, with their average number of territories per year, were Common Chaffinch (26), Robin and Wren (15 each), Blackbird (14), Blue Tit (13) and Yellowhammer (12). In all, 53 species were recorded, including Eurasian Curlew until 1984, House Sparrow until 1987, Reed Bunting until 1990 and Grey Partridge and Turtle Dove until 1991. A second survey was conducted at nearby Abberton over the earlier period of 1981-86. Although, at 296 ha, this plot was four times the size of Naunton Beauchamp, with 63 species it was only slightly more diverse and with just 432 territories a year, or 146 per km^2, the density of birds was 40% lower. The commonest birds here, with the average number of territories each year, were Common Chaffinch and Yellowhammer (51 each), Blackbird (42), Sky Lark (29) and Wren (27). During the time of survey Corn Buntings declined from 4 territories to none, while Grey Partridge, Tree Sparrow and Linnet numbers all halved. Curiously, though, Turtle Dove numbers increased from one to three pairs. Allowing for the difference in size, Yellowhammer densities were the same at both sites and Abberton had the greatest density of Sky Larks. All of the other main species occurred in higher densities at Naunton Beauchamp.

A later survey carried out on 62 ha at Drayton Field during 1993-2002 showed the average number of territories to be 136 a year, or a density of 248 per km^2, which was virtually identical to that at Naunton Beauchamp. The commoner species here were Yellowhammer (21 territories a year), Common Chaffinch and Sky Lark (15 each), Blackbird (10) and Wren (7). In all, 45 species were recorded. No species of significance were lost, but the one predictable gain was Common Buzzards in 1998. Allowing for size differences once again, the density of Sky Larks here was two-and-a-half times that at Abberton, whilst the Yellowhammer density was double that at the other two sites.

Between them, these three census plots support the general consensus that most of the typical farmland species were lost or declined during the 1980s. In the case of Drayton Field, they also show that, given the right management, the diversity and density of birds on open arable farms, where Yellowhammers and Sky Larks are dominant, can be as just as high as where there is more cover for species such as Wren, Robin and Common Chaffinch.

The Malvern Hills and Teme Valley

General Description

This is a relatively small, but very distinctive, sub-region, coving 263 km^2 along the western fringe of Worcestershire—or just under 4% of the total regional area. At its extremes, it measures 25 miles (40 km) from the edge of the Wyre Forest in the north to the southernmost tip of the Malvern Hills in the south and 13 miles (21 km) from Great Witley in the east to Tenbury Wells in the west.

As its name implies, the two dominant features are the range of the Malvern Hills (Area 1), which stretch from Abberley in the north to the Chase End Hill in the south, and the River Teme (Area 2), which bisects this range at the Knightwick gap on its journey eastwards from mid-Wales to its confluence with the Severn just below Worcester. Although we have combined these two areas into one Chapter, we have chosen to describe each separately. This accords with the Countryside Agency, which puts the Malvern Hills and Teme Valley into separate *Character Areas*, but

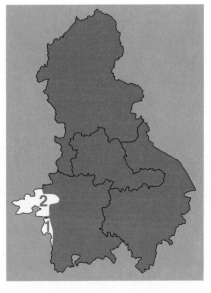

not with English Nature which includes them in a single *Natural Area*. Two small parts of the *Central Herefordshire Natural Area*, around Kyre and Clifton-on-Teme, are also included within this sub-region.

The Malvern Hills

Physical Features

The long ridge of the Malvern Hills proper measures nine miles (14 km) from north to south, reaches 425m at its highest point on Worcestershire Beacon and separates Herefordshire from Worcestershire. Northwards, the range then continues along what is known as 'The Malvern Axis' and eventually ends in the Abberley Hills.

The main part of the range comprises ancient Precambrian granites, diorites and volcanic rocks lying in a complex upfold. Collectively known as the 'Malvernian', these rocks are amongst the oldest in Britain. Their extreme hardness means they have withstood weathering, but this quality has also made them attractive for construction works and there was much quarrying in the nineteenth century, some of which still continues. Northwards Silurian limestones form the series of lower ridges and valleys that mark the Suckley and Abberley Hills. The Silurian outcrop narrows north of the Teme, but then broadens again around the breccia-capped Woodbury Hill before finally culminating in the 300m high, sweeping curve of the Abberley Hills. Beyond here the general thrust of the higher ground is then continued by the sandstone plateau of the Wyre Forest.

An intriguing feature of the sub-region is its drainage pattern, with both the River Teme and the Leigh Brook cutting through the line of the hills rather than following the valleys between them. It seems likely that this is the result of river capture by the Severn, following its post-glacial rejuvenation.

Landscape Character

The Malverns are one of England's most distinctive landscape features. From the surrounding lowlands they provide a towering scenic backdrop, whilst their summits afford commanding views in every direction.

So it is hardly surprising to find the ridge crowned by the two major Iron Age hill forts on Herefordshire Beacon and Midsummer Hill. Other ancient hill forts also occur at Berrow Hill and Woodbury Hill, along the lower range of hills extending northwards.

The Hills were declared part of a Royal hunting forest—known as the Malvern Chase—shortly after the Norman Conquest. Today they are managed by the Malvern Hills Conservators—a body established by Act of Parliament in 1884 with responsibility for commoners' rights and maintaining the hills for public enjoyment. The hills have long been an irresistible magnet, with people coming from far afield to enjoy the views, hike across the rugged terrain or hang-glide on the uplifting currents of air. While most remain oblivious to the great geological interest of the hills and the wealth of natural habitats, plants and animals to be discovered, the conservators still bear the responsibility for their conservation, which becomes ever onerous due to the erosion wreaked by countless visitors.

Settlements ring the foothills, with Great Malvern and Malvern Wells especially having flourished as spa towns in Victorian and Edwardian times. Even today the elegance of these periods shows through in many of Great Malvern's buildings, particularly the villas dotted amongst the wooded hillsides. Nor have the benefits of the spa been completely lost, as Malvern water is still bottled for drinking.

Above the wooded hillsides stands a jagged skyline of bare summits with poor, shallow soils that have little agricultural benefit and so remain as unenclosed rough sheep grazing. Southwards, this bare, rugged character gradually mellows into a gentler landscape of lower hills separated by heavily wooded valleys and dotted with old orchards and the occasional arable field. Here, too, commons such as Castlemorton, spread out from the foothills, but these are technically lowland grasslands and were covered in the Chapter on the Severn and Avon Vales. Finally, at their southernmost extremity, the hills end amongst an intricate blend of ancient woods, commons and small pastures.

To the north of the main ridge, the Suckley Hills consist of parallel ridges clothed with woodland. Separating the ridges, are deep, twisting valleys, with old orchards, small woods and pastures and a few arable fields. Narrow lanes wind their way between tall hedges, giving access to numerous scattered farms and cottages. Beyond the Knightwick gap, the ridge narrows as it forms the eastern flank of the Teme valley. Arable land is more widespread here, but the crest of the ridge still retains a more or less continuous finger of woodland. This eventually opens out again to embrace the conifer plantations on Woodbury Hill before culminating in the broad sweep of mixed woodland that clothes the Abberley Hills.

Key Habitats

Ecologically this is one of the richer parts of Worcestershire, with important woods, hedgerows and grasslands.

A large part of the Malvern Hills (732 ha) is a scheduled SSSI with habitats that grade from unimproved acid grassland on the summits, through taller herb communities on the lower slopes into woodland around the foothills. There are also small pockets of heathland, some flushes, a small reservoir and several exposed rock faces in the disused quarries.

The acidic grasslands of the summits form one of the largest expanses of this habitat within the region. Although not floristically rich, they do contain wavy hair-grass, sheep's sorrel, harebell and heath bedstraw, interspersed here and there with patches of heather and bilberry. There are also some important birds, of which the two most characteristic are Sky Larks and Meadow Pipits. In the late 1980s there were about 50 territories of each, but numbers have since declined—the former to 14 pairs in 2003. Tree Pipits, too, occur where scattered trees encroach onto the grassland, but their population collapsed from 70 singing males to just four in the ten years 1988-98. The short turf is also a traditional breeding site for one or two pairs of Northern Wheatears that nest in disused rabbit burrows on one of the hills. Common Ravens are now well established and a post-breeding flock of 22 seen over North Hill in October 2000 was a record number. At passage times Dotterel occasionally occur and in autumn the summits are the most likely place in the region to see Snow Buntings. A Shore Lark even appeared on North Hill in 1987 and a Dartford Warbler on the hills in 1999 was a surprising discovery.

Further down the slopes, where material has washed down and accumulated, the soils are deeper and great swathes of bracken enclose patches of gorse, scrub and secondary woodland. This is a good area for warblers, such as Blackcap, Garden Warbler and Common Whitethroat and for Common Stonechats, of which one or two pairs have nested regularly since 1993.

At the southern end of the range, the foothill woods comprise mostly sessile oaks, with an unusual combination of birch and hazel in the drier parts and ash and wych elm on the wet flushes. Four woodland birds are of particular interest. Until the mid-1990s there were up to 30 pairs of Common Redstarts, mostly on Midsummer Hill, but only nine sang in 1999 and by 2000 this was down to three. Wood Warblers suffered an even more calamitous decline, from 30-40 singing males in the late 1980s to six in 1991 and a final one in 1997. The cause of these declines is not known. Pied Flycatchers, on the other hand, were not recorded breeding until 1984, but, aided by the provision of nest-boxes, had increased to around 15 pairs within ten years. Numbers appear to have fallen since then, but at least two or three pairs are still breeding. Finally, Hawfinches have only been recorded regularly since 1985, though they were probably here before then. At that time there appeared to be a small breeding population of two or three pairs, but in recent winters up to 15 have been noted feeding under the hornbeams of Chase End Wood.

Much priceless information about the birdlife of both the hills and the commons has been gathered for the Conservators by the Malvern Hills Bird Group and published in a series of reports entitled *Birds on the Malvern Hills and Commons* (Parr 1996). In particular this has demonstrated the strength of the warbler populations, with counts during 1986-95 consistently showing phenomenal totals of 75-130 singing Common Whitethroats and around 400 singing Willow Warblers. Regretfully, there has not been a full census of either species since, but Willow Warbler numbers on a sample area halved between 1995 and 1997. The 2003 Report tells the same story, with 10 pairs on Raggedstone Hill being the lowest count ever and similar declines also noted on Midsummer and Chase End Hills.

The hills are also good for butterflies, including fritillaries, graylings and wood whites, whilst one of them hosts a rare clubmoss at its only known English site.

In autumn, many migrant birds use the valleys to pass westwards through the hills, often pausing to feed as they do so. Chats, thrushes, warblers, crests and finches are mostly involved, with Ring Ouzels, in particular, having occurred annually since 1983. Happy Valley, with its rich crop of rowan and hawthorn berries, is usually a favoured spot for many species.

The open hillsides also provide perfect hunting territory for raptors and almost any species might appear. Common Kestrels can often be seen hovering into the wind, Common Buzzards frequently spiral on up-draughts and sightings of both Red Kites and Peregrine Falcons have increased considerably in recent years.

Away from the Malverns proper, woodland remains a significant habitat. Moreover, there is great variety, ranging from semi-natural broad-leaved woods to conifer plantations. Thankfully, the area escaped the worst excesses of afforestation except on Woodbury Hill and parts of the Abberley Hills. The amount of woodland undoubtedly originates from the great Malvern Chase hunting forest, although past coppicing has precluded the survival of many veteran trees. Sweet chestnuts are a feature in many areas, yews occur on the Abberley Hills and many hedgerows contain a rich mix of woody species derived from former woodland cover.

Along the lower hills to the north, the underlying Silurian rocks yield basic soils that support a very different, more diverse vegetation than do the acidic soils of the Malverns. Although agricultural improvement has wreaked its customary havoc, some unimproved meadows are still graced by pyramidal orchids, dyer's greenweed and common rock-rose as well as plenty of insects and snails. Many of the ancient semi-natural woods were formerly managed as coppice-with-standards and typically contain a broad mix of trees including, oak, birch, yew and wild service, while small- and large-leaved limes are both characteristic trees. Indeed, there are even limes in some of the hedgerows, while Suckley and Crews Hill Woods contain some very ancient pollards and coppiced trees. In addition to these species, the north end of Crews Hill Wood SSSI has a canopy of sessile oak in association with hornbeam—an unusual feature for Worcestershire.

A few remnants of unimproved, neutral grassland can still be found among the smaller farms and holdings, while there are areas of semi-improved calcareous grassland along the Silurian ridge north to Abberley. There are also a few remaining fields of ridge-and-furrow. Although many of these grasslands are floristically rich, their value to birds is largely restricted to being feeding areas for corvids, Common Starlings and winter thrushes.

Old orchards also contribute to the habitat diversity, being rich in invertebrates and lichens. Once the haunt of Wrynecks, they are now much favoured by Green Woodpeckers and Little Owls. Finally, some of the quarry rock faces are important for ferns, mosses and flowering plants, but the huge quarry at the north end of the Abberley Hills has unfortunately encroached onto other wildlife-rich areas.

Green Woodpeckers are characteristic birds of the Malvern Hills area.

There has been one CBC to give an insight into the birdlife of the farmland in this area and this was carried out on 40 ha at Alfrick from 1986-2000. In all 54 species were recorded and there was an average of 203 territories a year. This is equivalent to 500 territories per km^2, which is a high figure that reflects the richness of habitat to be found in the area. The commonest species, with their average number of territories per year, were Robin (24), Blackbird (22), Wren (20), Blue Tit (19), Common Chaffinch (16), Dunnock (12) and Great Tit (10). Both Common Kingfisher and Dipper held territories, the former twice and the latter once, but surprisingly for a site this far west it was 1993 before Common Buzzards did so and 1998 before they became established. Other interesting species to be regularly recorded were Lesser Whitethroat and Bullfinch, whilst Turtle Dove and Tree Sparrow each held a territory on one occasion.

The Teme Valley

Physical Structure

The Teme rises in mid-Wales and, along with its tributaries, drains parts of south Shropshire and Herefordshire as well as north-west Worcestershire. Within the region, its valley forms a basin between Tenbury Wells and Newnham, but the flood plain then becomes progressively more constricted as the scarp slope of the Herefordshire plateau and the northern end of the Malvern-Abberley Hills range close in on either side. Eventually the river escapes down the narrow gorge it carved through the latter range at Knightwick and then meanders across the broad plain of the Severn and Avon Vales on its way to its confluence with the Severn.

Geologically the valley consists of an undulating area of Old Red Sandstone across which the Teme has cut its course. To the south-west the alluvial floodplain is clearly defined by a thin band of limestone, which occurs at the base of these sandstones, forming the pronounced scarp. A similar feature also defines part of the valley to the north, but this is then replaced by an undulating plateau of shales and sandstones, with deeply cut valleys along its southern edge.

Above the scarp is the Herefordshire Plateau, an elevated area of Dittonian sandstone between 150-250m high. The streams that flow north-eastwards from this plateau into the Teme have cut deeply incised dingles, or valleys, into this scarp slope. The Teme also has a steep gradient, but its fall is broken by rock reefs that create still pools between the faster-flowing sections.

Landscape Character

The overall impression is of an undulating, rolling valley encircled by woods. The most outstanding feature is the steep scarp slope to the south-west, with its incised dingles draped in semi-natural, ancient woodland. To the north is a plateau with steep, wooded valleys on its southern edge and to the east are the wooded Suckley-Abberley hills.

The rich, red, fertile soils support both arable land and agriculturally improved pastures within a farming mosaic that also includes orchards and hop fields on the warmer, south-facing slopes. Settlements are small and dispersed, with many isolated farms and hamlets and Tenbury Wells the only place of any size. Above the Teme, the Herefordshire Plateau also forms an undulating landscape dissected by narrow valleys and again characterised by rich red soils. These are mostly under arable cultivation in large fields enclosed by low hedges.

Key Habitats

The two main habitats are the rivers and the dingle woods.

Some uncommon plants occur amongst the flora along the banks of the Teme, while the river is rich in invertebrate and fish life and has been scheduled as an SSSI. The otter population here survived the collapse of the 1950s and 1960s, since when it has provided a springboard for animals to recolonise other areas. The high, clay banks along the Teme provide suitable sites for Common Kingfishers and Sand Martins to excavate their nest holes, while the faster-flowing stretches are the favoured haunts of Dippers and Grey Wagtails. A comprehensive survey along the 57 km of the Teme in Worcestershire during 1979 revealed one pair of Common Kingfishers to every kilometre (Green *et al.* 1991)—one wonders what a count today would show! Similar birds once occurred on the Leigh Brook, which is a major tributary stream, but unfortunately pollution as a result of run-off from agricultural fertilisers badly damaged the ecology of this brook. As a result the previously strong populations of mayflies and trout declined and Dippers were lost. However, Common Kingfishers and Grey Wagtails can still be seen at the WoWT's Knapp and Papermill reserve, which forms part of the Leigh Brook SSSI, while Goldfinches, Siskins and Lesser Redpolls also visit the brookside alders here in winter. Green Woodpeckers often feed on yellow ants in the meadow and Spotted Flycatchers may nest in holes in the walls of Papermill Cottage.

West of the river, the enclosing scarp faces north-eastwards, so its unique dingle woods are almost permanently shaded and very damp—conditions in which mosses, liverworts and ferns thrive in abundance beneath a canopy of majestic oaks, ashes and small-leaved limes. The woods are also very inaccessible and this allows some special plants, such as thin-spiked wood sedge, nettle-leaved bellflower and herb Paris to flourish. Indeed, these dingle woods frequently have a 'wilderness' feel to them. Hanley Dingle, which is now a WoWT reserve, also has probably the most extensive stand of large-leaved lime in the Midlands as well as much dead and fallen timber rich in invertebrates. In places, small springs issue from the base of the limestone and the calcium-rich water then spreads over rocks and vegetation, where it solidifies into tufa, which in turn supports many calcicole plants. Indeed, the tufa deposit at Southstone Rock is one of biggest in Britain. Little is known about the birdlife in these woods, but amongst a good range of woodland species are all the woodpeckers and tits, Blackcaps and Garden Warblers, and predators such as Eurasian Sparrowhawk and Common Buzzard.

Ancient woodland likewise clothes the deep, wet dingles carved into the coal measures by tributaries along the north side of the valley. Oak, small-leaved lime and wild service are again prevalent and some of the woods contain stools of former hazel coppice. One of the best examples is the Dumbleton Dingle SSSI, where coal was extracted from drift mines in the valley sides until the 1940s. Within the dingle, the WoWT's dense and impenetrable Hunthouse Wood reserve is dominated by oak, ash and birch. More noteworthy are the large-leaved limes and the huge wild cherries and rowans, while the birdlife includes all three woodpeckers, several warblers and both Dipper and Grey Wagtail along the stream.

Finally, the Teme Valley used to be noted for its cherry orchards, a few of which have survived amongst the smallholdings on sunny, south-facing slopes. The old orchard trees are full of holes that are ideal for nesting birds, while the rotting and dead timber is rich in invertebrates on which they can feed. A few of the old, lichen-encrusted trees form open canopies above grasslands that are botanically rich. The area is also one of the national strongholds for mistletoe, which is widespread throughout the valley. Time was when Hawfinches would have been attracted to the cherry orchards, but today there are perhaps too few to sustain many birds. Some have also been replanted with new, small varieties of trees that are covered with netting to keep any birds away. However, a couple of recent sightings of Hawfinches hint at the possibility of a few pairs remaining in the valley.

The Midland Plateau

The slopes of **Cannock Chase**, with their scattered birches, ancient oakwoods and sombre plantations of conifers complemented by broad sweeps of heather, form one of the most important habitats in the West Midlands. *(J.&G. Harrison)*

Amongst several unusual birds to be found here is a thriving population of the regionally scarce **European Nightjar**. *(Mike Wilkes)*

The Midland Plateau

The **Wyre Forest** is the largest and most important woodland in the region. A springtime walk alongside the attractive Dowles Brook is most rewarding for birds, with Dippers and Grey Wagtails on the stream and Common Redstarts and Pied Flycatchers in the woods.

(*J.&G. Harrison*)

Wood Warblers are also characteristic birds of this part of the forest, where their distinctive, trilling song is one of the welcome sounds of spring. (*S.C. Brown*)

The classical **Arden** landscape consists of small, irregularly-shaped fields, woods and copses, set amongst hedgerow oaks and narrow, winding lanes. (*J. &G. Harrison*)

This well-wooded landscape provides an ideal home for the **Eurasian Jay**. Generally a shy bird, its white rump and flash of blue in the wings attract attention as it flies away through the trees.

(*Mike Lane*)

The Midland Plateau

Once the province of pigeons, sparrows and starlings, **Birmingham City Centre** now provides homes for Peregrine Falcons, Lesser Black-backed Gulls and Herring Gulls.

(J. &G. Harrison)

The **Black Redstart** is an urban specialist, quick to exploit derelict and cleared sites. Its population has thrived during the reconstruction of so much of the inner city following the decline of manufacturing industry in the 1980s.

(Mike Wilkes)

The West Midland Bird Club's **Harborne Nature Reserve** is set in a surprisingly leafy suburb less than three miles from the centre of Birmingham. Consisting of disused allotments and developing woodland, it attracts a good range of birds for such a small area.

(*J.&G. Harrison*)

Several woodland birds visit the reserve. Amongst them, the elusive **Lesser Spotted Woodpecker** is recorded from time-to-time.

(*Mike Wilkes*)

The Midland Plateau

Sandwell Valley forms a wonderful breathing space between Birmingham and the Black Country, with the RSPB reserve providing an excellent centre for birdwatching in a heavily populated area.   (*J.&G. Harrison*)

The Valley is amongst the top five sites in the region for wintering **Goosanders**.   (*Mike Lane*)

The Meres and Mosses

The **meres and mosses** of west Staffordshire demonstrate a range of habitats from open water, through swamp, fen and marshy grassland to woodland. Several, such as **Aqualate Mere** NNR, seen here with its new bird hide, are of international importance for nature conservation.

(*J.&G. Harrison*)

The Staffordshire Wildlife Trust's reserve at **Doxey Marshes** is the result of subsidence from brine pumping. On the very edge of Stafford, this superb wetland has notched up an impressive list of birds, including a rare River Warbler. A more numerous bird is the Common Snipe, which can number several hundred in winter.

(*J.&G. Harrison*)

A high proportion of the region's breeding **Water Rails** can also be found skulking around the reedbeds at Doxey. (*Mike Lane*)

The Meres and Mosses

In 1977 the canal feeder reservoir at **Belvide** became the WMBC's first reserve, but bird-watchers had been visiting it for much longer than that. Designated an SSSI for its wintering wildfowl, the site is also good for passage waders and roosting gulls.　　　(*J.&G. Harrison*)

The **Eurasian Teal** is one of several species of dabbling duck that find Belvide's shallow bays and gently shelving, reedy shorelines ideally suited to their needs.　　　(*Mike Lane*)

Surrounded on all sides by urban development, **Westport Lake** is an oasis in the heart of the Potteries.

(J.&G. Harrison)

Park Hall Country Park epitomises Stoke-on-Trent's efforts to rid itself of a legacy of derelict land. Once a wasteland, its sandstone cliffs, swathes of heather and pine planta-tions now provide a valuable habitat for birds.

(J.&G. Harrison)

The Country Park is best known for its resi-dent **Long-eared Owls**, though being nocturnal they are difficult to see unless you chance across their daytime roost.

(Mike Lane)

The Churnet Valley

A gem of the valley's woods is the **Pied Flycatcher**—a summer visitor to upland oakwoods which often uses nest boxes. *(Mike Wilkes)*

The deep, steep-sided **Churnet Valley**, with its mantle of woodland, tiny meadows and bubbling streams, is a most beautiful area. It contains the RSPB's **Coombes Valley Reserve**, which provides the ideal introduction to the richly varied birdlife of the valley. *(J.&G. Harrison)*

The attractive **Common Redstart** can be found in good numbers in the Churnet Woods.
(Mike Wilkes)

The **moorland** mosaic of north Staffordshire, with its heather, wooded valleys, upland pastures, hay meadows and gritstone walls supports a very special range of birds. Sadly, many have declined due to changes in land management and recreational pressure. (*J. &G. Harrison*)

Despite a fall in numbers, **Red Grouse** can still be found amongst the wide expanse of heather. (*Mike Lane*)

The population of **Black Grouse** regrettably became too small to be sustainable and it is now believed to be extinct. (*Mike Wilkes*)

The Dales

The spectacular scenery of the **Dales**, with its upland pastures, ashwoods and deep river valleys is amongst the finest in England. *(J.&G. Harrison)*

Grey Wagtails enjoy the crystal clear rivers and streams of the Dales and usually nest in a hole in a bank or wall. *(S.C. Brown)*

The **Needwood** landscape is one of regularly shaped fields, blocks of woodland and old parkland trees. At its centre is **Blithfield Reservoir**, which is another WMBC reserve and one of the most important sites for wetland birds in the Midlands. (*J.&G. Harrison*)

Whilst wildfowl are most numerous, Blithfield is best known as *the* place in the region for waders. Most autumns bring **Curlew Sandpipers** that pause briefly on their way south.

(*Mike Lane*)

Large flocks of **Eurasian Wigeon** graze the banks around the reservoir and ringing has shown many of these come from Siberia to take advantage of our milder winters. (*Mike Wilkes*)

The Trent and Tame Valleys

The long string of gravel pits that stretches virtually the whole length of the **Trent and Tame Valleys** from Burton-on-Trent to Birmingham have provided the region with some of its richest and most valuable wetlands. *(J.&G. Harrison)*

A few **Whooper Swans** winter on the flood meadows and gravel pits around the confluence of the Trent and Tame, forming the only regular herd currently in the region. *(Mike Lane)*

Appropriately, the WMBC secured a lease on the **Ladywalk Nature Reserve** during the Club's 75th Anniversary year in 2004. This important link in the chain of wetlands along the Middle Tame Valley attracts a wide variety of waterfowl and waders and offers excellent birdwatching throughout the year.

In recent years Ladywalk has been *the* place to see **Eurasian Bitterns**, with up to four of these elusive birds present every winter and frequently giving good views.

(*Mike Lane*)

The Trent and Tame Valleys

The reclaimed gravel pits at **Kingsbury Water Park** are another crucial link in the Middle Tame Valley wetland chain. The nature reserve area is important for winter waterfowl and passage and breeding waders.
(J.&G. Harrison)

The most important feature is the breeding colony of **Common Terns**—one of the largest in the country inland.
(R.T. Mills)

The Systematic List

The Systematic List provides a synopsis for every species of wild bird recorded in the region, based on published information. Wild birds are defined as those included in Categories A-C of the British Ornithologists' Union's official *British List* (http://www.bou.org.uk), namely:

> **Category A**: species that have been recorded in an apparently natural state at least once since January 1st 1950;

> **Category B**: species that would otherwise be in Category A, but have not been recorded since December 31st 1949; and

> **Category C**: Species that, although originally introduced by man, either deliberately or accidentally, have established breeding populations derived from introduced stock that maintain themselves without necessary recourse to further introduction (referred to as feral in text).

> (All species within Categories A-C are included, even if there is reasonable doubt that they have ever occurred in a natural state within this region *e.g.* Lesser White-fronted Goose. Such cases are accompanied by statements qualifying the likely origin.)

Species in Categories D and E of the *British List* are included in the next Chapters.

Sequence and Names of Species
The sequence and scientific names used are those adopted by the BOU for the *British List* in 2004, except that in common with many authorities Yellow-legged Gull and Caspian Gull are treated as separate species. The English names used are those currently in use by *British Birds* magazine (*Brit. Birds* 1997 and 2004). Alternative names in recent use are shown in brackets.

Species Accounts
Each account begins with a statement of the species' status, based on the following categories:

Very rare	fewer than ten records ever.
Rare	ten or more records, but less than annual (recorded in nine or less of the last ten years). Breeding less than annually.
Scarce	fewer than 20 birds occurring, or 10 pairs breeding, annually.
Uncommon	20-100 birds occurring or 10-50 pairs breeding.
Frequent	100-500 birds occurring or 50-250 pairs breeding.
Fairly common	500-5,000 birds occurring or 250-2,500 pairs breeding.
Common	5,000-20,000 birds occurring or 2,500-10,000 pairs breeding.
Very common	20,000-50,000 birds occurring or 10,000-25,000 pairs breeding.
Abundant	>50,000 birds occurring or >25,000 pairs breeding.

The accounts, based largely on data from *WMBC Annual Reports*, summarise preferred habitats or localities, geographical and seasonal distributions, numerical trends, density, flocks, roosts, movements and ringing recoveries and give an estimate of the breeding population. For *very rare* and some *rare* species every record is listed. Otherwise the main analysis covers the period 1979-2001 (referred to as the current period), but refers back to *BWM* to provide a context. Authenticated records post-2001 are also included if these were received in time to incorporate into the accounts.

Rare Birds
In accordance with WMBC policy, records of national rarities are included only if they have been accepted by the BBRC. Those prior the BBRC's formation in 1958 have been included at the discretion of the authors and officers of the WMBC. Records of all regional rarities have been assessed by the WMBC on the basis of details provided or information available.

Population Estimates

Broad population estimates were first provided by the WMBC's pioneer *Atlas* (Lord and Munns 1970) and then refined in *BWM*, narrowing the ranges. The latter used CBC densities for farmland and woodland and multiplied them by the area of each within the region. Allowances were also made for birds in other habitats and for edge effects.

We have continued this tradition, partly because of the growing demand for local population data, *e.g.* to monitor Local Biodiversity Action Plans. Our starting point was the BTO's *Breeding Atlas*, which provided the most up-to-date baseline available (1989) and the best assessments of density, edge effects and other habitats. Population ranges were then derived by:

1. Using local surveys, where these were available and known to be reliable.
2. Multiplying the national population (source: Stone *et al.* 1997) by the proportion of nationally occupied 10-km squares falling in the region (source: *Breeding Atlas*) to establish a 1989-based population. This was then adjusted using the national CBC/BBS index 1989-2002 to give a regional population at 2002.
3. Multiplying the national CBC densities for farmland, woodland and other habitats (source: *Breeding Atlas*) by the extent of each habitat in the region (4,810, 456 and 2,088 km^2 respectively) to produce 1989-based populations. These were again adjusted using the national CBC/BBS index 1989-2002 to give a 2002 figure.
4. Taking the regional BBS data (1994-2002) and preliminary results of the two *Tetrad Atlases* as measures of current local densities and distribution and using them as checks against the national CBC densities and the *Breeding Atlas* 10-km square distribution.

This methodology would not stand up to rigorous statistical testing and the resulting population ranges should only be treated as a general guide.

Charts

Four basic types of charts are included, namely:

1. *Totals of Birds*: these show the number of birds recorded, either annually for residents and summer visitors, or over the 'winter' period (taken as July-June) for winter visitors.
2. *Indices*: these indicate population trends for species too numerous or dispersed to be fully counted. Two indices are normally shown, indicating the regional and national breeding trends respectively, based on CBC/BBS data. For wintering waterfowl the regional index is based on the summation of monthly maxima at all sites and the national index is taken from WeBS data (Pollitt *et al.* 2003). *Regional indices derived from CBC data are based on extremely small samples and are included only as a rough guide—they should be interpreted with extreme caution.* Where the population change between *BWM* and current estimates is at variance with trends, this is usually because more refined data is now available.
3. *Monthly Distribution of Birds*: these show occurrences by month or half-month, based either on arrival dates (where individuals can be identified) or the summation of monthly maxima (for more numerous species), which reflect general patterns of abundance.
4. *Best Sites for Birds*: these show the best sites for certain species, ranked by the number of records during the periods shown. The number of birds is also shown.

Species of Conservation Concern.

Where it is relevant to the region, reference is made to certain birds being on the *Red* and *Amber* alert lists. These species are of conservation concern, generally because their populations fell by more than 50% in the case of those on the *Red List* and 25% for those on the *Amber List*. For the full lists, definitions and reasons for inclusion see Gregory *et al.* (2002).

Notes: 1. The CBC/BBS Index values for 2001 have been taken as the mid-points between 2000 and 2002 because of the limited data available for 2001 due to access restrictions during the Foot and Mouth outbreak.
2. Average migrant arrival and departure dates may differ slightly from those in WMBC *Annual Reports* as a more sophisticated method of calculation has been used to take account of leap years.

Mute Swan *Cygnus olor*
Fairly common and increasing resident.

The powerful, yet elegant Mute Swan is a bird of slow flowing or still waters. It can be found on rivers, canals, pools, lakes, gravel pits and reservoirs right across the region, except for the extreme south and north, where suitable habitat is scarce. There was a worrying decline during the 1970s and 1980s, when many died as a result of ingesting lead shot discarded by anglers, but since the use of shot weighing over an ounce was banned in 1987 numbers have recovered well. Indeed, as the indices show, numbers nationally roughly doubled between 1979 and

2001 (Pollitt *et al.* 2003), but locally the increase appears to have been much faster. The species is *Amber* listed because of its unfavourable conservation status in Europe.

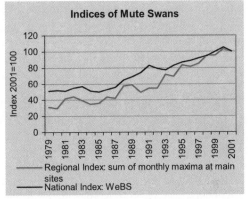

Factors likely to have contributed to its increase are better survival rates due to milder winters, improved river management and water quality leading to more aquatic vegetation, an increase in suitable habitat afforded by new gravel pits and the recovery after lead poisoning, which was especially bad on the Trent and Avon (Hunt 1977).

The *Winter Atlas* showed birds in 90% of 10-km squares, whilst they were recorded in 95% during the *Breeding Atlas*. Since then the WeBS index has shown an increase of about a quarter over the period 1990-2002. The last BTO census for which data was available was in 1990 and the totals of breeding and territorial pairs showed 120 pairs in Staffordshire, 37 pairs in Worcestershire, 36 pairs in Warwickshire and 37 pairs in the West Midlands. Taking account of all available information, the regional population is now estimated to be 300-400 breeding and territorial pairs compared to 230 in 1990.

Breeding success is often not good, with the 1990 Staffordshire survey showing only 56% of pairs rearing cygnets—the rest either failing or not even attempting to breed. Apart from nest failures, there are many threats to breeding success, but one of the most bizarre was suffered by a pair that nested in the middle of the ternery at Kingsbury Water Park. They came under such ferocious attacks from the terns that one of the pair had to be taken into care. Site fidelity is shown by a pair that nested for 17 consecutive years at Middleton Hall.

Many man-made hazards cause injury and death, most notably overhead wires and oil spills, whilst vandalism is a constant threat, with birds being shot and nests robbed or destroyed. Unwitting disturbance and accidental damage also add to their difficulties. Despite all this, many birds persist with nesting in urban areas, with nine pairs producing 55 young in Stoke-on-Trent in 1991 and 13 pairs nesting there the following year. However, the moulting herd at Westport Lake, which at one time numbered 100, has been much reduced in recent years due to the increasing numbers of feral farmyard and Canada geese that are coming to compete for food provided by the public. Breeding also occurs in the West Midlands Conurbation and some notable herds occur here, with counts of 37 at Witton Lakes in October 1999 and 39 in Sandwell Valley in June 2001.

Peak counts of Mute Swans mostly occur during July and August, when birds gather at favoured moulting sites, but then gradually decline through the winter as a result of mortality and movements. Alvecote Pools was once a traditional moulting site, regularly holding over 100 birds until 1989, but numbers have since fallen away and become much more variable.

Ringing has shown that Mute Swans frequently move short distances between sites and it is often surprising to discover how many different individuals use a site. Darvic rings help to determine this, but it must be remembered that these rings have to be replaced if they become damaged or worn. Even so, it was estimated at least 160 different birds visited Westport Lake during 1994. Of these, 145 were carrying rings, from which it was established that 103 originated from this site. At Chasewater in the mid-1990s well over 100 different individuals used the reservoir. Coleman *et al.* (1998) have provide an interesting account of the population trends in three south Staffordshire herds. With birds moving between sites, there is always a danger of double counting, but the most productive sites in recent years have tended to be along the main river valleys. The most outstanding area is that around the confluence of the Tame and Trent, stretching from the gravel pits at Elford and Fisherwick in the south to Burton-on-Trent in the north. This includes the lake and pools at Croxall and Whitemoor Haye, which are often the focal point. With several winter maxima of 250-300, this outstanding area is on the verge of the threshold of 260 at which a site qualifies as being of national importance. Staffordshire also has large herds at Chasewater and Blithfield Reservoir, with peaks of around 150 and 90 birds respectively, and overall the county attracted two-thirds of the birds recorded in the region during 1992-2001. Warwickshire's share was 22%, Worcestershire's 7% and the West Midlands 5%.

There is also a large herd on the Severn at Worcester. Numbers here had plummeted to less than 20 in the late 1980s. By 1992, they had recovered to 75 and the next year they shot up to 130, since when they have remained fairly stable. However, this increase has apparently been artificially aided by the release of birds from swan rescue centres. The same may also be true of Warwickshire's most famous herd, at Stratford-upon-Avon. Here, numbers had dwindled to six by 1975 and the local council became so worried that it established a swan sanctuary and appointed a warden to look after the birds. Gladly things have improved since then. By 1989 the herd had grown to 31 and in 1995 it reached 80. The following year there were 152 birds and around this level has been maintained since. The county's two other large herds are at Draycote Water, with a peak of about 90, and the Middle Tame Valley, where again counting is complicated by movement between sites but peak numbers almost certainly exceed 200. Interestingly, five cygnets from a brood of seven at Ladywalk in 1981 and one from a brood of five at nearby Nether Whitacre in 1985 were of the 'Polish' morph.

Mute Swans seldom travel far, but there have been a few surprising long-distance movements. One seen at Belvide and Chasewater in 1995 had been ringed in Dublin in 1992—only the second bird from the Dublin study to be recorded in Britain. Others involved six from a brood of eight ringed in Wednesbury in August 1974, which turned up 393 km away in Glasgow in August 1975 and one ringed at Gailey and found dead 764 km away, in Denmark.

Bewick's Swan (Tundra Swan) *Cygnus columbianus*
Frequent, though declining, winter visitor and passage migrant.

The Bewick's Swan is the smallest of our three swans and is a winter visitor to riverside flood meadows or the larger reservoirs. From the late 1950s onwards numbers increased dramatically, both nationally and regionally (*BWM*), but this growth subsided in the 1980s and has since shown a marked downwards trend. During 1979-2001, there were on average 250 birds a year, though the numbers each winter fluctuated widely, from an impressive 525 in 1985/86 to a meagre 19 in 1999/00. Between these two extremes, the five-yearly running mean showed a steady long-term decline and the species now seems to be heading towards becoming an uncommon visitor to the region. By comparison, the national pattern since the early 1980s has shown marked annual fluctuations, but with no evident decline overall (Pollitt *et al.* 2003).

More swans come to Britain when the weather on the Continent is harsh, so the recent mild winters across north-west Europe may partly explain the fluctuating numbers. In the winter of 2000/1, for example, peak counts at many sites suggested numbers in Britain were particularly low. Moreover, of those that have come to Britain, the vast majority have stayed on the Ouse and Nene Washes, rather than coming further west. Most of the birds seen in the West Midlands are on their way to or from Slimbridge and numbers on the Severn Estuary in recent winters were certainly much lower than average (Pollitt *et al.*, 2003).

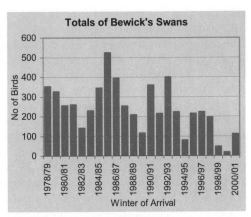

The pattern of occurrences has also changed. *BWM* noted that maximum counts generally involved transient parties, with large numbers only rarely remaining in the region for any length of time. Since 1979, however, there have been several instances of moderately large herds remaining for long periods during the winter, notably in the late 1980s.

Such occurrences were almost invariably on flood meadows, either along the lower Avon and Severn valleys or around the confluence of the rivers Tame and Trent—with the same areas also producing the highest counts. The lower Avon, especially around Bredon's Hardwick, has been the most favoured area, particularly in the four consecutive winters from 1984/5 to 1987/8 when birds were intermittently present from November or December into March. The peak counts in these four winters were also impressive, with

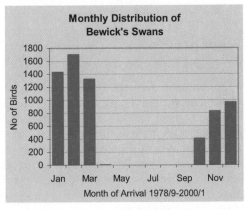

maxima of 156 on February 3rd 1985, 258—a regional record—on March 15th 1986, 143 on February 7th 1987 and 92 on December 15th 1987. These birds almost certainly came from Slimbridge and arrived either in hard weather or as flood waters were receding. Herds in the Tame/Trent valley have generally been smaller, numbering around 40 birds. For example, in 1986 up to 48 stayed around Alrewas from January 28th to March 16th. The only counts of passage birds to approach these totals were at Draycote Water on February 23rd 1980, when a herd of 60 that had been present during the day was joined by a further 35 at dusk; and at Whitemoor Haye, where, in 1991, 19 long-staying birds were joined by a further 150 on March 12th, with all departing the next day.

Otherwise, 80 flew over Dunhampstead on October 1st 1986, 70 were over Cannock tip on February 18th 1993 and herds up to 50 were reported from many, widely scattered, localities. Several such records referred to birds arriving in adverse weather, such as fog. The geographical distribution clearly shows the influence of Worcestershire's position close to the Severn Estuary, as it attracted 37% of birds, which is a far higher proportion than for many species of wildfowl. Of the other counties, 34% were recorded in Staffordshire, 25% in Warwickshire and just 4% in the West Midlands.

The vast majority of records during 1979-2001 fell between October and March. The earliest ever in the region was the herd over Dunhampstead quoted above, but generally few arrive before late October, after which there is a steady increase to a peak in February. Good numbers also occur during March, as birds begin their migration back to their breeding grounds, but by the end of the month most have left. A late individual was recorded at Tittesworth Reservoir on April 18th 1997, an adult lingered at Bredon's Hardwick from March 31st to May 8th 1987, an immature remained in the Tame and Anker valleys from 1994 until May 22nd

1995 and what was presumed to be an injured or escaped bird was at Barton Gravel Pit on the unusual date of June 9th 1992.

Bewick's Swans mingling with the region's herds of Mute Swans are invariably birds breaking their journey either to or from their wintering or breeding grounds. Local recorders are able to read the alpha-numerically engraved neck-collars of these shy and often easily disturbed birds and this has provided a fascinating insight into the remarkable journeys made by this species. Of the eight individuals to have been tracked in this way, six made spectacular movements from Russia, with four having been ringed in the Pechora Delta in 1992 and the others in the Yangutei River and Korovinskaya Bay areas in 1996. One of these was also seen twice in the Netherlands, a month either side of its appearance in Sandwell Valley in January 1997, whilst another was also seen in Germany and the Netherlands in the two years that elapsed between its being ringed and appearing at Upton-on-Severn in 1994. The remaining two, both seen at Belvide Reservoir, had been ringed elsewhere in this country, but one was known to have visited Denmark in the interim.

Whooper Swan   *Cygnus cygnus*
Scarce or uncommon winter visitor and passage migrant. Also a recent feral visitor.

Whooper Swans are winter visitors, mainly to northern Britain. Most come from Iceland, but some originate from Fennoscandia. This has always been the least common of the two wild swans and during 1979-2001 it was outnumbered ten to one by the Bewick's Swan. Whilst the latter species has been declining, however, the Whooper Swan has increased.

Birds were recorded in every winter between 1978/9-2000/1, although 1989/90 came desperately close to being a blank season, escaping only through a very late spring record—of a sick or feral bird which stayed at Baggeridge Country Park from May 15th until the following October. Since then, numbers have gradually increased, most notably since 1994/5. The peaks of 1991/2 and 1993/4 distort the true picture, since they involved an unusually large herd of 36 at the JCB Pool, Rocester, on March 24th 1992 and a party of 17 at Tittesworth Reservoir on Christmas Day 1993. The former was the third largest herd to be recorded in the region, the top two being 50 at Beaudesert in 1914 and 37 at Bittell Reservoir in 1953.

Over 500 birds were recorded during 1979-2001, though precise numbers are hard to determine because of mobility. For example, there were three records on November 19th 2000, when a herd of 13 flew south-east over Westport in the morning, one was at Blithfield and a party of 12 flew SSW over Smestow Valley. These records could easily have referred to the same party moving erratically south, with one bird dropping out on the way. But equally, if there happened to be a movement of swans that day, 26 individuals might have been involved.

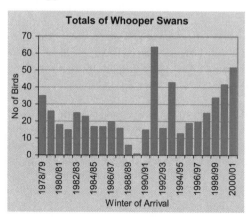

It was noted in *BWM* that the pattern of arrivals suggested birds fall into two categories: those moving spontaneously through, and into, the area during the November-December passage period, and those displaced into the region during mid-winter, hard weather movements. This is still very broadly true, with the first birds appearing in October, but the bulk arriving during November and December. The January peak that then follows includes some hard weather movements, though these have been less frequent during the recent run of mild winters. Since 1979, however, the return passage during February to April has been much lighter; the apparent March peak being largely attributable to the Rocester herd of 36 mentioned above. Otherwise few herds have exceeded a dozen birds.

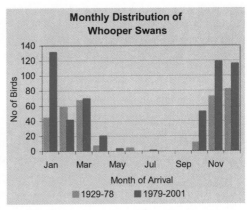

As might be expected of a bird coming from northern climes, Staffordshire has hosted the bulk of the birds (76%), with Warwickshire contributing 13%, Worcestershire 6% and West Midlands 5%. Only two areas have regularly held birds over several consecutive winters. In north Staffordshire, a herd visited the Longsdon Mill Pool-Rudyard-Tittesworth area for twelve consecutive winters from 1976/7 to 1986/7, its size varying from three to 15 birds. More recently, a smaller group of up to five birds frequented the flood meadows around the Tame-Trent confluence for the five consecutive winters 1995/6 to 1999/2000 and again in 2001/2. These birds favoured the Whitemoor Haye area, but also visited Barton Gravel Pit, Catholme, Croxall and occasionally Elford.

Away from these two areas the most favoured sites have been the reservoirs in Staffordshire, particularly Blithfield and Belvide. Other less frequently used localities, in descending order of visits, include Westport Lake, Draycote Water, Chasewater, Doxey Marshes and Bredon's Hardwick.

Two individuals prove that some of our wintering birds come from Iceland. The first was ringed in the north of that country in August 1993 and then visited Welney (Norfolk) in January before appearing at Belvide on March 21st 1994. The second followed a similar route, having been colour-ringed in Iceland in 1994 and recorded at Welney in November 1998 before turning up at Upton Warren on December 30th 1998. A few weeks later it, and its two companions, were at Ashleworth Ham (Gloucestershire).

In recent years presumed feral birds have further complicated record assessment, particularly in the West Midlands where two, which are believed to have escaped from the Cotwall End Nature Centre in 1991, roamed around the area until 1996, when one was found dead. More concern arose when one of a captive pair in Solihull was killed and its mate paired with a Mute Swan, producing several broods of young over the ensuing years. The hybrid offspring roamed widely along the Tame and Blythe Valleys and were even seen as far away as Brandon Marsh.

Bean Goose   *Anser fabalis*
Rare winter visitor.

There have been 21 records of Bean Geese, three of them historical, two during the *BWM* period and 16 since, all of which have occurred after 1985. The complete list is overleaf.

The county spread now shows nine records from Staffordshire, six from Warwickshire, five from Worcestershire and just a single historical one from inside the West Midlands county. However, it should be noted that the 1987 and 1988 Belvide records could refer to the same three birds, whilst the five records listed for Staffordshire in 1993 and 1994 could conceivably have involved anything from three to nine birds. The party of 20 at Bodymoor Heath in March 1986 was exceptional, no other group having exceeded five birds. Of those birds attributed to a particular race, all have been *A. f. rossicus*, or Tundra Bean Geese. Records have spanned the period October to April, but with a strong December-January peak that is typical for this species.

Regional Record Number	County Record Number		Year	Locality, Date and Notes
1	Warks	1	1841	Barford: unknown date, shot.
2	Warks	2	Pre-1904	Welford-on-Avon: unknown date, specimen collected.
3	W Mid	1	Pre-1908	Pelsall: Unknown date, reported as killed in Staffs (which Pelsall then was) and in Pelsall collection (Smith 1938).
4	Worcs	1	1941	Bittell Reservoir: March 27th.
5	Warks	3	1972	Alvecote Pools: January 30th to February 27th.
6	Warks	4	1986	Bodymoor Heath: 20 March 15th-26th., including 10 of the race *A.f. rossicus*, the others being indeterminate.
7	Staffs	1	1987	Belvide Reservoir: three adults of the race *A.f. rossicus* December 13th –31st, then moved to Wheaton Aston until January 3rd, 1988.
8	Staffs	2	1988	Branston GP/WP: January 9th.
9	Staffs	3	1988	Belvide Reservoir: three, February 6th-14th, assumed different to three from December 1987 to January 1988.
10	Warks	5	1990	Bramcote: adult of the race *A.f. rossicus*, February 3rd to March 13th, though not reported between February 5th and March 4th.
11	Worcs	2	1991	Bredons Hardwick: adult, April 16th.
12	Staffs	4	1993	Blithfield Reservoir: three, October 19th-23rd.
13	Staffs	5	1993	Doxey Marshes: November 19th., possibly one of those at Blithfield above.
14	Staffs	6	1993	Catholme: two, November 30th., possibly two of those at Blithfield above.
15	Worcs	3	1993	Bredons Hardwick: December 4th-5th.
16	Staffs	7	1993	Croxall GP: December 14th, possibly one of those at Catholme above.
17	Staffs	8	1994	Elford GP: two adults, January 15th to March 5th, possibly those at Catholme above. Also at Alrewas, Croxall, Whitemoor Haye and Wychnor .
18	Warks	6	1996	Draycote Water: adult of the race *A.f. rossicus*, January 1st-2nd.
19	Worcs	4	1998	Bredons Hardwick: two of the race *A.f. rossicus*, December 4th-6th.
20	Worcs	5	1998	Bredons Hardwick: five of *A.f. rossicus* race, December 24th-January 1st 1999, believed different to the two above. Same five, Mythe Bridge, December 27th.
21	Staffs	9	2001	Whitemoor Haye: three, December 15th.

Pink-footed Goose   *Anser brachyrhynchus*

Frequent passage migrant and winter visitor to Staffordshire, but normally rare further south. Also a scarce feral visitor or escapee.

Most of the Pink-footed Geese that come to winter in Britain originate from Iceland. In England, they form huge flocks on the Lancashire mosses and the north Norfolk coast and movements between the two result in birds crossing the region—a phenomenon first recorded in 1979, but now regularly noted. Elsewhere the species is rare and single birds or small groups attached to flocks of Canada or other geese are usually thought to be escaped or feral birds.

Increased numbers were recorded during the mid-1950s and again during the 1970s, with 80 in 1960 being the largest party prior to 1979 (*BWM*). Since then the concentrations in

Lancashire and north Norfolk have increased substantially and this has resulted in more coming through this region, with about 11,000 birds reported during 1979-2001. In autumn many birds go first to eastern Scotland and then move down to Norfolk, so the south-easterly passage across the region during September-December is small (20% of all birds), whereas in January and early February there is a much stronger north-westerly passage (80% of birds) as skeins move directly across Staffordshire to Lancashire.

The movements across the region broadly follow one of two routes. Some take a direct line across the southern Pennines, as instanced by several records from Rudyard and Tittesworth reservoirs and skeins flying over Coombes Valley, the Manifold Valley and Swallow Moss. Many, however, prefer to follow the easier, but more circuitous route along the Trent Valley, where there have been several records. Both routes converge on the Potteries and it is here that most birds have been recorded, including an astonishing 2,500 on January 31st 1996. As a result, 88% of all birds have been recorded in Staffordshire.

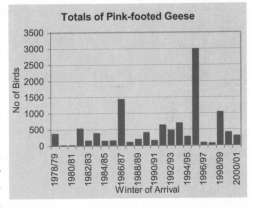

Some parties occasionally wander off these routes into Birmingham, the Black Country or north Warwickshire, with Warwickshire having had 5% and the West Midlands 4% of all birds, but large flocks further south are rare and generally associated with adverse weather. For example, it is likely that a north-westerly movement of 200 across the region on February 7th 1996 involved birds disorientated by fog. This skein, which was tracked at Fenny Compton, Kenilworth and Sandwell Valley, was the largest ever recorded in both Warwickshire and the West Midlands county. Further notable flocks in these counties were 120, at both Amblecote on January 16th 1982 and Whitacre Heath on October 21st 2001. Otherwise, groups seldom exceed 50 or 60. With just 3%, Worcestershire has the fewest birds, although small numbers occasionally appear along the Avon Valley, perhaps having wandered from Slimbridge. A flock of 84, which moved from Bredon Ham (Gloucestershire) to feed at Strensham on January 31st 1999, was easily the largest seen in this county, where groups seldom exceed 20.

The number of birds involved varies markedly from year-to-year, but, excluding the exceptional passage of January 1996, the long-term trend is fairly stable. *BWM* postulated that the region experienced hard-weather movements and there is some further evidence to support this, with the peak January passages of 1987 and 1996 both occurring when anticyclones were established over Scandinavia, bringing cold weather and easterly winds. However, movement is not just confined to cold weather, as significant passage was noted in nine of the ten winters during the 1990s—a decade with some of the mildest winters on record.

White-fronted Goose   *Anser albifrons*
Uncommon winter visitor and passage migrant. Also scarce feral visitor or escapee.

Two distinct races of White-fronted Geese winter in Britain, namely the Eurasian race *A. a. albifrons*, which breeds in the Russian tundra, and the Greenland race, *A. a. flavirostris*. The latter is an extremely rare visitor to the region, but flocks of the former are a regular feature just over the border at Slimbridge, in the Severn estuary. From here birds occasionally wander onto flooded meadows in south Worcestershire, whilst migrating skeins are also noted as they pass overhead or pause briefly at reservoirs.

In the 1940s, flights up to 500 strong were reported moving along the Avon Valley in January and then returning in March, with several reports of large skeins passing over at night, calling (*BWM*). Indeed, during 1929-78, some 5,000 birds were recorded compared to 1,800 during 1979-2001—averages of 100 and 78 a year respectively. Birds heading to the Severn estuary still have to pass over the region, yet far fewer are being detected, despite a huge increase in observers. This is probably due to a

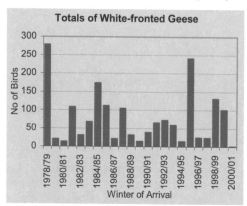

Totals of White-fronted Geese

national decline in numbers over the last twenty-five years, which has resulted in the species being *Amber* listed. This decline has arisen from a shift in the wintering population, with the recent mild winters and a ban on goose hunting since 2000 encouraging more birds to remain in the Netherlands (Pollitt *et al.* 2003). Regionally the main feature during 1978/9-2000/1 was the wide fluctuations in numbers from one year to the next, with no indication of a decline in the five-yearly running mean, which has consistently been between 50-100.

White-fronted Geese arrive late in Britain and leave early. It was noted in *BWM* that December, January and March were most productive, with several large flocks in the latter month as birds headed back to their breeding areas. In the current period, December and January remained the dominant arrival months, but more birds left early, with a rapid departure in February and a very small March passage. The short time spent here suggests birds mainly come this far west to escape hard weather and the largest counts support this, with those in 1978/9, 1984/5 and 1995/6 all coinciding with severe weather. Indeed, the first two of these winters were amongst the coldest on the Continent last century.

The largest flocks are almost invariably seen, or heard, flying overhead, with the biggest in recent years being 150 over Blithfield Reservoir on January 15th 1985. Also of interest were 95 heading ENE over Fenny Compton on February 1st 1999—a very early date for what was seemingly return passage—and a skein over Droitwich at 23.45hrs on November 23rd 1983, which was the last report of nocturnal movement.

Being close to the Severn estuary, Worcestershire has produced the most records (40%), but Warwickshire has had the most birds (35%), followed by Worcestershire with 33%, Staffordshire 30% and West Midlands 2%. No site consistently holds birds, but in rank order, those most frequently visited during 1991/2-2000/1 were Bredon's Hardwick, Blithfield Reservoir, Draycote Water, Belvide Reservoir, the Tame/Trent confluence and Grimley. Bredon's Hardwick produced records in fourteen of the seventeen winters 1984/5-2000/1, including a substantial flock of 79 on January 29th 2000. Since 1992/3 the flood meadows around the Tame/Trent confluence have also attracted a few birds, with records in five of the nine winters to 2000/1, including a maximum of 24 in 1995/6. Draycote's position on the direct flight line between the wintering and breeding areas helps to explain its importance, but that of Belvide and Blithfield Reservoirs is less clear. However, a small group of birds has historically been associated with the Belvide/Wheaton Aston area and it seems that south Staffordshire may have been a former winter staging area to which some birds occasionally return.

Few birds stay long, with two-thirds gone within a couple of days, but 14% have lingered longer than a fortnight. Records from north Staffordshire are rare, but birds are occasionally seen at Tittesworth Reservoir and two stayed for 94 days, from December 6th 1987 through to March 14th 1988, being joined by a further two from February 14th. Also noteworthy was a roost at Westwood Pool in 1993 that held up to nine birds between November 8th until January 22nd 1994—a period of 76 days.

The only records of the Greenland race *A. a. flavirostris* are the two from Belvide Reservoir that were documented in *BWM*, namely a family party of five that remained there from October 30th 1949 until February 27th 1950 and four adults that joined a flock of Eurasian birds on February 14th 1970.

Single birds and small groups are often considered to be feral or escapees from captivity.

Lesser White-fronted Goose   *Anser erythropus*
Very rare feral visitor or escapee.

The Lesser White-fronted Goose is a rare winter visitor to Britain from northern Eurasia. All records in this region are believed to refer to escaped, released or feral birds.

The only record quoted in *BWM* was of an escaped bird seen intermittently at Packington Park between January 28th and June 18th 1978. Since then there have been a further six individuals, as follows:

> Branston from May 31st-June 2nd 1985; Branston again from April-June 1987, with presumed the same individual again from October 19th-January 19th 1988; Kingsbury Water Park from May 17th-August 23rd 1987; Tittesworth Reservoir, where one released in 1988 was present until at least January 21st 1992; Leamington Spa from January 25th– February 12th 1991; and an unringed bird at Blithfield Reservoir from October 5th-17th 1991.

Greylag Goose   *Anser anser*
Frequent feral resident, mainly to north Warwickshire, but increasing and spreading elsewhere.

There are historical references to wild Greylag Geese having occurred in the region (Mosley 1863; Hastings 1834; Tomes 1904), but today all birds are considered to be of feral origin. Small flocks of these might be encountered at any gravel pit, lake, pool or reservoir across the region, though the larger flocks are concentrated into two or three areas. Often they consort with Canada Geese. Colonisation by feral birds began when the species was introduced into Packington Park in the mid-1960s and birds have bred in this area since at least 1967 (*BWM*). From here birds then spread northwards into the Tame Valley, with up to 90 at Kingsbury WP. Throughout the 1980s, numbers remained fairly stable, but during the 1990s there was a phenomenal increase, with the regional population now standing at around 500-700 birds.

The Tame and Blythe Valleys are still the stronghold, with generally around 300 birds, but

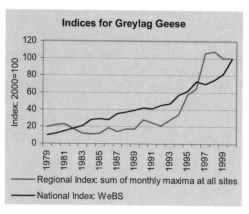

Indices for Greylag Geese

Index: 2000=100

Regional Index: sum of monthly maxima at all sites
National Index: WeBS

with a new regional record of 360 at Marsh Lane in December 2002. Another major flock, possibly arising from Packington, is centred on Brandon Marsh and Coombe Abbey. This began with some 15 birds in 1990 and now regularly numbers over 100 (maximum 165 in 2001). The largest flock in Staffordshire is at Branston. This began to form in the mid-1990s and now averages about 60 a year (maximum 105 in 2000). The only other site with a regular flock of any size is Blithfield Reservoir, where the average of the peak counts over the five-years 1997-2001 was 38.

Snow Goose *Anser caerulescens*
Scarce feral visitor or escapee.

Wild Snow Geese are very rare winter vagrants to Britain from their Arctic North American breeding grounds. So it is extremely unlikely that any West Midland record of either the white or blue colour phases has involved wild birds and all are regarded as feral or escapees.

The WMBC began to publish records of this species in 1970 and *BWM* documented 40 between then and 1978. Subsequently, there were a further 130 records, involving 215 birds, between 1979-2001—an average of nine a year. Birds were much commoner during the 1980s, however, averaging 15 a year, but since then, apart from 1996 with 17 birds, the average has fallen to five a year.

The most promising hint of possible genuine vagrancy came in 1980, when a gaggle of seven, at Kingsbury Water Park from April 30th-May 1st, coincided with a flock of 18 in the Netherlands that included one ringed three years previously in Canada (Lack 1986). At the time this was the largest party to have been recorded in the region, but it has since been equalled twice in circumstances less promising for potential vagrancy, at Chillington on May 13th 1984 and Dunstall Park on August 7th 1996. The seven at Chillington occurred around the time that up to half a dozen spent six months at nearby Belvide Reservoir.

Even if the above parties are excluded, the monthly distribution pattern of arrival dates still shows peaks in spring, late summer and January, but otherwise the random spread of records typifies a feral species, as does the broad geographical distribution across the region. Within this broad distribution, half-a-dozen clusters can be identified, in Staffordshire, around Aqualate, Belvide and Chillington in the west and the Tame/Trent confluence in the east; in Worcestershire around the lower Avon Valley and the Severn/ Stour valley below Kidderminster; in the West Midlands in Dudley and Wolverhampton; and in Warwickshire along the Middle Tame Valley. Overall, most birds (54%) have occurred in Staffordshire, 23% in Worcestershire, 12% in the West Midlands and 11% in Warwickshire.

Snow Geese quite often consort with Canada and other geese and hybrids do occur.

Canada Goose *Branta canadensis*
Common and increasing feral resident. Fairly common breeding species.

Canada Geese were introduced into England around the mid-1600s, but numbers remained low and birds were relatively scarce outside parks and country estates until the 1930s. A major population explosion began in the 1950s (*BWM*) and has continued ever since. As a result, birds are now well established throughout the region, breeding by gravel pits, lakes, ponds, reservoirs and rivers, even within urban areas. Large post-breeding flocks then gather at the larger lakes and reservoirs in late summer and autumn, during which time the moult occurs.

BWM said the regional growth rate had exceeded the national one. Subsequently, the increase continued nationally until the late 1980s, but then slowed and became more erratic. In contrast, regional numbers appeared to decline slightly in the early 1980s, but strong growth since, especially during 1987-96 when the population doubled, has brought them back in line with national growth. The BTO *Atlas* surveys recorded birds in 93% of 10-km squares. During 1990-2000 the number of adult birds increased nationally by three-quarters. However, no increase was evident in urban areas or in tetrads with a high percentage of water, where the goose population had probably already reached saturation point (Austin 2001)— situations which are typically found in this region. Today the wintering population is estimated to be 5,000-6,000 birds (*cf.* 2,230 in 1976 in *BWM*).

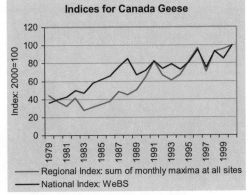

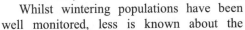

Whilst wintering populations have been well monitored, less is known about the breeding population. However, surveys undertaken for the WWT in June and July 1991 estimated 678 birds in Warwickshire and 1,591 in Staffordshire, where 70 pairs bred, producing 366 goslings. In good seasons, a 100 or more young have been produced at some sites, notably Kingsbury Water Park in 1979 and 1988, Kings Bromley in 1980, Elford in 1989 and Arrow Valley Park in 1991. Clearly, with so little information, the breeding population is very hard to estimate, but is almost certainly in the 'fairly common' range of 250-2,500 pairs.

The sheer weight of numbers has brought the Canada Goose into conflict with both agricultural and leisure interests, because of damage to crops and fouling of public places. As a consequence control measures have been instigated at certain sites. For example, 170 were culled at Aqualate Mere in 1992 and 1993, whilst productivity was reduced by egg-pricking at Coombe Abbey in 1997.

Blithfield Reservoir holds most birds, with an average peak over 1979-2001 of 768 and counts of over a thousand in four of the years, with a maximum of 1,212 in 1991. There have only been two other records of more than a thousand, namely 1,100 on Branston Golf Course in 1987 and 1,044 at Draycote Water in 1996. During 1992-2001 Staffordshire held 47% of birds, Warwickshire 26%, Worcestershire 19% and the West Midlands 8%.

Geese tend to travel along river valleys and most movements are within 40 km of the ringing site. Others ringed in the region have been recovered over 100 km away in Powys, Wiltshire and Buckinghamshire. There has been no recent evidence of our geese using the Beauly Firth as a moulting site as documented in *BWM*, but one moved to Fairburn Ings in North Yorkshire and another ringed on Tiree (Strathclyde) was found at Tamworth five years later. Our oldest known goose is a 25 year old bird, originally ringed in Tipton on July 1st 1978.

As observers have become more familiar with the characteristics of various races, so the number of records of these has increased from only around half-a-dozen in *BWM* to over 60 birds during 1979-2001. Some 40% have only been described as birds of one of the smaller races, but the same percentage have been considered to show the characteristics of the race *minima* (Cackling Goose). The remaining 20% have been attributed to the following races: *hutchinsii, parvipes, taverneri, interior, maxima* and *oxydentalis*. There are no indications as to the origins of these birds, but presumably they have escaped from captive collections.

There have also been many records of hybrid geese, most often between Canada Geese and one of a variety of other species. Feral geese readily hybridise and at times this causes confusion in identifying true species and races.

Barnacle Goose   *Banta leucopsis*

Rare winter visitor and passage migrant. Uncommon feral visitor or escapee.

This small goose breeds in the high Arctic and winters around the coasts of Britain and mainland Europe. Its history in the West Midlands is an intriguing one. Early authors described it as a rare visitor and there were no reports last century until 1960, after which records of feral or escaped birds became commonplace. Up to 1979 only three records, comprising flocks of 11, five and seven, were thought to suggest the possibility of wild birds (*BWM*).

During the 1980s the species' status was transformed. The first sign of a change came in 1980, when a flock of 24 was seen at Earlswood on December 6th. Although this was twice as large as any flock hitherto, it was still regarded as being of suspect origin. Then, on December 7th 1983, a similar flock of 29 appeared at nearby Bittell Reservoir. Over the ensuing years this gradually increased in size to a maximum of 146 in 1988. The possibility that these might be wild birds gained some credence from two events. Firstly, it was discovered that flocks of a similar size were arriving on Skomer island (Pembrokeshire) shortly after the Bittell birds left and it seems very likely these were the same birds. Secondly, in November 1987, there was a marked movement of birds, with 46 over Sandwell Valley on 12th and 53 over Branston on 13th as well as the 120 which arrived at Bittell on 15th. There were other large flocks in the 1980s that might have been wild birds, too, notably at Belvide, where 30 in 1984 were followed by 37 in 1985; and Upton Warren, where there were 26 in 1985. The Bittell phenomenon ended abruptly in 1989, when just six birds arrived in the autumn, but during the decade the annual regional average had increased from 32 for the first five years to 173 for the second five.

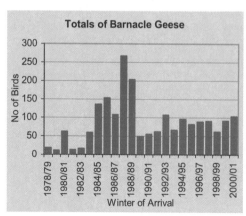

By comparison to the 1980s, the twelve subsequent winters have been lean ones, with an average of just 80 a year. During this time the largest flock was 24 at Westport Lake on October 4th 1994, but Blithfield Reservoir and Draycote Water were the most frequently visited sites.

The monthly distribution shows a marked influx of birds during September-December, with a very strong peak in November. However, the latter largely arises from the atypical numbers at Bittell Reservoir. This also explains why Worcestershire, with 41% of birds, was the most visited county, followed by Staffordshire with 34%, Warwickshire with 17% and the West Midlands with 8%.

Some idea of the strength of the feral population can be gauged from counts of 18 at Blithfield Reservoir in August 2001—too early a date for wild birds—and 14 at Draycote on December 21st 1999, which were considered to be of captive or feral stock. Indeed, feral birds have even begun to breed in recent

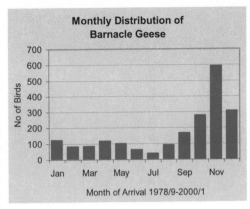

years, at Westport Lake in 1992; Edgbaston Pool in 1998; The Vale in 2000-2, with two pairs in the latter year; and on a private lake at Prior Marston, where three pairs bred in 2002.

Brent Goose   *Branta bernicla*
Scarce passage migrant and winter visitor.

Two races occur in Britain—the Dark-bellied Brent Goose *B. b. bernicla* from central Arctic Russia, which winters around our eastern and southern coasts, and the Light-bellied Brent Goose *B. b. hrota*, which nests in Arctic North America and winters in northern England and Ireland. Overflying birds, usually of the dark-bellied race, occasionally drop in to one of the region's reservoirs.

There are 11 fully documented historical records, involving 18 birds. To these a further 19 records of 44 birds were added during 1929-78—an average of just under one bird a year (*BWM*). By comparison the current period has produced another 94 records of 295 birds, at an average of 13 birds per annum. Despite this considerable increase, there were still five blank winters between 1978/9 and 2000/1, the last in 1999/2000.

Indeed, there were no birds in four of the first five winters and it was not until 1983/4 that numbers began to increase. Thereafter they have waxed and waned, but the numbers involved are small, with the peaks often resulting from just a single flock and there does not appear to be any correlation with weather patterns. The largest flocks were 32 flying over Chillington on April 1st 1988 and 25 over Doxey Marshes on February 21st 1993, whereas the largest mentioned in *BWM* was ten in 1941. Since 1993 no flock has exceeded 11 birds.

The monthly pattern of records shows a strong influx between October and January, after which new arrivals subside. The apparent return passage in April mainly comprised two flocks totalling 49 birds. The current period also brought the first May and July records—at Sandwell Valley in 1991 and Draycote Water in 1996 respectively—but both birds were considered to be of dubious origin.

As would be expected, the two largest reservoirs have been the best sites during the current period, with Draycote Water (17 records) almost twice as productive as Blithfield Reservoir (nine records). Sandwell Valley and

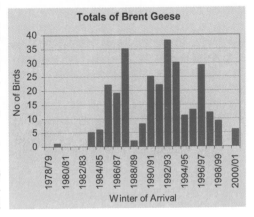

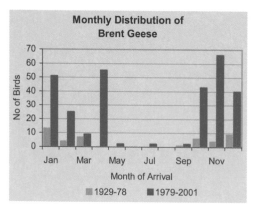

Belvide Reservoir were visited on seven and six occasions respectively.

Birds of the light-bellied race *B. b. hrota* were recorded on four occasions, with singles at Belvide on December 14th-15th 1984 and again on October 15th 1987, one at Jubilee Pools on April 17th 1994 and a party of six, five of them adults, at Chasewater on October 11th 1998.

Red-breasted Goose   *Branta ruficollis*
Very rare feral visitor or escapee.

Since the first record at Bodymoor Heath (now Kingsbury Water Park) between September 29th and October 14th 1973 (*BWM*), there have been four further sightings as follows.

Elford, August 31st and September 17th 1992: Bredons Hardwick, an unringed bird from September 15th to November 8th 1996: Belvide Reservoir, May 1st 2000: and Bredons Hardwick, an adult on May 10th 2001.

Red-breasted Geese breed in central Arctic Russia and wild birds are rare winter visitors to Britain. Many are kept in captivity, however, and all five of the region's records are considered to have involved escaped or feral birds.

Egyptian Goose   *Alopochen aegyptiaca*
Rare feral visitor or escapee.

Since the Egyptian Goose was admitted to the *British and Irish List* in 1970 there have been 68 records of 95 birds in this region. Of these, 50 records and 64 birds occurred during 1979-2001. All are presumed to have escaped from captivity or to have been feral birds.

Appearances have been erratic, ranging from none at all in three years to 10 birds in 1979 and nine in 1988, with a fluctuating long-term trend. The monthly distribution is typical of a feral population, with birds in every month, though most have appeared during April to June, or in August. This suggests possible breeding and in 1978 an abandoned egg was found south of Worcester, at High Green.

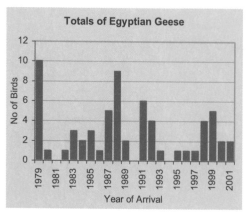

The largest party was nine at Upton Warren in 1971 (*BWM*), whilst during the current period five were at Bittell Reservoir in 1979 and four at Croxall in both 1991 and 1999. Birds were recorded at 38 localities during 1979-2001, with Staffordshire having 43% of all birds, followed by Warwickshire with 26%, Worcestershire with 20% and West Midlands with 11%. The sites where this goose has been seen fall into reasonably discrete areas, presumably reflecting dispersal from its point of escape or release. They have occurred along the Lower Avon, Severn, Tame and Trent Valleys (with Branston the most visited site); and in Needwood, the Black Country, the fringes of Cannock Chase, the Droitwich district and the Dunsmore area of Warwickshire. Apparently, two were deliberately released at Brandon Marsh in 1998, whilst birds were seen intermittently at Hollybush, in the Needwood area, from October 1985 through to 1991.

Ruddy Shelduck   *Tadorna ferruginea*
Scarce escapee or feral visitor and possible rare vagrant.

The populations of Ruddy Shelduck in north Africa and south-east Europe are decreasing (*BWP*), but studies have found there are no self-sustaining feral populations in northern Europe and have concluded that the species should be regarded as an irruptive vagrant to north-west Europe (Vinicombe *et al.* 1993 and Vinicombe and Harrop 1999). Nevertheless, records in this region are still more likely to involve feral or escaped birds.

There were two records prior to 1886, then none until 1974. Since then, birds have been seen in twenty-four years and in every year from 1985-2001 inclusive. Numbers have fluctuated from year-to-year, with most noted in 1979. However, the picture is obscured by at least a couple of long-staying, wandering individuals, which could in theory account for the bulk of records. Firstly, a female seen infrequently at Blithfield Reservoir for six years between August 31st 1992 and October 30th 1998 could have been the bird seen at Barton GP and Branston during that time, or even the one that visited Stubbers Green in most years from 1993-98. Secondly, a male intermittently roamed the Tame Valley in Warwickshire for four years from March 20th 1994 to October 11th 1998. During its stay it is known to have visited several sites and may also have been involved in records from Alvecote Pools and Dosthill Pool during this time.

Over 90% of records have involved just one, or sometimes two, birds, with higher counts of eight at Wilden on July 22nd 1979 and five at Holt in August 1979 and again in September-October 1985 and 1986. With Worcestershire having the majority of large parties it is not surprising that it has attracted nearly half (47%) of all birds, Staffordshire accounts for 22% of birds, Warwickshire for 21% and the West Midlands 10%. Three that arrived at Branston on July 6th 1994, when there was an influx into Britain, perhaps have the strongest claim to having been wild birds.

The most productive sites have been Upton Warren (eight records of 11 birds), and Blithfield Reservoir and Stubbers Green, with six records and six birds each. Interestingly, despite the presumption that most records refer to escapees or feral birds, the monthly distribution does show a strong late-summer peak between July-September and a subsidiary one in spring, during March and April, which might be interpreted as indicative of passage.

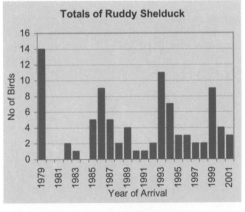

Totals of Ruddy Shelduck

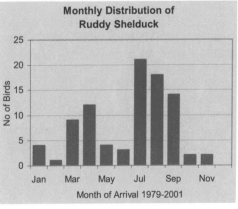

Monthly Distribution of Ruddy Shelduck

129

Common Shelduck   (Shelduck)   *Tadorna tadorna*
Frequent passage migrant and summer and winter visitor. Scarce or uncommon, but increasing, breeding species.

Normally found on muddy estuaries or sandy shores, the Common Shelduck is one of several coastal species that have increasingly spread inland over the last thirty years. It is now breeding at several of the region's lakes and gravel pits, often nesting in rabbit burrows or even old drainage pipes. At passage times birds pass through the main reservoirs as well.

As the national population increased during the latter half of the twentieth century, so birds began to move away from the crowded coast, but the first successful breeding, at Ladywalk in 1970, was easily the furthest inland at that time. It was soon followed by regular nesting along the Tame and Anker valleys in Warwickshire. Pairs then bred for the first time in Worcestershire, at Upton Warren in 1978 (but not again until 2000), and in Staffordshire, at Stretton Hall in 1979. Twenty years elapsed, however, before a pair bred for the first time in the West Midlands, at an undisclosed site.

BWM said this duck was a very scarce breeding species, with probably only one or two pairs each year, but by the time of the *Breeding Atlas* it had spread into 21% of the 10-km squares. Nevertheless, on average only half-a-dozen pairs have nested each year and their success has varied enormously as they contended with the vagaries of floods and predation, notably by mink. At times they might even frustrate their own endeavours, with 15 adults at Ladywalk in 1995 thought to have failed to breed because they were too preoccupied with territorial behaviour. Following the second successful breeding in Worcestershire in 2000, pairs bred at four different sites in 2001, so perhaps the population is beginning to consolidate its position. Currently there are between 5-15 pairs.

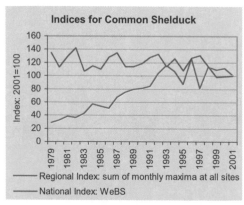

Indices for Common Shelduck

Index: 2001=100

—— Regional Index: sum of monthly maxima at all sites
—— National Index: WeBS

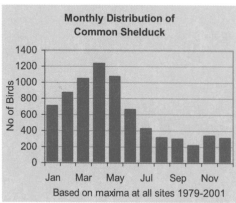

Monthly Distribution of Common Shelduck

No of Birds

Based on maxima at all sites 1979-2001

With the increase in breeding birds, the seasonal pattern has also changed from that shown in *BWM*, with spring now the dominant season and autumn and winter less important. Numbers begin to build up as early as January as the first territorial birds return. They then rise to a peak in April before steadily subsiding again during June-August as non-breeding birds, failed breeders and adults leave in that sequence for their moulting grounds. Most British birds travel to the Heligoland Bight or Wadden See to moult, though others moult in the Mersey Estuary, the Wash and Bridgwater Bay. The slight subsidiary peak in November-December indicates passage birds returning from their moulting grounds.

The largest flock mentioned in *BWM* was 43 at Kingsbury Water Park in December 1979. During 1979-2001 flocks up to 30 became reasonably common, especially in the Trent and Tame valleys where there were 43 at Branston in June 1994. The three largest parties, however, were 48 flying over Little Comberton in August 1984, possibly on their way to the moulting grounds in Bridgwater Bay, 50 at Bredon's Hardwick in March 2001 and 55 at Rough Hay on April 2nd 1997.

The colonisation by breeding birds has strongly influenced the geographical spread, with just over half of the birds during 1992-2001 occurring at five sites in the Trent and Tame Valleys, namely 13% at Branston, 12% at Dosthill-Kingsbury Water Park, 10% each at Barton Gravel Pit and Alvecote Pools and 7% at Ladywalk. The only other site to attract more than 5% of birds was Bredon's Hardwick. This heavy concentration into one area means that Staffordshire and Warwickshire between them have attracted 81% of birds (46% and 35% respectively), whilst 16% were recorded in Worcestershire and 3% in the West Midlands county.

Mandarin Duck   *Aix galericulata*
Uncommon, but increasing, feral resident and visitor.

The exotic plumage of the drake Mandarin makes this a popular species to keep in collections and escapees from these, plus deliberate releases, have established feral breeding populations.

The WMBC first began to document records when the species was admitted to the *British List* in 1971 and *BWM* mentioned 19 records of 39 birds between then and 1978. Throughout the 1980s population growth was slow, but from 1990 onwards it accelerated rapidly, making some duplication in counts inevitable. As a consequence, the current population cannot be stated with any accuracy, but is estimated to be up to 100 birds.

The species first became established in south Worcestershire, where 20 were at Aston Mill in 1978 and breeding was recorded for the first time in the region. From here birds spread to breed at several of the small pools that encircle Bredon Hill at Kemerton, Kinsham, Overbury, Westmancote and most notably Beckford, where the maximum was 23 birds in 1998. Other breeding records, from places such as Hinton-on-the-Green, Lower Moor, Nafford and Strensham, may also have emanated from the same source, with birds perhaps spreading even further afield to nest at Longdon Marsh and Mill Pond, at the foot of the Malverns. Meanwhile, breeding also occurred in north Worcestershire, along the Dowles Brook (Wyre Forest), where birds were first recorded in 1983 and a pair occupied a nest-box in 1988. Despite further records from here, including breeding again in 1998, there has been no sign of a colony developing. There has also been a single instance of nesting at Bittell Reservoir.

In Staffordshire, there was a well-established, free-flying colony of 30 birds at Trentham Park in 1994. Much reduced numbers were reported in 1998, but the following year they had almost recovered. It seems likely that other sightings around the Potteries, including a breeding record from Greenway Bank in 1998, stem from this source, though whether the scatter of records from the northern moors can be attributed to the same source is more questionable. There have also been isolated records, including one of breeding in the Needwood Forest area.

The first Warwickshire breeding record came in 1981, at Coombe Abbey, but, here too, it has been slow to consolidate its position. Sporadic breeding has also occurred at Henley-in-Arden and twice at Packington Park. Breeding has yet to occur in the West Midlands county, where most records have come from the Meriden-Marsh Lane, or Sandwell Valley-Walsall areas. Overall during 1979-2001, 55% of birds were seen in Worcestershire, 31% in Staffordshire, 10% in Warwickshire and 4% in the West Midlands. Outside the breeding season birds often favour the larger reservoirs, especially Belvide (16 records), Blithfield (20 records) and Draycote Water (13 records), whilst unusually one visited a garden pond in Bewdley in 1996.

Eurasian Wigeon   (Wigeon)   *Anas penelope*
Common winter visitor, scarce in summer.

The evocative whistles of Eurasian Wigeon echoing across a misty reservoir are a familiar winter sound. Visitors from Fennoscandia and northern Russia, they spend much time grazing the banks and fields around reservoirs and gravel pits and therefore prefer bodies of water with gently shelving shorelines and grassy surrounds. Large flocks also gather on riverside meadows at times of flood. Once almost exclusively a maritime species, birds began to appear more often inland during the 1930s, after the eel-grass on which they feed around the coast was struck by disease. In recent years there has also been an increase in summering birds.

Indeed, the WMBC recorded the first arrival and last departure dates for over fifty years, but ceased doing so in 1991 because of the growing incidence of summer records, often involving injured birds. As yet there have been no known breeding attempts, but it remains a possibility as successful breeding did occur in Nottinghamshire in 2001 (Ogilvie 2003).

Over fifty-two years the average arrival date was August 22nd, whilst the earliest bird seen was one on July 3rd 1975, though subsequently there were nine at Westport Lake on July 4th 1998 and 11 at Draycote Water on July 5th 2001. Over fifty-five years the average departure date for last birds was May 4th, with the latest ever on June 22nd 1984. These extreme dates illustrate just how close the first and last dates had come to overlapping and there was even an unusual summer record of 11 at Brandon Marsh on June 16th 1994. Normally the main arrival begins in September and numbers then steadily increase to their mid-winter maximum in January. Thereafter they decline slowly at first, but then very rapidly through March until few are left in April.

Birds are quite widely distributed and were recorded in two-thirds of the 10-km squares during the *Winter Atlas*. Numbers vary enormously according to the weather, but the regional index fairly closely mirrors that of the WeBS in showing an accelerating increase up to the mid-1990s, since when numbers have fallen slightly. The highest figures occur when the Continent is ice-bound, such as in January 1985 and 1987 and December 1995. By comparison, far fewer arrive in mild winters such as the one in 1987/8.

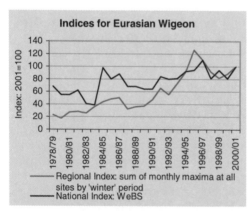

Regional Index: sum of monthly maxima at all sites by 'winter' period
National Index: WeBS

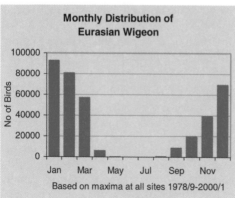

Based on maxima at all sites 1978/9-2000/1

Winter flooding can also bring some large influxes, especially to places such as Longdon Marsh, which held over 1,000 in February 1990 but in dry seasons has virtually none. *BWM* mentioned 2,500 at Belvide Reservoir in 1949 and 1,842 at Blithfield in December 1965 as the largest flocks. Compared with these, the current period has produced maxima of 2,000 at Draycote Water in December 1995 and 2,300 at Blithfield Reservoir in February 1987, whilst Bredon's Hardwick held 2,200 in March 1986 and 2,500 in February 1996, which equalled the previous record.

Bredon's Hardwick, with 5% of birds in the period 1991/2-2000/1, has also been the top site, followed by Draycote Water and Blithfield Reservoir, with 3% of birds each, and Croxall and the Dosthill-Kingsbury Water Park area with 2% each. Overall, Staffordshire proved the most productive county, with 41% of birds, whilst Warwickshire had 37%, Worcestershire 21% and the West Midlands just 1%. An unusual feature is the flock of up to 100 that grazes the lawns of the Chateau Impney hotel at Droitwich.

Eurasian Wigeon is the only species of duck regularly ringed within the region. A high percentage of ringing recoveries show movements of between three and four thousand kilometres to and from their breeding grounds in the far north and their over-wintering sites on our Midland reservoirs. The greatest movement recorded involved an adult female ringed at Blithfield Reservoir in January 1996 and shot in central Siberia in May 2000, after making a colossal journey of 6,498 km.

American Wigeon   *Anas americana*
Very rare vagrant. Six records.

There have been only six records of this North American duck, with the first in 1985.

Regional Record Number	County Record Number		Year	Locality, Date and Notes
1	Warks	1	1985	Kingsbury WP: male, June 15th. Same Ladywalk, June 16th-19th, and Coton Pools, June 22nd. *BB 79:535*
2	Warks	2	1987	Wasperton: adult male, May 9th-14th. *BB 81:546*
3	Staffs	1	1994	Belvide Reservoir: adult male, April 13th-21st. *BB 90: 462*
4	Staffs	2	1997	Blithfield Reservoir: male, February 9th-23rd. *BB 91:466*
5	Staffs	3	1998	Blithfield Reservoir: adult male, August 23rd to October 23rd. *BB 93:522*
6	Warks	3	2002	Ladywalk: male, April 13th-15th. (*records no longer considered by BBRC*)

It is somewhat ironic that Staffordshire and Warwickshire should share the records of this Transatlantic vagrant, while Worcestershire—the most westerly county—still awaits its first bird. All birds appeared between February and August, rather than in autumn which is the expected time for Transatlantic vagrants to arrive. However, full-winged birds are not uncommon in wildfowl collections and it is possible that, nationally, some accepted records relate to escapes (Dymond *et al.* 1989).

Gadwall   *Anas strepera*
Fairly common and increasing winter visitor. Uncommon breeding species.

The British breeding population of Gadwall was started in the middle of the nineteenth century from wild birds that were caught, pinioned and released in Norfolk (*Breeding Atlas*). Whilst this population has spread, it must have been augmented by genuinely wild birds from the wintering population to produce the rapid range expansion that this opportunistic species has enjoyed over the last thirty years. Gadwall require shallow areas of slow flowing or standing water, with a lush growth of submerged vegetation for food, and islands on which to nest. They have been quick to exploit the many reservoirs and gravel pits created during that time.

Until the late 1960s the species was only a scarce passage migrant and winter visitor. Breeding then occurred for the first time in 1970, at Belvide Reservoir in Staffordshire. This proved to be an isolated occurrence, however, and it was 1979 before any bred again, this time in Warwickshire at Brandon Marsh and Kingsbury Water Park (*BWM*). Since then, nesting has

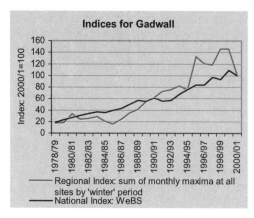

Indices for Gadwall

Index: 2000/1=100

—— Regional Index: sum of monthly maxima at all
sites by 'winter' period
—— National Index: WeBS

been an annual event in the region, with an average of around seven pairs a year, though the success rate has varied considerably. Pairs bred in Worcestershire for the first time in 1986, at Croome Park and Larford, whilst in the West Midlands the first definite proof of breeding came from Sandwell Valley in 2003, though a pair with young at Bradnock's Marsh in 1991 may have bred locally. Since these initial records breeding has been fairly regular in Warwickshire and Worcestershire. However, it has been most consistent in Staffordshire, and more especially at Belvide where birds have bred every year since 1986 with a maximum of 14 broods in 1998. The most recent figures published by the RBBP suggest a regional population around 20-25 pairs (Ogilvie *et al*. 2002 and 2003).

Whilst the *Breeding Atlas* showed 20% of 10-km squares to be occupied, birds are more widespread outside the breeding season, with the *Winter Atlas* recording them in 42% of squares. Nationally, the steady increase shown by the WeBS index is also reflected regionally, though it was the mid-1980s before the latter index began its climb.

The monthly distribution is very uneventful, showing numbers building steadily from July to a peak in December, then falling away again until by May only the breeding birds remain.

During 1991/2-2000/1 Belvide Reservoir was overwhelmingly dominant, accounting for 20% of the region's birds. Despite this, Staffordshire, with 38% of birds, came second to Warwickshire, with 40% of birds. Worcestershire, with 21%, was a long way behind and the West Midlands had a nominal 1%. Considering the habitat does not appear ideal for Gadwall, it is surprising that Draycote Water came second to Belvide, with 9% of birds, whilst Westwood Park, Coton-Lea Marston and Dosthill-Kingsbury Water Park all had 8%.

Eurasian Teal   (Common Teal or Teal)   *Anas crecca*
Common winter visitor. Uncommon in summer, but a rare breeding species.

The tiny Eurasian Teal is a bird of contrasting fortunes. It is best known as a winter visitor to our reservoirs, gravel pits, flood meadows and other wetlands. Occasionally a few pairs also nest in these situations, but as a breeding species it is really most at home amongst the peaty bogs and pools of the northern moors. The wintering population, swollen by immigrant birds from the Continent, is expanding, but the breeding population is in decline nationally and very precarious regionally.

In winter, birds are widespread, with records from 87% of the 10-km squares during the *Winter Atlas*. Numerically they have increased broadly in line with the WeBS index, except for a faster rate of growth in the late 1980s. Annual totals vary considerably, however, depending on several factors. Eurasian Teal take a wide range of food which they obtain by up-ending in shallows around the margins of open water. So if water levels rise during and after heavy rain, or the shorelines freeze over, birds will very quickly move to somewhere more suitable. In extreme conditions, they may forsake the region altogether, but conversely bad weather elsewhere, particularly on the Continent, might make the region the beneficiary of an unexpected influx. For example, when blizzards swept the country in December 1990, numbers at Blithfield shot up to 2,760 and then peaked at a regional record of 3,410 in January. These counts were more than double those of the months either side. In 1995/6 cold weather in mainland Europe again brought high numbers. Far fewer migrants arrived during the mild winter of 1992/3, while numbers were low in 2000/1 because of high water levels. Equally, the more frequent flooding since the late 1980s has also drawn in more birds, including 2,000 at Longdon Marsh in January 2001.

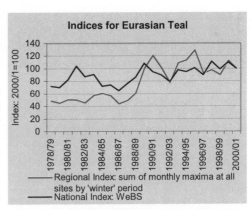

Although the first immigrant birds might appear at the end of June, it is usually August before numbers begin to rise noticeably. They then steadily increase to a peak in December, after which they decline again until few are left by April.

Most birds are found in small flocks up to a couple of hundred or so, but 400 are quite commonplace, especially at the five main sites, whilst during 1991/2-2000/1 there were eight records of gatherings building up to over 1,000, seven of them at Blithfield Reservoir. By comparison the most mentioned in *BWM* was 1,500 at Draycote Water in January 1969. During this same ten year period two sites were dominant, attracting between them a third of all birds. These were Blithfield Reservoir (18% of birds) and Belvide Reservoir (15%). With such high concentrations, it is not surprising that Staffordshire held most birds (57%), with Warwickshire second (25%) followed by Worcestershire (15%) and the West

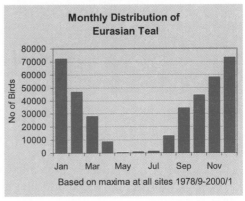

Midlands (3%). Three other sites held more than 5% of birds, namely Brandon Marsh (8%) and Draycote Water and Croxall (6% each). Interestingly, in November 1996 a sudden drop in numbers at Brandon coincided with the presence of a pair of Hen Harriers.

As a breeding species, the Eurasian Teal maintains a tenuous hold. On the moors of north Staffordshire, where the habitat is most suitable, Lord and Blake (1962) said pairs bred sparingly, whilst the RSPB surveys located six pairs in 1985 and smaller numbers (unspecified) in 1992. Since then there have been no records, but fewer observers seem to visit the area these days. In the lowlands, possible breeding was reported from the Middle Tame Valley in most years from the mid-1970s until at least the mid-1980s, but it then became increasingly sporadic and now seems to have ceased altogether. Reasonably regular breeding has also occurred at Doxey Marshes, where two or three pairs (once six) have nested on occasions since 1985. Apart from these instances, isolated breeding occurred on six occasions during 1979-2001, but, unless breeding is still occurring on the moors, it is doubtful if the regional population exceeds five or six pairs, which is slightly less than the 5-10 pairs postulated in *BWM*.

Eurasian Teal are rarely ringed in the region, but a recent remarkable movement of 1,426 km was recorded for this diminutive duck. The bird, an adult male, was ringed in Portugal in February 1999 and shot in Sardon (Staffs) in December 2000.

Green-winged Teal   *Anas carolinensis*
Rare vagrant.

Following the first record of this Transatlantic vagrant in 1953, there have been nine further records, all since 1980.

Regional Record Number	County Record Number		Year	Locality, Date and Notes
1	Warks	1	1953	Baginton: male, January 15th-17th.
2	Warks	2	1980	Kingsbury WP: male, April 17th. *BB 75:491*
3	Warks	3	1990	Draycote Water: male, February 4th. *BB 84:461*
4	Staffs	1	1990	Blithfield Reservoir: male, November 11th to February 17th, 1991. *BB 84:460.* Presume same, Blithfield Reservoir: October 27th to December 15th 1991.
5	Worcs	1	1992	Bredon's Hardwick: male, December 26th intermittently to January 5th, 1993.
6	Staffs	2	1995	Blithfield Reservoir: male, March 26th-29th.
7	Staffs	3	1995	Rudyard Reservoir: male, December 8th-10th, moving to Tittesworth Reservoir on latter date, then returning to Rudyard, but back again at Tittesworth on December 20th.
8	Warks	4	2000	Lighthorne Quarry: male, December 20th.
9	Warks	5	2001	Brandon Marsh: male, March 6th-8th. (Possibly same at Storton's Gravel Pit, Northampton, until March 5th.)
10	Staffs	4	2001	Blithfield Reservoir: male, December 23rd-31st.
Note:				BBRC ceased to consider records of this species as from January 1st 1991.

Unlike the regional records for American Wigeon, all those for this species fell between October and April inclusive, which is the more expected time for Nearctic vagrants to occur. There was one in each month, except December (four) and March (two). All also involved drakes, presumably reflecting the difficulty in separating the females from female Common Teal.

Mallard   *Anas platyrhynchos*
Common resident and very common winter visitor.

The Mallard is easily the commonest of our wild duck and can be found at all seasons and on any stretch of open water, from tiny ponds to vast reservoirs. It also frequents streams, rivers and canals, inhabits both urban and rural areas alike and often nests and feeds well away from water, sometimes in the most unlikely of situations. In winter, numbers are swollen by immigrants from the Continent, whilst the release of birds artificially reared for shooting adds further to the population. Inter-breeding with farmyard escapees also produces many hybrid birds with aberrant features.

Quantitative data on Mallard in the region are sparse and confusingly contradictory. Not surprisingly, the *Wintering* and *Breeding* Atlases both showed birds to be present in every 10-km square, with the breeding abundance generally above average except in the Vale of Evesham, where standing water is scarce. Nationally, the CBC/BBS and the WBS showed an average increase of just under 40% in breeding numbers during 1990-2002. In contrast, the WeBS index shows relative stability in the national wintering population through the 1980s followed by a gradual 30% decline through the 1990s. Mead (2000) attributed the difference between the breeding and wintering trends to a decline in winter visitors from the Continent.

Regionally, numbers have varied considerably from year-to-year, but with no clear long-term change. Weather has a major influence, with, for example, the cold spell of December 1995 bringing a noticeable influx that resulted in counts of 882 at Aqualate Mere and 1,000 at Draycote Water. Comparative data on the breeding strength at key wetlands is incredibly scanty, but during 1979-2001 the trends at certain major sites apparently varied widely. For example, the counts suggested numbers more or less halved at Alvecote Pools and Bittell Reservoir, but almost doubled at Upton Warren. Numbers at Doxey Marshes also showed an increase, but there was little change at Ladywalk, whilst the situation at Belvide Reservoir was indeterminate. From this it is safest to conclude that the breeding population is still within the range of 2,000-10,000 pairs estimated in *BWM*, but perhaps within the lower half. Among the more interesting breeding records there have been several of nests in trees 10-15m above ground, including one pair that used an owl nest-box. A very early brood was also seen on January 8th, at Kingsbury Water Park in 1989, but all disappeared after a few days.

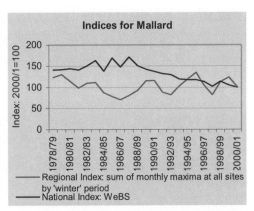

The seasonal pattern sees a late summer build-up of post-breeding flocks that peaks in August and September, when those sites used as moulting grounds often record their largest concentrations. Numbers then fall slightly during October before rising again to their mid-winter peak in December-January as immigrant birds arrive from the Continent. They

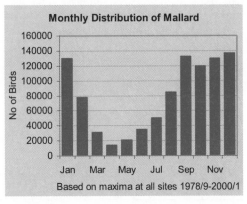

then decline rapidly during February and March as birds disperse back to their breeding areas.

Concentrations of 600 are still fairly regular at the larger reservoirs, though there have been recent references to declining numbers and *WMBC Bird Reports* mention 'evidence of decline' in the status summary of this species. Certainly at least three of the principal sites support this view. During 1978/9-1990/91, for example, Blithfield held over 1,000 in every winter, with a peak of 2,062 in January 1980. Aqualate and Belvide also had counts of 1,000 or more in nine of these thirteen winters, with Aqualate holding 2,539 in January 1982. However, numbers in the decade 1991/2-2000/1 were lower, with Blithfield reaching 1,000 in only seven winters, with a maximum of 1,690 in August 1999, whilst the highest counts at Aqualate and Belvide were 882 and 997 respectively. Moreover, none of the counts in either period approaches the huge gatherings of 3,100 at Belvide in 1969 and 4,200 at Packington Park in September 1974 mentioned in *BWM*. Such declines are clearly at odds with the general stability of the regional index, but whether they indicate a real decline in overall numbers, or simply birds taking advantage of the many new waters created in recent times by spreading themselves more thinly is a matter for conjecture.

During 1991/2-2000/1, Staffordshire was easily the most important county for Mallard, attracting 58% of birds, followed by Warwickshire with 23%, Worcestershire 15% and the West Midlands 5%. In all, 57% of birds were concentrated at the top ten sites. Of these, Blithfield Reservoir, with 12% of birds, was outstanding, holding 1% of the national population on occasions. Other important sites were Belvide Reservoir with 9%, Draycote Water with 7% and Aqualate Mere and Croxall with 5% each.

Although a very common duck, not many are ringed within the region. One adult, accidentally caught when ringing Eurasian Wigeon at Blithfield Reservoir in December 1996, was killed in Belarus (formerly USSR) in June 1997. It had made a huge journey of 1,868 km.

Pintail (Northern Pintail) *Anas acuta*
Frequent winter visitor and passage migrant, rare in summer.

Lowland shallow waters and adjacent grasslands are the preferred habitat of the Pintail. Their breeding grounds in Iceland, Fennoscandia and northern Russia are further north than those of any other dabbling duck. Many winter in Britain and every year a small, but increasing number utilise the region's larger waters on passage and in winter, but the greatest flocks are those that take advantage of transient flooding of riverside meadows. Occasional birds are also seen in summer and the behaviour of a pair at Dosthill Lake in 1999 could even have suggested the possibility of unsuccessful nesting.

This elegant duck was described as a regular, but scarce, winter visitor to the region in *BWM*, which mentioned just nine flocks between 20-40, all of them at reservoirs. There was no mention of birds visiting flood meadows, but at that time major floods were comparatively rare. Since then, however, numbers at the main reservoirs have risen, whilst the increased propensity for flooding since the early 1990s has brought much larger numbers to the periodic inundations of the Severn and Avon valleys.

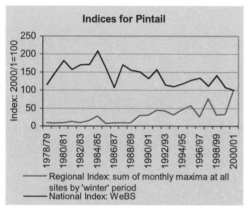

Indices for Pintail

Index: 2000/1=100

— Regional Index: sum of monthly maxima at all
sites by 'winter' period
— National Index: WeBS

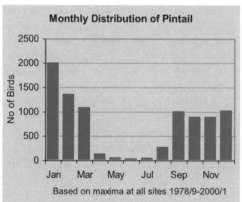

Monthly Distribution of Pintail

No of Birds

Based on maxima at all sites 1978/9-2000/1

Pintail mainly winter on estuaries and the distribution of the 35% of 10-km squares in which they were found during the *Winter Atlas* suggests that birds follow the river valleys inland into the region from the Humber, Severn and Wash. The WeBS index for this species is extremely variable, so it was expected that the very small regional sample would show even wider fluctuations, especially as this is a highly mobile species that responds quickly to the feeding opportunities offered by floodwaters.

The indices highlight two contrasting effects of weather on this species. Firstly the simultaneous peaks in the WeBS and regional indices for 1984/5 reflect the intense cold of early 1985, when many birds left the Continent for Britain. Within this region the influx eventually culminated in a flock of 110 at Ripple in March. Secondly, in 1997/8 and 2000/1 numbers nationally were low, but in this region they reached peak levels when heavy rain caused widespread flooding that attracted exceptional numbers to Longdon Marsh. Such disparities between national and regional patterns highlight the importance of local conditions.

In common with several other species of duck, the WMBC ceased recording first and last dates in 1991 because of the increase in summer records. Prior to then, the average first date for birds to arrive in autumn, over 46 years, was September 1st, whilst the earliest ever was on July 8th 1967. A regular passage then follows during September and October, particularly through the Staffordshire reservoirs, which sometimes record their peak counts at this time. For example, September flocks of 68 and 64 were at Blithfield Reservoir in 1999 and 2000 respectively, whilst the same site established a record for enclosed waters in the region, with 152 in October 1991. However, the highest numbers, and largest flocks, occur when flooding is most severe, which is usually during January to March. Small numbers coming inland from the Severn estuary were first recorded on floodwaters in the early 1980s, but the first substantial flock was 70 at Longdon Marsh in 1990. Subsequently there were 81 at Bredon's Hardwick in February 1996, but Longdon Marsh has a monopoly of the larger flocks, with 112 in January 1993, 190 in November 2000, 275 in March 2001 and a magnificent 475 in January 1998. During 51 years the average date of the last birds to leave was April 21st, with the latest ever, excluding summering birds, on June 8th 1983.

Whilst Longdon Marsh attracted the largest flocks, Blithfield Reservoir consistently held good numbers and, based on the monthly maxima during 1991/2-2000/1, incredibly held exactly a third of all birds. Longdon Marsh was close behind with 28%, whilst Bredon's Hardwick attracted 15% and Belvide Reservoir 6%. The overwhelming dominance of these four sites meant that Staffordshire (48%) and Worcestershire (39%) held the vast majority of birds, leaving just 12% for Warwickshire and 1% for the West Midlands county.

Generally birds seldom stay more than a few days, but in 1990/1 a female remained in the Avon Valley from July 19th to January 20th. Despite their reputation for being mobile, some individuals also exhibit strong site fidelity, with what was presumed to be same male visiting Sandwell Valley every winter from 1995/6 until at least 2000/1. As with so many wildfowl, observers need to be alert to the possibility of hybridisation, particularly with Mallard.

Garganey   *Anas querquedula*
Uncommon passage migrant and summer visitor, but rarely breeding. Very rare in winter.

The Garganey is unique in being the only species of wildfowl that is a summer visitor to Britain, with birds migrating to West Africa for the winter. Never numerous in the West Midlands, a few visit our wetlands each year, mainly the larger reservoirs or those waters with stands of emergent vegetation. They are very secretive, especially whilst breeding, when they spend much time hidden in cover.

This is usually one of the first summer visitors to arrive, with the average date of first birds over 57 years being April 1st and the earliest ever being on March 2nd 1969 at Hampton Lucy. In recent years the average date has crept forward and during 1992-2001 it was March 27th. Despite these earlier arrivals, the main spring passage slipped during the current period from April (*BWM*) into May. In all, 41% of birds were seen during March to May.

BWM showed a steady increase in numbers until 1969-73, by which time there were around 70 a year, followed by a decline to 30-40 a year during 1974-78. The current period began with an average of 23 a year during 1979-88, but in 1989 numbers suddenly doubled in what was a good year nationally, since when they have remained at around 48 a year. This is presumed to be due to more spring migrants overshooting from the Continent, but it has not resulted in more breeding records.

However, the Garganey is so secretive that proof of breeding is hard to obtain, except perhaps when well-grown juveniles appear late in the season. Nevertheless, it seems to have reached its regional peak during the late 1960s and 1970s, but even then it is unlikely that more than one or two pairs bred in any one year (*BWM*). The *Breeding Atlas* showed birds to be present in seven 10-km squares,

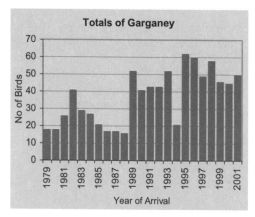

Totals of Garganey

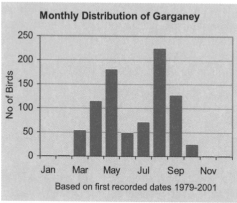

Monthly Distribution of Garganey

Based on first recorded dates 1979-2001

but with confirmed breeding only in the Trent Valley. Otherwise, there were no records of successful breeding during 1979-2001, but a predated egg was found at Ladywalk in 1980, a pair nested unsuccessfully at Little Wyrley in 1982, both display and mating were observed at Belvide and there were other sporadic records of summering pairs in suitable breeding habitat.

The return movement lasts from July to September, during which time 50% of birds are recorded with August clearly being the peak month. Excluding wintering birds, the average departure date of last birds over 56 years was October 1st, but during 1992-2001 it was October 16th, while the latest bird was one that remained at Upton Warren from August until November 5th in 1999. There have been six winter records as follows. A duck was at Upton Warren on December 29th 1984, an individual was at Belvide on February 15th 1989 and then another later in that year which remained at Beckford from November 5th to January 6th 1990, with presumably the same bird at Mythe Bridge on January 21st. Two were at Doxey Marshes in 1995—a male from January 6th-February 6th and a female on February 11th and 12th. Finally, an immature female remained at Belvide from October 9th 1998 to January 9th 1999.

Despite the increase in overall numbers during 1979-2001, parties have in fact been much smaller, with only two exceeding six birds, namely nine at Blithfield Reservoir in 1993 and eight at Belvide Reservoir the following year (*cf.* three flocks of 15-26 mentioned in *BWM*). It is assumed this might reflect a lack of family groups. During 1992-2001, most birds (41%) were in Staffordshire, with 31% in Warwickshire, 25% in Worcestershire and 3% in the West Midlands county. As regards sites, the main reservoirs were dominant, with Blithfield attracting 18%, Belvide 17% and Draycote Water 9%. The Middle Tame Valley and Upton Warren each attracted 8%, while 6% were recorded at Brandon Marsh.

Blue-winged Teal   *Anas discors*
Very rare vagrant. Eight records.

Following the first two records of this North American duck, which were documented in *BWM*, there have been a further six, bringing the total to eight records and nine birds, as shown opposite.

Five of the birds were drakes, three ducks and one an immature of unknown sex. Apart from the one in 1968, discovered in March, all arrived between July and October, with five birds in September and October, which are peak months for this Transatlantic vagrant to arrive in Britain (Dymond *et al.* 1989). The July individual, on the other hand, was unusual as few have appeared in Britain at this time. It is possible that the last two records involved the same individual returning here for a second time.

Regional Record Number	County Record Number		Year	Locality, Date and Notes
1	Worcs	1	1968	Upton Warren: male, March 6th-27th. *BB 62:464*
2	Worcs	2	1980	Upton Warren: two, a male and an immature, September 29th to October 11th. *BB 74:461* and *76:486*
3	Worcs	3	1982	Wilden: immature female, October 17th-31st. *BB 77:515*
4	Worcs	4	1989	Upton Warren: female, August 19th-27th. *BB 83:450*
5	Warks	1	1989	Brandon Marsh: adult female, September 19th to November 18th. *BB 84:461*
6	Staffs	1	1996	Blithfield Reservoir: male, September 21st-29th. *BB 90:463*
7	Staffs	2	2000	Blithfield Reservoir: male, August 6th to September 14th. *BB 94:463*
8	Staffs	3	2001	Belvide Reservoir: male, intermittently July 11th to September 3rd. Same, Blithfield Reservoir, September 2nd. *BB 96:556*

Notes: 1. The Upton Warren bird in 1980 was present from September 29th and not 27th, and until October 11th not the 12th, as stated in *BWM,* or November 11th as reported in *Brit. Birds.*
2. The bird at Blithfield Res. in 1996 was first seen on September 21st, not 22nd as stated in *Brit. Birds.*

Shoveler   (Northern Shoveler)   *Anas clypeata*

Fairly common passage migrant and winter visitor. Rare and decreasing breeding species.

The Shoveler can be seen throughout the year, but is most numerous during late autumn. Shallow, eutrophic waters with reedy shorelines are preferred to large expanses of open water. While the breeding population is relatively small, the region has a significant proportion of the British wintering population, with several sites holding nationally important numbers.

This highly migratory species is most numerous in September and October, when the resident breeding population is swollen by immigrants from north-western Europe as far east as Siberia. Both populations then move southwards into France and Spain, leaving steadily declining numbers through the winter. Return passage is virtually negligible, but there is just a hint of movement in March.

Although numbers have varied considerably from one winter to the next, the general trend has followed that of the national WeBS index. The rather specific habitat requirements mean that birds tend to congregate at relatively few sites and the *Winter Atlas* showed them in just 61% of 10-km squares.

The three shire counties attracted a broadly equal share of birds during 1991/2-2000/1, with 35% in Staffordshire, 32% in Worcestershire and 28% in Warwickshire, whilst the West Midlands' share was 5%. Based on monthly maxima, almost half of all birds appeared at just four sites, namely Blithfield Reservoir (12%), Belvide Reservoir and Westwood Pool (11% each) and Upton Warren (10%). However, there was probably some overlap between the last two of these sites, but to what extent is not known. In Warwickshire, Dosthill-Kingsbury Water Park was the most

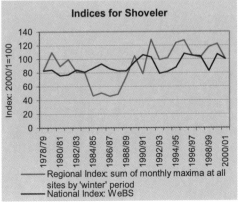

Indices for Shoveler

Regional Index: sum of monthly maxima at all sites by 'winter' period
National Index: WeBS

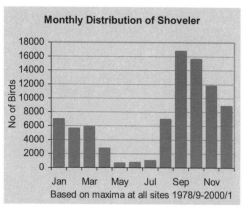

Monthly Distribution of Shoveler

Based on maxima at all sites 1978/9-2000/1

productive area, with 8% of birds.

Flocks up to 150 are fairly commonplace at favoured sites and the period 1978/9-2000/1 produced several of 200 or more. One notable feature is the way in which the relative importance of sites has changed, presumably due to changes in their ecology. For example, *BWM* noted that Belvide and Aqualate attracted the larger flocks from the late 1960s to the early 1980s, whilst numbers at Blithfield had declined. Indeed, Belvide set a new regional record with 570 on November 1st 1981. Numbers at Aqualate were more variable, with maxima of 475 in 1983, but only 14 two years later. By 1991/2-2000/1, however, this situation had completely reversed, with Blithfield dominating the larger flocks, claiming seven of the ten to exceed 200 and recording a maximum of 481 in October 1991. By comparison, the most at Aqualate was 358, in October 1997, and at Belvide a mere 187. The only other flock to exceed 200 during this period was one of 220 at Coombe Abbey in October 1994. All of these sites, plus the Middle Tame Valley, rank as being of national importance for this species (Pollitt *et al.* 2003).

The small breeding population appears to be in decline. *BWM* said it was doubtful whether more than five pairs nested in any one year. Subsequently only one to three pairs have bred in most years, although 1983 was a bumper year with nine broods and during 1989-91 the *Breeding Atlas* recorded birds in twenty-one 10-km squares (27%) with breeding confirmed in nine of these. However, there were no confirmed breeding records in 2000 or 2001. Most breeding records came from Belvide Reservoir, Brandon Marsh, Doxey Marshes and the Middle Tame Valley, with no instances of confirmed breeding in Worcestershire.

Red-crested Pochard   *Netta rufina*
Scarce visitor, with most probably escapees or feral birds.

This is a popular species in wildfowl collections and most records are assumed to relate to escaped or feral birds. A feral colony exists just outside this region in the Cotswold Water Park.

In *BWM* the Red-crested Pochard is recorded as a very scarce visitor, with generally less than five birds a year. Apart from a small influx in 1982, this pattern continued for most of the 1980s. Then, in 1989, there was a sudden, unexpected influx of 18 birds and from then until

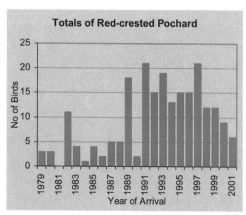

Totals of Red-crested Pochard

Year of Arrival

1997 numbers averaged around a dozen a year, except for 1990. Since 1997, however, they have declined sharply.

Between 1929-78, birds were fairly evenly distributed throughout the year, but since then a distinct autumn peak has developed. With all parties of four or more appearing between September and December, it is tempting to speculate that at least some of these might be wild vagrants from their European and Asiatic breeding grounds. However, others arriving as early as August do cast a shadow over the origins of those arriving later. For a discussion on the likelihood of some birds in Britain being wild see Vinicombe and Harrop (1999).

Most records relate to single birds, but two or more were seen on 22 occasions, with the most being five, at Blithfield Reservoir in September 1989 and at Belvide Reservoir in both September 1992 and October 1994.

During 1979-2001, the most regularly visited sites, with their number of records and birds respectively were Draycote Water (26; 34), Blithfield Reservoir (16; 22), Belvide Reservoir (12; 20), Kingsbury Water Park (10; 15) and Bredon's Hardwick (9; 16).

A hybrid male made a protracted stay in the Valley Park-Smestow Valley area from 1994 to at least 2002.

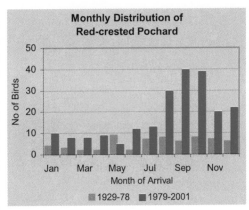

Common Pochard   (Pochard)   *Aythya ferina*
Common winter visitor. Scarce and declining breeding species.

Large flocks of Common Pochard winter on the region's larger lakes, reservoirs and gravel pits, but it is scarce and sporadic as a breeding species. Birds feed both by day and night, principally on the seeds, shoots and roots of aquatic plants.

The regional and WeBS indices both show little long-term change, though there has been a gradual decline since 1993/4 due to a reduction in the huge Tame Valley flock. Annual totals vary with the weather, however, so this reduction may be the result of milder winters. The highest numbers usually occur when hard weather on the Continent drives birds further west into Britain, as in January 1987 and November 1993. Conversely, many birds vacate the region during severe weather, whilst others resort to any unfrozen waters or seek sanctuary on rivers. Small numbers have also been seen on floodwaters, notably at Upton-on-Severn.

Flocks start to form in September and October, when the main influx of birds from eastern Europe begins. Immigration then continues steadily until numbers peak in January. Thereafter there is a fairly swift departure until the end of March, by which time it is mainly just breeding and summering birds that remain.

Within the region, a significant change in the winter distribution began in 1980/1, when large flocks first gathered at the new river purification lakes at Coton/Lea Marston. Initially these flocks also resorted to Hemlingford Water, at Kingsbury Water Park, and later to the newly formed Dosthill Lake until they were disturbed from there by water skiing. Shustoke Reservoir is also frequently used as a refuge when birds are disturbed from elsewhere.

Dean (1989) provided a comprehensive review of the development of this flock, which has reached numbers of national importance every winter since 1980/1 and averaged 1,500 a year during 1996/7-2000/1 (Pollitt *et al*. 2003). This represents 3% of the national population and makes this the third most important site in England for this species. During 1991/2-2000/1 the Valley held around a fifth of the region's wintering birds, with no less

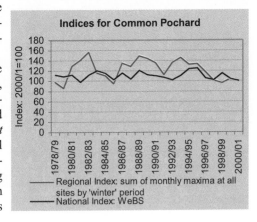

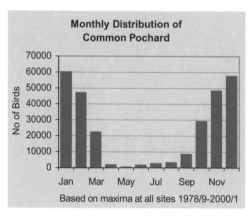

Monthly Distribution of Common Pochard

Based on maxima at all sites 1978/9-2000/1

than 14% at Coton/Lea Marston alone. Away from the Tame Valley, the most important sites were Belvide Reservoir (3% of birds), and Draycote Water and Westwood Pool (2% each). The county distribution is dominated by Warwickshire (52% of birds), followed by Staffordshire (25%), Worcestershire (16%) and the West Midlands (7%).

Not surprisingly, the Middle Tame Valley has also held most of the larger flocks, with gatherings over 1,000 recorded at Coton/ Kingsbury in sixteen of the twenty-one winters 1980/1-2000/1 and site maxima of 2,500 at Coton in February 1983, 1,500 at Shustoke in November 1996 and 632 at Dosthill/Kingsbury Water Park in January 1992. Away from the Tame Valley, the largest flocks were 875 at Aqualate in January 1982, 670 at Draycote in December 1978 and 415 at Blithfield Reservoir in November 1990.

During 1979-2001 breeding occurred in every year except 1995 and 2001, although in 1996 the only known pair, at Wormleighton Reservoir, was flooded out. The number of broods varied considerably, from an average of almost four a year during the 1980s to just one or two in the 1990s and survival rates were often poor. The best year was 1989, with eight broods, while the most regular breeding site until the early 1990s was Alvecote Pools, where up to six broods were noted annually. Since then there has been no consistent breeding site.

Ring-necked Duck   *Aythya collaris*
Rare vagrant.

There have now been 13 regional records of this species, which is the commonest of the North American ducks to occur in Britain.

Regional Record Number	County Record Number	Year	Locality, Date and Notes
1	Staffs 1	1977	Blithfield Reservoir: male, November 20th-22nd. *BB 72:515*
2	Warks 1	1977	Draycote Water: imm. male, December 24th to February 22nd, 1978. Same, Brandon Marsh, March 5th to April 5th, 1978. *BB 72:515* and *73:500*
3	Warks 2 Staffs 2	1978	Kingsbury Water Park: imm. male, January 7th-19th. Same, Alvecote Pools (Staffs part), January 14th and 19th. *BB 72:515* and *73:500*
4	Warks 3	1979	Kingsbury Water Park: adult male, May 3rd-9th. *BB75:493*
5	Worcs 1	1990	Bittell Reservoir: male, March 28th. *BB 84:462*
6	Warks 4	1992	Lea Marston: adult male, April 17th-19th. *BB 86:462*
7	Warks 5	1997	Dosthill Lake: female, intermittently May 2nd-8th.
8	Warks 6	1999	Draycote Water: female, May 16th.
9	Warks 7	2000	Coton Pools-Lea Marston: 1st winter male, October 31st to February 11th, 2001.
10	Warks 8	2001	Draycote Water: female, January 6th-8th.
11	W Mid 1	2001	Brookvale Park: male, May 17th-18th.

Regional Record Number	County Record Number		Year	Locality, Date and Notes
12	Warks	9	2001	Draycote Water: 1st winter male, November 17th. Presume same Abbots Salford Pool November 18th to December 10th and 22nd to January 5th 2002.
13	Warks	10	2002	Abbots Salford Pool: female, April 28th to May 1st. (Apparently also seen in Worcestershire, but details not received at time of going to press)

Notes: 1. The 1979 bird at Kingsbury was present as shown and not just on May 5th and 6th as per *BB*.
2. BBRC ceased to consider records of this species as from January 1st 1994.

Given their Transatlantic origins, it is strange that Worcestershire, the most westerly county, should have had only one record, whilst Warwickshire, the most easterly has had ten. Of the 13 birds, nine were males and four females. Six arrived in autumn or winter (October-January) and seven in spring (March-May), with four in May alone. Interestingly, following the initial flush of records in the late 1970s, there were none at all during the 1980s. The period 1990-2002 then brought nine—six of them in spring. Presumably these were wandering individuals that had arrived the previous autumn.

Ferruginous Duck *Aythya nyroca*
Scarce winter visitor, some probably being escapees or of feral origin.

The Ferruginous Duck is an endangered species due to decreasing breeding numbers across its entire range in eastern Europe and Asia and British records frequently come under suspicion as being of escaped or feral birds. Yet *BWM*, whilst doubting whether all records involved wild birds, did observe that a significant proportion occurred during the autumn months. More recently, Rogers *et al.* (2002) remarked on the distinct winter bias to this species' occurrence in Britain, which suggests a genuine wild origin for most individuals involved.

There were 13 records documented in *BWM* between 1949-78, one of which involved two birds. Since then, all records have been of singletons, but the exact number is confused by what might be the same individuals returning in successive winters. During 1978/9-2000/1 between 19 and 28 different individuals were reported, depending on how many were returning birds, but the charts include the higher figure. Of these, all but seven arrived during September to December, which is the time wild birds would be expected (*Winter Atlas*).

Records were few and far between for most of the 1980s, but birds have occurred in every winter since 1989/90. This is primarily due to a remarkable series of records from the Anker and Middle Tame Valleys. This began with a male at Alvecote Pools in 1989/90, followed by

another male at, or possibly the same one returning to, Lea Marston the following year. Then, in 1991/2 an immature male was discovered amongst the huge flocks of diving duck at Coton/Lea Marston, with what was presumed to be this same individual then returning every year until 1997/8. Its credentials as a wild bird, however, were tarnished when it arrived three times in August and once as early as July 25th, in 1992, whereas wild birds usually disperse from their breeding areas in September and October (Rogers *et al.* 2002). (Two blank years followed and then another was reported at Coton Pools from November

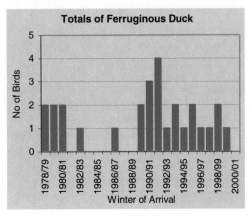

145

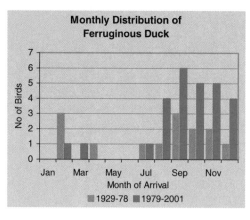

5th 2000 and again in 2001/2, but neither record has been submitted to the BBRC and they are not included in the charts.)

Away from the Tame Valley, the most frequently visited places were Upton Warren and Draycote Water, each with three records, whilst Bredon's Hardwick, Elford and Netherton Reservoir were each visited twice. The pre-eminence of the Middle Tame Valley means that, even allowing for the same individuals returning in subsequent years, 45% of birds have been in Warwickshire, with just 25% in Staffordshire, 20% in Worcestershire and 10% in the West Midlands.

Tufted Duck   *Aythya fuligula*
Common winter visitor and frequent breeding resident.

This is the commonest of our diving ducks, being widely distributed throughout the year on waters ranging from urban parks and canals to gravel pits, lakes, reservoirs, rivers and even floodwaters. Large flocks gather in winter, when numbers are swollen by immigrants from northern Europe. Tufted Ducks feed mainly on animal matter taken from the bottom or sometimes from submerged plants, but seeds form an important part of their diet in autumn and those in town parks also supplement these natural foods with that provided by the public.

The WeBS index shows a slight increase in winter numbers nationally since 1978/9, but the regional index shows a much faster growth during the 1990s and especially since 1996/7, which is due largely to the increasing numbers wintering in the Middle Tame Valley. The apparent fall regionally in 2000/1 is presumed to stem from incomplete counts due to the Foot and Mouth restrictions. Numbers also fluctuate according to the prevailing weather, with birds leaving the region during a big freeze, but equally more immigrants arriving if continental waters are frozen solid, as in December 1995. Specific influxes were also noted at Ladywalk during hard weather in 1979 and 1981, whilst small numbers resorted to the ice-free River Severn during the freeze of January 1987.

The monthly distribution shows a steady increase in numbers from June until the midwinter peak from November-January, after which there is an equally steady decline until May, when just the breeding and summering population remains.

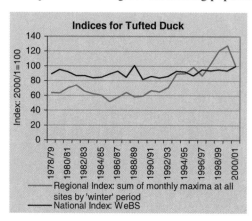

The initial build up from July into October mainly involves moulting flocks, firstly of males and later females. During the 1980s Belvide Reservoir was the region's principal moulting site, consistently producing the highest numbers during July-August, with a maximum of 843 in August 1981. However, during the 1990s numbers here have been much smaller, with the larger moulting flocks being at Blithfield Reservoir and the Middle Tame Valley. Numbers at the former have reached several hundred in recent years, with a peak of 769 in July 1997 following an exceptionally good breeding season across the region. This locality seemingly has an abundance of seed to sustain these late summer flocks, but presumably insufficient molluscs to feed wintering birds, numbers of which are quite small.

In contrast, since the formation of the Coton/Lea Marston purification lakes around 1980/1, the Middle Tame Valley has held impressive numbers throughout autumn and winter (Dean 1989). Moreover, unlike Common Pochards which appear to have passed their peak, the number of Tufted Ducks steadily increased, with up to 2,000 moulting birds in recent years and a new regional record of 2,240 at Coton/Lea Marston as recently as January 2001. The Valley as a whole has held numbers of national importance every winter since 1980/1, with an average of 2,274 a year during 1996/7-2000/1 (Pollitt *et al*. 2003). This represents almost 4% of the national population, making this the third most important site in England for this species. During 1991/2-2000/1 around a fifth of the region's wintering birds congregated in this valley, with just over 15% at Coton/Lea Marston alone. Away from the Tame Valley, the most important sites were Draycote Water and Chasewater (6% each) and Blithfield Reservoir (3%). The largest flocks here were 1,200 at Draycote in December 1995, 1,087 at Chasewater in October 1999 and 769 at Blithfield Reservoir in July 1997. As a result, the county distribution has been dominated by Warwickshire (49% of birds) and Staffordshire (37%), with just 9% appearing in Worcestershire and 5% in the West Midlands.

During 1979-2001, the number of breeding pairs reported from casual observations varied from 105 in 1987 to 34 broods in 1990, with an average of 65 a year, but no evident long-term trend. However, numbers at most of the traditional breeding sites such as Alvecote, Belvide, Blithfield, Ladywalk and Upton Warren have declined, but other, new waters have emerged. Water levels are also critical, with breeding occurring if they drop sufficiently to expose islands, such as at Draycote in 1997 when 21 broods were noted. Allowing for under-recording, it seems likely that the present population is within the range 200-300 pairs compared with the 150-220 pairs estimated in *BWM*. Many more pairs summer without apparently attempting to breed, whilst the success of those that do is often poor, with predation by mink and pike as contributory causes of lost broods.

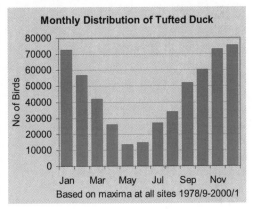

ing 1991/2-2000/1 around a fifth of the region's wintering birds congregated in this valley,

Greater Scaup   (Scaup)   *Aythya marila*
Uncommon winter visitor and passage migrant. Rare in summer.

The Greater Scaup is essentially a marine duck that comes to British coasts and estuaries from its Icelandic and west Siberian breeding grounds for the winter. Small numbers nevertheless find their way into the region every year, usually in the company of Common Pochards or Tufted Ducks. Great care is needed with identification, however, as *Aythya* ducks often hybridise, producing offspring that closely resemble this species.

On average there were 33 a year during 1978/9-2000/1 (*cf.* 10 a year between 1934 and 1978 *BWM*), but numbers ranged from as few as seven in 1989/90 to an exceptional 97 the following year. Such fluctuations are typical of many wintering wildfowl, but the Greater Scaup is unusual in that its peaks and troughs show little correlation with weather patterns. This perhaps suggests that our wintering birds come to us from Iceland rather than via the Continent, where they might be tempted to stay until conditions force them further west.

Whatever their origins, most arrive when immigration into coastal waters is at its peak dur-

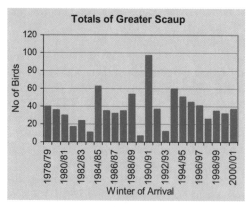

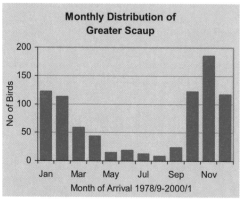

ing October and November. Subsequent arrivals from December to February presumably then result from birds either moving within Britain or coming from the Continent and these movements could be in response to hard weather. Finally, the few new arrivals in spring are perhaps indicative of a small return passage. Summering individuals also appear to be on the increase, with no fewer than 43 birds reported during June to August.

As noted in *BWM*, most records (89%) involve just one to three birds, but flocks up to ten do occur on occasions and during 1978/9-2000/1 there were half-a-dozen records of 12 or more. These included two groups of 14 in 1991, at Bartley Reservoir on February 12th and Dosthill Lake on March 9th, and a record 18 that visited Belvide Reservoir on November 19th 1988 (see also Red-throated Diver).

Just over three-quarters of all birds were shared more or less equally between Warwickshire (39%) and Staffordshire (38%), with the rest similarly divided between Worcestershire (12%) and the West Midlands (11%). The most prolific sites were the Middle Tame Valley (23%), Draycote Water (15%), Belvide Reservoir (11%), Blithfield Reservoir (9%) and Chasewater (7%), which between them accounted for almost two-thirds of all birds. Regular changes in the composition of the Middle Tame Valley flock make it difficult to know how long individual birds are staying, but one of the longest visits was made by a female that remained at Blithfield from January 24th-April 2nd 1987. Of those where the sex was specifically noted, slightly over half (51%) were males.

Hybrid Ducks

Perhaps here is the place to mention the vexed question of hybrid ducks, which at times resemble another species. This is especially true of hybrids of diving duck of the *Aythya* genus, which are recorded virtually every year. These often simulate Greater Scaup or sometimes rarer species, such as Lesser Scaup and Ferruginous Duck. Hyridisation is most likely when there is a surfeit of females of either species (Gillham *et al.* 1966), which perhaps arises more often in captive collections than in the wild. The young may then escape and pair with wild birds (see also Whooper Swan). Whatever the origin, the resulting progeny can provide identification pitfalls for the unwary and critical attention needs to be paid to size, shape, structure and the eye and bill colour as well as plumage. The incidence of hybrids is perhaps surprising. Smallshire (1986), from his observations in the Midlands, mainly at Belvide Reservoir, found that two out of every seven 'Scaup-type' birds were in fact hybrids, from which he concluded that in this region over 20% of birds that look like Greater Scaup are in fact hybrids. Dabbling duck (*Anas* genus) also hybridise, but Smallshire found the incidence of this to be only half that of *Aythya* species. Gillham and Gillham (2002) have provided an inventory to many of the pairings recorded in Britain over the years and when these pass through into back crosses, multiple hybrids and second or third generation hybrids the scope for confusion is infinite.

Lesser Scaup   *Aythya affinis*
Very rare vagrant. One record.

The first British record of this North American duck came from Chasewater in 1987.

Regional Record Number	County Record Number	Year	Locality, Date and Notes
1	Staffs 1	1987	Chasewater: immature male, March 8th to April 26th. (*BB 82:517* and *WMBC 56:29*)

This bird was a superb reward for the dedicated and meticulous observation of its finder, John Holian, and for John Fortey, who first identified it. Its lengthy stay in a readily accessible place also enabled hundreds of birders from as far afield as Scotland and France to come and see it. Once alerted to the prospect of the species occurring in Britain, further records soon followed and there have now been well over 50 nationally (Rogers *et al.* 2004).

Common Eider   (Eider)   *Somateria mollissima*
Rare winter visitor.

The Common Eider is our commonest sea duck, breeding and wintering mainly around northern coasts. It is a very erratic winter visitor to the region's reservoirs that seldom stays here for long.

The first records came in 1948 and by 1978 it had been noted on eighteen occasions—ten of them at Chasewater, which developed a reputation in the 1960s as *the* place in the region to see this species. During 1979-2001 there were a further 25 records, involving 62 birds. These figures are highly distorted, however, by the quite exceptional influx in the autumn of 1993, which produced 13 records of 45 birds.

Incredibly, between October 30th and November 19th around 30 birds passed though Draycote Water alone, where fresh arrivals were recorded on at least six dates and a flock of 18 on the latter date set a new regional record. There were also eight at Tittesworth Resevoir on October 31st, but surprisingly only two at Chasewater and none at the other large Staffordshire reservoirs. This influx was experienced across a wide area of the Midlands and involved over 200 birds (Dawson *et al* 1994). Most were seen in Nottinghamshire, Derbyshire and Northamptonshire, pointing to the North Sea as the source of these ducks.

The charts include this unprecedented influx, but if it is set aside the species' irregularity is well illustrated by the fact that it appeared in only eight of the twenty-three winters, while just six birds made 1999/2000 the second best winter. The monthly distribution

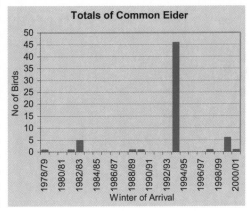

149

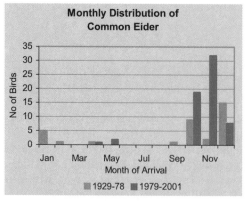

Monthly Distribution of Common Eider

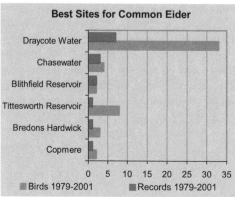

Best Sites for Common Eider

shows most arriving in late autumn, with December actually the peak month—as it was during 1929-78—if the 1993 influx is omitted. Spring records remain scarce, with just one in April and two in May during the current period.

Given their comparative sizes, the three larger counties have shared the bulk of the records fairly evenly, with 36% in Staffordshire, 32% in Warwickshire and 24% in Worcestershire, leaving 8% in the West Midlands.

Excluding the 1993 influx, Draycote Water had only one record, making Blithfield Reservoir and Chasewater the best sites, although neither could claim to have been outstanding. Certainly Chasewater has not lived up to its former reputation. However, Draycote Water holds the record for the longest staying birds, with three immature birds remaining from December 5th 1982 to April 14th 1983– a total of 131 days. This stay was exceptional, however, with only 13% of birds staying as long as a week and the vast majority (82%) leaving within one or two days.

Long-tailed Duck   *Clangula hyemalis*
Rare winter visitor, with occasional summer records.

The Long-tailed Duck breeds in Arctic regions and many winter around British coasts, mainly in the north. Occasional birds visit our lakes and reservoirs.

Occurrences in the West Midlands became more frequent during the 1950s and for the next three decades they remained fairly consistent at between two and three a year. Between 1979-2001 there were 44 records of Long-tailed Duck, involving 55 birds compared with 65 records

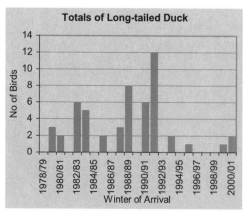

Totals of Long-tailed Duck

of 72 birds during 1929-78 *BWM.* Latterly, they have become scarcer, with only six birds in the nine winters from 1992/3-2000/1. One possibility is that with milder weather birds are spending the winters further north. Overall there were records in thirteen of the twenty-three winters in the current period. The best winter ever was 1991/2, with 12 birds.

The monthly distribution during 1979-2001 remained much the same as from 1929-78, with most birds arriving between October and February and an especially strong autumn peak in November. The few spring arrivals during April-June are evidence of a small pas-

sage of birds, the lateness reflecting the northerly latitudes of their breeding grounds. Most
records have involved just one bird, or occasionally two, but there were three at Frankley
on February 6th 1991 during a cold snap, four
at Fens Pools on November 2nd 1991 and four
at Alvecote Pools on November 13th 1983.

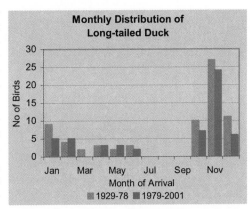

Records have been fairly evenly distributed between the three main counties, but the
number of birds shows an unexpected souther-
erly bias, with Warwickshire producing 35%,
Worcestershire 27% and the West Midlands
16%. Despite its many reservoirs, Staffordshire, accounted for only 22%.

The best sites also reflect this distribution,
with the top five containing two each from
Warwickshire and Worcestershire, but just
one from Staffordshire. Surprisingly, neither
Belvide Reservoir nor Chasewater are in the
top five sites. With only two or three records
separating these main sites, nowhere can truly
claim to be the best, but Draycote Water heads
the list, as it does for so many diving species.
Given that the Long-tailed Duck is usually
most at home in deep water, it is surprising to
find the shallower pools of Upton Warren and
Westwood featuring so highly.

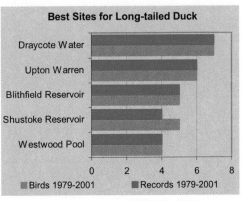

Although 40% of birds left within one day, Long-tailed Ducks tend to remain longer than
other sea-duck. The average stay was 16 days, with 20% staying a month or more, one for 103
days, from November 25th 1982 to March 7th 1983 at Upton Warren and Westwood Pool, and
another for 109 days, from December 1st 1988 to March 19th 1989 at Shustoke Reservoir.

Common Scoter   *Melanitta nigra*
*Uncommon passage migrant and winter visitor, principally in spring, late-summer
and autumn.*

Whereas other sea-duck occur inland only as
vagrants, the Common Scoter makes regular
movements across the country from east to
west in July-August and October-November,
then back again in April-May (Spencer 1969).
This is therefore the most likely maritime
duck to be encountered on the region's larger
lakes and reservoirs.

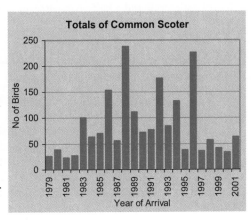

It was noted in *BWM* that the movements
in spring, and more especially July-August,
contain a high proportion of drakes, whilst
ducks predominate in the late autumn passage.
During the current period the sex ratio of
males to females in spring, as birds return to

151

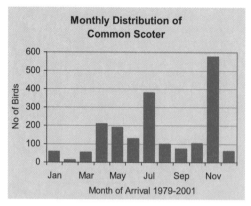

Monthly Distribution of Common Scoter

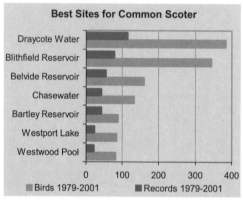

Best Sites for Common Scoter

their breeding grounds, was 60:40, but with males most dominant in April and roughly equal proportions in May. The July-August ratio was 75:25, as males and immature birds are the first to move to their moulting and wintering grounds, possibly in Carmarthen Bay. By late autumn this ratio was transposed to 25:75 as females and juvenile birds of the year followed on behind.

During 1979-2001, there were over 500 records involving almost 2,000 birds. The average number passing through each year more than doubled from 50 to over 100 during the 1980s, remained stable for the first half of the 1990s and then suddenly dropped to around 50 a year again since 1996. The most concentrated passages occurred in 1986, with 91 on July 12th, and in 1988, with a remarkable total of around 190 birds on November 19th-20th, while 1996 was also a good year with 87 in March and April and 108 in November.

Although birds arrived in every month, the spring, summer and late autumn peaks are still very evident, but the latter two now appear to be concentrated more into the single months of July and November. Winter arrivals are scarce, especially in February.

Staffordshire, with the most reservoirs, attracted nearly half the birds (47%), whilst Warwickshire had 29% and Worcestershire and the West Midlands 12% each. Once again the usual reservoirs attracted most birds, but Bartley Reservoir, which seldom features in the list of best sites, seems to suit this species.

The three largest flocks during 1979-2001 all occurred in autumn, with 53 at Blithfield on November 17th 1989, 72 at Draycote on November 20th 1988 and a record 90 over Sheepwash Urban Park on the same day. The latter two were part of the remarkable passage mentioned above. The most in spring was 38 at Draycote on April 7th 1996, whilst the summer maximum was 32 at Westport on July 3rd 1994.

An adult ringed in Coventry on July 3rd 1984 was recovered dead in Lincolnshire, near Belvoir Castle, four and a half years later, in January 1989.

Surf Scoter *Melanitta perspicillata*
Very rare vagrant. Three records.

There have now been two further records of this North American sea-duck to add to the historical one mentioned in *BWM*, as shown in the table opposite.

Of all the maritime species to occur in British waters, this must be one of the least expected inland. Indeed, the pre-1904 record always seemed incredulous until the arrival of a second, which itself was only the second to occur inland in England since the BBRC was established in 1958 (Rogers *et al.* 1987). Since then, however, the species has become more frequent in coastal waters and ceased to be a BBRC rarity from 1991. For a third to follow so soon after the second was therefore perhaps less surprising, but the species remains very rare inland.

Regional Record Number	County Record Number	Year	Locality, Date and Notes
1	Warks 1	Pre-1904	Near Stratford-upon-Avon: adult male, shot some years before 1904 (Tomes 1904).
2	Warks 2	1986	Draycote Water: adult male, October 26th. *BB 80:530*
3	Worcs 1	2000	Westwood Pool: adult female, October 21st. Possibly the bird seen at Dawlish Warren (Devon) the previous day.

Velvet Scoter   *Melanitta fusca*
Rare winter visitor and passage migrant.

The Velvet Scoter comes sparingly from its Fennoscandia and northern Russian breeding grounds to winter around the British coasts, principally along the East Coast. Its appearances in this region are rare and erratic. *BWM* documented 30 records involving 47 birds during the fifty years 1929-78, whilst the twenty-three years 1979-2001 produced a further 17 records of 33 birds. Thus, whilst the frequency of records has remained very similar, the number of birds has increased slightly.

The unpredictability of this species is well illustrated by the fact that it failed to appear in twelve of the winters 1978/9-2000/1. The best year was 1984, due largely to a party of seven—the largest recorded in the region—which dropped into Draycote Water on May 1st 1984. Four birds which arrived at the same place on November 23rd 1985 and another four at Sandwell Valley on December 3rd 1994 also swell the totals for those years.

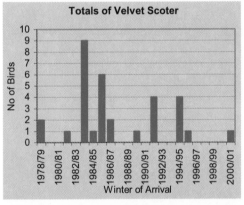

These parties, especially the seven in May, also distort the monthly distribution, which otherwise shows a distinct late-autumn peak of arrivals. There were no records in October, which during 1929-78 was the main arrival month, and also far fewer in January and none in February or March. These were not necessarily birdless months as some individuals have lingered for a considerable time. For example, one took up residence at Draycote Water from December 24th 2000 until April 15th 2001 (113 days), whilst one of the four that arrived at the same place on November 23rd 1985 finally left on April 4th 1986, after 133 days. Generally birds either leave very quickly or else stay for some time, with half moving on within two days, but three-quarters of the rest remaining for at least two weeks.

During 1979-2001 birds were seen at only seven localities. Warwickshire, or more specifically Draycote Water, proved overwhelmingly dominant, accounting for over half the number of records and birds. Staffordshire contributed 21%, West Midlands 15% and Worcestershire just 3%.

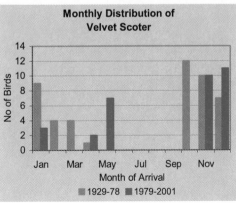

Common Goldeneye (Goldeneye) *Bucephala clangula*
Fairly common winter visitor. Rare in summer.

The Common Goldeneye is a regular winter visitor from Fennoscandia, principally to our larger reservoirs and lakes, where its ability to dive deeper and take food in suspension (*BWP*) enables it to feed in deep water and so avoid competition with many other diving duck. These characteristics also mean it is less affected by changes in water levels.

As the indices show, numbers visiting the region more than doubled during 1978/9-2000/1, which was a faster rate of growth than nationally. In recent years annual totals have shown very marked fluctuations, with major peaks in 1994/5 and 1998/9 separated by a trough that included the 1996/7 winter. The latter is perplexing, since this was one of the coldest winters for years on the Continent, bringing an influx into Britain as shown by the WeBS index. Just why this influx was not apparent in this region remains a mystery, especially as there were notable numbers of Smew and Goosander.

Over fifty years prior to 1992 the average date for the first birds to arrive was September 22nd, but generally few appear before late October and the main influx occurs in November. Numbers then build up to a peak early in the new year. Unlike many other ducks, Common Goldeneye delay their departure until early spring, so numbers remain high well into March or even early April, when many drakes are indulging in their splendid courtship display. The average date for last birds, based on data for 48 years, was May 8th. *BWM* also mentioned 28 records in June and July, but during 1979-2001 there were twice as many. However, these included one or two instances of birds summering for several years in succession, notably a drake which stayed at Kingsbury Water Park for six years. As a result, the WMBC ceased compiling data on first and last dates after 1991. Most of these summer records are believed to involve sick or injured birds, though it is worth noting that there has been a slow increase and spread of summering birds in England. (Ogilvie *et al.* 2003).

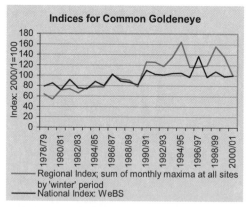

Indices for Common Goldeneye

— Regional Index; sum of monthly maxima at all sites by 'winter' period
— National Index: WeBS

Another indication of the growth in numbers is provided by flock size, with only two flocks of 100 or more mentioned in *BWM*, whereas at least two such flocks are now recorded annually. Indeed, during 1978/9-2000/1 many flocks exceeded 100 birds, with site maxima of 155 at Dosthill Lake in February 2000, 175 at Chasewater in December 1998 and, in the same winter, 185 at Draycote Water in January 1999.

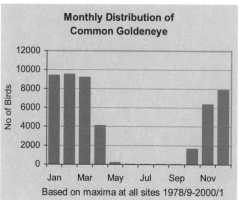

Monthly Distribution of Common Goldeneye

Based on maxima at all sites 1978/9-2000/1

Staffordshire and Warwickshire dominated the records during 1991/2-2000/1, attracting 58% and 36% of birds respectively, while just 4% visited Worcestershire and 2% the West Midlands county. Within this distribution, the top five sites accounted for over 40% of birds, with 14% at Chasewater, 13% at Draycote, 5% each at Dosthill/Kingsbury Water Park and Belvide and 4% at Blithfield. Interestingly, the average maxima at Draycote over the same ten years was 151, whilst at Chasewater it was 145—both just below the 170 limit needed to attain national importance.

Smew   *Mergellus albellus*
Uncommon winter visitor. Very rare in summer.

A few Smew visit the region every year and their discovery at a reservoir, gravel pit or along a river is one of the delights of birdwatching on a cold winter's day. Mostly we see immature or female birds—collectively known as 'redheads'—but occasionally an adult drake appears in its stunning black and white plumage.

In *BWM* the Smew was described as a regular, but scarce, visitor showing a distinct correlation with cold winters. Numbers vary annually, but are normally greatest when their wintering grounds around the Baltic and North Sea coasts (particularly the Netherlands) freeze and they move westwards into Britain in search of open waters. This is exactly what happened in the mid– to late 1990s, when successive winters brought relatively short, but very cold spells, both here and on the Continent. This resulted in unprecedented numbers during 1996/7-1998/9 even allowing for the fact that this is a highly mobile species so there was probably considerable duplication in the records.

As with many species, immature and female birds are more inclined to make these hard weather movements, with the result that adult drakes accounted for only 27% of those birds specifically aged and sexed. As well as being associated with cold weather, Smew also exhibit strong site fidelity and major influxes are often followed by birds returning for the next few years in gradually diminishing numbers. This perhaps explains why numbers remained high for two winters after the initial 1996/7 influx (*cf.* Goosander).

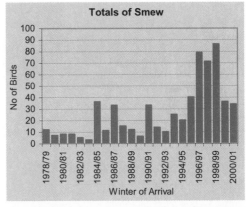

Although there were two October records during 1978/9-2000/1 (the earliest being on the 20th in 1990) and a few in November, the majority of birds (59%) did not appear until the coldest part of the winter in late December and January. Some fresh arrivals also came in February, but relatively few thereafter. Many of the earlier arrivals stayed well into March, however, when the main exodus occurs and a few lingered into April. Birds have occasionally been recorded in summer, too, but generally these were thought to be sick or injured individuals. Indeed, an injured drake stayed in the Gailey-Belvide area from the beginning of 1988 until at least February 1991, where it

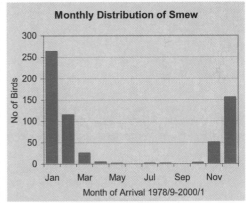

was later found dead, another remained in the Dosthill-Kingsbury area from the unusual date of July 23rd 1991 until April 15th 1992 and one appeared at Blithfield on August 30th 1991.

Around a quarter of all birds occur singly and two-thirds in small parties up to half-a-dozen or so, but the recent major influxes into the Trent and Tame Valleys resulted in a remarkable series of records three years running, with 17 at Croxall on January 26th 1997, a regional record of 19 at Coton Pools on February 20th 1998 and 17 at Coton in January-February 1999.

Large reservoirs such as Belvide and Blithfield used to be the most favoured localities. During the current period, Draycote Water, with 13% of birds was the most important single site. However, 22% of birds occurred in the gravel pits along the Trent Valley, principally at

Barton and Croxall, and 31% were in the Middle Tame Valley, especially at Coton/Lea Marston and the Dosthill-Kingsbury area. The county distribution showed 43% of birds in Staffordshire, 38% in Warwickshire, 16% in Worcestershire and 3% in the West Midlands.

Red-breasted Merganser   *Mergus serrator*
Scarce winter visitor and passage migrant. Probably bred in Staffordshire in 1994.

Until the middle of the twentieth century, Red-breasted Mergansers were rare visitors to the region. Then, in the late 1950s numbers began to increase and this continued at an accelerating rate throughout the late 1960s and 1970s until about seven a year were occurring on average

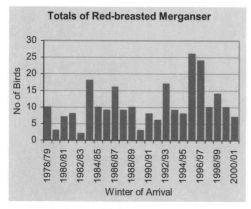

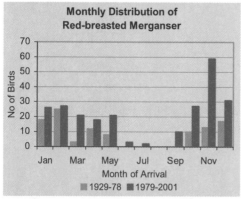

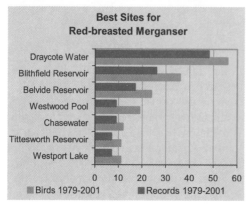

BWM. The species very quickly established itself as an annual visitor, with the last blank year being in 1964.

Almost 250 birds were recorded during the current period, although winter totals fluctuated quite widely, from a paltry two in 1982/3 to 26 in 1995/6. However, the general increase continued, albeit at a slower rate until the average peaked at just over ten a year. It then fell back to around seven a year in the early 1990s before recovering to reach a new peak of just over fifteen, since when there has been another decline.

The initial increase occurred around the time that Red-breasted Mergansers began to colonise north-west England, North Wales and the Peak District. The species has since consolidated its position in these areas and possibly bred in Staffordshire in 1994, when a duck was seen with 15 ducklings on the River Dove. Unfortunately, the river forms the boundary with Derbyshire and it is not known on which bank the nest was located.

Birds have arrived in every month except August, but most reach our lakes and reservoirs during October to December, with a very pronounced peak in November. This is a slightly different pattern to the period 1929-78, when January and February were the main months of arrival. Of the three June records, that at Sandwell Valley in 1990 concerned a confiding bird that was judged to be either injured or an escapee.

The vast majority of records (94%) involved just one or two birds, but there were six on two occasions between 1979 and 2001, at Blithfield Reservoir on November 14th 1986 and Westwood Pool on December 4th 1995, whilst the largest party comprised four pairs that headed north past Eymore Wood on

March 25th 1984, presumably *en route* to their breeding territories higher up the Severn.

Despite Draycote Water being the best individual site, Staffordshire has proved the most popular county, holding 45% of all birds, with Warwickshire's share being 30%, Worcestershire's 19% and the West Midlands 6%.

That most Red-breasted Mergansers just pass through is indicated by the fact that 71% left on the same day they arrived. However, a significant proportion (18%) stayed longer than a week, with half of these remaining for a month or more and a female spending 157 days at Blithfield from November 14th 1999 to April 18th 2000. Possibly the same bird also made lengthy stays in the following two winters.

Goosander   *Mergus merganser*

Fairly common winter visitor. Scarce in summer and a rare breeding bird in Stafford-shire and Worcestershire since 1990.

Long known as a winter visitor to the region's larger lakes and reservoirs, the Goosander has now begun nesting along certain rivers in north Staffordshire and west Worcestershire. Some also leave their winter roosting waters to feed on nearby rivers, where they catch small fish.

BWM noted a distinct bias towards waters in the Trent catchment area and said the only significant wintering population was at Blithfield Reservoir. This situation largely prevailed until the early 1990s, although by this time Belvide Reservoir was enjoying its resurgence as a favoured haunt and Draycote Water was beginning to hold significant numbers. Overall, birds were recorded in 37% of 10-km squares during the *Winter Atlas*, almost all of them in Staffordshire and north or east Warwickshire and most probably involving only a few individuals.

Goosanders are very mobile and frequently move from one water to another, making it difficult to eliminate duplication in records. Nevertheless, there was a noticeable increase during the 1990s, which, mirroring the national trend, culminated in a quite remarkable peak of over 1,000 in 1996/7. A sharp decline then followed (*cf.* Smew), although this is exaggerated in the indices by the effect of the 2001 Foot and Mouth access restrictions.

Numbers are greatest during hard weather and the mid to late 1990s peak coincided with several relatively short, but very intense cold snaps in successive winters, both here and on the Continent. However, the correlation with increased numbers of Smew perhaps points to influxes from the southern North Sea coasts, especially the Netherlands, rather than from elsewhere in Britain.

With the onset of breeding, the recording of arrival and departure dates ceased, but prior to 1992 the average first date, based on 46 years of data, was October 25th with the earliest arrival being two at Blithfield on September 9th 1984. It is November before significant numbers begin to arrive, however, and the main influx then continues until numbers

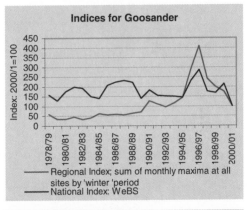

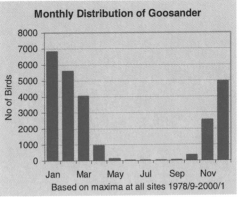

peak in January. A steady departure then ensues, with the main exodus during March. Over 43 years the average date for last birds was April 9th, with the latest ever being on May 25th, when individuals were at Blithfield in 1980 and again in 1990.

From 1979 until the beginning of the 1990s summer records were extremely rare, with the only one coming from Kingsbury Water Park on July 22nd 1984. However, Goosanders had been spreading southwards from northern England and eastwards from Wales for some years, with breeding first recorded in Derbyshire in 1981 and Herefordshire in 1988 (*Breeding Atlas*). In 1990 nesting in this region was suspected for the first time, in the Dove catchment area of north Staffordshire, and the *Breeding Atlas* (1988-91) confirmed nesting in this area and also recorded birds present along the River Dane. Successful breeding quickly followed in Worcestershire, along the River Teme in 1994. Since these initial records there have been regular reports of intermittent confirmed breeding, or presence during the breeding season, along the Rivers Dane, Churnet, Dove and Teme as colonisation takes place.

During 1991/2-2000/1 Staffordshire held 58% of birds, Warwickshire 22%, Worcestershire 11% and the West Midlands 9%. The most productive localities were Belvide and Blithfield Reservoirs, each with 14% of birds, Draycote Water with 9%, Sandwell Valley 5% (mostly since 1997), Chasewater 3% and Tittesworth Reservoir 2%. Except at Belvide and Blithfield, flocks seldom exceed 50 birds, but the 1996/7 influx broke most site records, producing maxima in January or February of 75 at Chasewater, 82 at Tittesworth, 174 at Draycote and an unprecedented 237 at Blithfield (*cf.* a maximum of 148 mentioned in *BWM*). Other notable concentrations at this time were 150 on the River Severn at Kempsey Lower Ham and 100 at Holly Bush, the latter presumably being part of the Blithfield flock. Strangely, Belvide's highest numbers came not during that influx, but in the winters either side, with 190 in January 1996 and 188 in December 1997. Sandwell Valley, another principal site, had a maxima of 66 in January 1998.

Ruddy Duck   *Oxyura jamaicensis*
Fairly common resident of feral origin.

This species is not native to Britain, but heralds from North America. It arrived here in 1948, when the then Wildfowl Trust (now WWT) imported three pairs into its collection at Slimbridge (Gloucestershire). Not all of their progeny were pinioned, however, and between 1952 and 1973 at least 70 juveniles escaped. By 1960 they were breeding in the wild and fifteen years later there was a feral population of over 50 pairs nesting in Britain (Hudson 1976).

Ruddy Ducks nest in little groups on waters fringed with emergent vegetation. Here they can be surprisingly secretive, often spending long periods hidden amongst dense stands of reed and reedmace. In winter they are much more evident when they flock together on the larger reservoirs, lakes and gravel-pits.

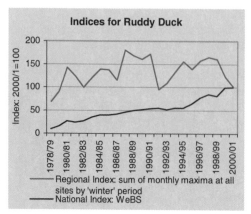

The first sighting in the West Midlands was in September 1959 at Belvide Reservoir. Pairs then bred for the first time in 1961, at both Belvide and Gailey Reservoirs, and in no time at all the region had become a national stronghold for the species, with an estimated 100 plus breeding pairs by 1980 (*BWM*). By the time of the *Breeding Atlas*, birds had already spread to most suitable waters in the region, being present in 57% of 10-km squares. So the subsequent doubling of the national population was not reflected in this region. However, the pioneering colonisation here helped to fuel the growth shown by the WeBS index.

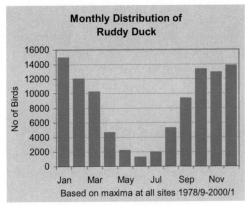

The region also holds a large wintering population of Ruddy Ducks. In the 1980s this was concentrated at Blithfield and Belvide Reservoirs, which between them held 810 birds in January 1981—or more than half of the known British population. A definite pattern of movement was established, with birds initially gathering at Belvide after their late summer moult and then moving to Blithfield in the new year in readiness for their second moult. Numbers steadily increased throughout the decade, especially at Blithfield, where there was a regional record of 909 in January 1988.

During the 1980s large concentrations also began to asemble on the newly formed pools of the Middle Tame Valley, particularly at the Coton/Lea Marston complex where 122 were present in February 1985. The distribution then changed during the 1990s, with numbers much reduced at Blithfield and falling at Belvide to the point where the species could no longer be regarded as regular. Nevertheless, in 2000/1 Blithfield and the Middle Tame Valley still ranked third and fourth in importance in Britain, with average winter peaks of 451 and 293 respectively (Pollitt *et al.* 2003).

From 1991/2 to 2000/1 Blithfield accounted for 21% of all recorded birds, the Middle Tame Valley 11%, Belvide just 3% and the roost at Westwood Pool 2%. Staffordshire was far and away the dominant county with 61% of birds, whilst Warwickshire attracted 26%, Worcestershire 11% and the West Midlands 2%. Peak counts in the same period were 602 at Blithfield in January 1995, 373 at Coton/Lea Marston in November 1997, 262 in the Dosthill/Kingsbury area in March 1996 and 182 at Belvide in December 2000.

Ruddy Duck numbers fluctuate according to water levels and weather. Low levels, such as occurred at Belvide in 1991, reduce breeding success and hence wintering numbers, whilst the species shows a readiness to move in response to weather conditions, with birds forsaking the area when waters are frozen. In 1991/2, for example, numbers were particularly low as unfavourable water levels coincided with freezing conditions during December and January.

Sadly, the Ruddy Duck's propensity to move may ultimately prove to be its downfall, as several birds of unknown origin have found their way to Spain, where they are threatening the integrity of the White-headed Duck population through inter-breeding. This produces hybrids, which unlike those of many species, are fertile. Following representations from the Spanish authorities, the Government launched a Ruddy Duck Control Trial to determine the feasibility and cost of reducing the UK population by 95%. The West Midlands was one of the areas included in this trial cull and this is reflected in the regional index, which shows a 40% decline in numbers between 1997/8 and 2000/1. Over the same three winters, counts in the Middle Tame Valley dropped by three-quarters. As a result of the cull, less information has been forthcoming on breeding, making it hard to estimate the current population, but *BWM* estimated 100 plus pairs and there might still be this many in the region.

The conclusions of the trial were that, given access to the main wintering areas, the population could be reduced by 95% within four-to-six years at a cost of £3.6-£5.4m. (Central Science Laboratory 2002). However, the cull is not universally supported. In particular there is concern about the disturbance it causes at key wildfowl sites. It is also likely that the residual population (which will be considerably larger than that which escaped in the first instance) will regenerate itself, creating the need for repeated culling beyond the six-year period which will prolong the disturbance to other waterfowl and add to the very high financial costs.

Drakes resembling the Peruvian race *O. j. ferruginea* were reported at Kingsbury in March 1991 and Bradnock's Marsh in May 1994, though these may have been aberrant or melanistic birds, whilst one resembling the Columbian race *O. j. andina* was at Kinsham on April 2nd 2000. In addition, reports of hybrid Ruddy x White-headed Ducks involved a male at Blithfield from December 1980-January 1981, with what was presumed to be the same bird at Belvide in March 1982, and a female at Lower Radbourn in May 1995.

Red Grouse   *Lagopus lagopus*
Uncommon and declining resident on the North Staffordshire Moors.

Since 1963 Red Grouse have been confined to the heather moorland of the southern Pennines and even here the resident population appears to be in decline. Heather forms the mainstay of their diet, with young plants the most nutritious. However, they also need taller plants for cover, so the age and size of the heather is vitally important, with birds being most abundant on well managed grouse moors.

In the early nineteenth century the species was more widespread, with breeding on the lower moors (Smith 1938) and isolated populations even on lowland heaths such as Chartley Moss and Sutton Park. Since then, there has been a steady contraction in the range, largely due to the loss of moorland and heath to agriculture. Despite subsequent claims, the last accepted record from Sutton Park came in 1868 and birds were extinct at Chartley Moss by 1897. Birds were also introduced onto Cannock Chase in the mid-nineteenth century and some of their descendants survived until the hard winter of 1963. However, subsequent attempts at reintroduction there have proved unsuccessful. Birds today are highly sedentary, but when heathland was more extensive they used to move from the higher moors to lower ground in winter—a habit that has long since ceased (Gribble 2000).

From surveys carried out during 1969-71 and repeated in 1992-4, Yalden (1994) estimated a population decline of about a third, mostly during the mid-1970s, and recorded approximately 67 territories in the latter period. Specific evidence of the reality of this decline comes from Gradbach Hill, where numbers collapsed from 16 pairs in 1974, when it was being managed as a grouse moor, to just three in 1985, by which time it was heavily grazed by sheep (Waterhouse 1985). Subsequently there was just one pair in 1992 and none in 1996. Comprehensive surveys of the moors by the RSPB in 1985, 1992 and 1996 showed a relatively stable population, with an estimated 100, 88 and 101 pairs respectively (Waterhouse 1985, Brindley *et al*. 1992 and McKnight *et al*. 1996). McKnight also reported a small, but gradual increase at Swallow Moss and the Roaches, but numbers recorded elsewhere since then suggest a further decline (Gribble 2000). Counts from three areas support this. At Baldstones numbers fell from five pairs in 1997 to three in 1998; at Gun Hill from seven birds in 1997 to none in 2000 and 2001; and at Roach End/Back Forest from seven territories in 1998 to one pair and a single male in 2000 and just three birds in 2001.

The reasons cited for these declines include degradation of the moorland through overgrazing by sheep; damage through land drainage; afforestation; and fewer keepers resulting in less rotational burning of the heather to maintain the optimum height for grouse. For example, when a prime area of 480 ha of the Swythamley estate came up for sale in 1977, the Peak Park Planning Board was outbid at auction and it was sold for intensive sheep rearing. Some years later, following extensive drainage grant-aided by the Ministry of Agriculture, Fisheries and Food, it came back on the market. This time the Planning Board's bid was successful and the area was secured for the public—but by then the heather moor had been extensively damaged, though it should recover in time. Since then the SWT has also acquired some 120 ha of overgrazed moorland and conifer plantations, with the intention, over a period of time, of felling the trees and restoring the whole area to moorland. At another key site, English Nature has reached a management agreement with the tenant farmer which should encourage heather regeneration. So there are prospects of a better future for the Red Grouse.

Black Grouse   *Tetrao tetrix*
Very rare and almost certainly extinct as a breeding species on the North Staffordshire Moors.

With the demise of birds on Exmoor in the late 1970s, the isolated population of Black Grouse on the moors of north Staffordshire became the most southerly in England. Here the habitat mosaic of heather moor, birch scrub and rushy pastures was ideally suited to its needs. Indeed, it was even enhanced in places by the planting of conifers, as young plantations provide winter shelter and roost sites as well as food.

Although confined to north Staffordshire, the Black Grouse was described in *BWM* as not scarce. As more sheep were introduced onto the moor, however, numbers began to fall and from the mid-1980s they plummeted to the point where the surviving population was no longer viable. It is now thought to be extinct as a breeding species, if not altogether.

In the nineteenth century it was much more widespread and 252 were shot in a single day on Cannock Chase (Lovenbury *et al.* 1978), but shooting pressure and habitat change led to a large decline and by 1924 the population here was extinct. For the same reasons, isolated populations in other counties were also affected, with that in the Wyre Forest becoming extinct in 1895 and the one in Sutton Park in 1897.

In Staffordshire, the range continued to contract until around 1945, by which time it was concentrated on the northern moors (*BWM*). For some time numbers appeared to be fairly stable as the preferred habitat changed very little until the 1970s. Estimating the population of a polygamous species is difficult, but Lord and Munns (1970) thought there were 60-100 birds,

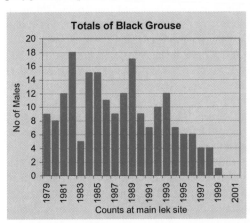

Totals of Black Grouse

No of Males

Counts at main lek site

whilst from surveys during 1973-5 Lovenbury *et al* (1978) deduced a total of 56 lekking males, or 85% of the total Peak District population. In 1982 numbers were down to between 33-37 lekking males and by the time of the first RSPB survey in 1985, only 17 lekking males and five greyhens were found (Waterhouse 1985). Subsequent surveys recorded 14 lekking males and four greyhens in 1992 and six lekking males and three hens in 1996. The latter year was the last in which definite breeding was confirmed (Brindley *et al.* 1992 and McKnight *et al.*1996). The chart plots the decline in males at the main lek at Swallow Moss.

Subsequent reports involved just four males and three females in 1997 and 1998, two males in 1999 and a female in 2000. With 2001 a blank year it was thought the species was extinct, but Gribble (*pers. comm.*) reports that a female has since been reported wandering into Staffordshire from a release scheme outside the county.

A major factor in the decline appears to have been drainage schemes, which caused the land to dry out, paving the way for increased grazing and the re-seeding of grassland. For instance, increased stocking on Gradbach Hill saw the numbers of Black Grouse fall from six males and four females in 1974 to no birds at all in 1985. However, the high number of visitors to the lek site cannot be discounted as a threat (McKnight *op cit.*). If this species has any future in the region now, it can surely only come from reintroductions.

Red-legged Partridge   *Alectoris rufa*
Common resident.

The introduction of the Red-legged Partridge into England as a game bird began towards the end of the seventeenth century, but it was the nineteenth century before any were released in the West Midlands. Today birds can be found in a wide variety of habitats, ranging from lowland valleys to the moorland fringe; and from heath and farmland to urban wasteland and even gardens. Their preferred habitat, however, remains as stated in *BWM*, namely dry, sandy arable land, although they are equally at home in the rough grassland found around power stations, reservoirs and gravel pits. This is a very sedentary species that seldom moves far and its distribution has not changed significantly in the past twenty-five years, although there has been some consolidation within its range in line with the spread in arable cultivation.

The first introductions appear to have been at Witley, where about a hundred brace were released on Lord Foley's estate around 1820 and at Teddesley some time before 1844 (*BWM*). The species took a while to establish itself and it was the first half of the twentieth century before numbers really began to increase. By the early 1980s the *Winter Atlas* showed birds in 88% of 10-km squares. This widespread distribution was later confirmed by the *Breeding Atlas*, which recorded birds in 91% of squares. Not surprisingly, birds were most abundant in the region's arable strongholds of the Feldon, the Lichfield district and the Mid-Severn Sandstone Plateau, whilst fewest were found on the uplands of north Staffordshire.

The CBC/BBS indicated a slight decline in the national population between 1980 and 2002, but regionally the sample size was too small to draw any conclusions. Some observers have referred to declines, notably in the Feldon district, whilst others have mentioned increases. Local populations vary considerably, however, according to the extent to which captive-bred birds are released by sporting interests.

Evidence of such releases comes from the frequency with which large gatherings are now being reported, especially around Bredon Hill. For instance, *BWM* said that coveys up to 20 were frequently noted between late-summer and February, but the largest party mentioned was one of 60 birds in 1977. No group of 50 or more was then reported until 1994, but there have subsequently been seven, the larger of which were 300 at Kinsham in 1998, followed by 100 there and 120 at Warrior's Lodge in 1999. Many of these larger groups are seen around estate feeding stations. Excluding known releases, the average reported covey size has remained stable at around 15-17 birds, with larger gatherings of 47 at Perton in 1984 and 55 at Stanford Bridge in 1996—very similar figures to those quoted in *BWM*. Nevertheless, releases aside, reports do suggest some reduction in numbers and the current population is probably in the range 4,000-6,000 territories compared with the 8,000-10,000 estimated in *BWM*.

Some of the more unusual situations in which birds have been seen include Snow Hill station in Birmingham before its redevelopment, Cradley Heath station car park, a building site at Tettenhall, the roof of a semi-detached house in Fordhouses and a chimney top at Bengeworth.

In the 1970s, several estates began to introduce captive-bred Chukar (*A. chukar*) or Red-legged Partridge x Chukar hybrids, known as 'Ogridges', and the first reports of these birds began to be received in 1981. (For details of Chukar records see under Exotica).

Grey Partridge   *Perdix perdix*
Fairly common, but rapidly declining, resident.

The Grey, or English Partridge as it is often known, used to be a common farmland bird. They are most active when feeding at dawn and dusk, whilst in winter they sometimes roost in ploughed fields. Described in *BWM* as a widespread and numerous-to-abundant resident, this partridge has since declined so markedly that it is now included on the *Red Alert* list of species of conservation concern. Typical mixed farmland, with dry arable fields, grassland, damp pastures, rough field margins and some water, suits it best, but such areas have largely disappeared with the specialisation in either livestock or arable farming.

The main causes of the decline have been widely researched and the general consensus points towards modern farming practices, particularly the use of pesticides which have reduced the population of insects, such as sawflies, on which the chicks are fed. Survival is further hampered by the species' highly sedentary nature, which means it is reluctant to forsake unsuitable areas and seek out new habitats. Between 1980 and 2002 the average size of reported coveys in this region fell by a third, from around 18 to 12, which is much less than the overall population decline, suggesting that causes other than chick survival are involved.

The general distribution is still similar to that shown in the two BTO *Atlases*, when birds were present in 95% of 10-km squares in winter and 92% in summer, but numbers have fallen dramatically and they are now very thinly, if widely, spread. Certainly a report of 12 birds on The Roaches in 1994 confirmed their continuing presence on the North Staffordshire Moors at that time, while a survey of Cannock Chase in 1997 revealed just one pair still lingering there then. The relict populations in the isolated green 'islands' of the Potteries and the Black Country have diminished, however, and the WMBC *Annual Report* for 1994 remarked that the species would soon be extinct in the West Midlands county area.

Few places could still be described as favoured localities, but 16 pairs at three sites in the Needwood Forest in 1999 was one of the more encouraging reports to have been received. Circumstances can soon change, however, with another favoured area, Whitemoor Haye, having 20 birds in 1999 and 25 in the winter of 2001, but none the following autumn.

The CBC/BBS data shows a sharp drop in numbers throughout most of the 1980s, but the decline slowed during the 1990s. The regional index is shown because it mostly follows the national trend, suggesting a similar decline of as much as 80%, but it is based on very limited data and should be treated with caution. National densities imply a regional population as high as 4,000 pairs, but this seems unlikely. Preliminary results from the tetrad surveys in the West Midlands and Warwickshire, for instance, show birds in just 6% and 19% of tetrads respectively. Taking all available data into account, a population of

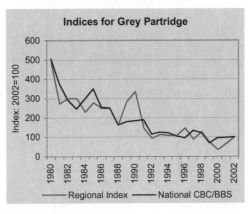

1,000-2,000 pairs seems more realistic. Between 14,000-24,000 pairs were estimated in *BWM*.

The WMBC's *Annual Report* for 1991 commented on there being fewer breeding records, but winter counts suggested it was holding its own. Undoubtedly the population is being supported by the release of captive-bred birds on shooting estates, but to what extent is unknown. Flocks arising from such releases include 55 at Larford in 1992, 50 at Bredon and 60 at nearby Kinsham in 1998, and 50 at Shustoke in 1999. In comparison, *BWM* said this species was more widespread and numerous than the Red-legged Partridge and that family coveys join together outside the breeding season, forming flocks of up to 40 birds, and exceptionally 80.

Common Quail   (Quail)   *Coturnix coturnix*
Summer visitor in fluctuating numbers, but usually scarce. Very rare in winter.

The Common Quail is a regular summer visitor to the region, though its numbers are erratic. It prefers open arable farmland, especially cereal crops, which means it is most common in western and south-eastern parts of the region.

There have now been almost 500 records of this species, over 300 of them during 1979-2001, and birds have occurred in every year since 1964. Despite such regularity, its small size and secretive habits make it difficult to observe, but during intensive survey work for the BTO *Atlas* during 1988-91 breeding was proved or suspected in twelve 10-km squares—or 16% of

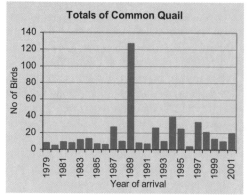

the total. Outside these years, there were just five proven breeding attempts, and two suspected ones, during 1979-2001.

Few birds are ever seen, the majority being identified by the characteristic 'wet-my-lips' call. Interestingly, several have been heard at night and one such occurrence concerned a bird calling in flight over Harborne at 02.00 hrs on June 20th 1984.

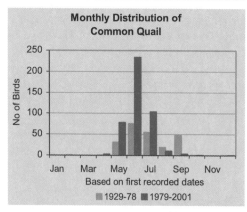

On average, around 15 birds a year reach the West Midlands, but Common Quail are renowned for their periodic influxes—the so-called 'Quail years'—when they arrive in large numbers. Such influxes usually occur during warm, dry springs and often coincide with south-easterly winds. *BWM* mentioned 1970 as the best such year, when 54 birds appeared, but this was surpassed in 1989, when 127 were recorded. Other good years were 1994 (39 birds) and 1997 (33 birds). In fact, the generally warm climate of the 1990s produced no fewer than five above average years.

Since 1989 WMBC *Annual Reports* have included the average first and last dates, but with such a secretive bird these can be very variable. During the current period there were two April arrivals, with the earliest on the 5th, at Sutton Park in 1980. However, May is the more usual month for birds to start arriving, with the bulk appearing during June. Birds continue to arrive in July (or remain undetected until then). Calling generally ceases in early August and most have left by early September. During the current period, an exhausted bird, presumably a passage migrant, was reported from a Witton garden on October 22nd 1986 and another was seen briefly at Whitemoor Haye on December 11th 1993.

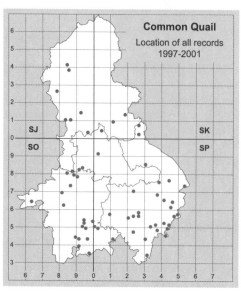

Almost half the birds (44%) in the current period occurred in Staffordshire, with 29% in Worcestershire, 23% in Warwickshire and 4% in the West Midlands. Birds were recorded most often at High Offley, but the largest concentration of calling males was six at Whitemoor Haye in 1994. A party of 10, possibly a family group, was seen at Seighford that year.

Common Pheasant (Pheasant) *Phasianus colchicus*

Very common resident, mainly in rural areas.

Believed to have been introduced into Britain in the late-eleventh century, perhaps by the Saxons or Normans, the Common Pheasant is now firmly established as the commonest game bird. It occurs throughout all rural parts of the region and can even be found sparingly within urban areas, where on occasions it visits gardens. It prefers wooded agricultural land and during the breeding season keeps mainly to the rank vegetation of field margins, scrub and woodland edges, emerging into fields to feed mainly at dawn and dusk. In winter small groups frequently feed in the open on arable fields.

By the 19th century artificially reared birds were being released and gamekeepers were controlling predators. Like it or not, pheasant shooting is a highly popular sport that makes a valuable contribution to the rural economy. Without it, many small plantations and game coverts would have disappeared, much to the detriment of our landscape and to many other birds.

The BTO surveys showed birds to be present everywhere except in the core of the West Midlands conurbation (95% of 10-km squares in the *Winter Atlas* and 99% in the *Breeding Atlas*) and this situation still prevails. Birds occasionally appear even in the Black Country, as records from Sheepwash Urban Park testify, but this is more likely in the winter. Elsewhere within the conurbation, they sometimes visit suburban gardens, again mainly in winter, but are most likely to be encountered in the few remaining enclaves of countryside, such as Harborne Nature Reserve, Sandwell Valley and Sutton Park. At the latter site, they were seen virtually every year until 1994, but reports then ceased and it seemed likely this isolated population had died out. However, two pairs again bred in 2001, so clearly it is lingering on. Other notable urban records include ten pairs at Minworth Sewage Works in 1994 and birds in the Potteries, at Westport Lake in 1997 and the centre of Kidsgrove in 1998. A few birds also occur on the moorlands of north Staffordshire.

Numbers are certainly increasing, with the national CBC/ BBS index suggesting that the population has broadly doubled since 1980. The regional index, however, was distorted by a major release of birds on one census plot between 1992 and 1993. Otherwise it would have shown a similar trend to that nationally.

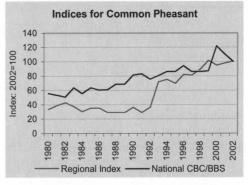

Although the population is probably self-sustaining, much of its increase is attributable to such releases, which take place on sporting estates every year. Judging from available counts, releases in the West Midlands are probably smaller than in some parts of the country, with the larger gatherings having been over 100 around Bredon Hill in 1995 and 1998; 185 at Coleshill in 1989; 200 at Berkswell in 1985 and Lower Radbourne in 2000; and 350 in 2001 at what has been developed as an internationally-rated shoot at Ilmington.

Apart from the CBC surveys, information on breeding density is sparse, but at Ladbroke there were 6 territories per km^2 in 1997 and 13 territories per km^2 in 2000—the latter more than twice the national CBC average. Estimating the populations of polygamous species such as the Common Pheasant is difficult. *BWM* suggested 11,000-13,000 'pairs', but it is now certainly higher, with perhaps 30,000-40,000 males and slightly more females. Of these, the number of males holding territory is perhaps 17,000-23,000.

Birdwatchers seldom pay much attention to Common Pheasants, but there have been reports of albino birds on several occasions and interbreeding with introduced Silver Pheasants and Silver x Common hybrids occurred at Crowle in 1984. Amongst the more unusual behaviour was one that took refuge down an occupied badger set when disturbed, others at Lady-walk which became expert at pecking holes in the nut-bags at the feeding station to get at their contents and a female at Belvide which clung like a Blue Tit to a nut feeder. Wing-tagging by the Game Conservancy has shown Common Pheasants to be highly sedentary, with few dispersing more than 2 km and most being shot within 400m of their release site (Lack 1986).

Golden Pheasant *Chrysolophus pictus*
Rare feral visitor or escapee.

This exotic pheasant was imported from China and first released onto sporting estates in Britain in the 19th century. Since then, feral populations have established themselves in East Anglia and Dumfries and the species was admitted to the *British List* in 1971. Birds are very sedentary, but sometimes their eggs are mixed with those of Common Pheasants at hatcheries, leading to sporadic, isolated occurrences. All records in this region are therefore considered to be of introduced birds, or escapees rather than of vagrants from feral populations elsewhere. *BWM* documented four records to the end of 1978, since when there have been a further eight as follows:

> 1980 Wheaton Aston, male April 8th; 1980 Sugnall, male in the autumn; 1985 Sutton Park, June 3rd; 1991 Burnt Wood (Staffs), April 18th; 1994 Brandon Marsh, pair June 27th; 1995 Maxstoke, male June 11th; 1996 Coton Clanford, pair March 8th; and 1998 Rushton Spencer, male August 23rd.

Red-throated Diver *Gavia stellata*
Rare winter visitor and passage migrant.

Red-throated Divers nest across northern Europe and sparingly as far south as the north and west of Scotland, but are better known in Britain as winter visitors to inshore waters. Inland occurrences are rare.

Compared to the period 1929-78, when there were just 33 occurrences involving 36 birds, they have become more frequent and numerous, with 76 during 1979-2001 and appearances in nineteen of the twenty-three winters. Most records were of single birds, but there were two together on four occasions and a quite exceptional party of 18 that arrived at Belvide Reservoir during a cold north-easterly wind on November 19th 1988. Most of these quickly moved on, but three remained until the next day. This party distorts the average, which otherwise was around four throughout the early 1990s, but has shown a significant downturn since 1996/7.

Good numbers also occurred early in 1979, when the weather was severe, and in the autumn of 1993, when there was also a major influx of Common Eider. Birds have occurred twice in May, in 1979 and 1993, coincidentally at Chasewater on each occasion. Otherwise all recent records have fallen between September and March. Excluding the exceptional November party mentioned above, the pattern shows a steady increase in new arrivals throughout autumn to a winter peak from December to February, after which birds quickly disappear. In contrast, the 1929-78 distribution included a higher proportion of records between April and July.

Staffordshire and Warwickshire have pro-

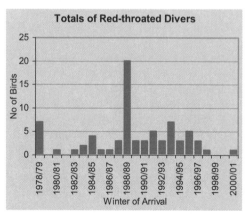

Totals of Red-throated Divers

duced most records (44% and 40% respectively), with West Midlands having 9% and Worcestershire 7%. The large reservoirs are especially favoured. Draycote Water was the most frequented site, with twice as many records as any other locality, but Belvide, by reason of the flock of 18, had the most birds. Otherwise its remaining records were all of single birds. Apart from those shown in the chart, there were records from seventeen other localities, but with no more than two at any.

Two-thirds of birds have remained for only one or two days, but seven have stayed longer than a fortnight. The most protracted stay was 64 days, from December 9th 1994 to February 10th 1995, made by a bird that was first at Larford, but moved to Bittell on January 28th. The two next longest visits were less than half this, being 27 and 28 days at Blithfield and Chasewater respectively in the early part of the years 1991 and 1996.

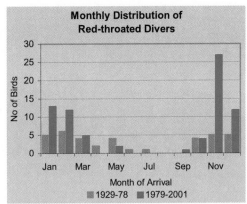

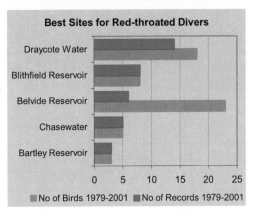

Black-throated Diver   *Gavia arctica*
Rare winter visitor.

The breeding range of the Black-throated Diver is similar to that of the previous species, but in Britain in winter it is restricted more to the northern and eastern coasts.

With just 37 birds recorded between 1979 and 2001, this species is the rarest of the three divers to visit the West Midlands. It was described in *BWM* as irregular, but since then it has become somewhat more consistent, having appeared in eighteen of the twenty-three winters during the current period, including twelve in succession from 1978/9-1989/90. On average, however, there are no more than one or two each year. Larger influxes appear to correlate with hard weather, such as that in 1978/9, when a severe freeze across the Baltic resulted in an unprecedented ten birds in this region, doubling the previous best of five in 1954/5.

Clearly the run of mild winters throughout most of the 1980s and 1990s was not conducive to more appearances, though an uncharacteristic cold spell in the second half of November 1996, when overnight temperatures fell to −11°C, did produce four birds along

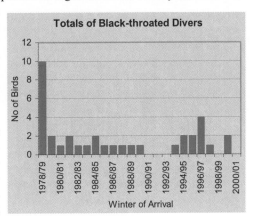

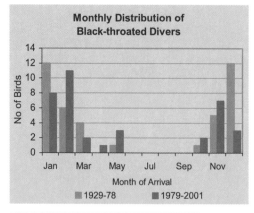

Monthly Distribution of Black-throated Divers

No of Birds / Month of Arrival

■ 1929-78   ■ 1979-2001

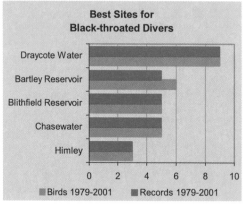

Best Sites for Black-throated Divers

Draycote Water
Bartley Reservoir
Blithfield Reservoir
Chasewater
Himley

0 2 4 6 8 10

■ Birds 1979-2001   ■ Records 1979-2001

with several Red-throated Divers.

Apart from 1978/9, when there were two at Draycote Water and up to three at Bartley Reservoir, all records have been of single birds, although Blithfield Reservoir had two in quick succession in November 1996.

All arrival dates since 1929 have fallen between October and May, but one did remain at Chasewater from May until September in 1960. The 1979-2001 period produced more in spring than occurred pre-1979. Otherwise both periods exhibit a strong winter peak during December-February, with the maximum numbers coinciding with the hardest weather.

Black-throated Divers seldom remain long, with over half leaving again on the day of their arrival and less than a quarter staying more than two days. However, in 1987/8 one spent 29 days at Chasewater, while in 2001 one remained at Draycote for 40 days from November 17th to December 26th.

Most records have come from Staffordshire, with 43%, followed by Warwickshire with 27%, West Midlands 19% and Worcestershire 11%.

As with all the divers, it is the larger, deeper reservoirs that have attracted the bulk of the birds, with Draycote Water again outstanding. It is worth noting, however, that birds have appeared three times on the relatively small lake at Himley Hall.

Great Northern Diver   *Gavia immer*
Rare winter visitor.

Great Northern Divers breed in arctic north America, Greenland and Iceland and some winter round the western coasts of Britain and Ireland. A few, perhaps carried on westerly winds, ar-

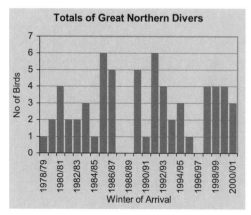

Totals of Great Northern Divers

No of Birds / Winter of Arrival

1978/79 ... 2000/01

rive inland, where this is the most frequent diver. Indeed, it has become an almost annual winter visitor to the region's reservoirs, having occurred in twenty of the twenty-three winters 1978/9-2000/1.

There were 64 birds during 1979-2001—a mean of almost three a year—which was considerably higher than Black-throated and marginally higher than Red-throated (discounting the exceptional party of 18 Red-throated Divers in 1988). What sets this species apart from the other two divers is its length of stay. Birds, usually immatures, regularly arrive in autumn and not infrequently stay into the winter or even through to the following spring. This pattern suggests some are deliberately penetrating inland rather than being driven by adverse conditions.

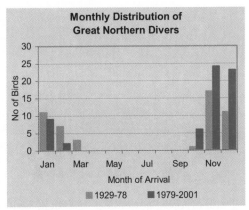

Since 1929 all birds have arrived during the period October to March, but there has been a subtle shift in pattern. Between 1929-78 there was a major influx in November followed by a steady decline in new arrivals through to March. Since 1978, however, there has been an even stronger peak in November and December, with significantly fewer in January and February and none in March. This pattern reinforces the view that most birds are arriving at the time of their autumn dispersal, while the recent run of mild winters has reduced the incidence of subsequent hard weather movements.

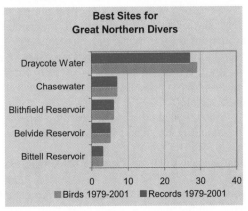

Between 1979-2001 Warwickshire had the largest share of records with 49%, followed by Staffordshire with 36%, Worcestershire 9% and West Midlands 6%. In all, birds were recorded at twenty-two localities, but only seven of these were visited more than once. As would be expected, the large, deep reservoirs were most favoured. The best site by far has been Draycote Water, with birds in fifteen of the twenty–three winters during the current period. Often it has hosted more than one bird at a time, with three or even four on occasions. Moreover, with several having remained here for some time, the species has almost become a regular winter visitor.

Indeed Great Northern Divers often make lengthy stays, with only 20 of the 64 birds leaving within one or two days, whereas 27 stayed for over four weeks. Again Draycote is dominant, having hosted nine of the ten longest staying birds, with the lengthiest being three that arrived on October 31st 1998 and remained until April 26th, April 30th and May 11th 1999 respectively.

Little Grebe   *Tachybaptus ruficollis*
Fairly common resident.

During the breeding season Little Grebes favour small, secluded pools and lakes, sluggish rivers and canals with plenty of emergent, submerged and floating vegetation. Some remain on their territories throughout the year, but others move to the larger waters or maybe even to the coast in winter, especially in hard weather.

The distribution is quite widespread in winter, but more restricted in the breeding season, with records from 92% of 10-km squares during the *Winter Atlas* and 75% during the *Breeding Atlas*. Birds avoid the higher ground of north Staffordshire at all seasons, but freely resort to suitable habitat within the main urban areas.

Information on the numerical strength is patchy, with no continuous data series, either nationally or locally, that monitored the populations in key habitats from 1980-2002. Birds are

169

known to be affected by hard weather, however, and all the indices fluctuate according to the severity of the winters. Often the effect on numbers is most apparent two years later, suggesting birds that survive the cold weather breed poorly in the following summer, so numbers are not replenished. Several observers have commented on poor breeding success and predation by mink is a constant threat. Indeed, the latter doubtless contributed to the WBS index, which monitors the linear waterways, falling by 40% between 1995 and 2000. Other, less common hazards faced by this species have included birds colliding with overhead power lines and young being predated by the Grey Heron.

In this region most records of breeding pairs in recent years have come from enclosed waters, many of them at gravel pits or ornamental pools remote from major watercourses. Taking account of the preliminary results from the *Tetrad Atlases* and the WeBS Index, which contrary to the WBS records a steady increase in numbers, the regional population is probably at the lower end of the range 400-700 pairs compared with the 200-300 pairs suggested in *BWM*. Much of this is due to an increase in gravel pits and man-made waters, cleaner rivers and milder winters.

Among the more regular breeding sites are Alvecote, Kingsbury Water Park, Ladywalk, Pirton and Upton Warren. Nesting also occurs well inside urban areas, notably along the canals of the Black Country and at places such as Edgbaston Park, Fens Pools, Sandwell Valley and Sheepwash Urban Park. Local populations vary considerably, often because of fluctuating water levels. At Ladywalk, for example, there were two or three pairs in the early 1980s, but generally only one during 1986-95. Since then numbers have increased again to five or six pairs, but breeding success is poor, with nests frequently flooded out. Numbers at Upton Warren also declined during the 1980s, but recovered in the 1990s to reach twice their former level, but at Brandon Marsh the population was stable through the 1980s, but has since declined.

After the breeding season many birds move to the larger reservoirs and gravel pits for the winter, when their numbers may be augmented by immigrants from outside the region. The highest counts occur between August and October. Thereafter there is a steady decline through the winter, presumably as birds gradually return to smaller waters in readiness for nesting. Autumn numbers vary considerably. In some years there are hardly any major gatherings, but in others the build up can be quite substantial, with notable examples being 100 at Kingsbury Water Park in October 1982 (and at Draycote Water in October 1976 following a drought that dried up many smaller pools *BWM*). Despite this variability, recent years have shown a discernable trend for larger gatherings. During the period 1991/2 to 2000/1 groups of 30-50 were noted most years, while in the autumn of 2001 there were 90 at Draycote Water in September and a record 115 at Lea Marston-Coton Pools in October. Throughout this period the most important site was the Middle Tame Valley, which held 14% of all birds recorded in the region and averaged 51 birds a year during 1996/7-2000/1, making it of national importance for this species (Pollitt *et al.* 2003). Other sites to hold more than five percent of birds were Pirton (9%), Upton Warren (8%) and Bishampton Vale Pool and Barton GP (6% each). Concentrations in the urban areas are smaller, but up to 20 have been reported along the Smestow Valley. The Little Grebe's habitat preference is reflected in the county distribution, with Worcestershire, which has many small, reed-fringed pools, holding 33% of birds between 1991/2 and 2000/1 compared with 32% in Warwickshire and 24% in Staffordshire, which have the larger reservoirs. The West Midlands' share was 11%.

Great Crested Grebe   *Podiceps cristatus*
Fairly common resident and winter visitor.

Great Crested Grebes occur throughout the region on most of the reservoirs and larger gravel pits and lakes. During the breeding season, they prefer waters with reeds, or other emergent or overhanging vegetation, that provide anchorages for their nests. In winter good numbers congregate on the more extensive bodies of water.

The colourful feathers of breeding birds were much prized by the millinery trade in Victorian times and the species was hunted almost to extinction. Legal protection followed and its power of recovery was such that within seventy years nearly all suitable waters were occupied (*BWM*). Around this time the species also began to winter in greater numbers, since when it has continued to consolidate its position, with the *Winter Atlas* confirming the presence of birds in 71% of 10-km squares and the *Breeding Atlas* in 75%. Today this grebe might be encountered anywhere, except the high ground of north Staffordshire, the Cotswold fringe and the Malvern Hills, or in the Teme Valley, where suitable waters are scarce.

Breeding success depends very much on water levels being stable. If heavy or continuous rain causes an unexpected rise, then nests are flooded, whereas a rapid draw-down of reservoirs in dry weather can leave nests high and dry and vulnerable to predation. For example, at Blithfield Reservoir, which is the region's principal breeding site, 40 young were reared in 1979 and a record 60 the following year. Numbers then fluctuated, with 35 young in 1983 and 30 in 1985, but none at all in the intervening year, when the water level was low. By 1987 productivity had fallen to just five young and in 1997 successful breeding was remarked upon as unusual. Then, with a high water level the following year, 12 pairs raised eight broods and 1999 and 2000 saw former productivity levels approached, with 30 and 32 juveniles respectively. Given the right conditions, breeding density can be very high, although 28 pairs along 50m of rushy shoreline at Dosthill Pool in 1993 was exceptional. The Great Crested Grebe also has a very protracted breeding season, with pairs beginning to indulge in their spectacular display in late January, whilst recently hatched young can been seen as late as October, as at Kidsgrove on October 9th 1991.

The WeBS Index increased by 80% between 1982/3 and 2000/1, whilst the regional index broadly followed suit, although numbers after 1997/8 were exceptionally high (the 2000/1 index probably being suppressed by foot and mouth access restrictions). There has been no comprehensive census of this grebe since 1975, but judging from all available data the summering population is probably between 800 and 1,100 birds compared with an estimated 598 in *BWM*.

After the breeding season, flocks build-up rapidly during July and August as birds move to their wintering sites before their autumn moult and many sites record their maximum numbers in these months. Numbers then continue to increase slightly to a November peak, suggesting some immigration into the region that might involve continental birds. By mid-February birds are beginning to return to their breeding territories and a subsidiary peak in March is indicative of this movement. The only recovery does show some movement as one ringed at Witton Lakes in March 1976 was found dead in Faversham (Kent) in February 1983.

Winter numbers vary considerably between months as well as years. For instance, there was a reduction of 70% during the severe cold spell in February 1979 and a massive 90% drop in the harsh weather of early 1982. The best winter ever was in 1999/2000,

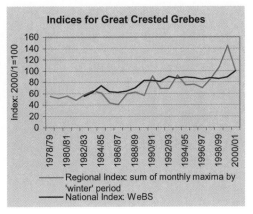

Indices for Great Crested Grebes

Index: 2000/1=100

——— Regional Index: sum of monthly maxima by 'winter' period
——— National Index: WeBS

when exceptional numbers totalling around 800 were present in December and January.

Gatherings of 50 or more are now quite commonplace at the larger reservoirs and lakes, with recent maxima of 104 at Dosthill-Kingsbury Water Park in September 1991 and 130 at Belvide Reservoir in December 2001. However the two top sites are Blithfield Reservoir and Draycote Water, both of which regularly hold between 150-200 birds each winter, making them nationally important. The highest recorded concentration during the current period was 309, at Draycote in November 1993, but Blithfield still holds the regional record, with 335 in August 1954 (*BWM*). These two sites plus the Middle Tame Valley each held 10% of all the birds recorded between 1991/2 and 2000/1, whilst Belvide attracted 7%, Bittell Reservoir 6% and Aqualate and Chasewater 5% each. Staffordshire (46% of birds) and Warwickshire (37%) were the leading counties, followed by Worcestershire (13%) and the West Midlands (4%).

Red-necked Grebe   *Podiceps grisegena*
Scarce winter visitor and passage migrant.

Red-necked Grebes are principally winter visitors to Britain from eastern Europe. Most remain in estuaries along the east and south coasts, but some penetrate inland and a few reach our larger reservoirs. Occurrences are most frequent when continental waters are frozen over.

The number of Red-necked Grebes visiting the region has increased significantly, from 37 during 1929-78 to 116 during 1979-2001. Yearly totals varied considerably, however, especially during the 1980s. The winter of 1978/9 brought the best showing ever, with 22 birds arriving as intensely cold weather across northern Europe during February drove them out of the Baltic and North Seas (*cf.* Red-throated and Black-throated Divers and Slavonian Grebe). Further good showings occurred in 1986/7, when there was a big freeze across Scandinavia in January, and in 1995/6, when the arrival of many birds again coincided with hard weather.

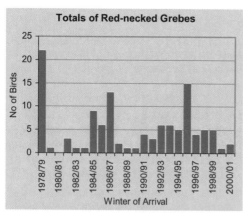

Most birds arrive between September and April. However, the current period brought much stronger passages in spring than in the *BWM* period. Summer records remain rare, with just three: at Belvide from 28th May to 4th June 1989, Dosthill from 9th-11th July 1994 and Tittesworth on August 8th 1996.

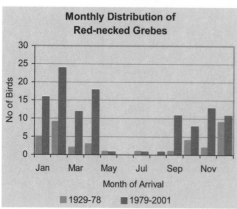

The majority of records (88%) involved single birds, but there were two together on ten occasions. Only Draycote has produced larger gatherings, with three in February 1985 and a quite exceptional seven during February 1979. Just under half of all birds (46%) stayed for only one or two days, but a substantial proportion (17%) stayed for over two weeks, with the lengthiest stays being 54 days, at Chasewater from September 19th to November 11th 1984, and 57 days, at Draycote from January 12th to March 8th 1987.

Warwickshire and Staffordshire, with their large reservoirs and more easterly location, have attracted most birds (43% and 34% respectively), whilst 13% have been in the West Midlands and 10% in Worcestershire. The larger reservoirs are the most favoured sites, with Draycote again outstanding. Birds were also recorded at 26 sites in addition to those shown on the chart, but all had less than five records.

One, in 1986, crash landed into a garden at Stoneleigh and is now in the Herbert Museum and Art Gallery at Coventry.

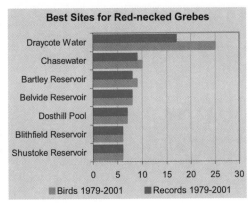

Slavonian Grebe   *Podiceps auritus*
Scarce winter visitor and passage migrant.

This species is a winter visitor to our sheltered coasts from northern and eastern Europe. Although it is the most maritime of our grebes, some come inland and two or three reach this region most years.

Slavonian Grebes were recorded in twenty-one of the twenty-three winters 1978/9-2000/1. During this period 90 birds were seen, compared with 94 during the previous fifty years. Annual totals vary markedly from year-to-year, but the long-term trend shows a steady increase in the five-yearly averages from one a year in 1964-68 to three a year 1974-78 and six per annum 1994-99. The winter of 1986/87 was particularly productive, with 12 birds, many of which arrived from mid-January onwards as anticyclonic air from Siberia sent temperatures plummeting across northern Europe and the North Sea. The winters of 1995/6 and 1996/7 also brought above average numbers, again during periods of cold weather.

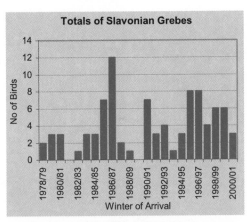

The monthly distribution shows all records during 1979-2001 being between September and May, with the main influx beginning in October and reaching its peak during November to January. Curiously, December arrivals were scarcer than in the 1929-78 period. The current period produced no summer records, whereas in the period of *BWM* there was one each in July (1951) and August (1946).

Most records (86%) have involved single birds, but two together have occurred on five occasions and three were on the river at Stratford-upon-Avon in 1997. Draycote has had the monopoly of larger groups, with four in November 1998 and November 1999, and five

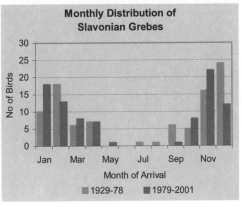

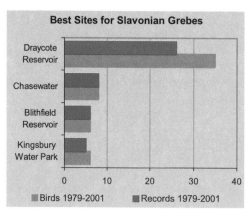

Best Sites for Slavonian Grebes

Draycote
Reservoir

Chasewater

Blithfield
Reservoir

Kingsbury
Water Park

0   10   20   30   40

■ Birds 1979-2001   ■ Records 1979-2001

on January 22nd 1987. Just over half of all birds (51%) have stayed only one or two days, but 21% have stayed longer than two weeks. The five longest stays have all been at Draycote, four of them since 1997, with the most protracted being 123 days from November 14th 1999 to March 15th 2000.

Records have been distributed between the counties as follows: 47% in Warwickshire, 30% in Staffordshire, 19% in Worcestershire and 4% in the West Midlands. Away from those sites shown on the chart, nowhere else was visited more than three times.

Black-necked Grebe   *Podiceps nigricollis*
Scare passage migrant and summer visitor, with sporadic breeding. Rare in winter.

Black-necked Grebes generally prefer quiet, secluded pools for breeding, but visit more open waters at other times. Breeding in the region is very sporadic and the species is best known as a passage migrant to reservoirs, gravel pits and other waters. It is now seen more regularly in the West Midlands than ever before.

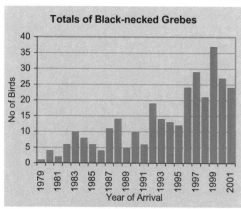

Totals of Black-necked Grebes

No of Birds

40
35
30
25
20
15
10
5
0

1979 1981 1983 1985 1987 1989 1991 1993 1995 1997 1999 2001
Year of Arrival

There was a sharp decline during the late 1970s, when numbers more than halved, but since 1977 birds have appeared in every year, with around 300 individuals recorded in the past twenty-three years compared with 184 in the previous fifty. It is impossible to arrive at an exact total, since the frequency, proximity and numbers involved suggest some possible overlap of records, especially in the last five years. The average number of birds increased from around six a year in the early 1980s to a dozen in the early 1990s, since when it has risen sharply to around 25-30 a year. This rapid growth is probably due to an expanding British breeding population.

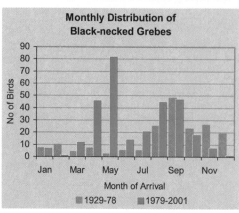

**Monthly Distribution of
Black-necked Grebes**

No of Birds

90
80
70
60
50
40
30
20
10
0

Jan   Mar   May   Jul   Sep   Nov
Month of Arrival

■ 1929-78   ■ 1979-2001

Within the region, breeding first occurred in 1954, but this was an isolated event. In recent years, however, there has been a noticeable increase in spring visits by pairs in breeding plumage, with display sometimes observed. Breeding had been attempted in Warwickshire back in 1984, nest building was observed in the same county in 1992 and finally successful breeding occurred in Staffordshire in 1996 and 2001. A late clutch in the latter county in 2002, however, failed to hatch (Ogilvie *et al.* 2004).

This upsurge in records has been accompanied by a significant shift in the monthly distribution pattern. Between 1929-78 there was a marked peak between August and December, followed by a few in the winter months. The quietest month was May. Since 1979 there has been an enormous increase in spring records, with May now the peak month of the year. This is followed by a late summer peak in August and September, but there are far fewer birds in winter.

Most records were of one to three birds, but four occurred twice, five were at Shustoke Reservoir on March 31st 1999 and six visited Barton GP on May 25th 1997. Sites producing more than five percent of records are shown in the chart. Of the counties, 38% of all records came from Staffordshire, 35% from Warwickshire, 20% from Worcestershire and 7% from the West Midlands, where Sandwell Valley has been the most visited site.

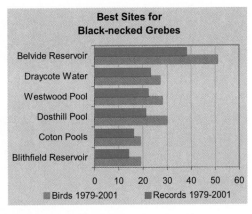

Fulmar *Fulmarus glacialis*
Rare vagrant.

In the land-locked West Midlands, the ocean-going Fulmar would be expected to be nothing more than a storm-driven vagrant. However, the pattern of occurrences suggests otherwise. Certainly most of the August and September records—when post-breeding dispersal can be disrupted by stormy weather—probably involved birds driven inland by strong winds. However, an equal number of birds have occurred in spring, and especially May and June, when adults are normally on their breeding grounds and the weather is generally quieter. Northern Gannets show a similar pattern, suggesting perhaps that some birds fly overland between the North Sea and the Atlantic on fishing trips to and from their feeding grounds.

Following two historical records, *BWM* documented a further 11 in the fifty years 1929-78. The current period then added the following 22, bringing the overall total to 35, all of them involving single birds.

Regional Record Number	County Record Number		Year	Locality, Date and Notes
14	Warks	2	1981	Avon Dassett: January 4th, found exhausted.
15	Warks	3	1981	Draycote Water: April 26th.
16	Staffs	3	1981	Blithfield Reservoir: August 20th.
17	Worcs	9	1982	Grimley: May 19th.
18	Warks	4	1985	Draycote Water: July 20th.
19	Warks	5	1987	Kingsbury WP: January 17th, crash-landed on ice.
20	Worcs	10	1987	Worcestershire Beacon: July 21st.
21	Warks	6	1988	Earlswood Lakes: June 13th.
22	Staffs	4	1989	Blithfield Reservoir: May 28th.
23	Staffs	5	1989	Blithfield Reservoir: August 25th and 27th.

Regional Record Number	County Record Number	Year	Locality, Date and Notes
24	Staffs 6	1989	Chasewater: August 25th.
25	Warks 7	1989	Draycote Water: September 10th.
26	Worcs 11	1989	Hagley: September 11th, found exhausted.
27	Staffs 7	1989	Belvide Reservoir: September 11th.
28	Worcs 12	1989	Upton-on-Severn: mid-September found exhausted, recovered in care.
29	W Mid 3	1991	Sandwell Valley: May 31st.
30	Staffs 8	1993	Chasewater: April 28th.
31	Staffs 9	1993	Tittesworth Reservoir: May 23rd.
32	Staffs 10	1993	Newcastle-under-Lyme: June 19th.
33	Warks 8	1994	Draycote Water: August 29th.
34	W Mid 4	1996	Bartley Reservoir: February 22nd-23rd.
35	Worcs 13	2000	Droitwich: November 27th found disorientated, taken into care.

All but two were seen for just one day—the exceptions being one, assumed to be the same bird, at Blithfield on August 25th and 27th, 1989; and one at Bartley from February 22nd-23rd, 1996. The majority of birds were seen either flying over or resting at reservoirs, or on rivers, but five were casualties of which four were found exhausted.

Cory's Shearwater *Calonectris diomedea*
Very rare vagrant. One record.

The sole record remains that documented in *BWM*, namely:

Regional Record Number	County Record Number	Year	Locality, Date and Notes
1	Staffs 1	1971	Chasewater: October 2nd. *BB 65:324*

Although Cory's Shearwaters occur annually off British coasts in variable numbers, this must surely have been one of the least expected species to be discovered so far inland. Unfortunately it was found in an exhausted condition and later died when released on the coast.

Manx Shearwater *Puffinus puffinus*
Rare, mainly storm-driven autumn vagrant.

Large colonies of Manx Shearwaters nest on islands off the west coast of Britain and the species is very prone to being driven inland by autumn gales. There have been 100 fully documented records, 21 of them historical, 32 during the *BWM* period and 47 in the current period—all of the latter involving single birds.

The 1980s were especially productive, with appearances in ten consecutive years 1981-1990 and exceptional totals in 1985, 1987 and 1988. Whether this unprecedented run of records is a reflection of more people reporting birds to rescue agencies (many birds are found exhausted, not necessarily by birders), or whether it reflects the more turbulent, stormy

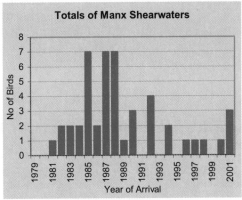

Totals of Manx Shearwaters

weather that seems to be a by-product of the changing climate is unclear. Certainly the majority of arrivals were closely associated with strong, predominantly westerly, winds.

The monthly and geographical distribution of records strongly reflects the autumn dispersal of this species from its west coast breeding sites. All records in the current period occurred between August and October, 81% of them in September alone, when westerly gales are most prevalent. It seems some birds are funnelled up the Bristol Channel and into the Severn Estuary, with 40% of records coming from Worcestershire. In contrast, the most easterly county, Warwickshire, accounted for only 19%, while Staffordshire's share was 23% and the West Midlands 17%. Ringing recoveries support a westerly origin, with several released here experimentally in the 1930s finding their way to Skokholm (Pembrokeshire) and two ringed on that island later being recovered here (*BWM*). To these can be added another ringed on Skomer (Pembrokeshire) on September 3rd 1982 and found dead seven days later at Needwood.

No fewer than 74% of records in the current period involved exhausted or dead birds, some of which were found in unlikely places such as gardens. Several of the former were taken into care by various bodies or individuals and 60% of these were subsequently released on local waters or at the coast.

European Storm-petrel   (Storm Petrel)   *Hydrobates pelagicus*
Rare, storm-driven vagrant.

Appearances by this diminutive seabird are extremely erratic and invariably the result of stormy weather. Overall there have been 26 documented records, 14 of them historical, eight during the *BWM* period and just the following four in the current period. So, despite more intensive watching these days, European Storm-petrels are becoming less regular.

Regional Record Number	County Record Number		Year	Locality, Date and Notes
23	Warks	6	1983	Draycote Water: October 15th, found dead. Now in Herbert Museum and Art Gallery, Coventry.
24	Staffs	3	1989	Blithfield Reservoir: October 29th.
25	Staffs	4	1989	Chasewater: October 29th.
26	Staffs	5	1990	Blithfield Reservoir: October 28th, found recently dead.

All four recent records occurred between October 15th-29th, with two of them, believed to have been different birds, on the same day in 1989. For three of the four records to have been in Staffordshire was quite remarkable considering that county had only been visited twice before. The first three all occurred during unsettled weather with westerly winds, whilst October 1990 began stormy, but had turned warm and dry by the time that year's bird was found.

Of the complete list of 26 records, 12 are in the West Midlands, six in Warwickshire, five in Staffordshire and three in Worcestershire. All dated ones fell between July 13th (1968) and January (1887), with 70% during September to November.

Leach's Storm-petrel (Leach's Petrel) *Oceanodroma leucorhoa*
Rare storm-driven vagrant.

Leach's Storm-petrel is a highly pelagic species, yet amazingly over a hundred have been recorded in the West Midlands. However, the species is well known for being prone to periodic 'wrecks', when storms drive birds well inland, and around half of these occurred during the major 'wreck' that occurred in 1952. At that time, violent storms around the western coasts of Britain during October 25th and 26th drove hundreds inland and at least 56 were discovered in the region. Unfortunately localities were not published for all of these, so it is impossible to give county totals.

There are documented records for at least 17 birds prior to 1929; for 15 during 1929-78 in addition to the 56 mentioned above; and for 22 during the current period of analysis from 1979-2001. There has also been at least one since, in 2002, as shown in the table below.

Year	Locality, Date and Notes	Year	Locality, Date and Notes
1979	Blithfield Reservoir: September 19th.	1989	Draycote Water: September 10th.
1983	Draycote Water: two, September 3rd.	1989	Belvide Reservoir: September 10th.
1983	Blithfield Reservoir: September 3rd.	1989	Trimpley Reservoir: December 17th.
1983	Blithfield Reservoir: September 4th, dead.	1989	Gailey Reservoir: December 24th..
1985	Chasewater: September 20th.	1989	Chasewater: December 24th, dead.
1987	Draycote Water: September 20th.	1989	Shustoke Reservoir: December 25th.
1987	Blithfield Reservoir: September 25th.	1989	Barton GP: December 31st.
1987	Chasewater: September 27th. Presume same, Bartley Reservoir and Sandwell Valley.	1997	Shustoke Reservoir: September 11th.
1988	Belvide Reservoir: September 5th.	1997	Kidderminster: October 6th, taken into care.
1988	Westport Lake: September 19th.	2000	Coton Pools: October 16th.
1988	Blithfield Reservoir: November 14th.	2002	Dunstall Park: February 6th.

In recent times, 1983 and 1987-9 proved to be the most productive years, with 1989 producing a small influx in late December. Arrivals have almost invariably coincided with stormy weather around the coasts. North-westerly gales regularly drive many birds onto the Wirral coast and some doubtless get swept inland. This could well explain the strong northerly bias, with Staffordshire having 56% of recent records: the other counties shares being 30% in Warwickshire, 8% in Worcestershire and 4% in the West Midlands.

All recent records (apart from the latest in 2002) have fallen during September to December, with two-thirds of them in September alone. Most birds have been seen at the larger reservoirs, with five at Blithfield, four at Draycote (including two together on September 3rd 1983), three at Chasewater and two each at Belvide and Shustoke.

Only two of the 21 recent occurrences involved birds found dead, although another was picked up, taken into care and later released on the coast. Doubtless others were close to exhaustion, but not all, as one individual managed to get round Chasewater, Sandwell Valley and Bartley Reservoir in the space of a day—something most birders would find difficult!

Northern Gannet   (Gannet)   *Morus bassanus*
Rare passage migrant and storm-driven vagrant.

The Northern Gannet is a rare, but fairly consistent visitor to the region. As with Fulmar, it would normally only be expected after gales, but, whilst many birds are storm-driven, there is also evidence of birds passing overland in calm conditions, perhaps between their breeding and feeding grounds.

There are pre-1929 records of 17 definite birds, the first of which, at Coleshill, was documented in Ray's *Ornithology of Francis Willughby* (1678) and is believed to be the earliest record for any species in Warwickshire. The *BWM* period then produced a further 30 birds, since when there were another 24 during 1979-2001. Whilst numbers are small, sightings are surprisingly regular, with birds in 15 years during the current period and in every year from 1987-97 inclusive. On average, there is about one a year.

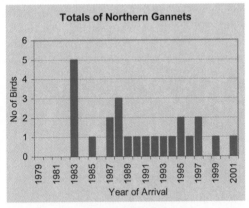

There does not appear to have been any real change in the monthly distribution between 1929-78 and 1979-2001, although there are some subtle differences. Autumn records, mostly after gales, dominated both periods, with peak numbers in September, whilst the unexpected summer records mentioned above featured in both periods. However, the latter period brought the first winter (January and February) records, but fewer in spring (March and April), which might indicate that birds are returning earlier to their breeding grounds. Outside the current period of this analysis, there were also three more May records from Warwickshire in 2002.

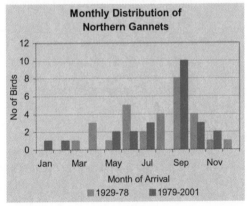

As with other seabirds, the geographical distribution shows a westerly bias commensurate with storm-driven birds being funnelled into the Severn Estuary. Worcestershire produced 52% of birds, including four together flying over Wilden on September 4th 1983; Staffordshire 20%; Warwickshire 16% and the West Midlands 12%. Apart from the Wilden record just mentioned, all other sightings were of single birds. Unlike other seabirds, Northern Gannets have not been especially associated with the major reservoirs such as Blithfield and Draycote, but have been reported from a wide variety of locations. Without doubt this is due in part to their being easily recognised, even in unexpected situations, such as over the M6 two miles from Junction 11! Of those specifically aged, 40% were adults.

Inevitably with storm-driven birds, there have been some casualties, with one picked up exhausted and later released; four picked up that later died; and two found dead. The latter included one that had been ringed as a pullus seven years earlier on Great Saltee, Ireland. There is a cautionary tale, too, in that a lady who rescued one bird had to receive hospital treatment for pecks to her face and, reportedly, only her glasses saved her sight. Sadly, the bird died of degenerative heart disease seven weeks later.

Great Cormorant (Cormorant) *Phalacrocorax carbo*
Fairly common winter resident and passage migrant. Scarce, but increasing breeder.

Any birder returning to the region after an absence of twenty years would be astonished by the number of Great Cormorants. Between 1979-2001 the population increased fourfold with the greatest growth occurring between 1987 and 1991. Staffordshire experienced a major rise first—with a count of over 50 at Blithfield Reservoir in 1976. *BWM* also records an exceptional roost of 240 at Kings Bromley in 1979, although numbers generally were much smaller, with 16 at Draycote Water in 1978 considered an atypically high count at that time! In Warwickshire it was 1987 before numbers began to take off, whilst it was not until the early 1990s that the smaller Worcestershire population began to grow significantly.

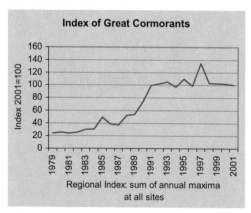

Index of Great Cormorants

Index 2001=100

Regional Index: sum of annual maxima at all sites

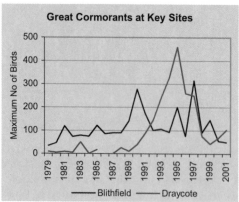

Great Cormorants at Key Sites

Maximum No of Birds

— Blithfield — Draycote

Great Cormorants consume a lot of fish and from the outset their spread became a contentious issue between conservationists and commercial fisheries. Organised culling, under licence, began at Blithfield Reservoir in 1977, but numbers were back to their previous level the following winter. Clearly creating a vacuum merely sucked in fresh birds to exploit a rich food supply—the carrying capacity of the reservoir being the critical factor. For example, three hatched at Puffin Island (Anglesey) in 1986 were shot in Staffordshire in August 1996, March 1997 and September 1998 respectively. It was also noted in *BWM* that Great Cormorants had not yet become a problem at Draycote Water, but that it would be instructive to follow developments there.

Charting subsequent events at both sites has proved revealing. At Blithfield, it seems the carrying capacity is around 100, since this threshold has been sustained over a period of years, but every increase above this level has been quickly followed by a reversion back to it. At Draycote, the carrying capacity is less easily estimated, since there has been no real period of stability. Throughout the 1980s numbers appeared to be below the expected threshold, but the phenomenal growth in the early 1990s, which culminated in a regional record of 459 in January 1995, was clearly unsustainable. Since then numbers have returned to what is probably a more 'normal' level, with the majority of birds now remaining at the Coombe Abbey roost site throughout the day. It is interesting to note that this extraordinary increase occurred during the 'rejuvenation phase' of Draycote, which followed the lowering of water levels during 1988-90 in order for the dams to be strengthened (Harrison 1996).

From the sightings of colour-ringed birds, it appears the increasing population is fuelled by immigration from both the Atlantic and North Sea coasts. The initial 1970s influx into Staffordshire centred on the Trent Valley and Blithfield, and was assumed to have come from the east coast, as was the first influx into Warwickshire, when unprecedented numbers moved into the Tame Valley during the winter of 1987/8. Some of these birds resembled the Continental race *P. c. sinensis* and several ringed birds were believed by the RSPB to be of Danish origin. A further influx in 1990 brought more individuals showing the main characteristics of this race, which were thought to have emanated from a cold weather movement of the Dutch population, since when sightings have become more regular, with reports from several other places as well. Even so, it is likely such birds are under-recorded because of the difficulty in separating them from elderly individuals of the nominate race, which can display similar plumage.

The first definite proof of the origins of our wintering birds came from Belvide Reservoir, where colour-ringed individuals in 1986 and 1989-91 were all found to have been ringed as nestlings on St. Margaret's Island (Pembrokeshire). Another, ringed there as a nestling, was shot at Packington in 1993, while three more from the same colony were at Draycote in that year. However, the original theory that birds were coming from the east rather than the west was given credence by three colour-ringed birds from Abberton Reservoir (Essex) which also visited Draycote that year, with another at Belvide in 2000, whilst one found dead at Westport Lake in 1990 had been ringed fourteen years earlier at Bradwell-on-Sea (Essex). There is also one record from an inland colony, with a bird from Besthorpe (Notts) being seen at Belvide in 1996. The only definite proof of immigration from the Continent also comes from Belvide, where an immature bird seen on October 20th 2000 had been ringed at Yderste Holm, Denmark, the previous May; while another in 2001 was traced back to Holland Vlieland, in the Waddensee area.

Apart from Blithfield and Draycote, Chasewater and Kingsbury Water Park are also regular feeding areas. At night birds usually move away to roost sites in trees, preferably on islands, with Aqualate, Chillington, Coombe Abbey, Gailey, Kings Bromley, Ladywalk and Westwood Park among the more favoured sites.

Because of the conflict with fishing interests, some secrecy surrounds the development of breeding colonies in the region. However, a pair raised three young in Staffordshire in 1981 and again in 1982, whilst in Warwickshire two occupied nests were discovered in the Tame Valley in 1997. Three nests were in the valley the next year, while at Coombe Abbey eight pairs reared at least two young in the heronry. The Tame Valley colony appeared to gradually subside, but that at Coombe had increased to 19 pairs by 2001—of which a dozen pairs were thought to have raised young. Meanwhile, breeding was again reported from Staffordshire in 1998 and by 2001 there was a small colony of 10 pairs in the west of the county.

Shag   *Phalacrocorax aristotelis*
Scarce visitor in all months, with occasional influxes in autumn and winter.

This, the smaller and more maritime of the two British cormorants, is a scarce, but regular, visitor to our reservoirs and other wetlands. It occurs mainly in autumn, when food shortages in coastal waters sometimes disrupt the normal dispersal of juvenile birds resulting in some being driven inland by prolonged onshore winds.

BWM documented 89 Shags between 1938 and 1978, but referred to the remarkable change in the status that began in the mid-1970s, when numbers suddenly increased from just one or two a year to around 10. Since then, birds have continued to appear regularly, with 1990/1 the only blank winter during the current period. However, numbers fell back slightly to around five or six a year during the 1980s and have generally remained around that level. The one major exception was in 1992/3, when two remarkable influxes brought a total of 97 birds—almost half of the 224 recorded during 1979-2001. The first 31 of these arrived at the typical time of August and September. They were then followed by a massive 61 in February—an

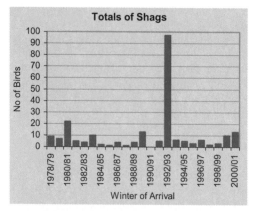

Totals of Shags

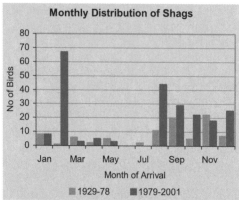

Monthly Distribution of Shags

■ 1929-78 ■ 1979-2001

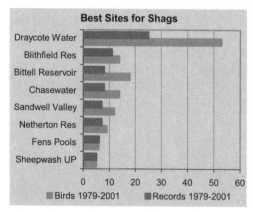

Best Sites for Shags

■ Birds 1979-2001 ■ Records 1979-2001

unusual time for birds to appear. At this time large numbers were spread right across the Midlands and presumably originated from an eruptive feeding flock in the North Sea, which became disorientated in poor weather and was driven inland on easterly winds.

Setting these influxes aside, the normal pattern is for the bulk of birds to arrive between August and December, with very few fresh arrivals in winter and spring. This strong autumn bias suggests storm-driven birds. Ringing recoveries show that birds may originate from both the west and east coasts, as one found on the M5 near Bromsgrove in November 1989 had been ringed as a nestling on a small island near Aberdaron (Gwynedd) the previous June, whilst another at Ladywalk in October 1999 had been colour-ringed on the Isle of May (Fife) in June of that year.

Records have been very evenly spread, with 30% from Warwickshire, 24% each from Staffordshire and the West Midlands and 22% from Worcestershire. Interestingly, the last four of the top eight sites are in the West Midlands county.

Multiple arrivals are not uncommon, with the largest parties being seven at Draycote in 1979, nine at Bittell in 2000, 13 at Draycote in 1992 and an incredible 24 at Edgbaston Reservoir on February 3rd 1993. Once here, Shags may remain for some time. Indeed three birds virtually became residents, staying respectively in the Netherton area for fourteen months from 1989-91; and at Draycote for two years and four months from 1992-95; and almost three-and-a-half years from 1992-96.

One thought to have shown the characteristics of the Mediterranean race *P. a. desmarestii* was at Draycote from August to December 1992, although this race has not officially been recorded in Britain.

Eurasian Bittern (Great Bittern or Bittern) *Botaurus stellaris*
Scarce winter visitor. Rare in summer.

Very much a bird of reedbeds, the Eurasian Bittern is included on the *Red Alert* list and is a priority species in the *UK Biodiversity Action Plan* because its breeding numbers have fallen to a dangerously low level in recent years. To combat this decline, efforts are now being made to create more 'Bittern-friendly' reedbeds in many parts of the country. The closest that the West Midlands has so far come to having breeding birds is at Ladywalk, where a male was 'booming' on New Year's Day 1994 and display has been noted once or twice in recent winters; and Brandon Marsh where one remained from June 5th 1995 to May 13th 1996 and another male was 'booming' on the more promising date of May 20th 2000. Whether breeding will occur in the future remains to be seen.

Meanwhile, a sustainable breeding population also requires productive wintering areas and the region has become renowned in recent years for the Eurasian Bitterns that winter on the WMBC's Ladywalk Nature Reserve.

Other sites have also been visited, albeit less consistently and for shorter periods, with the result that 92 birds were recorded during the current period compared with 45 during 1929-78 (*BWM*). There were records in twenty-one winters, with an average of around three in each until 1994/5, since when the average has doubled to six.

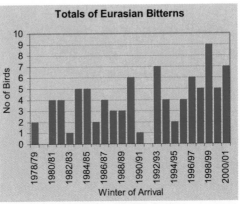

This increase largely coincides with events at Ladywalk, where one that arrived in December 1995 proved to be the precursor of an unbroken series of annual appearances through to the present (2004). During this time, both the number of birds and their length of stay has increased. Back in 1995/6 that first bird stayed just 19 days, from December 31st to January 18th. In 1997/8 the records spanned 117 days—from November 11th to March 7th and involved three, or possibly four, birds. Four birds were definitely present in the next winter and by 1999/2000 there were reports covering 179 days from September 11th to March 7th. Thus, what began as an isolated winter record has slowly developed into an established pattern of one bird returning as early as September, with others following, or being discovered, in October or No-

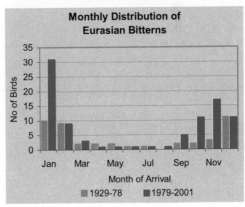

vember and again in the new year. Departure then takes place in late February or early March.

Away from Ladywalk, the second most favoured site—again in Warwickshire—is Brandon Marsh, where birds have been recorded on seven occasions. These two sites, along with Kingsbury Water Park, make Warwickshire easily the most visited county, with nearly half of all records (46%). Next comes Staffordshire (23%), where Aqualate, Belvide Reservoir and Chasewater have shared most of the county records; Worcestershire (19%), where Westwood Pool and Upton Warren have proved most attractive; and the West Midlands (9%), where Fens Pools has been most visited. In all, birds have been seen at around fifty localities, of which the most unusual was perhaps one feeding in a garden pond at Finstall.

The monthly distribution shows that arrivals commence in September and gradually increase to a sub-peak in November. There is then a lull in December before the main peak is reached in January. The latter is partly due to two small influxes of five birds each, in 1993 and 1997, neither of which appeared to be related to a specific weather pattern. It may simply be that birds are more easily detected at this time of year, although the *Winter Atlas* suggests that this is when birds arrive from north-west Europe. Surprisingly, new arrivals (or discoveries) have been recorded in each of the summer months. Away from the main sites, few birds are recorded on more than one day, but being so secretive they may stay longer.

Little is known about the origins of our wintering birds, but one at Ladywalk in 2000/1 was carrying an RSPB radio-transmitter. Sadly, this was not working, but it is known to have been fitted at either Leighton Moss (Lancashire) or Minsmere (Suffolk). Elsewhere one bird was found dead and two that were injured later died. However, another found in an emaciated state at Shard End in January 1987 was taken into care by the RSPB and later released successfully at Leighton Moss, where it was re-caught two months later during survey work.

Little Bittern   *Ixobrychus minutus*
Very rare vagrant. Eight records.

BWM listed seven records up to 1980, since when there has been just one more.

Regional Record Number	County Record Number		Year	Locality, Date and Notes
1	W Mid	1	Prior to 1836	Sutton Coldfield: two on unknown date(s), both shot.
2	Staffs	1	c1838	Kings Bromley: unknown date , shot.
3	Worcs	1	c1865	Badsey: unknown date, shot.
4	Staffs	2	1901	Near Hanley: May, shot.
5	Warks	1	Prior to 1904	Between Warwick and Stratford: unknown date, shot.
6	Warks	2	1976	Brandon Marsh: May 29th-30th. *BB 70:415*
7	Warks	3	1980	Kingsbury WP: adult male, June 24th to July 2nd. *BB 74:456*
8	Warks	4	1981	Brandon Marsh: juvenile, September 19th-20th. *BB 75:485*

This tiny heron is a declining summer visitor to western Europe that winters mainly in east Africa. Most British records involve overshooting birds that arrive in May, while Dymond *et al.* (1989) said the autumn distribution suggests birds probably originate from the Netherlands.

Night Heron   *Nycticorax nycticorax*
Rare vagrant.

BWM documented just four records up to 1979 inclusive. Since then there has been a noticeable increase, with a further 11 records.

Night Herons breed on the near Continent and winter south of the Sahara. Despite their proximity to Britain, those occurring here are frequently suspected of being escapees, but Dymond *et al.* (1989) suggested this was a largely unfounded stigma. However, free-flying birds from the well-known Edinburgh Zoo colony have been recorded in southern England and there is also a free-flying collection in the Midlands (Rogers *et al.* 1996).

Except for the early bird in 2000 and the one in July 1979, however, all those listed arrived between April 10th and June 17th—a typical time for overshooting migrants. Both 1983 and 1987, when two birds appeared in the region, were good years nationally. The geo-

Regional Record Number	County Record Number		Year	Locality, Date and Notes
1	Worcs	1	1870s	Bradley Green: unknown date, shot.
2	Staffs	1	1971	Moneymore GP: immature, June 13th. *BB 65:326*
3	Worcs	2	1978	Near Worcester: adult, June 17th-22nd. *BB 72:509*
4	Worcs	3	1979	Grimley: adult, July 27th., different locality to 1978. *BB 74:457*
5	Warks	1	1981	Coombe Abbey: first-year, May 26th-29th. *BB 75:486*
6	Worcs	4	1983	Bittell Reservoir: first-year, May 12th. *BB 77:509*
7	Worcs	5	1983	Stourport-on-Severn: second-summer, May 22nd-23rd. *BB 77:510*
8	Staffs	2	1984	Longsdon Marsh: second-summer, June 8th. *BB 81:542*
9	Warks	2	1987	Ladywalk: second-summer, May 5th. *BB 81:542*
10	Staffs	3	1987	Blithfield Reservoir: immature, age uncertain, May 10th-11th. *BB 83:443*
11	W Mid	1	1990	Hayhead Wood: adult, April 16th-25th. Same Park Lime Pits on latter date. *BB 84:454*
12	W Mid	2	1994	Foot's Hole: adult, May 6th-17th. *BB 88:499*
13	Warks	3	1998	Calcutt: adult, April 10th-16th, roosting in willows at a private pond. *BB 92:558*
14	Staffs	4	2000	Rolleston-on-Dove: first-summer, March 31st. Reportedly present for about a week beforehand. *BB 95:481*
15	Warks	4	2001	Brandon Marsh: adult, May 13th. *BB 96:550*, (unconfirmed reports until May 15th.)

graphical spread between the shire counties is remarkably even, although Worcestershire has not had a record since 1983.

Two birds have been excluded from the above list. The first is an adult at Kingsbury Water Park on May 24th 1995 (WMBC *Report* 62:22), which does not appear to have been submitted to BBRC: its exclusion reduces the regional total from sixteen (WMBC *Report* 68:21) to fifteen. The second is a triple colour-ringed immature bird seen at the same locality on various dates between October 24th and November 25th 1996, which was thought to be of feral stock.

Squacco Heron   *Ardeola ralloides*
Very rare vagrant. One record.

The sole record remains as follows.

Regional Record Number	County Record Number		Year	Locality, Date and Notes
1	Staffs	1	1874	River Dove, Coton-in-the-Clay: May 17th, shot

Squacco Herons breed from Iberia and north-west Africa eastwards into Asia and winter south of the Sahara. May is a typical time for overshooting migrants to appear in Britain.

With no record for 130 years, it should perhaps be mentioned that a well watched bird was at Blithfield Reservoir on May 25th 2004. At the time of writing, this record was still awaiting a BBRC decision.

Cattle Egret   *Bubulcus ibis*
Very rare vagrant. Two records.

There have been two appearances of Cattle Egrets accepted as being wild birds.

Regional Record Number	County Record Number		Year	Locality, Date and Notes
1	Staffs	1	1987	Doxey Marshes: January 7th. *BB 81:542*
2	Worcs	1	1993	Besford: October 25th to December 26th, intermittently. Same Bredon's Hardwick: December 27th. *BB 88:499*
	Warks	1	1994	Ansley: September 24th to December 23rd, possibly since early September, presumed same as Worcs above. *BB 89:488*

The Cattle Egret spread dramatically during the second half of the twentieth century and now breeds in northern France. A highly dispersive species, its expansion has been accompanied by a significant increase in British records.

These two birds nicely demonstrate the complexities of recording. The 1987 Doxey Marshes bird had been previously present in Derbyshire, where it visited three sites from December 22nd 1986 until the morning of January 7th (Rogers *et al.* 1988). The 1993 individual, seen first at Besford and then at Bredon's Hardwick, proved even more adventurous, since it was in Gloucestershire from March 19th to April 18th 1994 and again from July 29th until at least September 2nd, before reappearing again at Ansley later in that month (Rogers *et al.* 1995 and 1996). A third individual, seen at Crowle and Upton Snodsbury in December 1980, had a blue ring on its leg and was presumed to be an escapee. An escaped individual was also at Slimbridge shortly beforehand, but it is worth noting that three others, possibly of North American origin, also occurred in Britain at that time (*Brit. Birds* 74:160).

Little Egret   *Egretta garzetta*
Scarce, but increasing, visitor, mainly in spring or summer.

The Little Egret has proved to be one of the success stories of the late 20th Century. In France, birds made a significant jump westwards from their breeding grounds in the Camargue to colonise the Atlantic coast. From there they spread northwards and eventually crossed the Channel to reach England. Since then numbers here have rapidly increased, with over 3,000 birds now present in autumn. Breeding occurred for the first time in 1996 at Brownsea Island (Dorset) and there are now well over 100 pairs, mostly along the south coast.

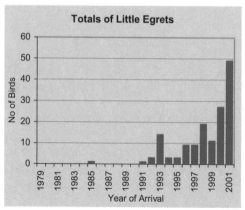

Occurrences within the West Midlands mirror this pattern. Apart from four records prior to 1836, *BWM* quotes only three records, of two birds in 1967 and singles in 1974 and 1978. This sparse, irregular pattern continued throughout the 1980s, during which time the only record was a bird at Coton Pools on May 20th 1985. Since 1991, however, the species has been an annual visitor, with an almost exponential growth and a five-yearly mean that has rapidly increased to over 20 birds a year. Indeed, there were almost twice as many birds in 2001 as in the previous year. In all, around 150 birds have been recorded since 1991, over 80% of them in just six years from 1996-2001.

There has been a significant change in the monthly distribution too, with fewer in spring, when the May peak of former years perhaps indicated overshooting migrants, but a dominant late summer influx, which no doubt indicates post-breeding dispersal. This begins in July and reaches its climax in August, when 60% of all birds arrive.

The records have a strong southerly bias, with three-quarters coming from Worcestershire and Warwickshire (38% and 32% respectively), but only 26% from Staffordshire and just 4% from the West Midlands. However, the latter county can lay claim to the largest party—seven at Marsh Lane Gravel Pits on August 12th 1998. Otherwise, five birds have been seen together on three occasions, namely flying over Claverdon in April 2000, flying over Tittesworth Reservoir in August of the same year and on the Gwen Finch Reserve at Nafford in August 2001. For all the increase in numbers, most birds are still seen only in ones and twos. An interesting record concerns a bird which plundered fish from several garden ponds in the Redditch area in April 1997.

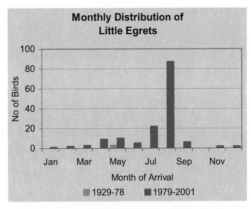

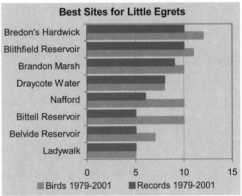

Great White Egret   *Ardea alba*
Very rare vagrant. Six accepted records.

Although nowhere near as dramatic as the spread of the Little Egret, the Great White Egret has been expanding its range too, with small colonies in the Netherlands and NW France (Rogers *et al.* 2003). The sightings listed below show a marked increase here since the first in 1992.

Regional Record Number	County Record Number		Year	Locality, Date and Notes
1	Warks	1	1992	Brandon Marsh: July 8th. (*BB 86:457*)
2	W Mid	1	1995	Meriden GP: Adult, July 24th to August 18th, intermittently.
	Warks	2		Same, The Somers: July 21st and Packwood House: July 28th. (*BB 89:488*)
3	Worcs	1	1999	Westwood Pool: September 11th-12th. (*BB 93:519*). (see details overleaf)
4	Warks	3	2000	Alvecote Pools: May 21st. *BB 94:459*
5	Staffs	1	2001	Copmere: Adult, July 22nd. *BB 97:571*
6	Staffs	2	2003	Whitemoor Haye: October 12th-19th. *BB 97:571*. (Same, Drakelow (Derbys) August 21st intermittently to October 12th.)

Note: The Alvecote Pools bird in 2000 is credited in *BB* to Staffs as well as Warks, but not in WMBC *Report*.

The European spread almost certainly explains these recent appearances in the West Midlands. A further record, of one at Stubbers Green on November 1st 2002, was belatedly submitted to the BBRC and is still under consideration. What is presumed to be same bird was also seen at Chillington (Staffs). If accepted, this will become the sixth regional record and that at Whitemoor Haye in 2003 the seventh.

This is a highly mobile species as shown by the 1999 bird. This was colour-ringed as a nestling on May 8th at Lac du Grande Lieu, France, crossed the Channel to the UK and was first discovered at Britford (Wilts). It spent one night at Westwood Pool and left again at dawn to return to Britford—a round trip of some 176 miles just for the pleasure of roosting somewhere different! It then appeared at Radipole (Dorset) on October 5th (Rogers *et al.* 2001 and 2003).

Grey Heron   *Ardea cinerea*
Fairly common resident.

The Grey Heron is probably more numerous now than ever before and can be seen, poised ready to pounce, along river and canal banks and around the margins of pools and lakes. Although shy, birds regularly take fish from garden ponds. They nest colonially at heronries in

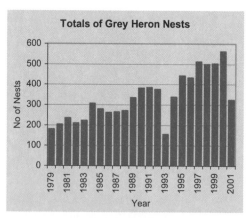

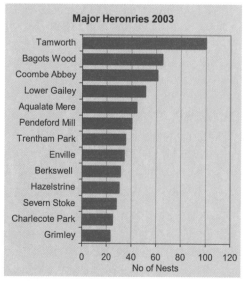

tall trees, often near water. Cleaner rivers, more waters, well stocked fisheries and milder winters have all contributed to its success. The region has more than its fair share of the British population, especially in Staffordshire where at least two heronries are of great antiquity. Its ringers have also been active at the Gailey heronry for very many years. So the species has a special place in the region's ornithology, which is why the WMBC adopted it as its new logo in 2003.

The number of nesting birds steadily increased throughout the current period, with the downturns in 1993 and 2001 being due to very incomplete counts. In 2000, the number of nests topped 500 for the first time—an increase of 150% between 1979 and 2000 compared with a national increase of only 33% 1972-96 (Mead 2000). However, Grey Herons are very vulnerable in hard winters and those of 1978/9 and 1981/2 probably meant the regional growth began from a low base. Even so, the most recent counts for the BTO's national census in 2003 showed a continuing increase to about 700 nests *cf.* 230 in 1978.

Staffordshire holds most of the larger heronries and during the current period had 80% of all nests, while Warwickshire had 14%, Worcestershire 6% and the West Midlands just 1%. For many years the largest heronry was at Bagots Wood, with over 100 nests, but recently there has been a sharp decline here, perhaps because of less favourable feeding conditions at nearby Blithfield Reservoir. At the same time the Tamworth heronry has expanded and this is now the largest in the region, with 100 nests in 2003.

Many heronries have a long history. For example, Smith (1938) said that Aqualate was in existence prior to 1686 and described the Bagots Park heronry as ancient. Conversely, others come and go, often because the host trees (particularly conifers) deteriorate through use. At Gailey, for example, nesting platforms were erected to compensate for the loss of natural sites. In Warwickshire, the principal heronry at Coombe Abbey continues to grow despite the competition from Great Cormorants, while the traditional heronry in Warwick Castle Park has re-established itself after being defunct from around 1974-2001. Worcestershire's two traditional heronries, at Croome and Westwood, were wiped out by the 1962/3 winter and breeding did not resume in the county until 1977, when two pairs reared eight young at Grimley. This heronry and another new one at Severn Stoke have since grown to 20-30 nests each. In the West Midlands the largest heronries are at Berkswell, where there were 31 nests in 2000, and Sandwell Valley with 18 nests in 2003.

Counts up to 30 are regularly reported outside the breeding season at places such as Bittell, Blithfield, Draycote, Ladywalk and especially Rudyard, where 50 or more have gathered on occasions with a peak of 68 in 1989. The largest reported concentration during the current period, however, was 80 at Blithfield in June 1980. Such figures are comparable to those mentioned in *BWM*, but, despite the population increase, the last count to exceed 50 was back in 1991. Perhaps birds are dispersing more to take advantage of the extra habitat now provided by cleaner rivers and the creation of new fisheries. Some interesting behaviour was observed at Ladywalk in 1987, when birds were seen to land on swimming Great Cormorants to steal their fish—then having to swim themselves when the cormorants dived again.

Grey Herons are mainly ringed as nestlings, with less than 1% being fledged birds. Most of the recoveries have come from the ringing programme at Gailey and these have shown the direction of movement to be fairly random, while one third of birds travelled less than 20 miles and fewer than a quarter more than 50 miles. Recoveries from the region's heronries as a whole show large numbers of birds moving to Wales and there appears to be a link between the Severn valley and the distribution of birds in Wales, with herons penetrating deeply into the river valleys adjacent to the Severn Flyway. Three birds ringed in summer within the region were recovered abroad in the following autumn—two in Spain and one in France—while five foreign-ringed nestlings have been recovered here—two from Sweden and one each from Norway, the Netherlands and Belgium. One that was colour-ringed in Greater Manchester in April 1992 was seen at Belvide Reservoir in May of the following year.

Purple Heron   *Ardea purpurea*
Very rare vagrant. Eight records.

During 1979-2001, five more records were added to the three documented in *BWM*, bringing the overall total to eight.

Regional Record Number	County Record Number		Year	Locality, Date and Notes
1	Staffs	1	1856	Wetmore: July 1st, shot.
2	Warks	1	1956	Near Earlswood: immature, August 31st to September 15th.
3	Warks	2	1970	Wormleighton Reservoir: adult, April 18th. *BB 64:343*
4	Worcs	1	1982	Upton Warren: adult, May 5th. *BB 76:482*
5	Warks	3	1990	Nuneaton: May 3rd, flying over.

Regional Record Number	County Record Number		Year	Locality, Date and Notes
6	Staffs	2	1993	Branston Gravel Pit/Water Park: May 2nd, flying over.
7	Staffs	3	1994	Westport Lake: April 25th.
8	Worcs	2	2000	Upton Warren: sub-adult, June 28th. Same, Oakley June 29th to July 1st.

Note: BBRC ceased to consider records of this species as from January 1st 1983.

Purple Herons breed on the near Continent and winter in sub-Saharan Africa. The pattern of records above mirrors that for the species in the UK generally, with five having arrived on typical dates in spring and just one in autumn. Slightly less usual, though, were the two late spring-early summer records in July 1856 and June 2000. Dymond *et al* (1989) suggested that the south-easterly bias in British records probably means most birds come from the Netherlands, rather than southern Europe, but the geographical spread of the above records suggests it would be unwise to speculate on the origins of these birds.

Black Stork   *Ciconia nigra*
Very rare vagrant. Three records.

All records occurred during the last fifty years.

Regional Record Number	County Record Number		Year	Locality, Date and Notes
1	Worcs	1	1956	Dowles Brook: May 31st.
2	Staffs	1	1983	Coombes Valley: May 29th. *BB 77:512*
3	Staffs	2	1985	Coombes Valley: June 2nd, flying over. *BB 79:532*

Black Storks breed in Iberia and from eastern France across to Russia and winter in eastern and southern Africa. The dates for all three birds fell within a five day period at a typical time for overshooting migrants from Southern Europe to arrive. Given the similarity between the last two records, it is tempting to think that the same individual might have retraced its 1983 route again in 1985. If so, did it do likewise in 1984 as well, but pass through undetected?

White Stork   *Ciconia ciconia*
Rare Vagrant. Escapees from collections occur.

Smith (1938) made reference to Garner's claim that "the species had occurred several times on the Dove" and also mentioned an undated claim of one "said to have been obtained in the neighbourhood of Abbots Bromley." However, the thirteen tabulated records are the only fully substantiated ones.

In Europe, White Storks breed in Iberia, and from the Netherlands and eastern France across to Russia, wintering south of the Sahara and in east Africa. The bird which roosted at Leamington Hastings on the night of April 20th-21st 1996 is known to have been ringed in the Netherlands. It was one of two first found at Holkham (Norfolk) on April 16th and subsequently appeared on the Ouse Washes from the 18th-20th before being tracked across Northamptonshire on the latter afternoon.

Regional Record Number	County Record Number		Year	Locality, Date and Notes
1	Warks	1	1896	Beacon Hill, near Coleshill: juvenile, September 26th; caught, died one week later.
2	Staffs	1	1981	Pillaton: June 4th. *BB 77:512*
3	Worcs	1	1984	Crowle: April 27th., flying over
4	Staffs W Mid	2 1	1986	Essington: June 21st, flying over. Same, Ashmore Park: June 21st, flying over
5	Staffs	3	1990	Doxey Marshes: June 1st. Same, Stafford: June 8th, flying over.
6	Worcs	2	1993	Upton Warren: May 28th.
7	Worcs	3	1995	Feckenham: June 18th., circling over.
8	Warks	2	1996	Leamington Hastings: April 20th-21st. Same, Draycote Water: April 21st.
9	Warks	3	1996	Between Coombe Abbey & Ansty: two, June 6th, flying north.
10	Warks	4	1997	Draycote Water: July 14th, flying over
11	Worcs	4	1998	Bredon's Hardwick: June 15th., flying north. Same, Droitwich, June 18th, flying over.
12	Staffs	4	1998	Chillington: April 28th, circling low, mobbed by a male Hen Harrier.
13	Warks Staffs	5 5	1999	Ladywalk: April 15th, flying over. Presume same, Branston: April 16th.

Note: BBRC ceased to consider records of this species as from January 1st 1983.

There have been four more recent records. In 2000, one visited Bishops Tachbrook (Warks) from July 25th-29th and Wellesbourne on the latter date, with what was believed to be the same bird seen again two months later, this time flying south over Kingsbury on September 23rd and then east over Long Lawford on the 25th. Subsequent investigations concluded that it was of captive origin, probably from a collection in the Bristol area. Another over Stone Manor (Worcs) on June 8th, and at Bredon two days later, was then seen in Gloucestershire, when any prospect of it being a wild bird was rendered unlikely by the discovery of a black plastic ring on its leg, but no metal one. Then, in 2001, one at Maxstoke and Packington on May 6th and Shustoke from September 21st-23rd was established to have escaped from a farm at Fillongley, whilst another at Sandwell Valley on January 16th was considered to be either a feral or escaped bird because of the unusual date. These four records illustrate the problems of assessing records of this species, especially those of overflying birds where the presence of rings cannot be established.

Glossy Ibis   *Plegadis falcinellus*
Very rare vagrant. One record

This historical record remains the sole one.

Regional Record Number	County Record Number		Year	Locality, Date and Notes
1	Staffs	1	1840	Fradley: unknown date, shot.

Smith (1938) also mentioned another bird shot at Walton-on-Trent (Derbys) in 1847 or 1848, but there is no evidence of it having been in Staffordshire, the River Trent in this vicinity being wholly within Derbyshire. In Europe, the Glossy Ibis breeds occasionally in France and Spain, but mainly in Ukraine, Romania and the Balkans, migrating to east Africa for the winter. In Britain it is now a great rarity (Rogers *et al.* 2004), although Witherby *et al.* (1943) described it as irregular, but often in small parties, so perhaps this old record is not quite as unusual as it first appears.

Eurasian Spoonbill   (Spoonbill)   *Platalea leucorodia*
Rare summer visitor.

The Eurasian Spoonbill breeds in the Netherlands, Spain and south-east Europe and winters around the Mediterranean and in northern Africa. Following five pre-1901 records and six during 1955-66, the numbers visiting the region's wetlands began to increase noticeably around

Totals of Eurasian Spoonbills

1972. In that year five arrived, including a party of four that visited Draycote Water, Brandon Marsh and Bartley Reservoir at the unusual time of October—the first time a group had been recorded in the region. Another seven birds followed up to 1978 (*BWM*), while 1979-2001 produced a further 34. Appearances are by no means regular, however, with several blank years during the current period. Mostly only one or two occur in a year, but there were four in 1982 and six in 1996.

The monthly distribution shows a strong spring bias, but with some evidence of birds beginning to arrive earlier, with 1979-2001 bringing the first April records and a strong May peak (including another party of four in 1996), compared to a June peak during 1929-1979. Apart from the four in October 1972, there are relatively few in autumn compared to spring.

The party of four in 1996 occurred on May 15th at Sheepwash Urban Park—an excellent record for an urban site—whilst two were recorded together on three occasions, coincidentally all in Staffordshire—at Blithfield Reservoir and Branston on August 10th 1980, Blithfield again on June 1st 1982 and Belvide on October 13th 1991.

Eurasian Spoonbills are highly mobile, with many birds visiting more than one site during their stay. During 1979-2001, the best localities were Blithfield, with seven records, and Belvide, with five: few other sites had more than one or two records. Staffordshire was the most favoured county, with 48% of records, followed by Warwickshire with 23%, Worcestershire 19% and the West Midlands 10%. The apparent restlessness of this species is also reflected in its short visits, with two-thirds being 'one day jobs'. However, a few have lingered for just over a week, but the only lengthy stay was one of 48 days at Handsacre and then Blithfield from July 11th to August 27th 1995.

Of those that were aged, almost three-quarters were adults, with the remainder described as either immature or first-summer birds.

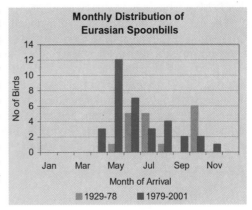

Honey-buzzard (Honey Buzzard) *Pernis apivorus*
Rare passage migrant and summer visitor; two nineteenth century breeding records.

The Honey-buzzard inhabits well-wooded districts and is a rare, but increasing, summer visitor to Britain. Nationally, breeding numbers have increased steadily, from just four pairs in 1979 to 20 pairs in 1989 and then 51 in 2000, when the first-ever national census was carried out (Ogilvie *et al* 2001).

As yet, the West Midlands has scarcely been a beneficiary of this expansion. Following a lean spell of twenty blank years 1967-86, sightings have certainly become more frequent, with birds in all but three of the fifteen years 1987-2001. Numbers, however, have remained very small, though recently there has been some sign of an increase. Indeed, breeding may have occurred in at least one county within the last year or two, although details are understandably confidential. A major reason for the lack of colonisation must be the shortage of suitable habitat, with the region's woodland cover being below the national average and much of what there is being too fragmented to suit Honey-buzzards.

The most outstanding event was the remarkable passage that occurred in Britain during September and October 2000 as migrating birds were forced westwards by persistent, strong south-easterly winds. This brought at least 28 birds to the region, 24 of them immatures, with just one adult and three of unknown age. Such an unprecedented influx naturally distorts the monthly pattern of arrivals for September and October, which otherwise shows that most birds have occurred ei-

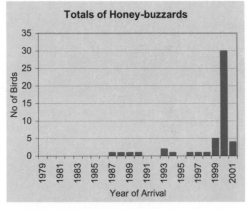

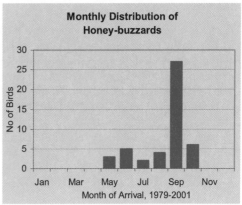

ther in May-June or in August-September.

The events of 2000 commenced nationally on September 19th, when the first immigrants from northern Europe appeared on the East Coast. This vanguard was followed next day by the main influx and thereafter birds moved slowly south across Britain, eventually reaching most parts. In this region, the first arrivals were five on September 23rd. The next day brought just one fresh arrival, but then on the 25th there were nine, including no fewer than seven through Belvide Reservoir alone. Thereafter one or two new arrivals appeared daily until October 1st, when there were four, and further stragglers on October 4th and 8th then concluded a quite remarkable passage. The highlight during this time was three spiralling together high over Bredon Hill on September 28th before leaving to the south.

Black Kite   *Milvus migrans*
Very rare vagrant. Three records.

All three records have been within the current period, with the first as recently as 1986. Black Kites breed throughout most of continental Europe and winter in Africa south of the Sahara. Records in Britain have increased since 1965, and particularly since 1979, as the species has expanded its range and the two in May arrived at a typical time for overshooting migrants (Dymond *et al.* 1979). That in March was unusually early, but there were others in this month in Suffolk during 1996 and 1997 (Rogers *et al.* 1997 and 1998), perhaps suggesting early migration stimulated by mild weather.

Regional Record Number	County Record Number		Year	Locality, Date and Notes
1	Worcs	1	1986	Defford: flying north, May 4th. Probably same, Hartlebury, 5th. *BB 80:531*
2	Staffs	1	1991	Morridge: May 14th. *BB 85:520*
3	W Mid	1	1998	Balsall Common: flying over, March 17th. *BB 92:568*

Red Kite   *Milvus milvus*
Scarce though increasing visitor, partly from released stock. Bred until the early nineteenth century.

What was a widespread and familiar bird in Britain until the early nineteenth century became virtually extinct a hundred years later, with just about a dozen individuals surviving in the hanging oakwoods and sheepwalks of mid-Wales. Elsewhere, including this region, it was little more than a rare vagrant. However, a reintroduction programme into Britain began in 1989, since when the Red Kite has gone from strength to strength.

BWM included records of Red Kites breeding until the nineteenth century, with the last recorded nest at Alfrick in 1840. Thereafter, the species became rare, with just seven dated sightings between 1848-84, while in the twentieth century there were only eight occurrences to the end of 1978. Apart from 1988, when there was an influx into Britain and five reached this region, Red Kites remained rare until the 1990s. Since then they have rapidly increased from less than one a year to an average of just over 15 a year. Overall, 163 birds were recorded during 1979-2001.

This growth accompanied the reintroduction programme instigated by the then Nature Conservancy Council (now EN) and the RSPB. Under this programme the first birds were released in England and Scotland in 1989 (Evans and Pienkowski 1991). By 2001 there were 113 pairs, raising over 200 young (Ogilvie *et al* 2001).

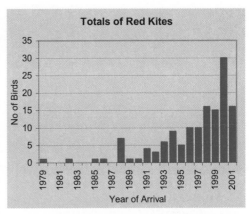

A least ten birds recorded in the region in recent years have been wing-tagged and, with the motorways providing Red Kites with plenty of carrion on which to feed, it has been widely assumed that this increase is largely due to birds moving along the M40 corridor from the reintroduction site in the Chilterns.

This theory received some support in 1992, when an individual from the English reintroduction scheme appeared at Beech, close to the M6 in North Staffordshire. However, not all have come from this most likely source. As far back as 1982 a Welsh-ringed bird was re-trapped and released at Stafford, whilst another, noted in November 2001 at Astwood Bank on the 11th, Spernall Ash on the 20th and then Haseley from December 5th-9th, may also have been moving slowly eastwards from Wales. More surprisingly, a wing-tagged bird at Conderton, south Worcestershire, in

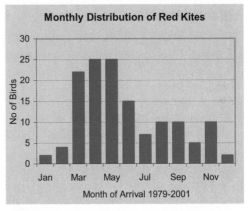

1996 came not from nearby Wales, but from the remote Scottish reintroduction scheme! Other birds in recent years have been specifically noted as not being wing-tagged.

The geographical distribution, with 39% of birds in Warwickshire and 33% in Worcestershire, nevertheless points to the Chilterns and Wales as the most probable sources. Staffordshire's share of birds has been 20% and the West Midlands 8%, which included one perched in a tree on the central reservation of the Solihull By-pass.

The vast majority of records have involved single birds, but there were two at Packington Park on May 20th 1995 and at Salford Coppice on May 1st 1998—both raising hopes of potential breeding. Then, in 1999 an adult and an immature were seen together during September in south Warwickshire and a local landowner claimed that nesting had occurred. Apart from this circumstantial evidence and hearsay, however, the first authenticated breeding record is still awaited. Perhaps one day recolonisation will occur.

White-tailed Eagle   *Haliaeetus albicilla*
Formerly a very rare vagrant. Two twentieth century records, the last in 1945.

There have been no further records to add to the six in *BWM*, which are listed over the page.

Five of the eight birds were specifically noted as being immature, whilst all except the birds of 1879 and 1905 were originally reported as Golden Eagles, but later adjudged to refer to this species (Harthan 1946, Norris 1947 and Smith 1938). White-tailed Eagles breed in eastern Europe and Fennoscandia. Adults are largely sedentary, but immature birds wander widely. A reintroduction scheme was started in Scotland in 1975.

Regional Record Number	County Record Number		Year	Locality, Date and Notes
1	Staffs	1	1792	Cannock Chase: two in early spring, feeding on a sheep carcass, one shot.
2	Warks	1	1879	Knavenhill: two, one of which, an immature, was trapped, November 22nd.
3	Warks	2	1885	Birdingbury: immature, December 2nd.
4	Warks	3	1891	Stratford-upon-Avon: immature, January 24th.
5	Staffs	2	1905	Cannock Chase: immature male, trapped, November 30th to December 4th.
6	Worcs	1	1945	Wannerton: immature, shot, December 25th. *BB 40:184*

Marsh Harrier *Circus aeruginosus*
Scarce passage migrant.

Thirty years ago the Marsh Harrier was a rare summer visitor to East Anglian reedbeds, with just a single pair breeding in 1971. Since then its numbers have grown considerably and it has taken to nesting in intensively farmed areas away from its traditional wetlands. It has also started to overwinter in Britain rather than migrating to the Continent or Africa, which has probably improved its survival rate (*Breeding Atlas*).

This has led to a significant change to its status within this region. Between 1919-43 there

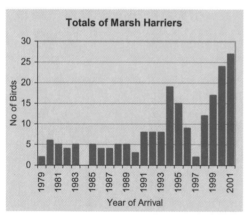

were no records, then 31 birds were noted in the thirty-six years 1944-78. By comparison, the period 1979-2001 produced almost 200 birds. Numbers were fairly stable at an average of about four per annum through the 1980s, but climbed sharply after 1991 to well over 20 a year by 2001. This rate of growth very much mirrored the increase in the British breeding population, which roughly doubled between 1992 and 2001 (Ogilvie *et al* 2003). During this period, 1984 was the only year in which Marsh Harriers failed to show, though birds were very scarce in 1990 and 1997.

Prior to 1979 most birds passed through in spring, while autumn brought very few, but during the current period a significant autumn passage has developed in August and September. Nevertheless, spring remains the dominant season, with April and especially May the peak months.

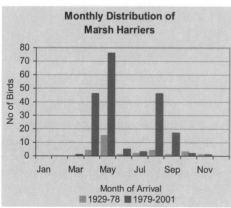

Concentrated movements occasionally occur, for example in 2000 there were six in five days during spring (May 3rd-7th), whilst in the same year a further six accompanied the Honey-buzzard influx, arriving during the seven day period September 23rd-29th. The latter included two together at Priors Marston on the 24th. Two were also seen together at

Brandon Marsh on April 5th 1998 and at Cuckoo Bank on August 22nd 2001. Otherwise all records have been of single birds.

Of those birds that were aged, 21% were adults and 79% immatures, whilst of those where the sex was noted 16% were males and 84% females.

Staffordshire and Warwickshire each had 36% of the birds, Worcestershire 24% and West Midlands 4%. Not surprisingly, the most frequently visited sites were wetlands with stands of emergent vegetation, particularly those with reedbeds.

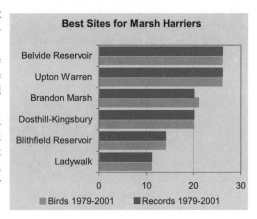

Hen Harrier *Circus cyaneus*
Scarce passage migrant and winter visitor. Bred in Staffs in 1974-5 and 1979.

The Hen Harrier is essentially a bird of moorland and upland heath and, in this region, is most likely to be seen drifting across the banks of heather on the North Staffordshire Moors, where birds have bred in the past, or systematically quartering the heaths of Cannock Chase.

Breeding has been very erratic. In 1974 a family party was observed, next year breeding was again attempted in the same area and a pair raised two young in 1979 *BWM*. There have been no records of nesting since then, although an immature ring-tail at Swallow Moss on June 6th 1999 might have been prospecting. However, birds have bred in recent years across the county boundary in Derbyshire and some of the Staffordshire sightings are doubtless from this source. Sadly, illegal persecution by sporting interests remains a major impediment to the consolidation and expansion of the small and vulnerable breeding population in the southern Pennines.

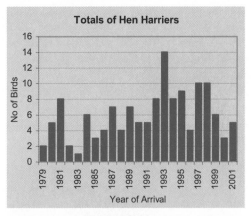

The species is better known as a passage migrant and winter visitor. Prior to the mid-1960s there were seldom more than one a year, but the 1970s brought a significant increase to around five a year *BWM*. Appearances in the early 1980s were erratic, but during 1985-98 they gradually increased to an average of eight a year, before inexplicably falling away again. In all, 136 birds were reported during 1979-2001.

The monthly pattern of records has changed very little over the two main periods of analysis, with the dominant feature being the autumn peak in October and November, during which some pass through whilst others

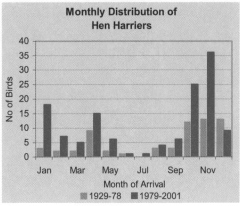

settle in for the winter. This may be followed by a small mid-winter influx if the weather elsewhere is harsh. Spring passage is weaker, but a small peak of records is evident in April. The only summer record away from the moors was one at Timberhonger on July 5th 1991.

In recent years, wintering has been most regular on the moors of north Staffordshire, where there have been sightings every year since 1988/89. The best period was from 1991/92 to 1994/95, when the records suggested three, or possibly four, individuals were present in some winters and a small roost formed at Swallow Moss in 1992/93, but there have apparently been fewer since 1995. Wing-tagging has shown that birds come to winter on the moors from a wide area, with individuals from the north of Scotland in 1992, Argyll in 1993, Dumfriesshire in 1995 and the Forest of Bowland in 1998.

Birds winter less regularly on Cannock Chase, but were noted in fourteen winters during the current period, with a continuous run from 1997/98 to 2000/01. Most records were of single birds, but two were present in 1988/89, 1993/94 and 1997/98. The pre-eminence of these two areas means that Staffordshire, with 63%, has had most birds, followed by Warwickshire with 20%, Worcestershire with 13% and the West Midlands with 4%. Two-thirds of the birds seen have been ring-tails, with 12% specifically identified as females, and one-third males.

Montagu's Harrier   *Circus pygargus*
Rare passage migrant, has bred.

The Montagu's Harrier is a rare and unpredictable summer visitor to Britain, with usually less than ten breeding males recorded annually (Ogilvie *et al.* 2004).

Regionally, up to and including 2001 there had been 27 records involving 29 birds, excluding young. The first of these concerned an adult male that was shot at Sutton Coldfield in the winter of 1839/40—a very strange time of year indeed for this species. There were then 12 records during 1911-73, including the region's only breeding record in 1926, when a pair raised three young at Hewell Grange. Since 1973 the following have occurred:

Regional Record Number	County Record Number		Year	Locality, Date and Notes
14	Staffs	5	1982	Belvide Reservoir: male, June 9th.
15	Staffs	6	1983	North Staffs Moors: first-summer male, July 10th to August 6th.
16	Worcs	5	1986	Bredon Hill: female, June 14th.
17	Warks	2	1987	Seckington: ring-tail, May 31st, left high to north.
18	Worcs	6	1991	Bredon Hill: ring-tail, April 27th, flying over.
19	Staffs	7	1994	Belvide Reservoir: female, May 15th.
20	Worcs	7	1995	Upton Warren: female, April 23rd, flying SW.
21	Warks	3	1995	Thurlaston: second-summer male, June 10th.
22	Staffs	8	1998	Seighford: female, May 28th.
23	Staffs	9	1998	Aquamoor: immature, July 16th.
24	Warks	4	1999	Shipston-on-Stour: first-summer male, May 1st, flying ESE.
25	Warks	5	2000	Upper Kingston: ring-tail, May 5th.
26	Staffs	10	2000	Belvide Reservoir: ring-tail, May 7th.
27	Warks	6	2000	Priors Marston: ring-tail, June 4th., with sightings of harrier sp. at Shotteswell 16th, Wormleighton Res 27th and Northend July 2nd probably the same bird.

The sightings in south Warwickshire in 1999 and 2000 provide an intriguing cluster and it seems probable that a bird summered in the latter year, but there were no sightings in 2001.

Harrier sp.   *Circus sp.*

Since specific identification of harriers is not always possible, it is worth noting that there have been at least 25 records of unidentified birds, 18 of them since 1979. Of these, over half involved ring-tailed birds, the majority of which were thought by the observers to be Hen Harriers. One record involved a male, which was either Hen or Montagu's, one was believed to have been Marsh and at least seven were not attributed to any species.

Northern Goshawk   (Goshawk)   *Accipiter gentilis*
Scarce to uncommon resident and visitor.

This large hawk favours well wooded districts, particularly those with conifer plantations or mixed woodland. However, because of the constant threat of persecution by egg collectors, falconers and gamekeepers, observers are understandably reluctant to disclose details of its whereabouts. The elusive nature of the species itself, especially around its breeding sites, also hampers detection, while the high risk of mistaking large female Eurasian Sparrowhawks for Northern Goshawks, particularly in distant views, complicates record assessment. Taken together, these factors have tended to obscure the recent history of this species.

There were three nineteenth century records from Staffordshire, the last being in 1877. No more reports were then received until the 1950s, when there were two possible sightings in Worcestershire, in 1954 and 1958 (*BWM*). By the 1960s, it was apparent that a breeding population, probably derived from deliberate releases and escaped falconers' birds, was re-establishing itself in Britain (Marquiss and Newton 1982, Vinicombe *et al.* 1993).

Exactly when the species returned to the West Midlands has not been documented. However, a pair—the female of which was an escaped bird wearing jesses—is known to have bred in the Wyre Forest in 1973 and breeding continued here for at least ten years. By 1977 there were several isolated reports from at least two counties and the following year breeding was reported for the first time in Staffordshire (Gribble 2000). Since then, nesting has occurred in twenty of the twenty-five years 1977-2001 and in every year since 1985. Numbers have remained small, however, with the most recorded being pairs at eight sites in 1999—five of them in Staffordshire. In 1987 a pair raised one youngster in the West Midlands county. In Warwickshire, which has less suitable habitat than the two other shire counties, a pair was observed in 1984, but it was 1994 before the first, tantalising evidence of possible breeding was provided by two adults accompanied by a juvenile in August. A gamekeeper then reported that a pair nested in 2002. Allowing for the secrecy surrounding this species, the current population is probably between 10-15 pairs, possibly a little higher.

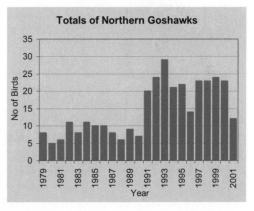

Between 1979 and 2000 the national population increased tenfold (Ogilvie 2003). By comparison, the increase in the West Midlands has been no more than threefold. Moreover, after a sharp rise between 1990 and 1993, the population now appears to have stabilised. British-bred Northern Goshawks are highly sedentary and suitable habitat for them is extremely limited in the West Midlands. It seems possible, therefore, that a saturation point has been reached, with further expansion precluded either by lack of habitat, or by its fragmented nature.

Staffordshire (50% of recorded birds) and Worcestershire (36%) have proved the most productive counties, with the concentrations of woodlands on Cannock Chase, in the Churnet Valley and the Wyre Forest being the most favoured areas. In comparison, Warwickshire (10%) and West Midlands (4%) have produced very few records.

Eurasian Sparrowhawk   (Sparrowhawk)   *Accipiter nisus*
Fairly common resident.

Despite being one of the commoner raptors, occurring right across the region, this hawk can be secretive. Coniferous and mixed woodlands are its preferred habitat, though small copses, clumps of parkland trees and even scrub are sometimes used for nesting. When hunting it also ventures into open country and farmland, often swooping low over a hedge in the hope of catching any small birds on the other side by surprise. Generally it is the larger female that makes these forays into the open, the smaller male tending to remain within the woods.

Until the 1950s, the Eurasian Sparrowhawk bred fairly commonly in most districts, but towards the end of that decade it had been brought to the brink of extinction by the widespread use of DDT and other pesticides which were ingested by its prey and passed up the food chain. At that time the known surviving pairs were virtually confined to well-wooded districts, such as the Churnet Valley, Cannock Chase and Wyre Forest. The ensuing recovery began during the 1970s, at which time a few birds began to appear in some of the more wooded urban situations. Since then the population has continued to increase, although numbers may have dropped slightly again in the last year or two.

The *Winter Atlas* showed birds in every 10-km square, whilst the *Breeding Atlas* showed them in 99% of squares. Abundance levels were below average in the Feldon area, where woodland is sparse, but above average in the main conurbations. Preliminary results from the *Tetrad Atlases* confirm this to be the case, with birds nesting in urban parks, cemeteries, open spaces and even large gardens.

Nationally the CBC/BBS index rose by 77% during 1980-2001, but the paucity of data makes it impossible to compile a regional index. However, there is no doubting the increase in numbers, with the Worcestershire recorder stating in 2000 that it was probably the commonest raptor in northern, central and western districts. In 1976, up to six were seen together over Cannock Chase during spring display flights, while in 2002—the first year in which the species was thoroughly surveyed here—there were 12 pairs. Otherwise, quantitative data is lacking, but the breeding population now is perhaps 600-1,100 pairs, compared with an estimated 200-300 in *BWM.*

The incidence of garden records grew steadily during the late 1980s, with birds quickly adapting to a fresh environment and taking advantage of its facilities by bathing in ponds and quite literally snatching a take-away from many a bird-table. A pair that bred within a mile of Birmingham City Centre in 1986 plucked hapless Common Starlings from their roosting ledges—though it is doubtful if this had much effect on the demise of the city centre roost (see Common Starling)! Other city birds have snatched Lesser Black-backed Gull chicks from their roof-top nests. Life in urban areas can be dangerous for the hawks as well though, with one seen weaving perilously through the traffic in Evesham and many others reported flying into windows. Indeed, a large number of ringing recoveries involve birds dying as a result of colliding with obstacles—chiefly patio doors—as they pursue their prey in gardens. This appears to be a common cause of death, not only for the hawks, but also for many of their intended victims.

The varied list of recorded prey includes a host of commoner birds up to the size of a Wood Pigeon, with the larger species generally being taken by the bigger females. Amongst the more unusual encounters were an unsuccessful attempt to take a Tufted Duck, one which snatched a Great Spotted Woodpecker from a nut-feeder and then carried it to the garden pond to drown it, and yet another which chased a Common Kingfisher along a river. As well as bird tables, reservoir shorelines also offer the prospects of a good meal and there are several records of waders being taken, including Ringed Plover, Northern Lapwing and Common Snipe. Reference should also be made to a Common Swift taken at Upton Warren in May 1986, since this is not a prey species mentioned in *BWP*.

Birds have also been observed contesting aerial space with Northern Goshawks, Common Buzzards and Peregrine Falcons. Although most sightings are of single birds, during the current period at least five individuals visited the Ladywalk feeding station during the autumn of 1989 and five were seen in the air together over Chesterton Wood in April 1999. Birds of prey are generally ringed as nestlings, but in addition a good number of adult Eurasian Sparrowhawks are caught in mist nets. Most recoveries are relatively local, showing movements of between two and 80 km, with only 8% of movements exceeding 100 km.

Common Buzzard   (Buzzard)   *Buteo buteo*
Fairly common and increasing resident, passage migrant and winter visitor.

The 'mewing' of Common Buzzards, circling overhead as they gain uplift from rising thermals, is now a familiar sound and sight throughout the region. So much so that is hard to remember they were a rare sight twenty years ago. This remarkable transformation—the result of birds spreading eastwards from their Welsh stronghold—was probably the most astounding ornithological event of the past decade. Their traditional haunts are open hillsides, heaths and wooded valleys, such as those along the Churnet Valley, around Kinver, in the Wyre Forest and Teme Valley and on the Malverns. The spread into lowland farming areas was unexpected, but already there seems to be a pair in every wood and even an overflow into tiny spinneys and hedgerow trees. Although they take a variety of prey and carrion, rabbits form a major part of their diet.

Common Buzzards probably occurred over much of the region until the nineteenth century, but they then dramatically declined and there were no breeding records at all from 1840 until 1944. By 1954 there were 15 pairs, but the rabbit population was then drastically reduced by an outbreak of myxomatosis and birds remained scarce until the mid-1980s. Numbers then began to increase slightly, topping 20 pairs for the first time in 1986.

Persecution still persisted, however, with

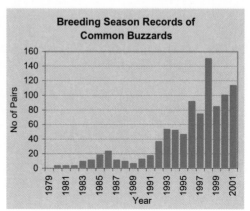

four shot in Staffordshire alone in 1983. Whether this thwarted some early colonisation attempts is unclear, but it was 1992 before numbers again reached 20 pairs. Around this time, birds were recorded in 28 (36%) of the 10-km squares during the *Breeding Atlas* survey. Thereafter they steadily increased and in 2001 over 100 pairs were reported, though the true figure was probably much higher. Using data from the West Country, Harbird (1998) showed a lapsed correlation between this increase and that of the rabbit, whose numbers grew dramatically after 1985. He attributed this time lapse to the site fidelity of young birds, which he thought retarded their initial dispersal.

As an indication of just how phenomenal the population growth has been, during 1988-2002 the CBC/BBS index showed a national increase of around 140%, but there was a tenfold growth in the number of pairs in this region, which was one of the first areas to benefit from the easterly spread. Initially the classic habitat of the Teme Valley became the stronghold, with seven in the air at once over Shelsley Walsh as early as 1984. By the early 1990s, parties of a similar size were being reported around Enville and 16 were seen on the nearby Sheepwalks in 1994. The same number also appeared at Aqualate Mere that year. Birds over the city centres of Birmingham and Wolverhampton were indicative of a spread into urban areas and sightings in Dudley Borough leapt from six in 1994 to 14 by 1996 and 20 by 1997. Scanning the skyline around Timberhonger in 1999 produced a count of 22 and the same number were at Belvide Reservoir on August 28th of that year. The latter included a flock of 15 drifting south—a movement typical of the post-breeding dispersal that occurs in late-August and September. By now parties of 10-14 were fairly widespread across Warwickshire and Worcestershire and two groups of 20 were seen in the Wyre Forest and Teme Valley areas in 2000.

The exceptionally high total for 1998 resulted from surveys undertaken in Worcestershire that year. These produced a total 50% above that normally reported and Harbird (*op. cit.*) estimated the Worcestershire population as 59-175 pairs at that time. Subsequently, preliminary results from the current *Tetrad Atlases* suggest birds are present in around a quarter of the urban tetrads and three-quarters of the rural ones. Even allowing for sizeable numbers of non-breeding birds and areas of unsuitable habitat, these figures suggest a population of 700-1,200 pairs—a phenomenal increase on the estimated maximum of five pairs in *BWM*. Indeed, numerically the species is now easily as common as the Eurasian Sparrowhawk and fast catching up the Common Kestrel.

The remarkable geographical spread is well illustrated by the accompanying chart, which shows the number of sites in each county at which birds were recorded in four progressive time periods. In Worcestershire, the spread began to increase in the 1980s and then accelerated rapidly in the early 1990s. Staffordshire, too, showed a marked spread in the 1980s, but progress appeared to falter in the early 1990s, though this may have been due to under-reporting. Further east, it was the early 1990s before the West Midlands and Warwickshire were colonised and it was not until the second half of that decade that birds became really widespread in the latter county.

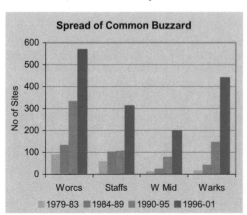

Spread of Common Buzzard

No of Sites

Worcs   Staffs   W Mid   Warks

1979-83 1984-89 1990-95 1996-01

Rabbits aside, birds have also been recorded feeding on a young Common Coot and killing a Moorhen. Two were also seen on a road with their talons locked and were only separated when the observer left his car and approached to within a few metres. Finally, a real David and Goliath act was played out over Warwickshire in 1991 when two birds regularly attracted the attentions of some local Hobbies.

Rough-legged Buzzard   *Buteo lagopus*
Rare passage migrant and winter visitor.

BWM cited around 25 records, including four or five undated historical ones, 10 between 1840-79, one in 1949 and 10 during 1966-78. Subsequently, the following 11 during the current period have brought the all-time total to 36.

Regional Record Number	County Record Number		Year	Locality, Date and Notes
26	Worcs	3	1979	High Green: March 15th.
27	Staffs	11	1979	Belvide Reservoir: immature, March 31st., found dead from poisoning. (Conceivably same as at High Green above. *WMBC Report 46:43*)
28	Staffs	12	1982	Gun Hill: October 2nd.
29	Staffs	13	1991	Codsall: January 5th.
30	Warks	12	1994	Nebsworth: immature, October 17th.
31	Staffs	14	1994	Swallow Moss: October 17th.
32	Staffs	15	1995	Swallow Moss: immature, March 9th. Presume same, Seven Springs March 15th and various sites back on the North Staffordshire Moors April 7th-14th.
33	Staffs	16	1995	Park Hall CP: adult, March 24th.
34	W Mid	3	1996	Bushbury: April 20th.
35	Staffs	17	1999	Park Banks: March 13th.
36	Staffs	18	2001	Apedale CP: April 20th.

Rough-legged Buzzards are annual winter visitors to Britain from Fennoscandia and Russia. Their numbers vary from year-to-year, but broadly follow a four or five yearly cycle of peaks and troughs that mirrors the population dynamics of the Siberian Lemming, which is the main prey on their northern breeding grounds (Fraser *et al* 2003). Most occur in eastern coastal counties and few penetrate as far inland as the West Midlands except during major influxes. The largest such influx last century occurred in the autumn of 1974 (Christie 1975), when five reached the region, whilst the second largest, in 1994 (Nightingale *et al* 1995), produced two birds here in autumn and a further two the following spring. The north-easterly origins are perhaps reflected in the all-time records, which show 18 in Staffordshire and 12 in Warwickshire, compared with just three each in the West Midlands and Worcestershire.

The seasonal and geographical distributions of the 11 records during 1979-2001 are interesting. Normally most records would be expected in autumn, but in this period there were more in spring, with five in March and two in April, compared with just three in October and a sole winter record in January. The spring bias, with most birds returning north-eastwards, perhaps explains the unusual geographical spread, with eight records coming from Staffordshire, six of them from the north, while the other three counties contributed just one each.

Golden Eagle   *Aquila chrysaetos*
No recent records.

The only references to this species ever having occurred in the West Midlands were summarised by Smith (1938), who surmised that "a few centuries ago Golden Eagles probably roamed Staffordshire in search of prey, even if they never actually bred amongst the cliffs in the north of the county." However, of the four or five specific references that he managed to glean, the author himself said "none of these records is absolutely definite. The migratory White-tailed Eagle resembles the Golden Eagle so closely in certain stages that *most* of these records *may* refer to the former species."

Witherby *et al* (1943) made no mention of Golden Eagles having occurred in Staffordshire, though he did mention them having been resident in the adjacent county of Derbyshire. Frost (1978) confirms that breeding took place in Derbyshire in 1668 and that fossil remains have also been found in a cave in that county.

All other claims of Golden Eagles in the West Midlands were reviewed by Anthony Harthan and Tony Norris and eventually attributed to having being White-tailed Eagles. The claim for this species' inclusion on the Regional List is therefore extremely slender, but with no fresh evidence on which to base a review we feel obliged to follow the precedent already set.

Osprey *Pandion haliaetus*
Uncommon passage migrant.

Sightings of this splendid raptor have steadily increased in line with the expanding British population.

Ospreys were recorded about 17 times in the nineteenth century and one was reported in 1906, but there were no further sightings until 1953. Then, with the recolonisation of Scotland, records began to increase and *BWM* documented 64 birds in the twenty-six years 1953-78. The steady growth in sightings has continued unabated ever since, with the current period producing no fewer than 296 birds. Indeed, there are suggestions that the rate of increase is rising, with 43 birds in 2000 easily setting a new annual record. Ospreys are now regarded as uncommon, rather than scarce, in the region.

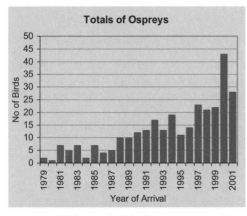

There was a subtle change in the pattern of passage through the West Midlands between 1929-78 and 1979-2001. During the former period, spring and autumn numbers were about equal, but in the latter the spring movement was stronger, with April and May quite clearly the best months. There has also been a tendency for birds to arrive earlier in recent years, with all 13 of the March arrivals occurring since 1993—the earliest being at Aqualate on March 11th 1997. Whether this reflects a response to climate change, or simply increased numbers is a matter for conjecture. One that remained at Packington Park until November 2nd 2001 also set a new record for the latest departure.

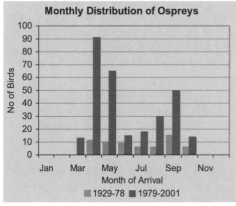

An even geographical distribution might be expected of a species that is moving either northwards or southwards through the region, but in fact there is a distinct bias towards Staffordshire (41% of birds), whilst Warwickshire and Worcestershire have had 28% and 23% respectively and the West Midlands just 8%.

Predictably, most birds are seen at the larger reservoirs, with Blithfield and Belvide perhaps most favoured because of the woodland nearby. Another feature of the records is that they are unusually widespread, with birds having been seen at 113 localities, including several well away from water. This no doubt reflects the ease with which a flying Osprey can be identified.

During the current period, all but two records involved single individuals, with the exceptions being at least two, possibly more, at Trimpley reservoir on October 7th 1981 and two flying north over Belvide Reservoir on April 13th 2001. With a spring bias to the records, it is not surprising that many birds simply fly straight through and almost 80% were recorded on just a single day. Only 9% remained for over a week, but a few of these lingered for some time in late summer, with the longest stays being 23 days, at Tittesworth from July 19th to August 10th 1999; 28 days, in the Middle Tame Valley from July 31st to August 27th 1990; and 35 days, at Blithfield Reservoir from July 24th to August 27th 1985.

Common Kestrel (Kestrel) *Falco tinnunculus*
Fairly common resident.

This is the commonest and most familiar of the region's raptors, occurring in practically every habitat from the northern moors to the lowland valleys and from the city centres to the deepest countryside. Its habit of hovering above open ground, especially along the region's many miles of motorway and roadside verges, also make it the most conspicuous. Voles are its staple diet, but birds and insects are also taken, while in winter especially, many take earthworms from cultivated land.

The *Winter* and *Breeding Atlases* both confirmed the widespread distribution, with records from every 10-km square. Both also showed birds to be most abundant in urban areas, whilst in winter there was a tendency towards higher densities on lower ground. Whether this arose from birds vacating the region's uplands, or whether it indicates immigration from elsewhere is unclear. Surprisingly, preliminary results from the *Tetrad Atlas* work contradict the two BTO *Atlases* by showing the percentage of occupied tetrads in urban areas to be well below that of rural areas. Within the urban fabric many birds nest on commercial or industrial buildings and in locations such as the Birmingham Art Gallery and Museum and the old signal box at Snow Hill station.

Nationally, the population declined by 28% during 1974-99, placing the species on the *Amber Alert* list of Species of Conservation Concern (Gregory *et al.* 2002). From 1980-2002, the CBC/BBS data show a 30% decline nationally, but unfortunately there is insufficient data to compile a regional index. Nevertheless, there is no doubt that the population has declined since 1980, although recent years have shown a slight recovery. Densities, however, vary according to the vole population, which has itself been high in recent years and this might account for any increase. A population range of 2,500-3,500 pairs was suggested in *BWM*, but, based on today's densities, 1,000-1,500 pairs seems more realistic.

Local decreases began to be widely reported in the early 1980s, with smaller clutches and poor fledging success implicated at least once. Yet in areas such as the Malvern Hills, where a record 19 were in the air together on July 27th 1985, numbers appeared to hold up well. Even so, in 1992 it was suggested that in Warwickshire the species was struggling to keep abreast of the Eurasian Sparrowhawk in its abundance, perhaps because of the removal of old trees and buildings. To reinforce this, the Banbury Ornithological Society recorded just one Common Kestrel to 59 Eurasian Sparrowhawks in the Feldon area that year! However, some increases have been reported from here in the last year or two and the mixture of sheep pastures and arable fields now appears to support a good population, with six pairs on 941 ha at Fenny Compton in 1999. The following year 15 birds were hunting this same area along with 13 on *c*900 ha of nearby land between Knightcote, Chapel Ascote and Hodnell. Meanwhile, in Worcestershire, birds were still present in every 10-km square in 1999, if rather scarce in the north-west.

Common Kestrels have become synonymous with the motorway network and during the 1990s the Department of Transport and the Forestry Commission encouraged them by erecting eleven nest-boxes between junctions 12 and 15 of the M40 in Warwickshire. These have proved particularly successful, with 118 nestlings ringed in the eleven years since they were erected. More recently, UK Highways put up further boxes, some of them outside this region, but for various reasons these have not so far been used (M. Tursner *pers. comm.*). As well as exploiting new opportunities, birds can also be very traditional and one site at Roach End has been occupied for over thirty years. Surprisingly little information has been received about food, or behaviour, but a juvenile was noted running after and catching beetles, whilst another individual fed on craneflies at Monkspath in 1984. Following the death of her mate, a female at Packington in 1990 showed signs of mourning, when for a week she became lack lustre and approachable. A party of five seen at dusk in Sheldon were assumed to be going to roost communally.

Common Kestrels, like most birds of prey, are usually ringed as nestlings and records show that a high percentage of the recoveries are less than 100 km from the ringing site. An exceptional movement was that of a bird ringed as a nestling on the Roaches in north Staffordshire in June 1995 and found dead in February 1997 at Deux-Sevres, France, 704 km from its natal site.

Red-footed Falcon   *Falco vespertinus*
Very rare vagrant. Six records.

Four records of Red-footed Falcon were documented in *BWM*, since when there have been two more.

Regional Record Number	County Record Number	Year	Locality, Date and Notes
1	Warks 1	1870	Welford-on-Avon: adult male in June.
2	Warks 2	1967	Middleton Hall: immature male, May 14th-21st. *BB 67:341*
3	Staffs 1	1973	Chasewater: immature male, May 28th to June 6th. *BB 67:319*
4	Staffs 2	1977	Brewood: male, August 23rd. *BB 71:497*
5	Worcs 1	2001	Westwood Pool: adult female, May 15th. *BB 95:490*
6	Warks 3	2003	Wormleighton Reservoir: first-summer male, May 15th. *BB 97:574*

Following three in eleven years (1967-77), it was surprising that twenty-four years passed before the next arrived, especially as this species has become more regular nationally. The 2001 record was the first in Worcestershire and the first known to be a female. Typically for this species, five have appeared in late spring and only one in autumn. Regrettably, the first

West Midlands record is still awaited, as the Chasewater bird in 1973 occurred before the county was constituted in 1974. Part of the area that it frequented was transferred to the new county at that date, but has since been transferred back to Staffordshire. Hence the West Midlands no longer has any claim to this record, either on the basis of the current boundary or that prevailing at the time. In Europe, Red-footed Falcons breed from eastern Hungary into temperate Russia, wintering in south-west Africa.

Merlin   *Falco columbarius*
Uncommon winter visitor. Rare breeding species on the northern moors.

The smallest of our falcons, the agile Merlin is essentially a bird of open moorland, where it makes dashing flights just above the ground, twisting and turning to follow the contours as it pursues its quarry. A tiny population breeds on the moors of north Staffordshire, where Meadow Pipits and Sky Larks are the most frequently taken prey. After the breeding season, Merlins move to lower ground for the winter and this brings immigrants into the region, where they frequent heaths, reservoirs, gravel pits or almost any open habitat where there are flocks of small birds. In recent times they have also taken to wintering on arable farmland.

The North Staffordshire Moors are at the southern extremity of the breeding range and breeding is sporadic. Smith (1938) thought it attempted to breed every year. In more recent times, however, a nesting pair in 1972 was the first for about fourteen years and this was followed by further breeding in 1974, whilst three pairs were present in 1978. This suggested annual nesting, though probably not more than two pairs a year (*BWM*). Breeding since has been more sporadic, with the 1980s an especially lean time, but an improved situation in the 1990s. Overall, probable or confirmed breeding was reported in eight of the twenty-three years 1979-2001, mostly single pairs, but with two in 1993 (when one pair was robbed), 1995 and 1999 and three confirmed breeding pairs in 1992 (when the RSPB undertook a comprehensive survey) and again in 1994.

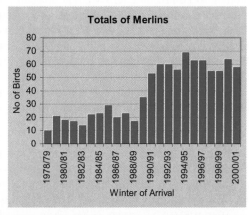

Outside the breeding season, there are no autumn or spring peaks to indicate that birds are passing through the region. Instead, Merlins are most numerous from October to March, suggesting that the majority are genuine wintering birds. Since many are seen only on a single day, it is assumed that a large proportion of individuals wander around, but at least a few establish winter territories where they remain for some time. One or two places have even become regular wintering sites, notably the Wishaw-Wiggins Hill area where two or three have been present every winter from 1991/2 until at least 2000/1. This discovery was the first indication that Merlins were to be found on open, arable land. Others have since been discovered in similar farmland situations, such as in the Fenny Compton area since about 1995. It is interesting that this ap-

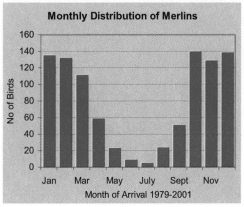

parently newly acquired habit coincided with a sudden leap in numbers during the early 1990s, from around 25 a year to approximately 60 a year.

The *Winter Atlas* showed birds in 23% of the 10-km squares, with a particular concentration in the areas of Cannock Chase and the Trent and Tame Valley. Geographically, Staffordshire, with 37% of birds, is the most frequently visited county, followed by Worcestershire (29%), Warwickshire (24%) and the West Midlands (10%). Apart from the locations already mentioned, occasional birds are noted on the moors throughout the year, whilst the major reservoirs such as Belvide, Blithfield and Draycote are usually visited once or twice each winter.

A juvenile male which died after flying into a window at Weston-under-Wetherley on August 17th 1993 had been ringed as a nestling in County Durham on July 1st—a movement of 264 km within six weeks of being in the nest.

Hobby *Falco subbuteo*
Frequent and increasing summer resident and passage migrant.

The aerial acrobatics of this splendid little falcon are now a regular summer sight, particularly in the south and east of the region. Pairs often take over an old crows nest, frequently in some remote, out-of-sight corner of farmland and preferably in an area of pasture or mixed farmland rather than arable land. They feed mainly on insects and small birds, paying regular visits to the region's wetlands to catch dragonflies, but turning more to small birds once their eggs hatch and there are young to be fed. Hunting frequently takes place at dusk.

Numbers have increased significantly since the late 1970s, when just four pairs were thought to be breeding (*BWM*). The *Breeding Atlas* showed birds in 69% of 10-km squares, with absences only from the high ground of the Moors and Dales of north Staffordshire, the Teme Valley and parts of Arden. The distribution is still broadly the same today, with 34% of birds occurring in Worcestershire, 32% in Warwickshire, 20% in Staffordshire and 14% in the West Midlands. Breeding is recorded most years in every county, but with Warwickshire seemingly having most pairs.

Assessing the actual population is extremely difficult, as records of confirmed or probable breeding almost certainly under-state the true breeding strength due to the retiring habits of nesting birds. There are also differences between the figures published in WMBC *Annual Reports* and the RBBP reports (Ogilvie *et al.* 1999-2003). Taking the latter figures, which, over the period 1997-2001 were the higher of the two, produces an average of 38 pairs a year, but the RBBP generally acknowledges its figures to be under-estimates. Clements (2001) suggested a figure for the British population that was approximately three times that indicated in the RBBP reports and if this factor is applied to the West Midlands then the regional population would be around 110-120 pairs.

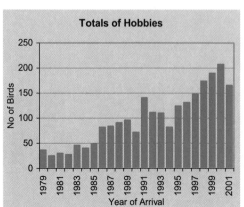

Totals of Hobbies

Year of Arrival

Clements went further and estimated the population for each 100-km square, which, taking the proportions of squares SJ, SK, SO and SP that fall within the West Midlands would give an estimated 176 pairs.

So far though, this region has not experienced the large pre-breeding concentrations reported elsewhere and this might indicate lower densities here. It seems more likely, therefore, that the current population is between 50-150 pairs—a range more in line with the annual totals being reported.

Hobbies arrive from their southern African

winter quarters during April and May. Over 33 years, the average date of first arrivals was April 21st, but during 1992-2001 it advanced to April 13th. Most birds depart during September, but a few stragglers linger into October with average last dates of October 4th over 36 years, but October 13th during 1992-2001. The extreme dates were March 17th, at Doxey Marshes in 1986, and October 30th, at Wyken Slough in 1994, but the former was exceptionally early with the next earliest date being April 4th, in 1987 and 1993.

Any large gatherings of birds will often attract a hunting Hobby and they frequently prey on flocks of Common Swifts, martins and Barn Swallows as they feed over water. Roosts of the latter two also provide easy pickings for juvenile birds as they learn to hunt in autumn. In addition, birds have been seen preying on a wader at Belvide Reservoir in 1990 and chasing moths. They are also partial to bats (Cramp *et al.* 1974-94) and one was observed well after dark attempting to catch bats in the lights of a public house car park at Furnace End in 1991. Such an exploit might explain why yet another individual, near Middleton in 1987, sought refuge in a tree to escape being mobbed by a medium-sized bat.

Hobbies are not uncommon visitors to urban sites, with individuals being seen to take a Common Swift at Sheepwash Urban Park and catch dragonflies at Fens Pools. Nor are they averse to visiting the high moorlands of north Staffordshire, despite generally being considered a lowland species. Indeed, one was in the company of a male Merlin at Swallow Moss in May 1993 and another chased a Common Kestrel at Rudyard in August of that year. The only recovery during the current period was of a bird ringed as a pullus in south-west Warwickshire in July 1980 and found dead locally in July 1983.

Gyr Falcon   *Falco rusticolus*
Very rare vagrant, no recent records.

The only records are the two historical ones quoted in *BWM*.

Regional Record Number	County Record Number	Year	Locality, Date and Notes
1	Staffs 1	Prior to 1844	Beaudesert Old Park: unknown date, shot (Garner 1844).
2	Warks 1	1852	Quinton: unknown date, shot.

Smith (1938) also mentioned a bird shot at Biddulph in October 1865, which was perhaps of this species, though efforts to trace it had proved in vain. Given that the identification was apparently uncertain, this record was not included in *BWM*.

The Gyr Falcon has a circumpolar Arctic breeding distribution. The populations in Iceland, Fennoscandia and Russia are largely resident, but those in northern Canada and Greenland are strongly migratory and most birds that occur in Britain are of the white form *F. r. candicans*, which predominates there (Dymond *et al.* 1989).

Peregrine Falcon   (Peregrine)   *Falco peregrinus*
Frequent winter visitor and passage migrant. Scarce breeding species.

This spectacular species goes from strength to strength. In this region it is best known as a passage migrant and winter visitor, usually to areas where potential prey congregates, such as the larger reservoirs, gravel pits and flood meadows. At night birds often roost in trees, or on pylons and other tall, man-made structures, such as cooling towers and churches. With the absence of natural cliffs, the small breeding population tends to be focussed on the rock faces of quarries or on tall structures such as cooling towers and telecommunication masts.

Peregrine Falcons suffered badly from the effects of organochlorine insecticides and their population crashed during the late 1950s and early 1960s (Ratcliffe 1963). Once these chemicals were banned, however, numbers began to recover slowly, from just two or three a winter in the 1970s to 28 in 1984/5. Even so, the *Winter Atlas* only recorded birds in four 10-km squares. An incredible increase then followed, such that little more than a dec-

ade later over 100 were regularly being reported each winter and this level has been sustained ever since. Indeed, with so many records, precise totals cannot be ascertained. Although the increase came in the wake of breeding being established in Derbyshire and at Symonds Yat (Gloucestershire), its scale was such that other sources must also have been involved.

Post-breeding dispersal brings a strong arrival in August, many of them immature birds and a steady influx then ensues until December. Thereafter the number of fresh arrivals gradually wanes, with no evidence of a spring passage.

As a breeding species the Peregrine Falcon has but a brief history. Smith (1938) considered it had probably nested in Staffordshire and Norris knew of one Warwickshire record, in 1892.

During the *Breeding Atlas* (1988-91), it was recorded in five 10-km squares, with probable breeding in one moorland square. The first definite breeding record for Staffordshire then fol-

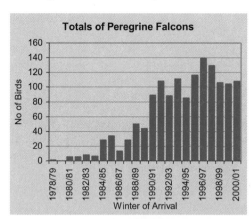

lowed in 1992, since when possible breeding birds have been reported somewhere in the region in every year except 1998. Numbers remain small, however, usually just a pair or two, but there were five probable nesting pairs in 1997 (though in one of these the female was found dead in her nest) and four in 2001.

In Worcestershire, birds were first noted in the breeding season in 1992, but it was 1996 before breeding was confirmed for the first time. This was quickly followed in 1999 by the first positive proof of breeding from the West Midlands county, in Birmingham city centre. In Warwickshire, a pair bred in a northern quarry in 2001 and 2002—the first confirmed breeding in the county since the pair at Warwick Castle in 1892.

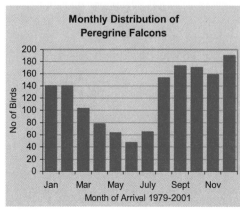

Tall buildings and structures are an obvious attraction and in some instances birds, or even pairs, have taken up residence on these for considerable periods of time—a trend that began at Meaford Power Station in 1985 before subsequently spreading to Hams Hall and more recently Worcester Cathedral, where a pair remained throughout 2001. One also took a liking to the spire of Lichfield Cathedral in 1994, whilst another roost site in recent winters has been the tower of St Mary's Church in

Warwick. Elsewhere, a summering female at Upton Warren roosted on the nearby radio transmitter masts, whilst at least one other bird summered at the Birmingham University campus, where the clock tower acts as a vantage point.

Birds are also regularly seen outside the breeding season at reservoirs and gravel pits. The bulk occur in Staffordshire (42%), with 27% in Worcestershire, 21% in Warwickshire and 10% in the West Midlands. At Belvide Reservoir, for example, at least 15 different individuals were reported in 1999, while at least one regularly attends Blithfield in the autumn—effectively emptying the reservoir of waders, much to the annoyance of some birders!

Water Rail   *Rallus aquaticus*
Frequent winter visitor and uncommon resident.

Water Rails spend most of their time skulking amongst the thick vegetation and muddy edges of reedbeds, marshy pools and slow-flowing streams. In winter they also venture onto wet fields and along ditches with emergent vegetation.

The BTO *Atlases* show birds to have been present in 62% of the 10-km squares during the winter and 27% during the breeding season, with nesting confirmed or suspected in 16%. During 1979-2001 as a whole, around ten pairs per annum definitely or probably bred, but the second half of this period was the more productive, with around 14 pairs a year after 1989. This increase was due almost entirely to one site, the SWT reserve at Doxey Marshes, which accounted for almost two-thirds of all the breeding records in that period. Two or three pairs were reported here in 1987, but this rose to 12 pairs in the early 1990s and a peak of 15 pairs in 1997. Since then numbers have varied considerably, but have mostly been in double figures.

The two other regular breeding sites are Brandon Marsh and Upton Warren. At Brandon birds probably bred in seventeen years during 1979-2001 and there were eight territories in 1982 and 1983, though subsequently four to six have been more usual. In the same period breeding was recorded in fifteen years at Upton Warren, where one or two pairs were the norm, but as many as three, or possibly even four, were noted on occasions.

Water Rails by no means shun the urban environment and, within the Black Country, a pair bred at Clayhanger in 1986 and others probably did so at Mushroom Green Marsh in 1990, Clayhanger again in 1995, Buckpool in 1998 and Sandwell Valley in 2001. In addition to these breeding records, at least half-a-dozen birds summer most years, mostly in Warwickshire, and sporadic breeding is occasionally reported. Based on this recent evidence, the breeding estimate in *BWM* of just 3-20 pairs perhaps needs revising upwards to between 15 and 30 pairs. With roughly half of these at a single site, however, the population must be regarded as vulnerable and liable to fall again at any time.

Outside the breeding season, small numbers up to 10 are reported from around thirty to forty sites most years, although this varies with the weather. In a hard winter, such as that in 1982, when large areas are frozen over, many birds forsake the region altogether and search for milder places. The geographical spread of wintering sites has been fairly even, with 29% in Worcestershire, 27% in Warwickshire, 26% in Staffordshire and 18% in the West Midlands. The biggest numbers occur between October and December as continental migrants mingle with local birds for the winter. Again weather is a significant factor,

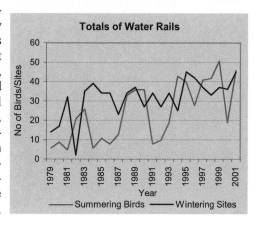

with more birds arriving when Europe is in the grip of freezing temperatures. The largest concentrations all occurred at Ladywalk, where 20 were recorded every autumn from 1999 to 2002. Elsewhere, there were 15 at Upton Warren in 1996 and 12 at Doxey Marshes in 1992. Within the built-up area, half-a-dozen or so regularly wintered at Mushroom Green Marsh from 1989-98, with an impressive peak for an urban site of 10 in 1990.

In the winter months, the species is also a regular visitor to feeding stations, especially at the WMBC's reserve at Ladywalk. Aggressive behaviour is by no means uncommon in such situations and one was seen to kill a female Brambling at Upton Warren in 1987. Water Rails are secretive birds that are seldom caught and ringed. Their capacity to move long distances, however, is well illustrated by an adult that was ringed at Stubbers Green in October 1982 and shot the following month in Vendee, France, 677 km from its ringing site.

Spotted Crake *Porzana porzana*
Rare passage migrant and winter visitor. Has bred.

The Spotted Crake is a secretive visitor to the region's reedbeds and marshy wetlands, almost invariably on passage and usually in autumn. In recent years it has become slightly more frequent, but this might simply mean more are being detected. The British breeding population is very small, so the majority occurring in this region are probably on their way to or from their continental breeding grounds. Birds occasionally occur in winter, with records from this region between December and February (*BWM*), but most European birds winter in east Africa.

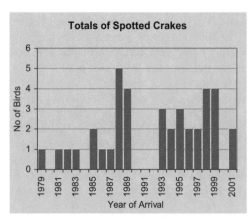

Totals of Spotted Crakes

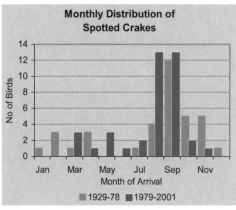

Monthly Distribution of Spotted Crakes

Between 1947-78 there were 36 birds reported (*BWM*)—an average of about one a year. Appearances continued at a similar rate from 1979-87, with eight in nine years, but the fourteen years 1988-2001 produced 31 birds—an average of just over two per annum. The sole breeding record came from Sutton Park around 1880 (not 1886 as stated in *BWM*). One or two records have concerned birds calling at night, but the only slight hint of possible breeding came from Staffordshire in 1989, when one was seen on eight occasions between June 10th and August 18th, but without any sign of a mate or young.

There have been two notable changes in the monthly distribution of records. Firstly, there has been only one winter arrival (in November 1988) compared to ten between November and February during 1929-78. It seems, therefore, that the species' status as a winter visitor is getting progressively more tenuous. Secondly, there have been more birds in spring (eight during March-June) compared to 1929-78, when there were just four. Notwithstanding this, the 'autumn' passage remains much the stronger, but there are now as many in August as in September, but fewer in October.

All records during 1979-2001 referred to single birds, except for two at Doxey Marshes from September 1st-5th 1993 and a possible second bird at Ufton Fields on September 6th 1998, which was only glimpsed briefly. The geographical spread was fairly even, with Staffordshire and Warwickshire each having 28% of birds, West Midlands 26% and, rather surprisingly, Worcestershire only 18%. The most productive sites were Sandwell Valley (six birds), Doxey Marshes (five) and Brandon Marsh and Upton Warren (four each). Of the fifteen other sites visited, none had more than two birds.

Sadly, Spotted Crakes often end up as casualties, with several old records referring to birds found dead beneath overhead wires, but happily only one since 1979 concerned a corpse.

Little Crake *Porzana parva*
Very rare vagrant. One record.

The only record remains that documented in *BWM*, namely:

Regional Record Number	County Record Number	Year	Locality, Date and Notes
1	Warks 1	1974	Ladywalk: adult male, November 7th to December 12th. *BB 68:315*

Breeding in central and eastern Europe and wintering in east Africa, Little Crakes are rare visitors to Britain, with just over a hundred records (Rogers *et al.* 2004). November is a typical month for birds to arrive (Dymond *et al.* 1989).

Corn Crake (Corncrake) *Crex crex*
Rare passage migrant, formerly bred.

The likelihood of seeing or hearing a Corn Crake in the West Midlands is now extremely slim.

In the 1930s and 1940s, the hay meadows of the lower Avon and Severn valleys were a well-known haunt, but, as elsewhere, birds fell victim to agricultural change, when mechanised mowing earlier in the season destroyed nests and young. The last confirmed nesting occurred in the 1960s, at Wick in 1967 and Chesterton in 1968 and 1969 (*BWM*).

Since then appearances have gradually become fewer, with the only hint of nesting coming from east Staffordshire, where birds were present at the same site from 1978-80, with three calling males in the latter year. Otherwise birds were seen or heard in five years during the 1980s, with as many as six in 1980 and five in 1988. By comparison, the 1990s produced only one record, of a bird heard at Packington Park on July 8th and 9th 1994,

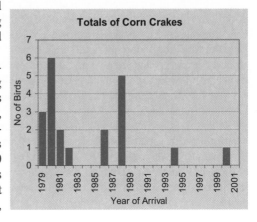

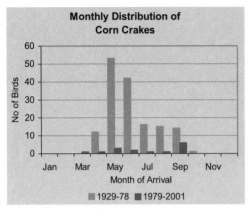

Monthly Distribution of Corn Crakes

No of Birds / Month of Arrival

■ 1929-78 ■ 1979-2001

while the most recent record concerned one flushed from a cereal field during harvesting at Clifford Chambers in September 2000.

All records since 1979 have fallen between March and September, with the majority in the latter month. One at Longsdon Mill on March 25th 1986 was the earliest ever reported in the region, apart from an unusual winter record in January 1908. Given the species' traditional affinity with the Avon and Severn valleys, it is interesting that 67% of the birds since 1979 were in Staffordshire, with the rest being shared between Worcestershire (19%) and Warwickshire (14%).

Moorhen   *Gallinula chloropus*
Very common resident.

Moorhens inhabit virtually every stretch of lowland water, from the tiniest of streams and farm ponds to the largest rivers and reservoirs. Nests are built wherever there is emergent vegetation or lush bankside cover. Although resident pairs defend their territories throughout the year, in winter birds often gather in small groups to feed on open fields and patches of short grass, especially when ditches and streams are frozen.

There were records from every 10-km square during both *Atlas* surveys, with abundance levels above average everywhere except the moors and dales, the Teme valley and the fringes of the Cotswolds. Here the fast-flowing rivers and streams generally provide insufficient food and cover to meet the species' needs, although 46 territories were found along 57 km of the River Teme back in 1979 (*BWM*).

Moorhens are sedentary and, except when they exhibit aggressive behaviour towards another species, they seldom receive more than a cursory glance. Furthermore their wide, but sparse, distribution means there are few studies of population trends and densities. The CBC/BBS index provides some guide, but does not focus specifically on their aquatic haunts. Moreover the regional sample is too small to identify trends. The hard winters of 1979 and 1982 caused significant losses, but these were gradually made good and nationally the CBC/BBS index showed little overall change during 1980-2002, whilst the WBS showed a modest 12% growth between 1986 and 2002.

Most local information is subjective rather than quantitative and includes references to reduced numbers as a result of predation by mink or competition from the expanding Common Coot population. For instance, in the early 1990s a fall to just five pairs from an average of 10-20 pairs at Doxey Marshes was put down to mink. Numbers here have since recovered to around 20 pairs. Nests are also prone to predation by Carrion Crows and mammals too if water levels drop low enough to make nests accessible. For their part, Moorhens themselves are avid egg thieves, plundering the nests of waders and terns. In 1999 one was seen to eat a clutch of Common Redshank's eggs at Upton Warren.

Recent data on densities include 11 pairs on 941 ha of farmland around Fenny Compton, where there are several farm ponds, and 14 pairs along a 9 km stretch of the Worcester and Birmingham canal compared to 15 territories along a different 6 km stretch in 1982. The first of these examples is a very high density, however, which is unlikely to be representative of the region as a whole. Taking account of all available data, the regional population probably lies between 15,000-20,000 territories rather than in excess of 20,000 pairs as suggested in *BWM*.

Birds are not shy to exploit urban situations and several pairs can be found nesting around park lakes or along rivers and canals in built-up areas. They also visit feeding stations and one at Kingsbury Water Park actually clambered up a small bush to get to a suspended tit feeder.

Most groups comprise less than 20 birds, but *BWM* remarks that concentrations outside the breeding season can be large and this remains true, although none in recent times has come near the 550 at Blackbrook Sewage Farm in 1956. In fact, apart from September counts at Belvide of 200 in 1979 and 100 or so in the following two years, no gathering has reached three figures, with the most elsewhere being 68 at Brandon Marsh and 65 at Alvecote Pools.

Common Coot   *Fulica atra*
Fairly common resident, common in winter.

The Common Coot is one of our most numerous and widespread waterfowl, nesting around lakes, flooded gravel pits, reservoirs and less often along slow-flowing rivers and canals, even within urban areas. It prefers shallow, nutrient-rich waters, where it dives to feed from vegetation at the bottom. Numbers are swollen considerably by immigrants from north-west Europe in winter, when large flocks form, mostly in the Middle Tame Valley and at the larger reservoirs.

The distribution remains much the same as that described in *BWM*. During the *Breeding Atlas* it was recorded in 94% of 10-km squares, but was noticeably absent from areas such as the Dales, Moors and Teme Valley, where there are few large pools and the rivers and streams are fast-flowing. Across most of the region it occurred at well above average abundance, but was less numerous in southern Warwickshire and Worcestershire, again because there is less standing water.

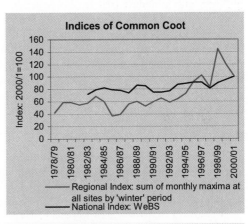

The *Winter Atlas* showed a slightly wider distribution, with birds in 96% of 10-km squares. Indeed, they were absent only from the Moors and Dales. Winter flocks gradually disperse during February and March as immigrants return to the Continent and resident birds return to their breeding territories.

Information on breeding numbers is sparse and somewhat contradictory, but it does highlight some significant declines. At Belvide numbers fell from a peak of 110 pairs in 1979 to 40 by 1982, probably because of lower water levels. Since then numbers have fluctuated widely, but seldom exceeded 20 pairs. At Alvecote Pools they fell from 15 pairs in 1980 to around five in the late 1990s, whilst at Brandon Marsh they dropped from 20-30 pairs in the late 1970s to about 10 pairs in the 1990s. On the other hand, the breeding population at Doxey Marshes has virtually doubled to around 20 pairs since the early 1980s and Upton Warren appears to have experienced a similar increase over the same period. Moreover, there are now many new waters to provide a wider choice of nest sites. However,

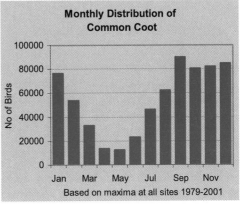

recent evidence points to poor breeding success, with for instance 18 pairs producing only 16 young at two sites in Warwickshire during 2002, partly because of the predation of eggs and chicks. Overall there is little evidence to suggest any significant change from the population of 1,000-2,200 pairs suggested in *BWM*, though it may currently be towards the lower end of this range.

Large late-summer moulting flocks were also a feature at Belvide, with a peak of over 2,000 in 1980, but these too declined shortly afterwards when low water levels reduced the available food supply and coverings of blanket weed made it less accessible. However, as the regional index shows, winter numbers have generally increased, particularly since the forma-tion of the Coton and Lea Marston lakes in 1980/1. During 1996/7-2000/1 especially, the an-nual peak numbers both in the Middle Tame Valley and at Blithfield Reservoir averaged 1,760, rendering both sites of national importance for this species.

The build-up of numbers starts in late summer, as birds begin to gather at favoured feeding and moulting sites, and peaks during September-November as new arrivals flood in from as far away as Fennoscandia and Russia. After the end of January they then tail away quickly until, by the end of March, only potential breeding birds remain. Common Coots spend much of their time grazing and tend to favour sites such as Blithfield Reservoir and Draycote Water, which have adjacent expanses of grass. Although many birds leave the region in cold weather (*BWM*), a small minority, probably our resident birds, are reluctant to go.

During 1991/2-2000/1 five sites stood out as holding high concentrations of Common Coot. The Middle Tame Valley was most important, with 11% of all birds, followed by Blith-field Reservoir, Draycote Water and Chasewater with 7% each, and Belvide Reservoir with 6%. As a result, Staffordshire, with 51%, and Warwickshire, with 36%, held the vast majority of birds, with a modest 10% in Worcestershire and just 3% in the West Midlands. The largest flock mentioned in *BWM* was that of 2,050 at Belvide in August 1980 referred to above, but since then there have been 2,200 at Draycote in October 1997 and a record 2,305 at Blithfield in September 1998. Indeed, the autumn of 1998 brought exceptional numbers to the region, with counts implying numbers some 75% above average. However, it seems likely that there was considerable movement between sites. Other notable counts include 950 at Shustoke Res-ervoir in November 1983, 1,020 at Aqualate Mere in November 1984 and 1,710 at Coton and Lea Marston in December 1988.

Common Coot are remarkably mobile birds with 45% of all ringing recoveries showing movements of over 50 km. Most birds have been ringed during the winter months and recov-eries showed them in summer quarters during the following or subsequent seasons in Shrop-shire, Northamptonshire, Derbyshire, Nottinghamshire and Anglesey. Our only foreign recov-ery was for an adult ringed at Blithfield Reservoir in December 1973. This bird was found dead in Loiret, France, in April 1974.

Common Crane   *Grus grus*
Rare vagrant.

The table opposite shows that, of the eleven records to date, eight have occurred since 1979— all of them during typical passage periods. Seven of the eight were in spring, between March 13th and June 6th, with five of these being in Staffordshire. The sole autumn record involved the splendid spectacle of six birds flying south over Ladywalk in October 2000.

A crane, calling as it flew west over Draycote Water on February 9th 2001, was probably this species, though unfortunately the light was too poor for the similar Demoiselle Crane, which occasionally occurs as an escapee, to be eliminated.

Common Cranes nest very sparingly in Norfolk, but otherwise breed in Fennoscandia and eastern Europe and winter in Spain and Africa.

Regional Record Number	County Record Number		Year	Locality, Date and Notes
1	W Mid	1	1903	Knowle: pair, December 1st, shot, believed wild.
2	Staffs	1	1971	Blithfield Reservoir: October 1st, circled over. *BB 65:331*
3	Warks	1	1977	Welford-on-Avon: three, two adults and an immature, January 3rd to February 13th. *BB 71:498*
4	Staffs	2	1979	Belvide Reservoir: May 5th. *BB 73:504*
5	Staffs	3	1983	Rudyard Reservoir: two, May 26th, flying N into Cheshire. *BB 82:520*
6	Staffs	4	1990	Rudyard Reservoir: April 1st, flying SE.
7	Staffs	5	1991	Belvide Reservoir: two, April 25th-26th, left to SW.
8	Worcs	1	1999	Childswickham: immature, March 13th. Same, relocated Kinsham, 20th-21st.
9	Staffs	6	2000	Blithfield Reservoir: adult, March 25th, circled over. Same later over Cannock Chase.
10	Warks	2	2000	Ladywalk: six, October 19th, flew S at dusk, not relocated next day.
11	Warks	3	2002	Packington Ford and Tip: adult, June 6th.
	W Mid	2		Same, National Exhibition Centre: June 6th.

Note: BBRC ceased to consider records of this species as from January 1st 1988.

Little Bustard   *Tetrax tetrax*
Very rare vagrant. Two or three historical records.

The only records are those listed in *BWM*, namely:

Regional Record Number	County Record Number		Year	Locality, Date and Notes
1	W Mid	1	Pre 1893	Birchfield: unknown date, shot.
2	Staffs	1	c1899	Warslow: unknown date, shot. *BB 2:148*

Another, at Thickbroom, near Tamworth, sometime before 1886 was placed in square brackets by Norris (*BWM*), implying some uncertainty about its acceptance.

Little Bustards breed in France, Iberia, north-west Africa and eastwards through southern Europe to Kazakstan, but are rare visitors to Britain.

Great Bustard   *Otis tarda*
Very rare vagrant. One historical record.

Great Bustards bred in Britain until the early nineteenth century and attempts are currently being made to reintroduce them onto Salisbury Plain. The only record is that listed in *BWM*, namely:

Regional Record Number	County Record Number		Year	Locality, Date and Notes
1	Worcs	1	Pre 1828	Near Worcester: unknown date a few years prior to 1828, shot.

Oystercatcher   *Haematopus ostralegus*

Frequent passage migrant. Scarce winter visitor and breeding species, the latter mainly in the Trent and Tame Valleys.

Traditionally Oystercatchers nest around the coast or on northern uplands, but in recent years they have begun to spread into lowland river valleys, where they nest at sand and gravel quarries or reservoirs. Increasing numbers also appear on passage in the same situations during spring, autumn and occasionally winter.

Initial colonisation of the region appeared to emanate from the North Sea coast via the Trent Valley. Breeding was first confirmed at Branston in 1970, although circumstantial evidence suggested birds may have bred at Draycote Water the year before. Regular nesting then began along the Trent and Tame Valleys in 1979. Colonisation was slow, however, with two pairs in 1979 increasing to around three throughout the 1980s and eventually building to perhaps five or six pairs during the 1990s. Many early breeding attempts also met with mixed success. For example, whilst pairs at Branston and Elford managed to raise one or two young most years, at Kingsbury Water Park nesting was attempted in 1983, but it was another ten years before successful breeding was confirmed there.

Away from the Trent and Tame Valleys, breeding was attempted in Worcestershire at Bredon's Hardwick in 1993, but Herring Gulls predated the nest. Eventually this site produced the county's first breeding success in 1997, but in 1999 two nests, one here and one at Upton Warren, were both lost to flooding. It seems likely that this colonisation arose from birds moving inland from the Bristol Channel and evidence of penetration even further along the Avon Valley came from Salford Priors Gravel Pit, where a pair nested successfully in 2001. Outside the major river systems, pairs bred successfully for the first time at Coldmeece in 1997 and The Somers, Belvide Reservoir and Blithfield Reservoir in 1999, with summering birds or failed nesting attempts at several other places. Among the causes of the latter, Carrion Crows took young from a nest at Belvide and an adult was killed by a car on the causeway at Blithfield. Overall, in both 2000 and 2001 there were seven successful breeding pairs.

With the onset of inland nesting, the number of birds coming into or through the region has perhaps increased tenfold from around 40 a year during 1969-78 (*BWM*), although it is no longer possible to determine precise numbers. There were almost certainly over 400 in 2000, which was a record year.

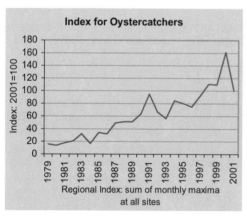

Index for Oystercatchers

Index: 2001=100

Regional Index: sum of monthly maxima at all sites

Comparing the monthly distribution with that in *BWM* shows some significant changes. To begin with, both the passage periods have advanced, with the protracted spring passage now beginning in early February and continuing through to May. During this time two different populations are probably involved, with British birds, including those nesting locally, arriving in February and March, whilst those coming later are on their way to more northerly situations. Secondly, *BWM* said birds

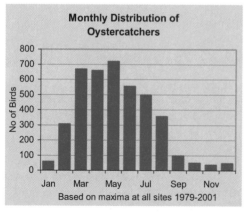

Monthly Distribution of Oystercatchers

No of Birds

Jan   Mar   May   Jul   Sep   Nov

Based on maxima at all sites 1979-2001

were equally divided between the spring and autumn passage, but spring passage is now very definitely the dominant one, with 56% of birds occurring during February-May compared with just 23% between July and September.

Thirdly, significant numbers are now being recorded in June. As local populations alone are too small to account for the numbers involved, some must be passage birds. With earlier spring movements and reduced numbers in August (*cf. BWM*), these are probably adult birds, whilst juveniles are now following in July rather than August.

Most birds pass through singly, or perhaps in pairs, and seldom stay long, but larger groups do occasionally appear. The largest mentioned in *BWM* was 17, at Belvide in March 1965, but this has since been exceeded on four occasions, with a maximum of 24 at DM Kineton on October 31st 1991. Reports during the September-January period remain unusual, amounting to nine or ten birds a year—or just 7% of all dated records. Many of these appear to be hard weather movements, as they refer to birds standing on ice and, in one instance, to an individual seen on the moors in freezing conditions. Other records have referred to birds heard calling overhead at night. There is still little hard evidence as to where our birds come from, apart from that mentioned in *BWM* of a bird ringed at Heacham (Norfolk) and recovered six-months later at Minworth.

Two-thirds of the birds recorded during the ten years 1992-2001 occurred in Staffordshire, 19% in Warwickshire, 11% in Worcestershire and 5% in the West Midlands. The vast majority of these (44%) were seen in the Trent and Tame Valleys, where the principal sites, in descending order of importance, were Elford, Croxall, Dosthill-Kingsbury, Barton and Branston. Elsewhere the most notable sites were Blithfield Reservoir (7% of birds), Belvide Reservoir (6%) and Bredon's Hardwick (5%).

In 1983, a bird at Eccleshall followed children into school and inspected their shoes while a WMBC member gave a talk on the species. It was later released at Doxey Marshes, where it associated with anglers and a working party erecting a hide before finally moving to a Stafford car park.

Black-winged Stilt   *Himantopus himantopus*
Very rare vagrant. Six records.

Since the first record in 1968, which is documented in *BWM*, there have been a further five occurrences of this elegant wader.

Regional Record Number	County Record Number		Year	Locality, Date and Notes
1	Staffs	1	1968	Belvide Reservoir: June 11th-16th. *BB 62:470*
2	Worcs	1	1986	Larford: first-summer, June 14th-16th. *BB 81:555*
3	Warks	1	1987	Alvecote Pools: pair, May 28th to June 4th. *BB 82:521*
4	Staffs	2	1987	Belvide Reservoir: two juveniles, September 1st-7th. *BB 81:555*
5	Staffs	3	1991	Croxall GP: male, April 28th to May 13th. *BB 85:522*
6	Staffs	4	1995	Blithfield Reservoir: two, May 11th. *BB 90:468*

Black-winged Stilts breed widely across southern Europe, but they depend on the right water levels. In very dry years, they may abandon their traditional haunts and wander further north, perhaps as far as Britain, in search of more suitable conditions (Gibbons *et al.* 1993). This is reflected by the above records, five of which occurred in spring. Indeed, the Alvecote

Pools birds were seen to copulate, although it was believed that at least one of the pair had not reached maturity. The sole autumn record of two juveniles at Belvide Reservoir in 1987 was thought to involve the progeny of a pair which bred in Norfolk—the first successful nesting in Britain since 1945. The Croxall individual was probably that seen at Dunstable (Bedfordshire) on April 26th and 27th (Rogers *et al.* 1992).

Avocet   *Recurvirostra avosetta*
Rare passage migrant. Has recently bred.

In recent years, with the expanding British breeding population, this most elegant of waders has become a more frequent visitor to the region's wetlands.

The first ever record was of eight birds at Aqualate Mere back in the 17th century (Plot 1686), but there were only two 19th century records and none in the 20th century until 1958. From 1958 to 2001, 96 birds were recorded, 56% of them during the period 1979-2001. As the chart shows, however, annual numbers varied considerably from year-to-year, with none at all in nine years, but 10 in both 1984 and 1996. The larger flocks were a superb party of nine displaying at Ladywalk on April 26th-27th 1999, six in the Potteries at Westport Lake on March 24th 1984, and five at Draycote Water on May 19th 1996. Otherwise, there was one party of three, with the rest appearing just in ones and twos. With five records, Draycote has also been the most visited site.

The spring passage lasts from March to May and is far and away the stronger of the two, with that in autumn being quite a weak affair. Comparing the two periods 1929-78 and 1979-2001, there has been a noticeable rise in March records (even allowing for the flock of six mentioned above). This is probably a reflection of the increasing numbers wintering in Britain and then making an early return to their breeding grounds. The earliest regional spring record came from Draycote Water on March 9th 1991. The main feature of the autumn passage has been three late birds, two in November and one in December, with the latter—at Barton Gravel Pit on December 3rd 1995—the latest ever in the region.

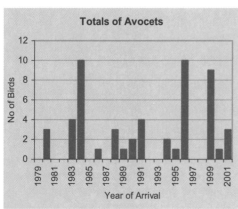

Visits by Avocets are generally brief, with two-thirds of all birds departing on the same day as they arrived. However, 10% stayed at least a week, with the longest stays being 10 days at Blithfield Reservoir from August 14th-23rd 1990 and 11 days at Grimley from April 11th-21st 2000.

Birds were reported from 21 sites during 1979-2001, with the vast majority being seen in Warwickshire (48%) and Staffordshire (36%). Despite its southerly location, Worcestershire had only 12%, while the West Midlands accounted for just 4%. However, in 2003 Worcestershire received more than adequate compensation for its lack of records with the region's first breeding record, when a pair successfully raised four young at Upton Warren. Inland breeding records are most unusual, but the brine that seeps into the lagoons at this site might just provide the level of salinity that the species requires. At the time of writing it would appear that successful breeding has occurred again in 2004 and it will be interesting to see whether nesting becomes a regular feature in the future.

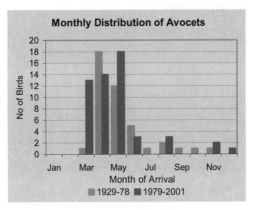

Stone Curlew   (Stone-curlew)   *Burhinus oedicnemus*
Rare vagrant.

Hastings (1834) wrote of the Stone Curlew "that a few pairs bred among the stony barren parts of the Broadway and Bredon Hills", but it is thought breeding ceased soon after 1840. Eight definite records were then listed in *BWM*—three of them in the first half of the twentieth century. There were then none between 1956 and 1991, since when there have been four.

Regional Record Number	County Record Number		Year	Locality, Date and Notes
1	Worcs	1	Unknown	Eardiston: two, killed on unknown date(s) prior to 20th Century.
2	Worcs	2	1834	Twyning: juvenile on unknown date, caught alive .
3	Warks	1	1847	Wilmcote: October 19th, taken.
4	Warks	2	1853	Weston-on-Avon: January 1st, shot.
5	W Mid	1	1861	Sutton Coldfield: unknown day in May.
6	W Mid	2	1927	Harborne: August 9th.
7	W Mid	3	1952	Handsworth: May 3rd.
8	Staffs	1	1956	Blackbrook SW: December 28th.
9	Worcs W Mid	3 4	1991	Frankley Reservoir: May 6th. Same, Bartley Reservoir: May 6th.
10	Worcs	4	1995	Bredon Hill: May 1st.
11	Worcs	5	1996	Defford: April 21st.
12	Warks	3	2001	Shipston-on-Stour: May 29th.

It is interesting that the three most recent records were all close to the outlying Cotswold hills, which were the former haunts of this species. One notable point is that the 2001 record from Warwickshire, of a bird calling at night, was the first in the county for nearly 150 years. In Britain Stone Curlews are largely confined to the Brecklands of East Anglian and the Wessex downs.

BWM also mentions a bird, probably of this species, near Alveston in 1951, but, as there was some uncertainty about its identification, it has not been included in the above list.

Collared Pratincole   *Glareola pratincola*
Very rare vagrant. Two records.

There have been just two records of this very rare wanderer from southern Europe, south-west Asia and Africa, namely:

Regional Record Number	County Record Number		Year	Locality, Date and Notes
1	Worcs	1	1994	Bredon's Hardwick: May 4th. *BB 88:508*
2	Warks	1	1996	Draycote Water: May 12th-13th. *BB 90:468*

Both followed a fascinating itinerary. The Bredon's Hardwick bird firstly flew across the county boundary into Gloucestershire and was later presumed to be that seen near Hereford on May 20th (Rogers *et al.* 1995). The Warwickshire individual—clearly identifiable by the missing tail feathers on its right-hand side—proved even more adventurous. It began by leaving Draycote for Northamptonshire, where it visited Earls Barton from May 13th-25th. It then moved over to the North Sea coasts, where it was seen in the Netherlands in May; then back in Britain, at Muston (N. Yorks) on June 3rd, Hornsea Mere (E. Yorks) the next day, Burnham Norton (Norfolk) the day after that and Dunwich (Suffolk) on June 8th; before reappearing again in the Netherlands in June. The same bird actually visited various parts of Britain every year from 1994 to 1999 (Rogers *et al.* 1996-2001).

Little Ringed Plover   *Charadrius dubius*
Frequent summer resident and passage migrant.

Little Ringed Plovers are summer visitors to the region's gravel pits and bare post-industrial sites. Unrecorded in the region until 1945, they have quickly exploited the vast increase in suitable habitat, especially during the 1970s and 80s, and can now be found at suitable sites across all four counties. They do have a preference for working quarries, however, and will often nest near machinery, probably because a human presence keeps predators away (*Breeding Atlas*).

From the first, unsuccessful, breeding attempt in 1952, numbers rose to a peak of 32 pairs at 16 sites in 1977 and, by the time *BWM* was published, around 25-30 pairs were nesting each year. Within the space of seven years numbers had doubled, with the BTO census of 1984 showing 57 pairs at 34 sites. Special censuses invariably produce higher counts than casual observations, but this number of pairs has never been equalled since. During the 1990s the average number of territories was consistently around 40 and this is probably the current breeding population. One recurring theme is the persistent reference to poor breeding success, with many failed nests and low fledging rates. This is attributed to numerous causes, ranging from flooding and site destruction to egg collecting and predation, with Moorhens being implicated more than once. At some reserves, cages with a small mesh to keep out predators have been provided and these have helped to improve breeding suc-

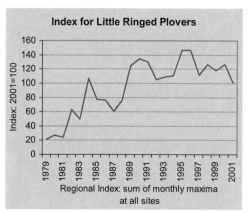

Index for Little Ringed Plovers
Index: 2001=100
Regional Index: sum of monthly maxima at all sites

cess. Despite the pressures mentioned above, in a few instances pairs have raised two broods.

Little Ringed Plovers are one of the first summer visitors to return each spring from their African wintering areas, with the average date of first arrivals over 36 years being March 19th. As with most migrants, however, the first dates have been getting earlier in recent years and the average during 1992-2001 was March 11th, whilst the earliest ever was at Belvide Reservoir on March 1st 1994. By the end of April most pairs are back on territory and well into breeding.

Arriving at true totals is impossible, but the regional index shows a substantial growth during the 1980s, since when numbers have fluctuated widely without showing any clear long-term trend. During 1992-2001, 40% of birds occurred in Staffordshire, 28% in Worcestershire, 19% in Warwickshire and 13% in the West Midlands. The top sites, holding 5% or more of the recorded birds, were Upton Warren (13%), Belvide Reservoir (7%), Blithfield Reservoir (6%) and Dosthill-Kingsbury Water Park (5%). Also noteworthy is Marsh Lane, which although a new site, has proved very attractive to this species. Overall, the top ten sites held half of all birds.

Spring parties rarely exceed a dozen, so 22 in the Dosthill-Kingsbury area in May 1993 was noteworthy. Peak numbers then follow in late July or early August, when up to 20 are quite usual as birds gather for their return migration. The most mentioned in *BWM* was 34 at Kingsbury Water Park on August 2nd 1979, whilst more recent counts include 32 at the same locality in July 1987 and a new regional record of 39 at Blithfield Reservoir in late July 1984.

Unlike spring, the pattern of departure has changed little, with numbers falling away quite rapidly during August and September. October 3rd has been the average date for last birds, both over 35 years and over the last ten years, while the latest in the current period was October 23rd 1996 at Chasewater. However, a record on October 27th 1972 at Chasewater, quoted in *BWM*, remains the latest ever.

Two birds, ringed as nestlings in the region, show easterly movements. The first, ringed at Draycote Water in July 1988, was recovered in July 1990 near Ely (Cambridgeshire) and the second, ringed near Sudbury (Derbyshire) in June 1990, was recovered in August of that year at Cantley (Norfolk). They represent movements of 110 km and 222 km respectively.

Ringed Plover   (Great Ringed Plover)   *Charadrius hiaticula*
Frequent passage migrant and scarce summer resident. Rare in mid-winter.

As with Oystercatcher, the Ringed Plover is another wading bird normally associated with coastal areas that has recently begun to colonise inland areas. Around the coast, its favoured sandy beaches increasingly suffer from human disturbance, whereas, inland, sand and gravel quarries offer a similar habitat with greater security. Birds are widespread during passage periods, with the major reservoirs sometimes attracting large concentrations.

Annual numbers fluctuate according to the conditions prevailing at passage times, but the general trend showed a steady increase in the early 1980s, a dramatic rise during 1987-89 and a gradual decrease since (see chart overleaf). Breeding was first recorded in the region at Bittell Reservoir in 1902 and subsequently at Branston in 1979, while three pairs nested in the Tame Valley in 1980 (*BWM*). As predicted at the time, these early nesting attempts turned out to be precursors of regular breeding along the Tame and Trent valleys, with birds moving between gravel pits to take advantage of the best conditions at the time. Breeding success was often poor, but nevertheless the number of pairs steadily increased to a maximum of seven or eight in the early 1990s, since when it has fallen slightly to around four or five.

Elsewhere, a pair bred at Bredon's Hardwick in 1984—the first Worcestershire record since that in 1902 mentioned above—but this proved to be an isolated occurrence. In 1990 a pair nested at Chasewater and thereafter breeding became more widespread, with reports from

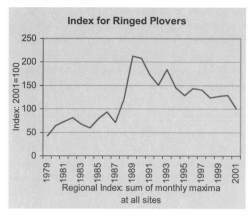

Index for Ringed Plovers

Index: 2001=100

Regional Index: sum of monthly maxima
at all sites

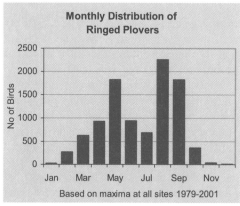

**Monthly Distribution of
Ringed Plovers**

No of Birds

Based on maxima at all sites 1979-2001

Belvide Reservoir, Berkswell, Brandon Marsh, Doxey Marshes, Draycote Water, Lymedale Business Park, Marsh Lane and Westport Lake.

During 1929-78, spring passage was virtually all concentrated into May (*BWM*), but these days it begins in early February and gradually builds to a peak in May. Parties during this time are usually less than 20, but up to 35 were in the Dosthill-Drayton Bassett-Kingsbury Water Park area in May 1999 (*cf.* 59 at Blithfield in *BWM*). The current trend for earlier arrivals correlates with increased breeding and almost certainly involves local birds returning to claim territories, whereas the May peak coincides with birds returning to their breeding grounds in Iceland and Greenland.

The first returning birds begin to trickle through in late June, but passage does not reach its peak until August and September, when the largest flocks are noted. Of the sixteen parties during 1979-2001 to exceed 40 birds, no fewer than nine occurred at Blithfield Reservoir, where there were August maxima of 96 in 1997, 116 in two separate overflying flocks in 1993 and 125 in 1989. Of the remaining seven flocks, there were two each at Belvide Reservoir, Draycote Water and Kingsbury Water Park, while Chasewater had one. However, all of these were eclipsed by the record 166 at Blithfield on August 23rd 1970 (*BWM*). Most birds have left by October, but there were mid-winter records in fifteen of the twenty-three years 1979-2001, mostly involving just single birds.

Some evidence of the origins and destinations of birds passing through the region is provided by an adult, colour-marked in Greenland in the summer of 1972 and seen here the following August and one ringed here in 1963 and recovered four years later in Portugal (*BWM*). The only recent recovery is of a bird ringed at Chasewater in August 1985 and recovered five years later in Pentney (Norfolk) in July 1990.

Within the region during 1992-2001, the geographical distribution showed 60% of birds in Staffordshire, 21% in Warwickshire, 15% in Worcestershire and 4% in the West Midlands. The vast majority of birds (61%) appeared at just six sites, with Blithfield Reservoir attracting 18%, Belvide Reservoir 13%, Draycote Water 12%, Barton Gravel Pit and Dosthill-Kingsbury Water Park 7% each and Upton Warren 5%.

Kentish Plover   *Charadrius alexandrinus*
Rare passage migrant.

Kentish Plovers breed around the coasts of mainland Europe and winter along Mediterranean and African shores. The first record for this region came as recently as 1940 and there have still been only fifteen. Indeed, even with the intensive amount of watching these days, it remains a rare bird, with just seven sightings during 1979-2001.

Regional Record Number	County Record Number		Year	Locality, Date and Notes
1	Worcs	1	1940	Bittell Reservoir: juvenile, July 15th. *BB 34:90*
2	Staffs	1	1948	Belvide Reservoir: adult male, May 2nd. *BB 42:94*
3	Staffs	2	1950	Belvide Reservoir: September 13th.
4	Staffs	3	1970	Blithfield Reservoir: immature, September 11th-16th.
5	Warks	1	1974	Draycote Water: August 21st.
6	Warks	2	1976	Draycote Water: female, April 22nd.
7	Staffs	4	1976	Chasewater: female, April 28th.
8	Warks	3	1977	Bodymoor Heath: male, May 14th.
9	Staffs	5	1979	Branston: male, May 7th, flew briefly across from Drakelow (Derbys).
10	Warks	4	1980	Lea Marston: male, May 3rd.
11	Staffs	6	1981	Belvide Reservoir: female, May 16th.
12	Staffs	7	1981	Westport Lake: female, May 18th.
13	Staffs	8	1983	Belvide Reservoir: female, April 11th.
14	Warks	5	1993	Draycote Water: male, May 14th-15th.
15	Staffs	9	1995	Tittesworth Reservoir: adult male, June 15th.

Although regarded as separate records, *BWM* recognised there was a possibility of the two 1976 records being the same individual. The same also applies to the two in 1981.

Spring passage is the strongest, with two-thirds of the records falling between April 11th (1983) and May 18th (1981). Of the remaining five, there was one each in June, July and August and two in September.

Dotterel   *Charadrius morinellus*
Rare passage migrant, very rare in winter.

In recent years the Dotterel has been noted more frequently on the region's hills, usually in small numbers, but occasionally in larger parties known as 'trips'. The best time to search for them is in spring, when they sometimes pause briefly as they journey from their wintering grounds in north Africa to breed on the mountains of Scotland and Fennoscandia.

There are ten documented historical records, to which *BWM* could add only six between 1950 and 1978. The only sizeable 'trips' included in these were 10 on Cannock Chase on May 15th 1875 and nine at Grove End on May 13th 1978. During 1979-2001 birds were recorded in just eleven of twenty-three years, although the frequency of occurrence was slightly higher in the 1990s (eight years out of 10).

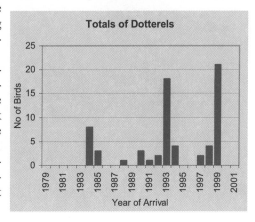

Totals of Dotterels

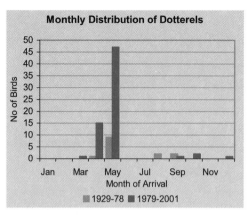

Monthly Distribution of Dotterels

The vast majority of these records (94%) were in spring, with the earliest being a bird on North Hill, Malvern, on March 23rd 1997. The bulk of the passage, however, was concentrated between late April and mid-May and all of the larger 'trips' occurred at this time. These included five on the Morridge on May 8th 1993 and a remarkable series from Bredon Hill, which produced eight on April 20th 1984, between 11-14 during May 3rd-6th 1993 and a regional record of 20 on May 13th 1999. Autumn passage, in comparison, has been virtually non-existent in recent times, with singles on the Malverns in September 1997 and October 1993 and one at Wellesbourne Airfield, again in October 1993. Of more interest was the region's only winter record, from the Wasperton-Wellesbourne Airfield again, where one remained with a large flock of European Golden Plover from December 17th 1988 until January 24th 1989.

The 1979-2001 records have been dominated by three sites, which between them have produced 94% of all birds. The most outstanding has been Bredon Hill, which alone has accounted for 69% of birds, with occurrences in 1984, 1993, 1994, 1998 and 1999. A further 11% were seen on the North Staffordshire Moors, particularly in the Morridge area where birds appeared annually from 1990-93. Lastly, the Malverns, with records in 1983, 1993 and 1997 (spring and autumn) held 9% of birds. With two of the top three sites in Worcestershire, it is no surprise to find that county top of the list with 78% of the birds recorded. Staffordshire comes next with 19%, whilst Warwickshire is a poor third with 3%. There has been no record from the West Midlands county area since 1978.

American Golden Plover   *Pluvialis dominica*

Very rare vagrant. One record.

There has been just one record of this vagrant, which breeds in Arctic North America and the extreme north-east of Asia and winters in South America.

The date is typical for British appearances, 90% of which are in autumn, mostly in September and October (Dymond *et al.* 1989). British records of this American wader have increased more than tenfold since the 1970s and by 2003 almost 250 had been reported. Much of the increase is probably due to more active observers and a better understanding of field identification (Rogers *et al.* 2004).

Regional Record Number	County Record Number	Year	Locality, Date and Notes
1	Warks 1	1991	Grandborough: juvenile, October 18th. Same Draycote Water 22nd-23rd and near Willoughby 26th. *BB 86:477.*

European Golden Plover (Golden Plover) *Pluvialis apricaria*
Common passage migrant and winter visitor. Scarce and declining breeding species on the North Staffordshire Moors.

This handsome plover is best known as a passage migrant and winter visitor to the region's farmland and wetlands. It is decidedly local, however, having traditional areas, known as 'flock ranges' within which birds gather to feed and roost. Generally these are on flat or gently undulating farmland, with well-drained neutral or basic soils, which is where earthworms and other soil invertebrates are most abundant during the winter. Passage birds or itinerant flocks do occur outside these traditional areas, particularly at reservoirs or on flood meadows, and a few pairs may still nest on the moorland of north Staffordshire.

As a winter visitor *BWM* noted that the species was apparently becoming more numerous and the index shows this trend has continued, with seemingly a large increase in numbers during the late 1980s and early 1990s. Annual totals are very variable, though, as birds are susceptible to cold conditions and many arrived in January 1984, along with Northern Lapwings and thrushes, to escape the blizzards across northern Britain at that time. It is possible, therefore, that the increase during the recent milder winters reflects birds coming into the region to escape colder conditions elsewhere, particularly on the Continent. Whatever its cause, it has also been accompanied by an increase in the number of regular flocks, from the thirteen shown in *BWM* to between 17-20, although counting is compounded by movements between these.

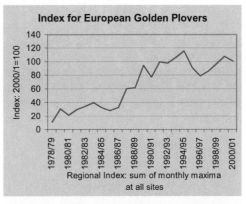

Wintering birds are normally present from August to April, but a few may arrive earlier or leave later. Over 50 years, the average date for first birds to arrive was August 10th, whilst the average for the last ten years was just a couple of days earlier. Three at Brandon on the unusual date of July 6th 2000 were the earliest ever recorded by three days.

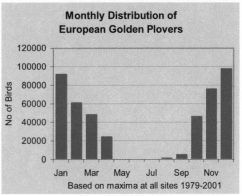

Numbers then build up through the autumn to a December– January peak, before falling away quite sharply. *BWM* noted an influx during March and April, when British birds are usually back on their breeding territories, and assumed this comprised birds from northern Europe. Presumably this passage still occurs, as evidenced by 20 birds of the northern race *P. a. altifrons* at Coton in April 1984, but is now masked by the much larger wintering numbers. Over 52 years the average date for last birds has been April 27th, but during the last ten years it was May 8th. The latest ever recorded was on May 15th 1980 at Kingsbury Water Park.

European Golden Plovers were first proved to be breeding on the moors of north Staffordshire in 1925 and up to five pairs, or even ten on occasions, were subsequently reported in most years (*BWM* and Gribble 2000). However, an RSPB survey in 1985 revealed 12 pairs (Waterhouse 1985), showing the importance of thorough coverage. Habitat changes then began to have an adverse effect, with little burning of the heather, rough pastures being drained and improved, and stocking rates increased. As a consequence, numbers began to drop and a

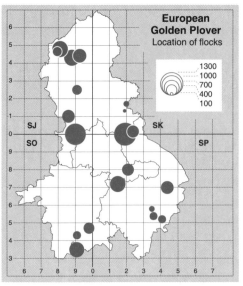

repeat RSPB survey in 1992 found only four pairs (Brindley *et al.*1992). Since then, breeding was reported from three areas in 1993, a single pair bred in 1996 (McKnight *et al.* 1996), display was noted in 1997 and finally breeding was again suspected in 1998 and probably at two sites in 1999. Subsequent sightings indicate that a small population may still be surviving in this southernmost extremity of the Pennines, although there has been no confirmation of breeding.

The wintering population was estimated in *BWM* as 5,000-7,500 birds, with the largest flock being 1,200 in 1971. During 1978/9-2000/1 nine flocks exceeded 2,000—four of them at Wellesbourne airfield, where a record 4,000 assembled in October 1993. However, the roost here has been more erratic since helicopter flights were introduced. Elsewhere the most recorded were 3,000 in the Church Lawford-Draycote area in January 1993. More recently, a flock of 2,000 at Dunstall Park in January 2002 was an excellent record for an urban locality. Currently there are probably 12,000-20,000 birds wintering in the region.

During 1992-2001 just over a third (37%) of all birds occurred in Warwickshire, with 28% in Staffordshire, 18% in the West Midlands and 17% in Worcestershire. The six principal sites, in descending order of importance were Wellesbourne Airfield (10% of birds), Draycote Water and Bredon's Hardwick (7% each), Hockley Heath and Dosthill-Kingsbury Water Park (5% each) and Park Hall Country Park (4%). Overall, half of all birds occurred at just ten sites.

Grey Plover   *Pluvialis squatarola*
Uncommon passage migrant and winter visitor.

Grey Plovers come from western Siberia to winter around British coasts. Small numbers regular visit the region, mostly on their spring and autumn migrations, when they can occasionally be seen at the main reservoirs and gravel pits.

Birds have been recorded annually since 1953, with *BWM* citing around 395 during 1929-78. Since then there were at least a further 750 during the twenty-three years 1979-2001. The species' fortunes during this time, however, have been mixed. Numbers varied substantially from year-to-year, the poorest years being 1981 and 2001 with just six and five birds respectively. Conversely, the two best showings, in 1990 and 1993, produced 84 and 93 birds respectively. Such fluctuations are commonplace, especially with migratory species, but the long-term trend is interesting in exhibiting a rapid and substantial increase between 1983 and 1993, during which time the national WeBS index doubled (Pollitt *et al.*

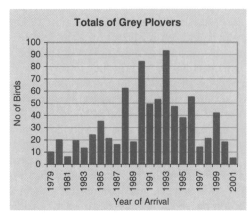

2003). Since then the numbers nationally have remained fairly stable, but there has been a very sharp decline regionally, suggesting that fewer birds are coming inland.

Birds have occurred in every month and the spread is similar to that shown in *BWM*. There is a concentrated spring passage in May (24% of records), when many adult birds are in their distinctive summer plumage, and a stronger return one from September to November (42% of records), when juveniles are arriving in Britain from Siberia. The main differences between the two periods are that the November passage was weaker during 1929-78, whilst the first March records occurred during 1979-2001. Seasonal variations can be quite marked too, with, for example, none in the spring of 1995 for the first time since 1979. Winter records are often associated with spells of cold weather, such as that in 1995/96, when at least a dozen arrived between December 30th and January 6th. At such times birds may mingle with flocks of Northern Lapwings and European Golden Plovers to feed on flooded meadows and are occasionally noted roosting on the ice at frozen reservoirs. Intriguingly, the seasonal fluctuations sometimes vary from to county to

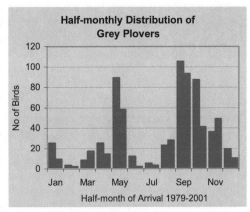

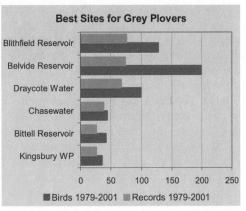

county as well, with 1994, for example, being a poor year in Warwickshire, but not elsewhere.

Almost 90% of birds are seen singly, or in twos, but there have been several parties up to ten. The four largest flocks have all been at Belvide Reservoir, where there were 15 on November 19th 1994, 18 on October 30th 1999, 24 on September 23rd 1990 and 38 on September 14th 1993. However, these were all eclipsed before the current period by an incredible flock of 110 that flew over the same place on August 12th 1969. Away from Belvide, the largest flocks were 12—at both Draycote Water on September 22nd 1990 and Blithfield Reservoir on September 14th 1993. Indeed, almost half of all the records (46%) have come just from these three localities. The distribution of birds between the counties was 56% in Staffordshire, 28% in Warwickshire, 14% in Worcestershire and 2% in the West Midlands.

White-tailed Lapwing (White-tailed Plover) *Vanellus leucurus*
Very rare vagrant. One record.

A major highlight of recent ornithological history in the West Midlands was the discovery of this bird, which constituted the first ever record for Britain and Ireland of a species that breeds in south Russia, the Middle East and west-central Asia.

Regional Record Number	County Record Number	Year	Locality, Date and Notes
1	Warks 1	1975	Packington Gravel Pits: July 12th-18th. *BB 69:334 & BB 70:465*

This bird was a superb find for John Fortey, Mrs E. Green and Eric Phillips and was enjoyed by several hundred birders from all over Britain during its seven day stay. The record, at first sight, appeared to be an astonishing one, though it was later discovered that others reached seven other European countries, namely Austria, Finland, Hungary, Italy, the Netherlands, Poland and Sweden, in the same year. (Rogers *et al.* 1976 and Dean *et al.* 1977).

Northern Lapwing   (Lapwing)   *Vanellus vanellus*
Common migrant and winter visitor. Fairly common to common breeding species.

The Northern Lapwing is a flagship species in the fight to save our farmland birds. It was once widespread and common across the region, nesting in rushy pastures on the northern moors, in damp meadows and wetlands in the lowlands, and on cultivated land. In winter huge flocks could be seen on arable fields, old ridge-and-furrow pastures and at reservoirs and gravel pits. It is now scarce and local as a breeding species and numerically much reduced in winter.

Pairs prefer bare ground on which to nest and grassland nearby in which to rear their chicks in safety—a combination which virtually every modern farming practice, be it the drainage of wet meadows, early cutting for silage, autumn sowing, or over-stocking, seems designed to deny them. As a consequence they now nest in tight colonies at the few remaining suitable sites—a far cry from the one nest per tilled field of the 1950s (J. Winsper *pers. comm.*). They have also taken to nesting in strawberry fields (C. Brown *pers. comm.*). Even in winter, birds favour areas of mixed farming, where they spend much time feeding on grasslands, often at night, but choose ploughed fields for roosting.

At the time of the *Winter Atlas*, there were birds in every 10-km square, though the density was lower on the uplands of Staffordshire. The *Breeding Atlas* confirmed their presence in 96% of squares, but at this season they were more plentiful in the predominantly dairy areas of central and north Staffordshire. The distribution at this broad scale has changed very little since, but, at a more detailed level, preliminary results from the two *tetrad atlases* indicate only a quarter to a third of the tetrads are occupied.

One of the most important breeding populations is that on the North Staffordshire Moors. Here RSPB surveys revealed a decline of 59% in just seven years, from 306 pairs in 1985 to 128 in 1992 (Brindley *et al.* 1992), followed by a further drop to 85 pairs in 1996 (McKnight *et al.* 1996). Poor breeding success seems to be a significant factor here. For example, in 1997 four pairs in one study area made nine nesting attempts, but only five of their 25-32 eggs hatched and just one chick was thought to have fledged, while at a second site all five nesting attempts failed (Lawrence 1997). A further survey of the lowland river valleys in Staffordshire in 1998 revealed 182 pairs. Elsewhere, in 1997 the species was considered to be almost absent from arable land in west Worcestershire and no breeding birds were found in the 10-km square east of Worcester. The following year just one bird was seen during the May count at DM Kineton, compared with a maximum count of 54 birds in 1989, whilst at Brandon Marsh numbers fell from an estimated 20 pairs in 1973 to between four and six in the 1990s.

Nationally, the CBC showed a population decline of 44% during 1974-99, which qualifies for *Amber Listing* as a Species of Conservation Concern. Regionally the numbers present on CBC plots were too small to show any trend, but the current regional population is

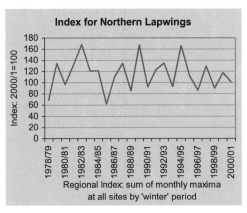

Index for Northern Lapwings

Index: 2000/1=100

Regional Index: sum of monthly maxima
at all sites by 'winter' period

possibly around 4,000-6,000 pairs compared to the 14,000-18,000 pairs estimated in *BWM*. Surprisingly the index in the accompanying chart, which is based on monthly maxima counts, shows little long-term change, presumably because more records are being published now that the species has become much scarcer. However, it does show the volatile nature of the population, which is frequently up one year and down the next. Indeed, it even varies considerably from month to month, as Northern Lapwings will vacate the region altogether to escape heavy, prolonged frosts or a covering of snow. For example, in 1984/5

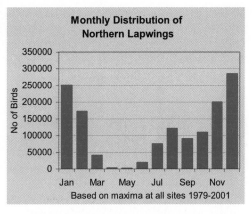

there were 19,500 in December, but a severe cold spell in January reduced this to 400. However, by February over 4,000 had returned. At such times substantial movements can be seen, such as 809 heading west over Stafford in one-and-a-half hours on December 12th 1983.

Northern Lapwings nest early and so are one of the first species to form post-breeding flocks, with small parties beginning to appear in late May and flocks of a hundred or more by June. Boosted by immigrants from the Continent, numbers then steadily increase to a mid-winter peak in December and January before falling away quite rapidly in February, as birds return to their breeding territories. *BWM* referred to regular feeding flocks of 3,000, with occasionally 5,000 and once up to 8,000 in the Kingsbury area in 1979/80. There were then two more flocks of 7,000 in 1983—one near Draycote and the other on floodwater at Bredon—and another of 8,000 in the Coton-Kingsbury area again in November 1984. However, with the population in decline, flocks have since become smaller. There were 6,000 at Hixon Airfield in December 1991 and at Draycote Water in December 1997, but since then none has exceeded 2,500. Currently the wintering population is probably in the range 10,000-20,000, though numbers vary from year to year according to the weather.

Relatively few Northern Lapwings are now ringed compared with the high numbers in the 1960s and 1970s. Recoveries, however, continue to show our birds moving south or south-westwards to over-winter on the mainland of Europe (see also *BWM*), with birds ringed in late summer in Staffordshire, Worcestershire and Warwickshire recovered during the winter in Spain and France. Interestingly, one ringed in Germany in June 1985 and found dead in Tamworth in November 1990 was perhaps further proof of the winter immigration of birds from eastern Europe documented in *BWM*. Our oldest known Northern Lapwing was a bird ringed at Blithfield in November 1976 and recovered in Poland in November 1986.

The monthly maxima counts during 1992-2001 show a very even spread of birds between the shire counties, with 37% in Staffordshire and 29% each in Warwickshire and Worcestershire, while the West Midlands' share was 5%. Despite Staffordshire's slight majority, the two best sites were in Worcestershire and Warwickshire respectively, with Upton Warren attracting 11% of birds and Draycote Water 10%. These two places were well ahead of Kingsbury Water Park-Dosthill, with 6%, and Barton Gravel Pit and Bredon's Hardwick, with 5% each.

Red Knot (Knot) *Calidris canutus*
Uncommon passage migrant and rare winter visitor.

Red Knots have become more frequent visitors to the region during the past twenty years and might be encountered at passage times at any of the major reservoirs.

BWM recorded some 400 birds in the fifty years 1929-78, whereas the period 1979-2001

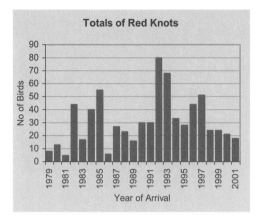

Totals of Red Knots

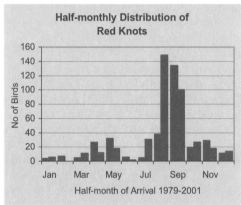

Half-monthly Distribution of Red Knots

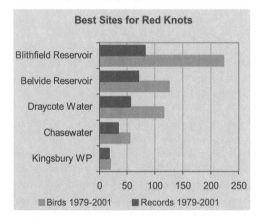

Best Sites for Red Knots

produced just over 700. During that time the average grew from around 17 a year in the early 1980s to almost 50 a year in the early 1990s, since when it has dropped back again to below 30 per annum. The long-term trend conceals quite wide differences in the annual totals, which have ranged from just five in 1981 to at least 80 in 1992. Included in the latter count, however, was an exceptional flock of 56 at Blithfield Reservoir on August 30th, without which the year would have barely been an average one.

The monthly pattern shows that birds have occurred in every month, but the most noticeable feature is the very strong peak during late-August and September. This is the time when juvenile birds reach Britain from northern Greenland and high Arctic Canada, having travelled via Iceland (Wernham *et al* 2002). Adults often return earlier and they account for most of the July records, which were proportionately fewer during 1979-2001 than in the *BWM* period. Conversely, the spring passage, from March to May, though still numerically small, has been proportionately stronger. It is thought this comprises birds moving across to Morecambe Bay, where they congregate to re-fuel for the long flight back to their breeding grounds. The small February influx evident during 1929-78 now seems to have faded away and winter records are fairly few. A third of the November arrivals came during an unusual influx in the autumn of 1996.

The Staffordshire dominance which was remarked upon in *BWM* has continued, although the proportion of birds recorded in that county has fallen from three-quarters to around two-thirds (65%). Warwickshire also has a significant share (26%), due largely to the importance of Draycote Water, but neither Worcestershire (8%) nor the West Midlands county (2%) have attracted many birds.

The major reservoirs have proved most productive, with two-thirds of all records having come from just four sites. These are also where the largest flocks have occurred. Both Belvide Reservoir and Draycote Water have had maxima of 21, on September 21st 1994 and September 7th 1997 respectively, but Blithfield Reservoir has claimed the two largest flocks, with 27 on September 16th 1985 and, of course, the 56 mentioned earlier. However, the vast majority of records (88%) involved only one or two birds. The majority of birds only stay for two or three days at the most, but about 30 have stayed for around a week and another five for two weeks or so. The longest stay was one of 26 days, at Upton Warren from November 24th to December 19th 1998.

Two juvenile birds ringed in the Lea Marston area in August 1982 were sighted in Wainfleet (Lincolnshire) the following August. One of these birds was later shot on the Alt Estuary in Merseyside.

Sanderling   *Calidris alba*
Uncommon passage migrant, rare in winter.

Every year a few Sanderlings find there way to the region's larger reservoirs during their long migrations between the breeding grounds of the high Arctic and the wintering areas on oceanic beaches as far south as West Africa. Most occur in spring, often when overflying birds are forced down by adverse weather.

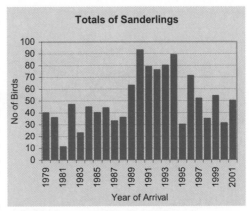

There are surprisingly few historical records of Sanderlings, but *BWM* recorded 666 birds during 1929-78. They have since increased to the point where accurate totals are difficult to compute, but there were at least 1,150 between 1979 and 2001, with an intriguing increase in numbers from 1989 to 1994, since when there has been a corresponding decline back towards the level of the early 1980s.

During 1979-2001 birds were recorded in every month, except February, but the spring passage was the dominant feature, with 77% of birds passing between late-April and early-June—80% of them in May alone. The much smaller return passage occurs principally during late-July and August, with just a few stragglers in September. Only nine birds were recorded in winter.

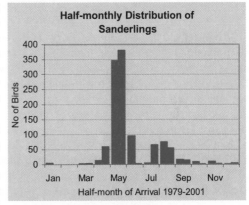

Sanderlings often pass through in small flocks, the largest of which was 25 flying straight through Chasewater on June 1st 1990. The same locality also had 17 on May 20th 1996, whilst 14 paused at Draycote Water after heavy rain on May 29th 1992 and 13 were at Belvide Reservoir on May 15th 1994. The vast majority stay for only a day and few remain longer than two or three days, though a couple have stayed for a week and one spent 13 days at Kingsbury, from May 21st-June 2nd 1983.

Most records come from the four major reservoirs, which means that Staffordshire—with 54%—has had most birds, followed by Warwickshire with 31%, whilst Worcestershire's share has been just 11% and the West Midlands 4%. For once, however, Chasewater has provided as many records as Draycote and

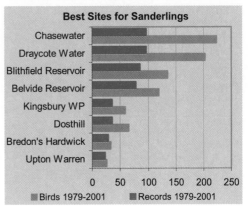

233

more than Blithfield! In all, birds were recorded at 44 different sites, with one on the North Staffordshire Moors at Boarsgrove on January 3rd 1993 perhaps the most unusual.

Little Stint   *Calidris minuta*
Uncommon autumn passage migrant, in variable numbers. Rare in spring and winter.

Little Stints breed in the Arctic tundra and winter in sub-Saharan Africa. They are most likely to be encountered on migration at the region's reservoirs, lakes and gravel pits, especially during autumn when low water levels expose muddy margins where they can feed.

BWM remarked on the great increase in records during the 1960s and 1970s, when there were maxima of 86 in the autumn of 1973 and 66 in 1976. Such numbers were maintained, and often improved upon, during 1979-2001, when there were at least 1,400 birds. However, this included a quite exceptional total of at least 400 in the autumn of 1996, which was nationally one of best autumns ever (*Brit. Birds* 90:544). If this unprecedented passage is excluded, the average was almost 50 a year. Numbers vary considerably from year-to-year and there were five autumns in this period that produced less than 20 birds, with the lowest being just nine in 1987. At the opposite end of the scale, there were particularly good passages in 1993, 1996 and 1998, with over 100 birds in each year.

Passage usually begins with a small movement of adults in late July and early August. Juveniles then follow from late August to October, with a customary climax in late September although in some years this comes a week or two earlier. At this time large flocks are sometimes recorded, with, for example, 103 at Blithfield Reservoir, 75 at Draycote Water and 37 at Upton Warren—all between September 22nd-27th 1996. Excluding this outstanding year, the largest flocks were 38 and 29, at Blithfield on September 10th 1993 and September 11th 1998 respectively, 26 at Belvide Reservoir on September 13th 1993 and 25 at Draycote on September 11th and 22nd 1993. By way of comparison, 26 was the largest flock quoted in *BWM*.

Compared to autumn, very few are seen in

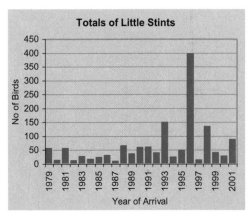

Totals of Little Stints

No of Birds — Year of Arrival

spring, but up to a maximum of seven did pass through in eighteen of twenty-three years 1979-2001. Outside the current period of analysis, a flock of six at Fisher's Mill GP on May 18th 2002 was the second largest ever recorded in spring, the highest being eight at Chasewater back in 1958 (*BWM*). Little Stints can be late migrants, so it is sometimes difficult to judge whether individuals in June are spring passage birds or early returning ones. Later in the year, birds will often linger well into autumn, especially when reservoir water levels are low enough to expose large areas of mud. For example, one that arrived at Blithfield on November 4th 1988 was last seen at Doxey Marshes on January 24th 1989. November arrivals such as this are not rare and fresh birds have been recorded in every month, except January. Winter records are rare, though, so the three from Barton Gravel Pit on November 15th 1997, during December and again in February 1998, probably referred to the same over-wintering individual.

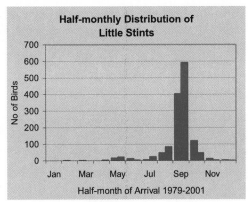

As with so many waders, Staffordshire, with 52%, received the most birds during the current period, followed by Warwickshire with 28%, Worcestershire 18% and the West

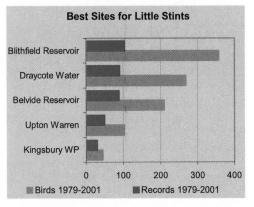

Midlands 2%. The three major reservoirs have been dominant, with almost half of all records being shared evenly between them, though Blithfield, with its larger expanse of mud, has attracted significantly more birds than either Draycote or Belvide. The chart also shows that Upton Warren is a regionally important stop-over point for migrating Little Stints.

Temminck's Stint   *Calidris temminckii*
Rare passage migrant, mainly in spring.

This tiny little wader is always a welcome sight whenever it appears at one of the region's gravel pits or reservoirs on passage between its central African winter quarters and its breeding grounds in northern Fennoscandia and Russia.

There appear to have been only two historical records, whilst during 1929-78 there were just 34, involving 43 birds. Records became noticeably more frequent from about 1972, however, and this has continued ever since, with birds failing to appear in only four of the thirty years 1972-2001. Otherwise numbers varied from one to six a year. From 1979-2001 there were sixty records involving 64 birds. The majority were single birds, but two

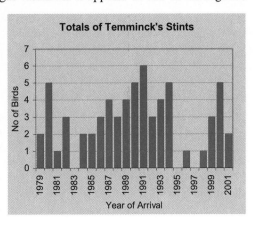

235

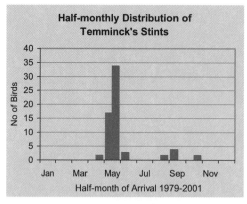

Half-monthly Distribution of Temminck's Stints

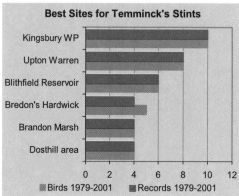

Best Sites for Temminck's Stints

were at Wasperton on May 15th 1989, Larford on May 22nd 1989, Bredon's Hardwick on May 30th 1991 and Barton Gravel Pits on May 21st 1994.

Spring records predominated during 1979-2001, accounting for 88% of all birds, with 60% of these concentrated into the second half of May. During the current period the earliest arrival was on April 24th, at Kingsbury in 1993. Autumn passages during the same period were very meagre affairs, involving just eight birds, of which the latest was at Upton Warren on October 23rd 1985.

Warwickshire, with 43%, has received most birds, followed by Staffordshire and Worcestershire, with 26% each, and the West Midlands with just 5%. Temminck's Stints definitely favour gravel pits and smaller waters rather than the large reservoirs, with Kingsbury Water Park and Upton Warren having been visited most often. Somewhat surprisingly, Belvide Reservoir has attracted very few.

As would be expected of a mainly spring migrant, birds generally pass through quite quickly, although less than half actually left on their day of arrival. Instead a significant proportion stayed for two or three days, but only two remained longer than a week. Of these, the longest stay was fifteen days—at Kingsbury Water Park from May 7th-21st in 1986.

Least Sandpiper   *Calidris minutilla*
Very rare vagrant. Three records.

Amazingly, the first record of this rare Transatlantic vagrant in 1971 (*BWM*) has now been followed by two more.

Regional Record Number	County Record Number	Year	Locality, Date and Notes
1	Staffs 1	1971	Chasewater: August 9th-11th. *BB 65:333*
2	Worcs 1	1988	Upton Warren: adult, August 13th-15th. *BB 82:523*
3	Staffs 2	2002	Drayton Bassett GP: May 23rd-25th. *BB 96:568*

Least Sandpipers breed from Alaska, across northern Canada to Labrador and Newfoundland and winter around the Caribbean and in South America. Up to 2002, there had been only thirty records in Britain. That 10% of these should have occurred in the West Midlands—which is not noted for rare birds—is quite remarkable. The 2002 record was only the second spring record for Britain, the first being in Hampshire on May 22nd 1977 (Rogers *et al.* 2003). The similarity in dates of the first two records is also noteworthy, as is the attraction of this species to birders, with nearly a thousand coming to see the Upton Warren individual in 1988.

White-rumped Sandpiper   *Calidris fuscicollis*
Very rare vagrant. Four records.

The first record of this Transatlantic vagrant, which came just in time for inclusion in *BWM*, has now been followed by a further three.

Regional Record Number	County Record Number	Year	Locality, Date and Notes
1	Staffs 1	1979	Blithfield Reservoir: immature, November 10th-12th and December 8th-11th. *BB 73:507*
2	Staffs 2	1984	Tittesworth Reservoir: adult, July 6th-7th. *BB 78:547*
3	Staffs 3	1989	Rudyard Reservoir: juvenile, November 3rd. *BB 83:462*
4	Worcs 1	1996	Bredon's Hardwick: September 15th-16th. *BB 90:472*

White-rumped Sandpipers are one of the more regular vagrants from North America, having occurred in Britain just over 340 times by 2003 (Rogers *et al.* 2004). The most notable features of the four records above are the appearance of two in north Staffordshire and the wide spread of dates, with arrivals in July, September and November (twice). However, these months do span the period when the majority of British records occur (Dymond *et al.* 1989).

Baird's Sandpiper   *Calidris bairdii*
Very rare vagrant. Two records.

Coincidentally, the only two occurrences of this rare Transatlantic vagrant were both in the same year.

Regional Record Number	County Record Number	Year	Locality, Date and Notes
1	Warks 1	1996	Draycote Water: juvenile, September 28th. *BB 90:476*
2	Staffs 1	1996	Blithfield Reservoir: juvenile, November 2nd-7th. *BB 90:476*

The Warwickshire individual was also seen at nearby Daventry Reservoir (Northants) from September 29th to October 2nd. September is the classic time for juveniles to appear in Britain, but November records are exceptional (Rogers *et al.* 1997).

Pectoral Sandpiper   *Calidris melanotos*
Rare or scarce passage migrant, mainly in autumn.

Pectoral Sandpipers breed in the coastal tundra of eastern Siberia, Alaska and Canada and winter mainly in South America. The species is nevertheless an annual visitor to Britain, chiefly in autumn. The first regional record came as recently as 1957, but by 1978 there had been seventeen (*BWM*). Of these, fifteen fell in the period 1967-78, twelve of them in just four years between 1970-73.

The current period then produced a further 32 birds, including two together at Coton Pools on September 15th 1984 and Blithfield Reservoir on September 7th and 8th 1994. During this time, birds failed to show in seven of the twenty-three years—all in the 1980s and early 1990s—but appeared annually between 1992 and 2001. The best year was in 1984, when five

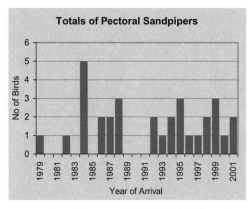

Totals of Pectoral Sandpipers

No of Birds (y-axis: 0–6)
Year of Arrival (x-axis: 1979–2001)

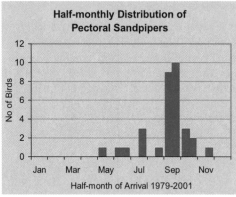

Half-monthly Distribution of Pectoral Sandpipers

No of Birds (y-axis: 0–12)
Half-month of Arrival 1979-2001 (x-axis: Jan–Nov)

were reported, but generally there are just one or two a year.

Although arrivals have been spread between May and November, the majority of birds arrived in autumn, 59% of them in September, which is when most birds, usually juveniles, arrive in Britain. The only definite spring records involved single birds at Bredon's Hardwick on May 4th 1987 and Kingsbury on June 14th 1986, although an adult at Upton Warren on June 27th 1984 could have been either a late spring migrant or an early returning bird. Apart from this bird, only two other adults were reported, typically both in July. The vast majority (86%) of those that were specifically aged were juveniles and their arrival dates spanned the period August 27th-November 20th.

Birds have been fairly evenly spread between the three main counties, with 11 in Worcestershire, 10 in Staffordshire and nine in Warwickshire, with the West Midlands county claiming the remaining two. In terms of sites, Blithfield Reservoir, with eight birds, has clearly been dominant, whilst Bredon's Hardwick has attracted five birds and Kingsbury Water Park three. The rest have been shared by nine sites, seven of which have had two birds.

Just under a third (31%) of birds have only stayed for one day, but significantly the same percentage has stayed for over a week, with two remaining for fifteen days, one at Kingsbury Water Park from September 15th-29th 1982 and the other at nearby Coton Pools, coincidentally on the same dates in 1984.

Curlew Sandpiper   *Calidris ferruginea*
Uncommon autumn passage migrant in variable numbers. Rare in spring.

The Curlew Sandpiper's long migration between its breeding grounds in arctic Siberia and its winter quarters in sub-Saharan Africa regularly brings birds into Britain, especially juveniles in autumn. As with the Little Stint, it is an annual visitor to the region's reservoirs, lakes and gravel pits at this season, when low water levels expose suitable feeding areas. Birds are much rarer on spring passage.

Again, like the Little Stint, this species has good and bad years, its numbers affected by breeding success, weather patterns during migration and water levels at the region's reservoirs when it arrives. Often, but not invariably, these coincide with the good and bad years for Little Stints, especially in 1996 which was the best year ever for both species. *BWM* cited 1969, 1975 and 1978 as good years for Curlew Sandpipers, with 35, 53 and 54 birds respectively. Since then, numbers appear to have increased, with over 800 recorded during 1979-2001. The poorest years were 1984 and 1989, with just one and two respectively! Conversely the totals in good years have steadily improved, with at least 48 in 1985, 79 in 1991 and 118 in 1996.

Adult birds are first to arrive, in late July and early August, when they are often still in their brick-red summer plumage. They are then followed from mid-July to early October by the passage of juvenile birds, which peaks in the first half of September, slightly ahead of that for Little Stint. The largest flocks during the current period were 26 at Blithfield Reservoir on August 30th 1991, 25 at the same locality on September 25th 1996 and 28 at Draycote Water on September 22nd 1996. In Worcestershire the largest party on the ground was 15 at Bittell Reservoir on August 26th 2000, but when they left and flew south over Upton Warren they were joined by a bird from there, so technically the latter site holds the record.

If conditions are right, some birds may stay for a week or more, though by mid-October most will have left for their winter quarters in southern Africa. However, unusually late birds were recorded at Blithfield on November 16th 1997 and Draycote on December 3rd 1995—the latter being the latest ever.

Birds are rare in spring, with records in just 12 of the twenty-three years 1979-2001 and never more than four in a year at this season. The 1980s were particularly lean, with records in only two years, but there have been spring occurrences in ten of the twelve years since 1989.

With the large expanses of mud uncovered most autumns, Blithfield Reservoir has clearly been the most outstanding site for this species. Given its small size, Upton Warren also emerges as a site of some importance, as it does for Little Stint. With Blithfield enjoying such pre-eminence, it is hardly surprising that 57% of all the birds in the current period were in Staffordshire, with Warwickshire's share being just 24%, Worcestershire 18% and the West Midlands 1%.

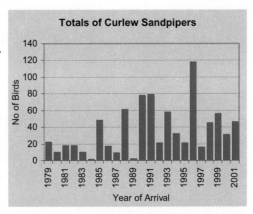

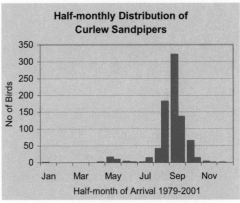

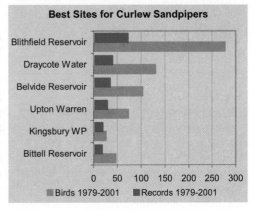

Purple Sandpiper *Calidris maritima*
Rare passage migrant, very rare in winter.

Purple Sandpipers are essentially maritime and relatively few winter in Britain south of a line from the Mersey to the Humber (Lack *et al.* 1986). Not surprisingly, they are therefore rare visitors to the region's major reservoirs and large waters.

The incidence of this species has changed very little over the years. *BWM* included one definite historical record and a further 21 during 1930-78, including an exceptional party of at least four at Walsall Sewage Farm on October 2nd 1930. There have subsequently been a further 19 as listed below.

Regional Record Number	County Record Number	Year	Locality, Date and Notes
23	Worcs 3	1981	Bittell Reservoir: September 16th.
24	Warks 6	1982	Ladywalk: adult, August 7th.
25	Staffs 13	1982	Chasewater: October 22nd.
26	Warks 7	1983	Draycote Water: August 29th.
27	Staffs 14	1983	Blithfield Reservoir: November 5th.
28	Staffs 15	1984	Blithfield Reservoir: January 15th.
29	W Mid 4	1985	Tividale: adult, July 28th-29th.
30	Staffs 16	1986	Blithfield Reservoir: October 28th to November 1st.
31	Warks 8	1987	Draycote Water: October 30th.
32	Worcs 4	1988	Bittell Reservoir: adult, August 24th.
33	Warks 9	1988	Draycote Water: adult, September 13th.
34	Warks 10	1988	Draycote Water: first-winter, September 18th-26th.
35	Warks 11	1991	Draycote Water: October 27th.
36	Staffs 17	1991	Blithfield Reservoir: November 17th.
37	Staffs 18	1992	Blithfield Reservoir: October 28th.
38	Warks 12	1993	Draycote Water: juvenile, September 4th.
39	Staffs 19	1995	Westport Lake: December 7th.
40	Staffs 20	1998	Blithfield Reservoir: juvenile, September 26th.
41	Staffs 21	2000	Belvide Reservoir: juvenile, December 17th.

Most years have produced just one or two birds, but there were three in 1972 and 1973, then again in the autumn/winters of 1983/84 and 1988/89. Indeed, as the table shows, the 1980s were the most productive years, since when occurrences and numbers have been fewer.

During the current period, birds were recorded in every month from late July to early January, but most arrived between late August and October. Summers (in Lack *et al*. 1986 and Wernham *et al*. 2002) states that birds from Norway start arriving on the East Coast in July, whereas the later arrivals that reach our northern and western coasts in October and November probably originate from Arctic Canada. It is possible, therefore, that those arriving in this region during July-September are of Scandinavian origin, whilst those coming during October-January may have travelled from across the Atlantic.

Dunlin   *Calidris alpina*
Fairly common passage migrant and winter visitor.

The Dunlin is one of the commoner waders to regularly pause at the region's reservoirs, gravel pits and lakes on passage. Although a few appear in spring, most stop-over in autumn, when the normally lower water levels expose muddy shores for feeding. They are less frequent in winter, but sizeable flocks sometimes gather on flooded pastures.

Unfortunately the moors of north Staffordshire lack the tracts of wet cotton-grass above 400m that are preferred for nesting and the species has never bred in the region, although a pair once nested just 200m over the boundary into Derbyshire at Axe Edge (*BWM*). Birds were also seen displaying on two or three occasions during the early 1980s.

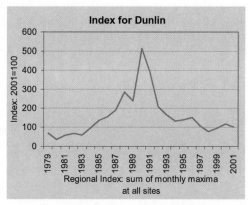

The most obvious feature of the regional index is the pronounced peak around 1990, which was due to the large winter flocks that gathered on the extensive Avon floods around that time. If these were excluded, the index would show little change. These flocks have also had a significant effect on the monthly distribution, shifting the emphasis from that of a passage migrant into a winter visitor. *BWM* noted that it was usually scarce in winter.

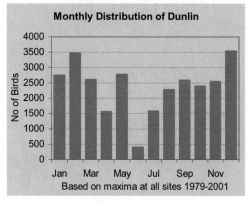

The migration pattern is complex, with several influxes as birds of different ages and from different geographical populations move through. *BWM* drew attention to some interesting differences between the pre-1967 and 1967-78 periods, showing how the culmination of spring passage had advanced from early May to late April, whilst the return passage had retreated from a July-August peak to one of October– November. These proved to be temporary shifts, however, as the spring maximum reverted to May during the current period, whilst that in autumn was in September.

Around 29% of birds pass through on spring passage (March-May), usually in small groups up to about 20, but with occasional parties up to 50. The most recorded at this season were 50 at Barton Gravel Pit and 53 at Belvide Reservoir in May 1994 and up to 68 in the Kingsbury Water Park-Drayton Bassett-Dosthill area in May 1999.

The main return passage brings slightly more birds (40% during July-November), but spread over a longer period. At this season up to 50 are not unusual and in excess of 100 were recorded four times during 1979-2001, whilst the maximum was 362 at Blithfield Reservoir on October 25th 1991. The first arrivals, in late July and early August, are believed to comprise birds of the southern race, *C.a. schinzii*, which breeds in south-east Greenland and north-western Europe, including Britain. Adults normally precede juveniles in this passage. There are then two further influxes of birds of the northern form *C. a. alpina* from northern Scandinavia and Siberia, one during August and September and the other during October and November (*Migration Atlas*). Unfortunately, the WMBC's current practice of simply recording monthly totals obscures the subtleties of these movements. Significant late autumn or early winter flocks are very evident, however, with 18% of birds occurring during November-December, including 68 at Belvide Reservoir in November 1996 and 311 at Blithfield Reservoir in December 1992. The only evidence of movements provided by ringing recoveries is that documented in *BWM*, namely three birds at Draycote of which two had been previously ringed on the Wash and the other was subsequently re-trapped in Sweden.

As mentioned above, winter floods sometimes draw flocks of Dunlin from the Severn estuary onto the meadows of the lower Severn and Avon valleys, notably around Bredon's Hardwick and at Longdon Marsh. Between 1984 and 1990 a series of flocks at Bredon's Hardwick provided some impressive totals for an inland site, with 306 in 1984/5, 480 in 1986/7, 420 in 1988/9 and a record 730 on February 23rd 1990. Occasional birds have also been noted in winter associating with Northern Lapwings on arable fields.

Based on monthly maxima during 1992-2001, just over half of all birds (55%) have occurred in Staffordshire, with 23% in Worcestershire, 18% in Warwickshire and 4% in the West Midlands. Birds are very concentrated, with almost three-quarters (73%) occurring at just eight sites. Of these, Blithfield Reservoir (21% of birds) has been by far the most productive, followed by Bredon's Hardwick (12%), Belvide Reservoir (11%), Draycote Water (10%), Chasewater and Dosthill-Kingsbury Water Park (6% each), and Barton Gravel Pit and Upton Warren (4% each). Amazingly, one caused a few problems as it dodged traffic in the centre of Walsall on January 3rd 1997—an interesting diversion from cones on the M6!

Broad-billed Sandpiper   *Limicola falcinellus*
Very rare vagrant. One record.

Most British records of Broad-billed Sandpipers are in spring and involve a westerly displacement of birds from their normal migration route through the eastern Mediterranean, Black and Caspian Sea areas *en route* to their breeding grounds in Fennoscania and northern Russia.

This was one of five that were recorded in Britain in 1985 (Rogers *et al.* 1986). The date was typical for this species (Dymond *et al.* 1989).

Regional Record Number	County Record Number	Year	Locality, Date and Notes
1	Warks 1	1985	Coton Pools: June 1st-4th. *BB 79:546* (recorded as Lea Marston by *BB*)

Buff-breasted Sandpiper   *Tryngites subruficollis*
Very rare vagrant. Five records.

Following the first in 1978, there were four more during the current period. All five birds arrived between September 2nd and 26th, which is the classic time for this Transatlantic wader

Regional Record Number	County Record Number	Year	Locality, Date and Notes
1	Staffs 1	1978	Chasewater: September 14th. *BB 72:523*
2	Staffs 2	1980	Blithfield Reservoir: September 7th-22nd. *BB 75:502*
3	Warks 1	1993	Draycote Water: juvenile, September 26th intermittently to October 9th.
4	Warks 2	1994	Draycote Water: juvenile, September 2nd-16th.
5	Warks 3	1995	Draycote Water: juvenile, September 7th.

Note: BBRC ceased to consider records of this species as from January 1st 1983.

to reach Britain (Dymond *et al.* 1989). If it was not for the fact that the three Draycote birds were all juveniles, then records from the same locality in three successive years might have suggested the same individual repeating a set migration pattern. Nationally, the location of arrivals appears to have shifted northwards during the 1990s (Fraser *et al.* 2003) and this might account for the recent run of records in this region.

Ruff   *Philomachus pugnax*
Frequent passage migrant, though in variable numbers. Scarce in winter.

A few Ruff visit the region's reservoirs, gravel pits and flooded meadows every year, usually in late summer on their way to West Africa for the winter. Far fewer pass through in spring, although passage at this time always brings the exciting prospect of one or two resplendent males adorned with ruffs. Winter sightings are comparatively scarce, but flood waters will often attract one or two.

Annual totals vary considerably according to weather patterns at the time of migration and water levels at the main reservoirs. The regional index wavered through the 1980s, then suddenly built to a dramatic peak in 1993 before falling back almost to its original level.

In spring Ruff travelling from their wintering grounds in sub-Saharan Africa to their breeding territories in north-east Europe mostly follow a direct route across central and eastern Mediterranean regions and inland Europe. As a consequence, spring passage here is modest, with just 22% of all birds passing through from March to May. Males, or ruffs, are the first to arrive, with the smaller females, or reeves, following from the middle of April onwards. Most pass through singly or in small groups, but just occasionally a larger party arrives. In fact, despite this being the smaller passage, an exceptionally strong passage in 1987 brought 154 birds, including a record party of 47 at Bredon's Hardwick on April 16th. Conversely, the passage in 2000 brought only 15 birds. Flocks of mixed sex are sometimes stimulated to lek, for instance at Upton Warren in 1984, although this is a rare event.

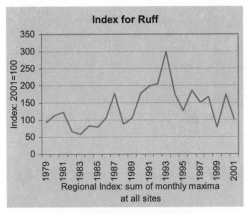

Late June and July then see the first signs of the return passage, which reaches its climax in August and September. At this season birds follow a more westerly migration route that brings many to Britain and the period July-September is easily the most productive, accounting for 63% of birds. Again most pass through in small groups, but larger flocks are more prevalent at this time. During 1979-2001 ten flocks exceeded 20 birds, several of which were at Blithfield Reservoir. The best passage was in 1993, when 33 were at Blithfield in August, 28 at Belvide Reservoir in September and 45 at Draycote, also in September.

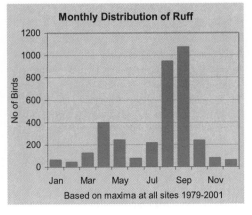

After September, only a few stragglers or potential wintering birds remain. Sorensen, in the *Winter Atlas*, says that Ruff winter in single-sex flocks and the majority of birds are

243

males. The *Atlas* also shows that most inland birds are found in the East Midlands and the five 10-km squares where birds were found in the West Midlands were all close to that region, suggesting that some birds penetrate just a little further inland. However, birds also occur in the Severn and Avon valleys following inundations of the flood meadows and these are assumed to come from the Severn Estuary. In general, winter is a quiet time for this species, with just 7% of birds occurring during November-February. Small flocks occasionally winter, with a good example being up to six which remained at Kingsbury Water Park from December 1988 to March 8th 1989.

During 1992-2001 half of the birds (52%) occurred in Staffordshire, with 25% in Warwickshire, 20% in Worcestershire and 3% in the West Midlands. To a large extent Staffordshire's share is due to the dominance of Blithfield Reservoir, which attracted 21% of all birds. Other favoured sites holding more than 5% of birds were Draycote Water (12%), Belvide Reservoir (11%), Dosthill-Kingsbury Water Park (8%) and Bredon's Hardwick and Upton Warren (7% each).

Jack Snipe   *Lymnocryptes minimus*
Frequent passage migrant and winter visitor.

Jack Snipe are regular winter visitors to Britain from their breeding grounds in Fennoscandia and northern Russia and small numbers are recorded annually in this region. Mostly they occur on passage in spring or more especially autumn, but providing they are not driven out by freezing weather a few stay throughout the winter. The species has very exacting habitat re-

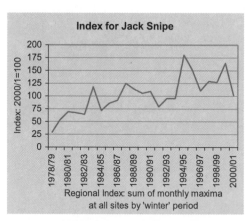

Index for Jack Snipe

Index: 2000/1=100

Regional Index: sum of monthly maxima
at all sites by 'winter' period

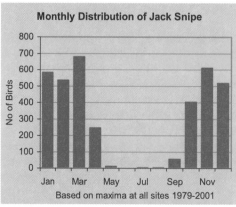

Monthly Distribution of Jack Snipe

No of Birds

Based on maxima at all sites 1979-2001

quirements, which restrict its distribution to wet grasslands or marshes with shallow water, mud and plenty of rushes, sedges and decaying vegetation to provide cover and camouflage. Birds almost invariably sit tight during the day and so remain undetected unless flushed, but become active at dusk, when they can be seen characteristically 'bobbing' up and down as they feed. Their diet consists of adult and larval insects, molluscs, worms and seeds.

Although numbers are small, we have chosen to represent trends by way of an index as the secretive nature of this species makes it impossible to estimate the number of birds actually present. Annual numbers are extremely variable, but the general trend appears to show a progressive increase. Whether this represents a real increase, or simply indicates that birders are finding more, remains unknown. Despite their fastidious habitat requirements, birds are extremely widespread and were indeed reported from 47% of 10-km squares during the *Winter Atlas*. The wintering population is probably in the range 100-150 birds, but may be higher.

The 'winter' of 1990/1 was unusual in that it produced both the earliest and latest dates on record—the extremes being July 15th at Bredon's Hardwick and May 29th at Belvide Reservoir. The Bredon's Hardwick record was a full twelve days earlier than the previous first on July 27th 1952, whilst others have occurred in August. A dog flushed the very late bird at Belvide, which otherwise may not have been discovered.

More typically, the first birds arrive towards the end of September, with the 26th being the average date over 58 years, although the last ten years have produced an average five days earlier. The main arrival then occurs in October and November, but, as some birds pass straight through the region, numbers in December are lower. They then rise again in the new year, reaching a peak in March with the reappearance of passage birds. The increase in winter sightings might just reflect the fact that it is easier to detect birds when the vegetation has died back and the combination of short days and cold weather forces them out into more open situations. By April most have left, with the average last date over 54 years being the 20th.

During 1991/2-2000/1 Worcestershire and Staffordshire held most birds (34% and 32% respectively), but the West Midlands did exceptionally well with 23%. Warwickshire, on the other hand, only drew 11% due to the scarcity of suitable habitat. Five sites held at least 5% of the birds recorded during this period, namely Upton Warren (12%), Goscote Valley (8%), Sandwell Valley and Chasewater (6% each) and Abberton (5%).

Mostly only ones and twos are detected, but parties up to twenty are not uncommon. During 1984/5-90/1, Sandwell Valley produced some excellent counts, with 22 in December 1986, 35 in March 1988 and 29 in March 1990. However, these were all eclipsed by an unbelievable 52 at Doxey Marshes in December 2001. Also noteworthy were 18 at Wasperton in January 2003, which was a good party for Warwickshire.

Among the more unusual records were groups of 11 and 12 flushed from virtually dry areas of *Chenopodium* on the settling beds at Wilden in October 1979 and December 1980 respectively, one on a roadside near Dunhampstead in December 1985, another in an Olton garden in October 1992 and one at the Wyevale Garden Centre, Colwich in 1999.

Common Snipe   (Snipe)   *Gallinago gallinago*
Fairly common winter visitor and passage migrant. Frequent, though much declined, as a breeding species.

Common Snipe are secretive birds that spend much of their lives concealed within the dense vegetation around the shorelines of shallow pools, gravel pits and reservoirs. Here they probe the mud for invertebrates, feeding most actively at dusk and dawn. During the breeding season they move into wet, rushy grasslands along river valleys and on the higher ground of the northern moors. They then become more conspicuous as they perch on posts and engage in display flights, circling above their territories before swooping down whilst making the characteristic 'drumming' noise with their tail feathers.

As a breeding species the Common Snipe has declined nationally in both the lowlands and uplands because the lowering of water-tables and the draining of marshes and wet pastures has left the ground too hard to probe. Higher stocking rates have also increased the trampling of nests and chicks. As a result of its declining numbers, it is now on the *Amber List* as a Species of Conservation Concern (Gregory *et al.* 2002).

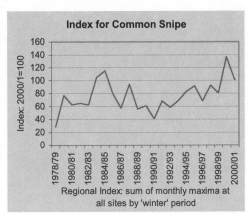

Regional Index: sum of monthly maxima at all sites by 'winter' period

Regionally, the *Breeding Atlas* indicated its presence in 90% of squares across Staffordshire (north of the A5), but in only 38% of those in the other three counties to the south. In lowland situations, however, they are now extremely local, having disappeared from many areas, whilst even on the moors, where they were more widely but thinly spread, numbers have fallen drastically.

For instance, none now nest in Warwickshire (J. Bowley *pers. comm.*), where they were last reported 'drumming' in the mid-1990s, while fieldwork for the *BBCBB Atlas* confirmed breeding in only two tetrads in the West Midlands. Likewise, none at all have been reported in Worcestershire in the breeding season since 1995. Here the decline is typified by Wilden, where river improvement works destroyed a prime habitat, reducing the population from 20 pairs in 1972 to just one during the late 1980s.

In Staffordshire, surveys of the moors by the RSPB showed a decline of 52%, from 656 to 315 pairs between 1985 and 1992. Even so this still represented 1% of the British breeding population at a time when the species was a candidate for inclusion in the *Red Data Book* (Brindley *et al.* 1992). Since then numbers have fallen further, to 178 in 1996 (McKnight *et al.* 1996). Other surveys of 50 km^2 of moorland fringe, carried out by the WMBC, showed a parallel decline of 60%, from 100 pairs to 40, between 1978-98 (Gribble *et al.* 1998). Elsewhere in the county, the 1998 survey found a further 25-27 pairs or drumming birds, including eight pairs at Doxey Marshes and four in the Churnet Valley. Birds had disappeared from the Dove and the Lower Trent/Tame catchments, however, and were much reduced in the Upper Trent catchment, whilst small numbers were holding on in the Tern catchment around Aqualate Mere and some of the surrounding wet meadows. Currently the regional population is probably no higher than 150-250 pairs (*cf.* 600-700 estimated in *BWM*).

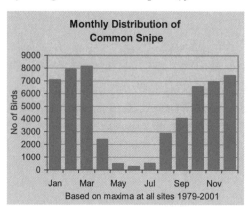

Monthly Distribution of Common Snipe
No of Birds
Based on maxima at all sites 1979-2001

Common Snipe are more numerous and widespread in winter, when the population is augmented by immigrants from Scandinavia and eastern Europe. Evidence of this is shown by birds ringed at a number of wetlands in the region, including some at Stubbers Green during the autumn and winter months which were recovered in subsequent summers in Finland and Russia, movements of well over 2,000 km. Similar movements have been recorded for birds ringed at sites in Staffordshire and Worcestershire. Most recoveries involve birds that have been shot.

Numbers begin to build up in the region from late July, but the main influx occurs in October and November and during the *Winter Atlas* birds were recorded in 95% of 10-km squares. Weather permitting, many then remain throughout the winter, resorting to rivers and even small streams if standing waters freeze over. However, they can suffer greatly during a prolonged freeze, so often they move further west at the onset of hard weather, returning in February or March on their way back to their breeding territories. Most wintering birds have left by the end of March. Numbers vary considerably from winter to winter, but, despite falling breeding numbers, the regional index shows signs of a welcome increase during the 1990s. There have also been some good sized flocks, in particular at Doxey Marshes where 420 in March 1991 and a new regional record of 734 in October 2001 compare favourably with the 600 recorded there in October 1971 (*BWM*). More recently, 100 at Sandwell Valley in December 2002 was a good number for an urban site. The total wintering population of the region probably averages around 1,000-2,000 birds.

Based on monthly maxima during 1991/2-2000/1, most birds were seen in Staffordshire (38%), followed by Worcestershire (30%), Warwickshire (20%) and the West Midlands

(12%). Slightly over half of these (53%) were concentrated at ten sites, of which just four held more than 5%. These were Upton Warren (12%), Doxey Marshes (11%) and Brandon Marsh and Dosthill-Kingsbury Water Park (6% each). Interestingly, Upton Warren tops the list by virtue of consistently holding good numbers, as opposed to the more variable ones at Doxey.

Occasionally birds appear in unusual situations, such as 40 feeding in open grassland, 15 in stubble, 35 in set-aside and one drinking from a roadside puddle. One was even on the bird-table at Belvide Reservoir during freezing conditions in 1991, another visited a garden at Penn in February 2002 and there have been other reports of birds moving into urban settings during cold, snowy weather.

Great Snipe   *Gallinago media*
Rare vagrant. Only three records since 1916.

There are several historical records of Great Snipe. Smith (1938) suggested at least a dozen had occurred in Staffordshire up to 1916 and Norris (1947) listed five or six birds between 1875 and 1894, but a big gap followed before the next in 1950. In view of the imprecision involved with many of these early records, only those from 1950 onwards have been tabulated. For completeness, however, the county and regional totals include fifteen earlier records that were reasonably substantiated. There have been no Worcestershire records and only two within the current Warwickshire boundary, the last of which was in 1878.

Regional Record Number	County Record Number	Year	Locality, Date and Notes
16	W Mid 4	1950	Sutton Park: May 6th.
17	Staffs 11	1954	Whittington SW: April 25th.
18	W Mid 5	1995	Sandwell Valley: August 22nd-23rd. *BB 89:501 & BB 90:478.*

Although commoner in the past, the Great Snipe's range has retracted northwards and eastwards in Europe during the last two hundred years (Cramp *et al.* 1974-1994), which explains, at least in part, the dearth of recent records. The 1995 bird was therefore a superb find that stayed just long enough for 200 or so lucky birders to see it.

Long-billed Dowitcher   *Limnodromus scolopaceus*
Very rare vagrant. Two records.

Two records of this snipe-like, North American wader within the space of eight years were totally unexpected. Both dates were typical for this species.

Regional Record Number	County Record Number	Year	Locality, Date and Notes
1	Warks 1	1983	Draycote Water: age uncertain, November 10th. *BB 78:549*
2	Worcs 1	1990	Westwood Pool: juvenile moulting to first-winter, October 9th-20th. *BB 84:471*

Another dowitcher sp., probably Long-billed, was at Draycote Water from August 23rd-26th 1990. Unfortunately, separating Long-billed and Short-billed Dowitchers in the field requires good views and this bird frustratingly remained on an island, where the long-range and heat haze made determination of its precise characters difficult (*BB 86:481*).

Woodcock   *Scolopax rusticola*
Frequent or fairly common resident and winter visitor.

Woodcock are best known for the males' eerie, twilight roding flights just above the tree tops. Although they inhabit a wide range of woodland, most are to be found in conifer plantations or birch scrub, especially those with damp or wet feeding areas and dry nesting areas. Woodland structure is important, with birds preferring woods with clearings, rides or an open canopy. The species is on the *Amber List* as being of medium conservation concern (Gregory *et al.* 2002) and its conservation status within Europe is also unfavourable (Tucker *et al.* 1994).

Woodcock are crepuscular birds, spending most of the day concealed amongst the leaf litter on the woodland floor, where their superbly cryptic plumage ensures they are virtually invisible. Only at dusk do they venture forth to feed. With such secretive habits, this is a difficult species to census and most estimates of breeding numbers have to rely on the counts of roding birds. Unfortunately, these are known to be an unreliable indicator, because the males are often polygamous, so there is no indication of how many females are present. Woodcock also nest early and wintering birds may commence roding before they migrate. In the late 1970s, however, the regional population was tentatively put at 500-1,500 'pairs' (*BWM*). The CBC recorded a 76% decline nationally between 1974 and 1999, but the data has a south-easterly bias, so it may not be representative of the UK as a whole. However, it is probably appropriate to this region, although Woodcock have been recorded on too few regional CBC plots to verify this.

The decline in numbers has also been accompanied by a contraction in range, which, between the two BTO *Atlases*, was 29% nationally, but 35% regionally. Within the region the retraction was not uniform, being less marked in Staffordshire (20%) and most severe in Worcestershire (40%) and Warwickshire (55%) where birds virtually disappeared from the small woods across the Severn and Avon Vales, along the Cotswold fringe and in the Dunsmore and Feldon areas. During 1988-91 Woodcock were found in just about half (52%) of the 10-km squares in the region, and it seems likely there has been a further reduction in range since. Taking into account what evidence is available, an equally tentative estimate now of roding males would be towards the lower end of the range 100-400.

The core of the population is now concentrated into the three most wooded parts of the region, namely Cannock Chase, the Churnet Valley and the Wyre Forest, but even from these places it is hard to establish any firm trends. Thorough surveys of Cannock Chase in 1992, 1997 and 2002 revealed 27, 30 and 15-20 roding males respectively. This suggests some recent decline and numbers were considered to be down in the conifer plantations. Territories are large and flight paths overlap, however, so it is also possible that a more cautious approach was taken in 2002 (Bennett *et al.* 2002). Data from the Churnet Valley is even sparser, but there were five roding birds at Coombes Valley in 1987 and 1992, while counts along the Dowles Brook area of the Wyre Forest, where birds were reported in nineteen years, ranged from seven in 1985 to three in 1996, five in 1999 and three in 2000. Better data are available for some of the smaller sites, however. For example, in the Arden area, the number of roding birds at Bentley Park Woods between 1986-2001 ranged from two to five, with the higher numbers in recent years. Conversely, in The Gullet area of the Malverns, eight were roding in 1989 and 1994, but this then declined to four and then three in the next two years. Overall, the average number of sites from which roding birds were reported each year steadily declined from the early 1980s until 1995, since when it has halved.

Outside the breeding season, the Woodcock population is swollen in winter by variable numbers of immigrants from the Continent. Again it is difficult to quantify the scale because more records are submitted as birds become scarcer. The largest recent counts came from the Packington estate, where a shooting party flushed about 20 birds in 1999, and at DM Kineton, where there were 14 in 1990. On average, though, only around 60 a year are reported from the whole region—which must be a very small proportion of the true numbers present.

Birds are naturally scarce within the region's urban areas, but they were present on the WMBC's Harborne reserve in consecutive winters from 1998-2000. There have also been several records of them turning up in suburban gardens during the winter months, both in the Potteries and the West Midlands county, while one even appeared on the car park at New Street station in Birmingham, where it unfortunately flew into a car windscreen and was killed. Birds sometimes become disorientated in bad weather, turning up in unlikely situations, such as the one on top of the Malvern Hills in thick fog in 1987. The only ringing recovery for the current period involved a juvenile bird, which was ringed at Packington in January 1991 and shot at Worksop (Nottinghamshire) in the following January.

Black-tailed Godwit   *Limosa limosa*
Frequent passage migrant, rare in winter.

The elegant Black-tailed Godwit is now seen with increasing frequency around the shorelines of the region's reservoirs, lakes and gravel pits, mainly during its spring and autumn migrations. Two races pass through Britain at these seasons—the declining *L. l. limosa*, which breeds in western Eurasia, including sparingly in Britain, and winters mostly in western Africa; and the expanding *L. l. islandica*, which breeds largely in Iceland but winters on our estuaries.

In *BWM* the species was described as scarce, but regular—a situation that remained true during the early 1980s, when on average between 25-30 passed through each year. Numbers then increased at a steadily accelerating rate to reach around 100 a year in the early 1990s and almost 240 a year during 1997-2001. This increase correlates with that of the national WeBS index and coincides with favourable breeding conditions in Iceland (see Prater 1975 and Pollitt *et al.* 2000). At least 385 birds were recorded during the fifty years 1929-1978 (*BWM*), but this pales into

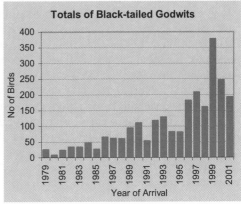

249

insignificance compared to the 2,400 noted in just twenty-three years during 1979-2001.

This huge increase has been accompanied by a significant shift in the seasonal distribution. During 1929-78, almost half of all birds (48%) occurred in spring, but the equivalent proportion during 1979-2001 was just less than a third. Moreover, the latter included a phenomenal flock of 172 that fed along the north shore at Belvide Reservoir on May 11th 1999. If this quite extraordinary flock—which needless to say set a new regional record—is excluded, then the proportion falls below a quarter (23%). The current period also brought the first birds ever to arrive in winter (December-February). These began with one at Ladywalk on February 19th 1980, but it was the 1990s before more followed. Between 1991-2001 there was then a small spate of records, with five in December (1991, twice in 1998, 2000 and 2001), three in January (1993 and twice in 1996) and one in February (1997). In addition, following the arrival at Draycote Water of a small flock in the autumn of 1996, there were various sightings across Warwickshire until early January 1997, probably involving at least some of this flock.

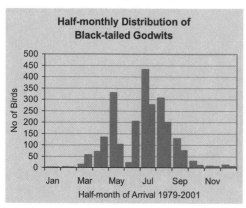

Half-monthly Distribution of Black-tailed Godwits

No of Birds

Half-month of Arrival 1979-2001

Spring passage sometimes begins with a trickle of birds in March and then intensifies in late April and early May. At this season, most pass quickly through, either singly or in small groups, with large parties being unusual. Apart from the exceptional flock of 172 mentioned above, the most reported was 27 at Bredon's Hardwick on April 19th 2000.

Return passage begins quite early, with a good number of adult birds arriving in late June. These then peak in early July, to be followed by the juveniles in August. Significantly, both peaks are about two weeks earlier than they were during 1929-78 (*BWM*). Finally, there is a definite 'tail' to the autumn passage, with new arrivals continuing into November. The return passage also brings the larger flocks, with reports of several up to 20 strong and the highest being 37 at Belvide on August 12th 1992 and 40 at Blithfield Reservoir on July 25th 1999. In comparison, the largest flocks quoted in *BWM* all occurred in spring and none exceeded 15. Returning birds may also stay for some time, with one remaining at Wilden for 37 days in 1998 (from September 19th-October 25th), while another lingered at Upton Warren from August 4th to the end of September in 1979.

In the current period, just over half of the birds (53%) occurred in Staffordshire, whilst Warwickshire and Worcestershire received 23% and 22% respectively. Even allowing for the small size and highly developed nature of the West Midlands county, with only 2%, its habitats are clearly not attractive to this species. During the ten years 1992-2001 Black-tailed Godwits were seen at about 60 widely scattered localities, but almost half of the birds were concentrated at just three sites, namely Belvide Reservoir (19% excluding the exceptional flock of 172), Upton Warren (17%) and Blithfield Reservoir (12%). Other sites holding 5% or more of birds were Kingsbury Water Park and Bredon's Hardwick (6% each) and Brandon Marsh, Dosthill and Draycote Water (5% each).

There have been several references to birds showing the characteristics of the Icelandic race *L. l. islandica* and definite proof that some birds originate from there is provided by two individuals. The first was one of four juveniles that arrived at Marsh Lane Nature Reserve on September 12th 1999, having been colour-ringed as a chick in Iceland on July 14th of that year, and the second was one of a party of 14 birds at Tittesworth Reservoir on July 17th 2004, which had been ringed in northern Iceland on June 16th 2003. Between times it had also been seen at Clonakilty Bay (County Cork, Southern Ireland) in August 2003 and on the Humber estuary (Lincolnshire) in January 2004. Other evidence of movements is provided by two birds that were colour-ringed on the Wash in 1996 and 1998. The first of these found its way to Upton Warren on July 27th 1999, while the latter, ringed at Terrington Marsh (Norfolk) in August, had moved to the Netherlands in March 1999 before arriving at Belvide Reservoir on July 21st. Nine days later it was back on the east coast at Snettisham (Norfolk).

Bar-tailed Godwit   *Limosa lapponica*
Uncommon passage migrant, rare in winter.

Bar-tailed Godwits come from their Arctic breeding grounds to winter around our coasts, but occur less often inland. Nevertheless, despite being the scarcer of the two godwits, small numbers are seen on migration every year, mostly at the region's larger reservoirs.

During the period 1929-78 Bar-tailed and Black-tailed Godwits appeared in virtually equal numbers, with *BWM* reporting 355 of the former over the fifty years. Since then the Bar-tailed Godwit has increased fourfold, with the twenty-three years 1979-2001 producing almost 800 birds, but even this has failed to keep pace with the phenomenal growth in Black-tailed Godwits. Occurrences during the current period seem to have followed a cyclical pattern, but the long-term trend remained stable at around 34 birds a year. The worst year was 1980, when only four were recorded, whilst the best years were 1984, with 86, and 1992, with 85. However, numbers in both of these years were swollen by the two largest parties of the period, with 31 pausing briefly at Belvide Reservoir on April 26th 1984, during an especially strong spring passage, and 50-60 flying through Chasewater on May 5th 1992. The former party, incidentally, was also seen at Blithfield Reservoir the next day.

Such movements are typical of late April and early May, when large numbers of Bar-tailed Godwits are moving north-eastwards through the English Channel. Some presumably are displaced by adverse weather and end up here, whilst others may choose to cross overland, perhaps from the Severn to the Wash. Certainly their appearances are often typical of birds brought down by poor weather, such as the party of 28 that landed at Draycote Water during a thunderstorm on April 26th 1999. In all, 41% of birds occurred in late April and early May—a very similar figure to the 37% recorded in *BWM*.

Exactly the same percentage of birds (41%) was recorded on return passage (*cf.* 51% in *BWM*). Movement at this season is much more protracted, however, beginning in late July, peaking in early September and then continuing to the end of the month, with a few stragglers into October and even November. Small flocks are also noted in autumn, often just flying over. Examples include 21 that flew straight through at Tittesworth Reservoir on August 9th 1998 and some over the urban parts of the region, such as 20 moving west over Seabridge, in the Potteries, on September 6th 1979 and the same number moving north-

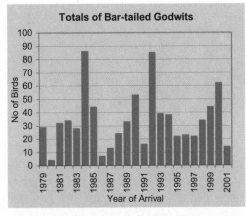

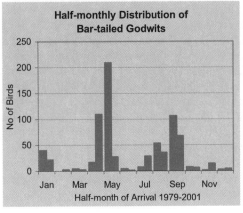

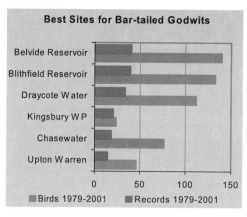

Best Sites for Bar-tailed Godwits

■ Birds 1979-2001 ■ Records 1979-2001

west over Kingstanding, Birmingham, on September 18th 1985. Since the current period of analysis, a flock of 24 was seen flying over Fenny Compton on September 1st 2002. Birds are more likely to stay around in autumn than they are in spring, with one having spent 20 days at Blithfield, from September 3rd-22nd 2000, another 27 days at Coton Pools from September 20th-October 16th 1983 and one 52 days at Blithfield, from September 17th-November 7th 1982. That many over-flying birds might be making involuntary stops, however, is reinforced by the fact that a staggering 95% left within two days.

As might be expected of an estuarine wader, the larger reservoirs, together with the chain of wetlands along the Middle Tame Valley (including Kingsbury Water Park) have attracted most birds. This means that Staffordshire tops the list of counties, with 55% of birds, followed by Warwickshire with 30%, Worcestershire 11% and the West Midlands with just 4%.

Whimbrel   *Numenius phaeopus*
Frequent passage migrant.

Migrating Whimbrel pass through the region in spring and autumn as they journey between their African winter grounds and their northern breeding territories. The distinctive, seven-note whistle of birds flying overhead makes detection easy, even at night.

BWM described this as a scarce species and mentioned only 840 birds in the fifty years 1929-78—an average of 17 a year. Even by the end of that period, though, numbers were running at a higher level and during the early 1980s the average was around 50 a year. It then climbed to about 75 during the late 1980s before rising to a mean of over 150 a year in the early 1990s. Since then it has fallen slightly, to approximately 100 a year. Overall, the period 1979-2001 produced just over 2,000 birds.

This increase in numbers has been accompanied by a significant shift in the seasonal distribution. During 1929-78 only about 30% of birds occurred in spring, whereas from 1979-2001 the proportion was 53%. Moreover this shift appears to be on-going, as the table at the bottom of the page shows. Just why the spring/autumn ratio should have changed from 1:2 to 2:1 and so quickly is unclear.

Spring passage is concentrated very much into the four weeks from mid-April to mid-May, with the peak in the last two weeks. Whilst the earliest record during 1929-78 was on April 2nd (1939), the current period has produced four in March, the earliest of which was on the 24th, at Defford in 1996. At this season most birds move quickly through, but in 2001 one remained at Draycote Water for 13 days from May 12th-24th, during which time song and display were noted, whilst an-

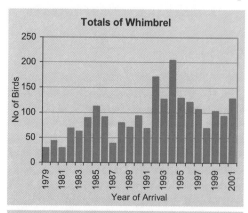

Totals of Whimbrel

Percentage of Birds in Spring				
1980-84	*1985-89*	*1990-94*	*1995-99*	*2000-01*
36	48	48	63	73

other lingered at Bredon's Hardwick for 14 days, from May 7th-20th 1996. *BWM* noted that no spring party had ever reached double figures, but several have since, with the larger ones being 28 at Chasewater on May 11th 1985, 33 at Draycote on April 30th 1995 and 40 at the same locality on May 7th 1994. The latter occurred on a day of heavy rain, when around 80 birds were noted at various sites across the region, including 20 that paused to rest at Swan Pool, Sandwell Valley.

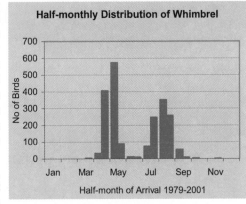

Return passage usually begins in July, reaches its climax towards the end of that month and during August, then peters out in September. Small flocks are more frequent at this season, with the larger ones being 28, at Blithfield on August 18th 1985 and Draycote on July 30th 1994; 30 flying north-west over Kingstanding (Birmingham) on August 19th 1984; and separate groups of 24 and 32 that contributed to a total passage of 64 birds at Upton Warren on August 9th 1992. A feature of the autumn passage at this latter locality is that birds sometimes join the roost of Eurasian Curlew, as indeed they also do at Ladywalk. There were two or three October records, while an exceptionally late individual at Belvide Reservoir on November 22nd 1990 is the latest on record.

Geographically, Staffordshire fared best in the current period, with 35% of birds, but, unusually, Worcestershire (32%) came ahead of Warwickshire (26%), while the West Midlands attracted just 7%. The best locations, with their number of records, were Belvide (139), Upton Warren (131), the Middle Tame Valley (121), Blithfield (82), Bredon's Hardwick (78) and Draycote Water (74).

Eurasian Curlew   (Curlew)   *Numenius arquata*
Fairly common summer resident and passage migrant. Frequent in winter.

The bubbling calls of Eurasian Curlew have long been one of the most evocative sounds of spring and summer on the moorland of north Staffordshire. Between the 1920s and 1960s the breeding range expanded tremendously, as these splendid birds spread firstly into lowland river meadows and then onto arable land. Now they have largely retreated again as this newly-claimed territory has been rendered unsuitable by progressive land drainage and changing agricultural practices. In winter the species has always been less common, but it is more so now

with the loss of permanent pastures for feeding. Those birds that do winter, frequently gather at one or two traditional roost sites.

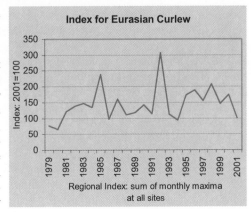

Nationally the distribution is strongly biased towards the uplands of north and west Britain and this comes out as a strong feature within this region too, with the *Breeding Atlas* showing birds in 90% of the 10-km squares covering Staffordshire and Worcestershire, but in only 52% of those covering Warwickshire and the West Midlands. Since then the range has contracted still further, at least in the latter two counties, where surveys provisionally indicate the presence of birds in only

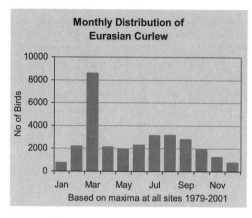

Monthly Distribution of Eurasian Curlew

No of Birds

Jan   Mar   May   Jul   Sep   Nov

Based on maxima at all sites 1979-2001

5% of tetrads. In Warwickshire, generally less than 20 pairs were reported each year before these more thorough tetrad surveys began, but the population is now thought to be around 30 pairs (J. Bowley *pers comm*.) Assuming a similar ratio, there are perhaps 40 or more pairs in Worcestershire compared with the combined total of 50 pairs estimated for Warwickshire and Worcestershire in *BWM*.

In Staffordshire, three major surveys carried out on the moors by the RSPB in 1985, 1992 and 1996 revealed an overall decline of 60%, from 421 pairs to 280 and 173 pairs respectively (McKnight *et al*. 1996). A further survey of waders along the river valleys, carried out by the WMBC in 1998, showed 28-32 pairs, but in many cases birds were thought to be nesting on arable or set-aside land away from the flood plains, which they used primarily for feeding. Roughly two-thirds of the sites covered had also been surveyed in 1982 and little change was found between the two dates (Gribble and Jennett 1998).

These surveys show up as pronounced peaks in the regional index, which surprisingly fails to reflect any long-term decline—presumably because this has been cancelled out by greater reporting. In all, the current regional population is probably about 200-300 pairs—slightly less than the 250-400 pairs quoted in *BWM*, which with hindsight was almost certainly an underestimate. The Eurasian Curlew is on the *Amber List* of Species of Conservation Concern (Gregory *et al*. 2002) and its future is rightly being accorded a high priority in the Peak Park, where it has been included in the Biodiversity Action Plan. Given a sympathetic approach by landowners, such as that in parts of north Warwickshire in the late 1980s, its survival might even be secured in the lowlands as well.

Numbers start to increase from February, as birds begin to reoccupy lowland territories, and over a quarter occur in March, when the main movement back to their breeding grounds takes place. The return movement is less obvious, as it spans from late summer through to autumn. In winter the distribution is more restricted and birds are fewer, with just 9% occurring during November-January. During the *Winter Atlas*, birds were recorded in 50% of 10-km squares in Staffordshire and Worcestershire, whilst the comparative figure for Warwickshire and the West Midlands was 31%.

The largest concentrations are usually to be found at roosts. At Upton Warren and Coton-Ladywalk these may form throughout the year, although they are often absent or very small during the breeding season. Maximum numbers are normally reached either during February-March, or after the breeding season in late summer or autumn and during 1991/2-2000/1 the average sizes were 103 and 23 birds respectively. The Upton Warren roost has held over 100 birds on many occasions, with peaks of 120 in July-August 1985 and September 1988. However, the largest numbers have been at two spring roosts in north Staffordshire where birds gather in March prior to returning to their breeding territories. For many years that at Longsdon Mill Pool regularly held the highest numbers, including 574 in 1982 and a record 600 in 1987, but more recently the larger numbers have been at Tittesworth Reservoir, where the most recorded was 310 in 1995.

During 1992-2001, Worcestershire and Staffordshire were the most visited counties, with 46% and 42% of birds respectively, though it must be pointed out that Worcestershire's dominance stemmed largely from regular counting of the Upton Warren roost, which accounted for 18% of all birds. In Staffordshire, by comparison, little information was received from the moors apart from the RSPB surveys in 1992 and 1996, so this area's share of birds was only

11%. The only other site worthy of mention was Tittesworth Reservoir, on the edge of the moors, which attracted 4%. Warwickshire's share of birds was 11% and the West Midlands 1%. Indeed, Eurasian Curlews are seldom seen in urban situations, other than at oases such as Sandwell Valley, so individuals at Salford Bridge in 1984 and on a cricket pitch at Netherton Hill in 1996 were noteworthy.

Two ringing recoveries are of interest. One shows an adult, ringed at Ombersley in June 1986, moving 407 km into France, where it was shot in October of the same year. The other involved a bird, ringed as a juvenile in Wellington (Shropshire) in August 1980, that was killed against wires near Droitwich Spa in February 1997, when it was a least sixteen-and-a-half years of age.

Upland Sandpiper   *Bartramia longicauda*
Very rare vagrant. One nineteenth century record.

This was the first fully-dated British record of this vagrant from North America.

Regional Record Number	County Record Number	Year	Locality, Date and Notes
1	Warks 1	1851	Compton Verney: October 31st, shot. *Witherby et al. 1938 Vol IV:181*

At the time of its occurrence, the species was known as Bartram's Sandpiper—and this is still perpetuated in its scientific name. Although this record is generally claimed to be the first for Britain, it is interesting that Witherby *et al.* (1938-44) also mention one on the River Parrett (Somerset) *circa* 1850, which could conceivably have pre-dated this one. The Upland Sandpiper remains one of the rarer Transatlantic vagrants to visit Britain, with just 44 records up to 2002 (Rogers *et al.* 2003).

Spotted Redshank   *Tringa erythropus*
Scarce or uncommon passage migrant, very rare in winter.

Spotted Redshanks have become increasingly scarce, so it is always a pleasure to find one of these graceful waders, with their long, thin bills, at one of our wetlands. They breed in lowland Arctic regions and winter in sub-Saharan Africa.

BWM noted that this species had increased dramatically as a migrant to the region in recent decades, with roughly 45 birds a year recorded during 1969-78. This level was broadly maintained until 1982, since when numbers have inexplicably halved to an average of about 20 a year. During this time the worst showings were in 1985 and 1997, with nine and seven respectively, whilst the best years were 1990, 1996 and 2000, with 35, 33 and 32 birds respectively—but all still well below the earlier average. Furthermore, the long-term trend since 1991 has been progressively downwards. Overall, there were 704 birds between 1929-78 compared with 576 in the current period.

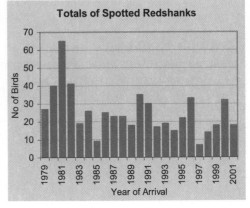

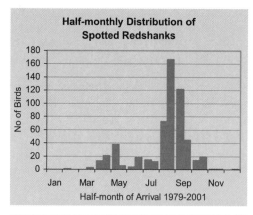

Half-monthly Distribution of Spotted Redshanks

No of Birds / Half-month of Arrival 1979-2001

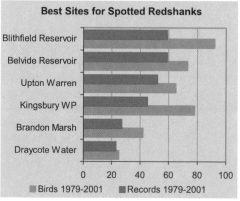

Best Sites for Spotted Redshanks

Blithfield Reservoir / Belvide Reservoir / Upton Warren / Kingsbury WP / Brandon Marsh / Draycote Water

■ Birds 1979-2001   ■ Records 1979-2001

The seasonal pattern remains much as it was during 1929-78, with a small spring passage during April and May that reaches its maximum in early May and a much stronger, well-spread return passage from July to October, with most between mid-August and mid-September. However, the percentage of birds occurring in spring has doubled, from 7% during 1929-78 to 15% between 1979-2001. One feature common to both periods is the unusual number of records in late June and early July, which are probably of females arriving in Britain to moult. A peculiarity of this species is that the males remain behind on the breeding grounds to tend their young. Males and juveniles then come later in the main passage.

At this time small parties are sometimes recorded, with the largest in the current period being eight, at Blithfield Reservoir on September 5th 1979 and Alvecote Pools on September 16th 1981; and 11 at Kingsbury Water Park on September 12th 1981. The only spring party of note comprised eight birds at Brandon Marsh on May 1st 1990. Three-quarters of all records involved just single birds. Autumn also produced a couple of really long-staying birds, with one spending 48 days at Blithfield, from September 3rd-October 20th 1997, and the other 64 days at Belvide, from July 6th-September 7th 1985 during which time it moulted into winter plumage.

Winter records are very rare, but the present period produced two: a bird which remained in the Coton-Kingsbury area from December 27th 1980 until April 25th 1981—which is still the only recorded instance of a protracted wintering stay in the region—and one which remained for just a month at Bredon's Hardwick from February 5th-March 9th 1998.

The distribution of birds between the counties shows the majority (41%) in Staffordshire, 35% in Warwickshire, 22% in Worcestershire and just 2% in the West Midlands. Amongst the sites, 40% of all the records have been shared more or less equally by Blithfield, Belvide and Upton Warren.

Common Redshank (Redshank) *Tringa totanus*
Frequent passage migrant and summer resident. Uncommon winter visitor.

The frequent piping calls of these highly vocal birds readily betray their presence around the shores of reservoirs and gravel pits, amongst the rank vegetation of wetlands or in damp riverside meadows. Spring and summer are when most are seen, but winter occurrences are not infrequent. Regular over-wintering is not yet established, although the current run of mild winters may well encourage it before long.

As a breeding species, the Common Redshank has declined markedly. The *Breeding Atlas* recorded birds in 36% of the region's 10-km squares, mostly those covering the lower valleys of the Severn and Avon, the Trent and Tame valleys and the many reservoirs and gravel pits

particularly in south Staffordshire. Nationally, the CBC recorded a decline of 63% during 1974-99, resulting in its inclusion on the *Amber List* of Species of Conservation Concern (Gregory *et al.* 2002).

In this region the biggest losses have been in lowland meadows, where drainage, re-seeding of permanent pastures, early cutting for silage and trampling by more livestock have all impeded successful breeding. But losses have also been recorded from the rushy pastures of the northern moors and even favoured wetland areas have suffered declines.

In 1978 the population of Staffordshire was thought to be around 40 pairs (*BWM*) and this was confirmed by the 1982 survey of wet meadows, which found 36 pairs at fifteen sites. In 1998 just 25 pairs were found at an equal number of (but not necessarily the same) sites. A comparison of those sites common to both surveys showed a decline of 50%, mostly in the upper Trent catchment. Up to five pairs also bred on the moors until 1985, but by 1992 these had all gone due to drainage of the regular site on Morridge (Gribble 2000).

Information from the other counties is less detailed, but the Warwickshire population was estimated in *BWM* as 20 pairs, whilst that of Worcestershire was implicitly put at less than 50 pairs. In Warwickshire probably no more than 15 pairs now attempt to breed, while Worcestershire might be down to a dozen pairs and the West Midlands just one or two. In all, the regional breeding population could now be as low as 40-70 pairs, which is less than half the 100-150 pairs suggested in *BWM*.

Numbers begin to increase in February as birds return to their breeding grounds, peak in March and April and then steadily decline from June onwards as birds drift slowly away again. All too often an early exodus seems to be prompted by failed breeding attempts. Despite the widespread decline in breeding numbers, the regional index (based on monthly maxima), though erratic, shows a steady long-term rise, presumably due to greater reporting. However, flocks have also been getting larger, with up to 20 occurring fairly regularly and several exceeding the most mentioned in *BWM*, which was 30 in March 1968. The five largest flocks all occurred at Bredon's Hardwick during March, with 41 in 1989 and 1991, 43 in 1994, 45 in 1992 and a regional record of 49 in 1990. Away from this locality, the most was 33 in the Coton-Kingsbury Water Park area in March 1989. Substantial autumn flocks are more unusual, as most birds have left the region by this time, but September counts reached 22 at Draycote Water in 1992, 25 at Belvide Reservoir in 2000 and 30 at Blithfield Reservoir in 1994.

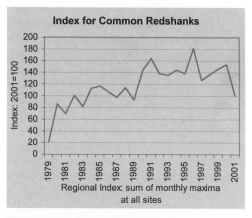

Index for Common Redshanks

Index: 2001=100

Regional Index: sum of monthly maxima at all sites

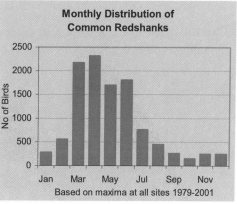

Monthly Distribution of Common Redshanks

No of Birds

Based on maxima at all sites 1979-2001

Despite the *Winter Atlas* showing birds in 36% of 10-km squares—a similar distribution to that in summer—relatively few occur at this season, with just 8% during October-January, mainly in ones and twos. This is because the shallow water in which they feed readily freezes, so in cold spells they are more vulnerable inland than on the coast. Two examples of the influence of weather were provided in 1987, when one resorted to feeding along a small stream at Arley during a freeze in January, then later in the year 15 were grounded at Bittell Reservoir in thick fog in October. *BWM* referred to the Tame Valley as a popular wintering area, with groups up to 15. This area, together with the Trent-Tame confluence, remains popular, but numbers have been smaller recently, with no count reaching double figures. Complete over-wintering remains rare, but did occur on two or three occasions during 1978/9-2000/1. The possibility that at least some of these wintering birds are of the Icelandic race *T. t. robusta* was raised in *BWM*, but conclusive proof is still lacking.

The monthly maxima show that almost half of the birds recorded during 1992-2001 were in Staffordshire, which attracted 45%, with Worcestershire (29%) and Warwickshire (23%) making up the other half, leaving only 3% in the West Midlands. Although Common Redshanks tend to be more widespread than many other waders, they still have favoured sites, with Bredon's Hardwick and Belvide Reservoir each attracting 5% of birds, Dosthill-Kingsbury Water Park 4% and Upton Warren and Brandon Marsh 3% each.

Ringing recoveries show movements to and from the coast. A nestling, ringed at Kingsbury Water Park in July 1989, was shot on the Wirral at Hoylake (Merseyside) in August 1989 and a juvenile, colour-ringed at Southport (Lancashire) in June 1988, was sighted at Belvide Reservoir in March 1998.

Marsh Sandpiper   *Tringa stagnatilis*
Very rare vagrant. One record.

This record was only the nineteenth for Britain and was unusual in being both inland and the first ever in June (Smith *et al.* 1975).

Regional Record Number	County Record Number	Year	Locality, Date and Notes
1	Staffs 1	1974	Belvide Reservoir: June 22nd. *BB 68:317*

Marsh Sandpipers breed from Finland and the Baltic eastwards through Siberia and winter from Africa eastwards through India to China, south-east Asia and Australia.

Greenshank   (Common Greenshank)   *Tringa nebularia*
Frequent passage migrant, rare in winter.

Migrating Greenshanks regularly interrupt the long journeys between their breeding territories in north Scotland and Scandinavia and their winter quarters in west Africa to feed and rest at the region's reservoirs, gravel pits and marshy areas. They are usually most numerous in late summer, when the low water levels expose areas of mud for feeding.

Although numbers vary considerably from year to year, the regional index based on monthly maxima counts during 1979-2001 points to a steady increase, possibly because there is more suitable habitat.

Spring passage is usually fairly weak and only 12% of the birds recorded during 1929-78 occurred at this season (*BWM*). During the current period the comparative figure was 15%, hinting at a slight shift in the spring-autumn balance. There is also some evidence of birds arriving earlier in recent years, with the first March record in 1989, since when the total for that month has risen to 14 birds of which the earliest was one at Ladywalk on March 12th 1994. Nevertheless, May is still the main time for birds, with 62% of the spring passage occurring during this month.

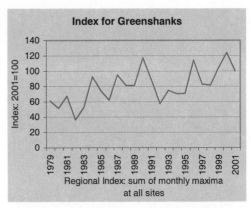

The first returning birds then begin to appear towards the end of July and passage culminates in August and September. Around 84% of birds are seen at this time (*cf.* 87% during 1929-78 *BWM*), mostly during late August-early September, with just a few occurrences in October or even November.

Winter records are rare, but not unknown. Indeed, there have been a series of them recently in the Tame and Trent Valleys. This began with one that remained in the Alrewas-Barton Gravel Pit area from January into March during 1994. Others then followed in 1997, when one was at Clay Mills on January 1st, with perhaps the same individual returning to wander the gravel pits during the following November and December. A repeat performance in 1998 saw two at Barton

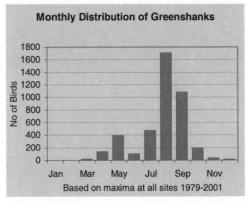

Gravel Pit in November, with presumably the same two then at Drayton Bassett Gravel Pits in December. One was also at Belvide Reservoir on December 19th 1999.

Although spring passage is the weaker of the two, small parties sometimes occur at this season, with groups of 10 noted at both Belvide Reservoir and the Dosthill-Kingsbury Water Park area in May 2000. The largest concentrations, however, are invariably in autumn, when double figure counts are not unusual, but few parties exceed 20 birds. The most mentioned in *BWM* was 26 at Blithfield Reservoir in mid-July 1976, but the same locality has since attracted 34, in August 1996. Elsewhere, other notable gatherings during the current period were a flock of 18 that circled Grimley on August 19th 2001, setting a new Worcestershire record, 17 at Belvide Reservoir in September 1992 and the same number at Elford in August 1996. The geographical spread during 1992-2001 shows that Staffordshire attracted 44% of birds, Warwickshire 27%, Worcestershire 22% and the West Midlands 7%. The high percentage in Staffordshire is due largely to the importance of Blithfield and Belvide Reservoirs, which attracted 13% and 10% of birds respectively. The only other sites to hold more than 5% of birds were Upton Warren, with 7%, and Dosthill-Kingsbury Water Park, Draycote Water and Brandon Marsh, each of which had 6%.

Lesser Yellowlegs *Tringa flavipes*
Very rare vagrant. Two records.

Although the Lesser Yellowlegs is one of the North American waders that occurs quite regularly in Britain, with over 250 by 2003 (Rogers *et al.* 2004), there has only been one further record in the West Midlands to add to that in 1979, which was documented in *BWM*.

Regional Record Number	County Record Number	Year	Locality, Date and Notes
1	Staffs 1	1979	Blithfield Reservoir: adult, September 15th-30th. *BB 73:509*
2	Staffs 2	1995	Knighton Reservoir: juvenile moulting into first-winter, November 11th-16th. *BB 89:502*

The Blithfield individual occurred in what was a poor year for the species nationally, but arrived on a typical date. The Knighton bird, though rather late, was in a year which saw two others in the East Midlands (Rogers *et al.* 1996).

Green Sandpiper   *Tringa ochropus*
Frequent passage migrant and uncommon winter visitor.

Green Sandpipers are one of the commoner passage waders to visit the region, especially in late summer when they migrate from their breeding grounds in Fennoscandia and eastern Europe to spend the winter in western Europe or Africa. They have a marked preference for running water and are just as likely to be found along the feeder streams of reservoirs, lakes and gravel pits as round their muddy shorelines. Sometimes they visit quite small farm ponds, streams and even drained stretches of canal.

Numbers vary quite noticeably from year-to-year, depending on breeding success, weather conditions and water levels, but the long-term trend showed a steady increase during the 1980s and peaked in 1990/1. This was followed by a sharp drop over the next two winters, since when numbers have slowly recovered.

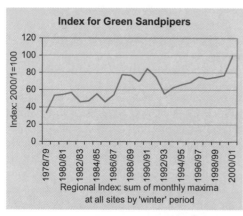

Index for Green Sandpipers

Regional Index: sum of monthly maxima at all sites by 'winter' period

Two-thirds of Green Sandpipers are seen on their late summer passage, which is one of the earliest for any wader, sometimes beginning as early as the second week of June. Numbers then increase rapidly during July and reach their maximum in August. Thereafter they subside again until most have left by the end of September. A further 19% then occur during the winter, with some staying throughout before joining with the very weak spring passage in March and April that accounts for 10% of birds. One or two late stragglers sometimes hang on until the first few days of May, but records from then until mid-June are extremely rare, though one was at Bredon's Hardwick on May 9th-10th 2000.

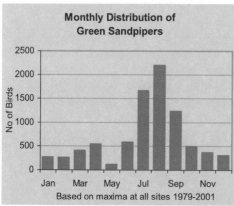

Monthly Distribution of Green Sandpipers

Based on maxima at all sites 1979-2001

Loose flocks regularly build up during the summer, with up to a dozen commonplace and 20 quite normal at favoured localities such as Brandon Marsh and Upton Warren. The largest gathering mentioned in *BWM* was 26 at Grimley in August 1977, but during the current period there were 27 at Brandon in August 1997, 31 at Upton Warren in August 2001 and 34 at Brandon in July 1993. Indeed, these two sites had a monopoly of all the largest flocks, with Brandon having the most in thirteen years and Upton Warren in nine years, while in the remaining year they were equal. In all, Brandon Marsh held 18% of birds and Upton Warren 15%. Otherwise, Dosthill-Kingsbury Water Park had 8% and Grimley 6%, but no other site exceeded 3%. Thus virtually half the birds were concentrated at just four sites and this largely determined the county distribution, which during 1991/2-2000/1 saw Warwickshire, with 35% of birds, as the most visited county, followed by Worcestershire (32%), Staffordshire (27%) and the West Midlands (6%).

Wintering birds seek out those places least likely to freeze over, such as canal locks, saline flashes, sewage works and streams. This is also the most likely time for them to appear at small farm ponds, as exemplified by individuals at Lower Smite Farm and Oddingley in January 1995 and Warndon in January 1997. Numbers appear to have changed very little from the wintering population of 25 estimated in *BWM*.

Wood Sandpiper *Tringa glareola*
Uncommon passage migrant. One record of wintering.

Reservoirs, pools, gravel pits and even tiny pools in flooded meadows suffice to provide migrating Wood Sandpipers with somewhere to feed and rest. They breed in Fennoscandia and north-east Europe and winter in Africa.

Although numbers are small, birds do occur annually. *BWM* charted an increase from around 12 a year in the 1950s to 15 in the 1960s and 24 in the 1970s, and attributed this to an apparent growth of the population in the northern Palaearctic forests (Ferguson-Lees 1971).

As sometimes happens with an expanding population, numbers fell back to around 15 per annum in the early 1980s before increasing again to an average of around 28 a year in the early 1990s, since when there has been a further slight fall. The best year, with 38 birds, was 1991, whilst the worst, with just eight birds, was 1981. As much as anything, the year-to-year fluctuations are a reflection of weather conditions at the time of migration and are a characteristic feature of many passage waders.

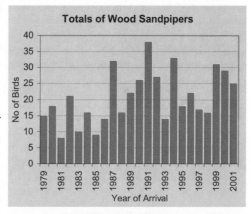

Spring passage sometimes begins in April, with the earliest during 1979-2001 on the 11th, at Brandon Marsh in 1995. The main movement is in May, when 29% of all birds pass through. Interestingly, this is double the percentage recorded in *BWM* for 1929-78, indicating a clear shift towards stronger spring passages. At this time birds seldom stay for long as they are intent on reaching their northern breeding grounds as soon as possible, with one at Dosthill Pool on May 27th 1998 already singing and indulging in display flights.

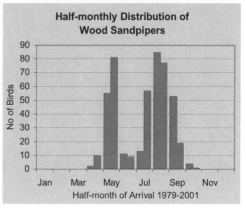

Almost before the last of the spring migrants have passed through in early June, the first returning birds start to appear at the end of the month. Indeed, with some individuals,

Best Sites for Wood Sandpipers

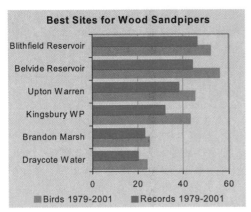

Blithfield Reservoir
Belvide Reservoir
Upton Warren
Kingsbury WP
Brandon Marsh
Draycote Water

0   20   40   60

■ Birds 1979-2001   ■ Records 1979-2001

such as that at Belvide Reservoir from June 14th-20th 1990, it is impossible to know whether they are travelling north or south. The bulk of the return passage then occurs between mid-July and mid-September, but mostly in August. At this season, birds will often linger for some considerable time, with stays of two or three weeks not unusual. In recent times the more protracted stays have lasted 31 days, at Dosthill from July 29th to August 28th 1990, and 32 days, at Blithfield Reservoir from September 1st to October 2nd 1996.

Amazingly, the longest stay of all was made by a bird which arrived in the Middle Tame Valley on October 30th 1982 and left on May 3rd 1983—possibly the first instance of a bird over-wintering in Britain. Apart from this bird, there were four others in October during 1979-2001, with the latest on the 11th—at Belvide in 1990.

As would be expected of a species that is equally at home on small as well as large waters, the geographical spread of birds is more even than that of some waders, with Staffordshire having 41%, Warwickshire 34%, Worcestershire 21% and the West Midlands 4%. The distribution of records also reflects this, with Upton Warren having been visited almost as often as Belvide and Blithfield Reservoirs, whilst in Warwickshire both Kingsbury Water Park and Brandon Marsh have produced more records than the much larger Draycote Water.

Common Sandpiper   *Actitis hypoleucos*
Fairly common passage migrant. Scarce summer resident and winter visitor.

The Common Sandpiper is a characteristic bird of the upland streams and reservoirs to the north and west of the region and a few pairs breed in north Staffordshire. On passage it is one of our commoner waders and is often seen along rivers and canals, or at reservoirs, lakes and gravel pits, as it skims low across the water on flickering wings, or works its way steadily along the shoreline as it feeds. Being a bird of fast-flowing, boulder-strewn streams, it is just as much at home amongst the gravel, shingle, rocks and man-made dams and embankments as on expanses of mud. Occasional birds are also seen in winter.

Historically Common Sandpipers used to breed on many of the fast-flowing streams and rivers in north Staffordshire, such as the Dane, Hamps, Manifold, Churnet and Dove and also along the Teme and its tributaries in west Worcestershire. Nesting was even recorded, or at least suspected, in several lowland situations as well. However, the species is known to be susceptible to disturbance from activities such as angling and hiking (Yalden 1992). Its range has also been contracting around the periphery (*Breeding Atlas*) and in this region birds have gradually retreated or disappeared from virtually all of these locations.

It was noted in *BWM* that there were less than five pairs left in the moorlands, mainly in the less disturbed areas, but none could be found at any of the traditional territories in 1980 and 1981 and the species was thought to be extinct in the region. However, at least two pairs bred at Tittesworth Reservoir in 1982, and possibly in the previous two years, and this has since become a regular site. Common Sandpipers will breed in quite small sanctuaries and the nature reserve at this reservoir seems an ideal location for them. The number of pairs increased to six or seven at times, although not all necessarily bred, and in 2004 three or four pairs were present and at least one bred successfully (A. Lawrence *pers comm.*).

Tittesworth appears to be the most southerly of the Pennine sites in regular use, although elsewhere around the moorland fringe breeding occurred at least once at each of Denford (1983), Rudyard (1984) and Leek (1994). The *Breeding Atlas* also showed confirmed breeding in six 10-km squares and birds present in a further 21 squares. Although the majority of the latter were almost certainly passage birds, isolated lowland breeding does still occur, with successful pairs at Doxey Marshes in 1988 and a gravel pit at Salford Priors in 2002—the latter being the first breeding record for Warwickshire.

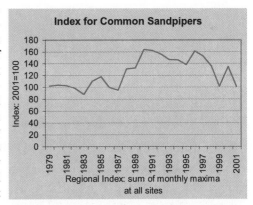

As a passage migrant, the number of Common Sandpipers moving through the region increased sharply in the late 1980s, but then fell away again a decade later, leaving little long-term change. Records of first and last dates were kept for over fifty years until 1991, by which time it had become impossible to distinguish migrants from wintering individuals. Prior to then, the average date for the first birds to arrive, calculated over 54 years, was April 6th, with the earliest ever being on March 9th, as far back as 1944. A strong passage during April and May then accounts for

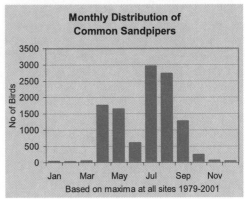

almost 30% of birds. Mostly these pass through singly, or in small groups of less than ten, with the largest party at this season being 20 at Sandwell Valley in April 1994. Return passage typically starts towards the end of June and lasts until the end of September, during which time around 60% of birds occur. Again, many pass through singly, or in small groups, often along rivers where they go largely unnoticed, but flocks of 20 or more are also fairly commonplace. Indeed, Blithfield Reservoir has frequently held more than this and on twelve occasions during the current period recorded the highest annual count, including a maximum of 43 in July 1991. In the last two years, however, it has had no more than eight! Elsewhere, 37 were in the Coton-Kingsbury Water Park area in August 1988 and 36 at Tittesworth Reservoir in July 1996. The regional record, however, remains that quoted in *BWM*, namely 50 at Blithfield Reservoir on August 5th 1970. By October only a few stragglers or potential wintering individuals remain and over 50 years the average last date for migrant birds was October 23rd.

Winter records began to increase during the 1970s and *BWM* referred to half-a-dozen or so instances of successful over-wintering, particularly in the Middle Tame Valley. The 1980s certainly saw more birds staying into late autumn and, aided by the milder weather, at least one individual has probably over-wintered in most years since. Food can be hard to find, however, and at Draycote Water one was observed picking insects from the carcass of a gull. Sadly another managed to survive through to late February at Chasewater in 1983 only to finish up dead on the end of a fishing line.

Based on the monthly maxima during 1979-2001, most birds (41%) were seen in Staffordshire, with 24% in Worcestershire, 22% in Warwickshire and 13% in the West Midlands. During the same period the principal sites were Blithfield Reservoir and Draycote Water (each with 10% of birds), Belvide Reservoir (8%), Tittesworth Reservoir (6%) and Upton Warren and Bredon's Hardwick (5% each).

BWM recorded three movements of birds between the Pennines and this region. During the current period, a colour-ringed bird from Ladyside, in the Scottish Borders, was at Belvide Reservoir on April 16th 2000. Unfortunately, because the position of the BTO ring was unclear, it could have been either of two individuals, one ringed in 1998 and the other in 1999.

Spotted Sandpiper   *Actitis macularius*
Very rare vagrant. Four records.

After three in six years between 1977-82, there has been only one further record of this North American wader.

Regional Record Number	County Record Number		Year	Locality, Date and Notes
1	Warks	1	1977	Draycote Water: adult, May 8th-10th. *BB 71:504*
2	Warks	2	1980	Draycote Water: juvenile, September 10th-25th. *BB 74:472*
3	Staffs	1	1982	Belvide Reservoir: adult, May 18th. *BB 76:498*
4	Warks	3	1990	Draycote Water: adult, May 29th-30th. *BB 86:484*

The three spring adults posed no identification problems, whilst the sole autumn juvenile obligingly stayed long enough to ensure that the finer points of separation from a juvenile Common Sandpiper could be noted. Unusually, three of the four were at the same locality, namely Draycote Water. Autumn is the classic time for Nearctic vagrants to arrive and it is likely that those in spring had made the crossing in a previous autumn and were following their normal migratory instincts on this side of the Atlantic.

Turnstone   *Arenaria interpres*
Uncommon passage migrant, rare in winter.

The description of the Turnstone in *BWM* as a passage visitor to reservoirs and gravel pits in small numbers remains true, although its numbers have increased since that time. It is, of course, a common winter visitor to British coasts from its Arctic breeding grounds.

The fifty years 1929-78 produced 546 birds, but half of these appeared in the decade 1969-78, when there was a mean of around 30 birds a year and an annual maximum of 47. By comparison, during the twenty-three years 1979-2001 almost 1,000 birds passed through—an average of about 40 per annum—with the best year being 1993 when 109 were recorded. Numbers were low in the early 1980s, but climbed strongly over the next decade to reach a peak of around 60 a year in the early 1990s. Since then they have declined to about 40 again. However, the WeBS index shows a decline of 15% in wintering birds throughout the period 1978/79 to 2000/01.

It would be interesting to know where the Turnstones that pass through the region come from. Unfortunately there are no ringing re-

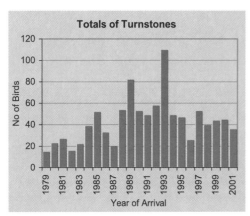

turns to provide direct evidence, but there is evidence of some movements between south-east England and west Greenland and north-east Canada (Wernham *et al.* 2002). Migration following a direct route would bring these birds over the West Midlands, where perhaps more have been grounded by the volatile weather of recent years.

There was virtually no change in the seasonal pattern of records between 1929-78 and 1979-2001. Spring passage begins in late April, but most birds appear in the first half of May after which numbers quickly subside in early June. The first returning birds then appear in July, with numbers rapidly building later in the month to reach a peak in August. Thereafter passage continues through the first-half of September, but then falls away rapidly.

During the current period the extreme passage dates were April 16th (1988) and November 1st (1986), whilst overall 39% of birds passed through in spring and 59% in autumn (*cf.* a third in May and about half in September *BWM*). Outside these passage periods, there were just ten records, including one in late November, four in December involving 17 birds, three in January and two in March.

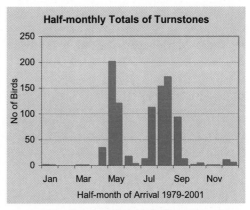

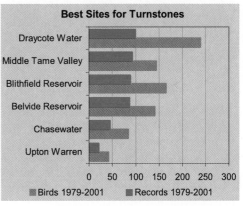

Two-thirds of all records involved just single birds, but parties up to four or five were not uncommon and double figure counts were recorded on five occasions, with the largest of these—27 at Draycote Water on August 17th 1993—setting a new regional record. Unusually, the same locality also produced the second and third highest counts, with 17 on August 11th 1993, followed by 15 on the 28th. Of the winter records, eight flying through Blithfield Reservoir on December 1st 1985 and five at Sheepwash Urban Park on December 18th 1995 were noteworthy. Most birds pass quickly through, but there have been some moderately long stays, with half-a-dozen remaining for at least a fortnight. Blithfield Reservoir claims the record, with one of three that arrived on July 22nd 1999 staying 18 days and the other two 25 days until August 15th.

As with most passage waders, Staffordshire (49%) has claimed the largest share of birds, followed by Warwickshire with 38%. By comparison, both Worcestershire (9%) and the West Midlands (4%) are relatively unimportant for this species. This is largely due to the nature of the best sites, with Draycote Water, Blithfield Reservoir, Belvide Reservoir and Chasewater all having significant lengths of the hard, stony shorelines favoured by this species. A surprise has been the attraction of the Middle Tame Valley, where the habitat is generally less suitable.

Wilson's Phalarope *Phalaropus tricolor*
Very rare vagrant. Three records.

Wilson's Phalaropes breed in North America and winter in South America, so are only rare vagrants to Britain. The first in this region came in 1985 and there have now been a total of three, as listed in the table overleaf.

Up to the end of 2003 there had been just over 200 British records of this fine-billed, delicate wader, many of them dating from the 1970s and 1980s. Recently, though, occurrences have declined to about one a year (Rogers *et al*. 2004). These three all arrived in September and October, which is a typical time for Transatlantic vagrants to occur (Dymond *et al*. 1989).

Regional Record Number	County Record Number	Year	Locality, Date and Notes
1	Worcs 1	1985	Upton Warren: juvenile moulting to first-winter, September 14th. Probably same, Slimbridge (Glos) earlier in day. *BB 79:551*.
2	Warks 1	1988	Draycote Water: first-winter, September 12th-23rd. *BB 83:464*.
3	Warks 2	1996	Draycote Water: juvenile moulting into first-winter, October 1st. Same, Daventry Reservoir (Northants) the previous day. *BB 90:482*.

Red-necked Phalarope   *Phalaropus lobatus*
Rare passage migrant.

This much sought after little wader is rarer than the Grey Phalarope and its infrequent visits always attract the region's birders. There were eighteen records mentioned in *BWM*, ten of them between 1963-78. Its subsequent occurrences, listed below, have continued at a similar rate, with numerous blank years, but with two birds in 1999 and three in 1989.

Regional Record Number	County Record Number	Year	Locality, Date and Notes
19	Staffs 11	1981	Belvide Reservoir: adult female, May 30th.
20	Staffs 12	1985	Chasewater: female, May 31st.
21	Warks 4	1986	Shustoke Reservoir: female, May 28th.
22	Warks 5	1988	Shustoke Reservoir: September 28th to October 2nd.
23	Staffs 13	1989	Belvide Reservoir: male, June 1st.
24	Worcs 4	1989	Upton Warren: adult female, June 6th-7th.
25	Worcs 5	1989	Wilden: female, July 10th.
26	Staffs 14	1996	Belvide Reservoir: female, May 4th-5th.
27	Worcs 6	1999	Upton Warren: adult female, May 25th.
28	Worcs 7	1999	Gwen Finch NR: juvenile, August 22nd-25th.
29	Warks 6 / Staffs 15	2000	Kingsbury Water Park: male moulting into breeding plumage, April 24th-25th. Same, Fisher's Mill and Drayton Bassett, 26th and Dosthill Pool, 27th.

Eight of these birds arrived in spring and three in autumn. Red-necked Phalaropes are late migrants, often not arriving on their breeding grounds until early June in Scotland or even later further north. The above included two early birds, one on April 24th and the other on May 4th, with the remaining six typically concentrated into the two weeks May 25th-June 7th.

On return passage, a female on the early date of July 10th served as a reminder that in this species the sexual roles are reversed, with the drabber coloured males incubating the eggs and tending to the young.

All recent records have involved single birds, but a pair was shot at Moseley back in 1893.

Grey Phalarope   *Phalaropus fulicarius*
Rare passage migrant in autumn, often storm-driven. Very rare at other times.

Grey Phalaropes breed in the high Arctic and winter at sea. As they are late autumn migrants, they often get caught up in storms that drive them inland.

BWM observed that this species is almost exclusively an autumn visitor and that still remains the case. During 1929-78 all but one bird occurred between late August and December 7th, whilst during 1979-2001 all but one occurred between August 25th and December 21st. The exceptions were a female in full-breeding plumage at Blithfield Reservoir on June 15th 1976 and one at Chasewater on January 9th 1994.

During the current period the annual numbers of birds ranged from one to four, except in 1987 when the infamous 'Great Storm' of October 15th-16th swept seven into the region. Two have occurred together twice, at Arrow Valley Park on October 16th 1987 and at Draycote Water on September 25th 1988, but otherwise all records have been of single birds.

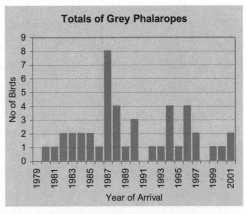

Exactly half of all the birds were recorded in Staffordshire, principally at the main reservoirs with Blithfield having seven, Belvide six and Chasewater three, while in the Potteries, Westport Lake attracted four. Warwickshire was the second most productive county, with 22% of birds, including five at Draycote. Worcestershire and the West Midlands each had 14% of birds. Of the eighteen other sites in the region that were visited, none had more than two records.

Few stay for long, with 77% going within two days. Three or four have stayed up to a week, however, but only two have remained longer—coincidentally both in 2001, when one was at Westport Lake for eleven days from October 2nd-12th and another at the Abbey Fields, Kenilworth, for twelve days from October 5th-16th.

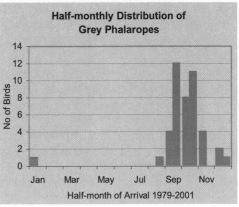

Grey Phalaropes, especially storm-driven birds, often end up on quite small pools and one near Netherton Reservoir in 1987 was described as being on 'little more than a puddle'. Also of interest, one at Sandwell Valley in 1993 ended up as the unlikely victim of a Eurasian Sparrowhawk.

Pomarine Skua   *Stercorarius pomarinus*
Rare storm-driven vagrant, mainly in autumn. Very rare in spring and winter.

This species was described in *BWM* as one of the less frequent skuas, even on the coast. However, it is now known to be more regular than previously thought, with birds moving up the west coast of Ireland and Scotland or through the English Channel during May, then returning along the East Coast in late autumn. It is during the latter period, when they are susceptible to being blown inland by gales, that most have occurred in this region. Pomarine Skuas breed in the Arctic tundra of Russia and winter at sea, chiefly in the northern hemisphere (*BWP*).

Regional Record Number	County Record Number		Year	Locality, Date and Notes
1	Warks	1	1869	Shipston-on-Stour: September, shot.
2	W Mid	1	1879	Oldbury: dark morph, October, shot.
3	Staffs	1	Pre 1910	Chasewater: adult, unknown date, killed and mounted for lady's hat.
4	Staffs	2	1912	Shugborough: male, October 30th. Same Cannock Chase, where later shot.
5	Worcs	1	1936	Bittell Reservoir: adult, October 21st. Only one of three skuas to be positively identified.
6	Staffs	3	1970	Belvide Reservoir: adult light morph, October 21st, exhausted later died.
7	Staffs	4	1977	Branston: September 20th, flew across Trent from Drakelow (Derbys.).
8	Warks	2	1978	Draycote Water: immature, December 31st to January 3rd, 1979.
9	Staffs	5	1985	Blithfield Reservoir: adult pale morph, November 2nd-3rd.
10	Staffs	6	1985	Chasewater: adult pale morph, November 10th.
11	W Mid	2	1985	Tividale: adult, November 10th-11th.
12	Staffs	7	1985	Chasewater: immature, November 18th-19th.
13	Warks	3	1985	Seeswood Pool: adult pale morph, November c10th, found exhausted.
14	Staffs	8	1987	Chasewater: adult pale morph, October 16th.
15	Staffs	9	1991	Chasewater: adult, October 21st.
16	Worcs	2	1991	Westwood Pool: juvenile pale morph, December 18th.
17	Worcs	3	1995	Westwood Pool: immature, January 4th.
18	Warks	4	1997	Draycote Water: two adults, May 11th.
19	Worcs	4	1999	Westwood Pool: juvenile, December 22nd.

The two adults at Draycote Water in 1997 were unusual in constituting the only spring record and the only time two have appeared together. Four birds have also appeared in the winter months of December and January, with three of them being seen at Westwood Pool, in 1991, 1995 and 1999. Indeed, this location has hosted three of the last five birds. Of the remaining fourteen records, two were undated and twelve occurred in autumn, with the extreme dates being September 20th-November 18th.

Whilst some overlap between the five records in November 1985 is possible, there is no conclusive proof of this and, as the birds' arrival coincided with major influxes on the East Coast on the 2nd and 18th, they have all been treated as referring to separate individuals. These movements also involved Arctic Skuas, sea-duck and Kittiwakes. Other definite storm-driven birds were one at Chasewater in 1987, whose arrival coincided with the 'Great

Storm' (*cf.* Grey Phalarope) and another there in October 1991, which occurred at a time when large numbers were off the East and Welsh coasts.

Arctic Skua   *Stercorarius parasiticus*
Rare passage migrant, mainly in autumn. Very rare in winter.

This piratical seabird is an infrequent visitor to the region, but is sometimes seen at the larger reservoirs during, or after, stormy weather, when it pursues flocks of terns inland.

There were half-a-dozen nineteenth century records, but only four twentieth century ones up to 1965. The period 1966-78 then produced 30 records involving 41 birds—an average of three a year (*BWM*). Occurrences continued at a very similar rate from 1979-86, during which time birds were recorded in five of the eight years. The frequency of appearances and the number of birds then increased quite noticeably, with records in eleven consecutive years from 1987-97, during which time the average number of birds rose to over six a year. Since 1997, though, there have been only two records involving four birds. Overall, there were 99 birds during 1979-2001, with a maximum of 13 in 1997. The best year on record, however, remains 1973 with 17 birds.

The monthly distribution shows a few subtle differences to that shown in *BWM*. The period 1929-1978 included the sole winter record to date—an adult at Draycote Water on February 20th 1977—and the only July record—near Tewkesbury on the 22nd 1960. The current period, on the other hand, includes the first ever June occurrences, with two records involving three birds in 1982, one in 1985 and another in 1993. The lack of winter records is probably due to the fact that birds winter at sea, mainly off the south African and Argentine coasts.

During 1979-2001, 88% of birds appeared in autumn, mostly between mid-August and the end of September, with the remainder in spring. The largest party comprised seven adults that flew through Belvide Reservoir on September 14th 1980. This equalled the original regional record, set at Chasewater on August 21st 1973. There were also three records involving five birds and one of four birds, but the majority (67%) concerned just singles.

Of those where age was specified, 69% were adults (*cf.* 48% in *BWM*), whilst the proportions of dark morph birds were 61% in the current period and 71% during 1929-78. Apart from one individual that stayed for two days, no bird has remained for more than a day.

During 1979-2001 there were records from twenty-one localities, with Draycote Water having 13 records (23 birds), Blithfield Reservoir 12 records (24 birds) and Belvide Reservoir 8 records (16 birds) the only sites to be visited more than four times. Not surprisingly, the county distribution reflects the dominance of these sites, with 48% of birds in Staffordshire, 29% in Warwickshire, 14% in Worcestershire and 9% in the West Midlands.

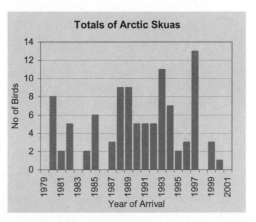

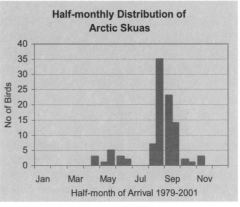

Long-tailed Skua   *Stercorarius longicaudus*
Very rare vagrant. Seven records.

Incredibly, following the first, historical, record in 1874, there was not another until 1987, when two arrived. Although a further four since then have brought the overall total to seven, this remains a very rare vagrant in the region.

Regional Record Number	County Record Number		Year	Locality, Date and Notes
1	Staffs	1	1874	Lichfield racecourse: immature, October 7th, shot.
2	Staffs	2	1987	Blithfield Reservoir: adult, July 27th.
3	Worcs	1	1987	Upton Warren: adult, August 8th.
4	Staffs	3	1990	Hanchurch: immature, October 3rd-4th.
5	Staffs	4	1991	Blithfield Reservoir: immature, September 29th.
6	W Mid	1	1991	Fens Pools: adult pale phase, October 21st.
7	Staffs	5	1994	Belvide Reservoir: immature, September 15th.

Long-tailed Skuas breed in the Arctic tundra of Scandinavia and Russia and winter at sea, mainly south of the equator.

The two arrivals in 1987, at Blithfield and Upton Warren, coincided with northerly winds in late July and early August that produced a strong skua passage nationally. That at Hanchurch in 1990 was doubly interesting in that it was found in a field and was also the only bird to stay more than a day.

Great Skua   *Stercorarius skua*
Rare passage migrant, very rare in winter.

The Great Skua, or 'Bonxie', as it is often called, is a rare visitor to the region's large reservoirs, almost invariably after storms. In total, there were 39 records involving 60 birds up to the end of 2001, of which 24 occurred between 1979 and 2001 involving 45 birds.

After two early records in 1896 and 1909, there were none until 1957 and 1967. The decade 1971-80 then brought a further 12 records, whilst a spell of unusually heavy snow in late April 1981 produced the first ever spring records, with singles at Draycote Water on April 25th-26th, Blithfield Reservoir on May 3rd

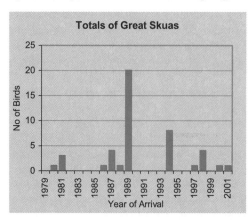

and Belvide Reservoir on May 10th.

The years 1986-89 were particularly productive ones, with four birds in 1987, two of which arrived at Draycote Water on October 18th, in the wake of the 'Great Storm', and an unprecedented 20 birds in 1989. The latter was an astonishing year that began with one at Belvide Reservoir on March 24th, which was only the second year to have any spring records. The remaining 19 then arrived during September 8th-10th. All but one of these were at Draycote Water, where two on the 9th were followed next day by a party of 14 that flew straight through and a further two later in that day. All were moving south-westwards, swept along by gale-force north-easterly winds that also brought a Fulmar, Leach's Storm-petrel and Sabine's Gull to the same locality!

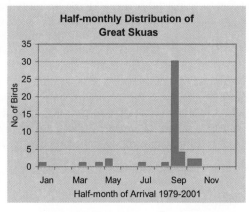

Another four blank years elapsed before 1994 produced a further mini-influx of eight birds between September 14th-26th, including a party of five at Chasewater on the first date. Again the weather conditions were a significant factor, as an intense depression developed over the North Sea on the 13th, bringing heavy rain and strong north-westerly to north-easterly winds.

The sole winter record, of a bird at Fens Pools on January 3rd 1998, coincided with four days of strong south-westerly winds, culminating in a ferocious gale that drove several Great Skuas into the Bristol Channel. Again, in the autumn of that year, the remnants of two Atlantic hurricanes brought three more birds to our region in September, including one at Draycote on the 18th, when 13 passed through nearby Boddington Reservoir (Northamptonshire) on the same day. Unusually, one was discovered in a ploughed field at Timberhonger on October 6th 2000, where it remained until the next day. This was one of just four occasions when birds have remained for a couple of days—all other records having been for a single day.

The geographical spread of records 1979-2001 was restricted to only eight sites. Of these, Draycote Water was dominant, with nine records (29 birds), followed by Belvide Reservoir, with six records all of single birds, and Chasewater, with three records involving seven birds Given this concentration on a few sites, it is not surprising to find Staffordshire (10 records, 14 birds) and Warwickshire (nine records, 25 birds) were the best counties, with West Midlands (three records, four birds) and Worcestershire (just two records of two birds) well behind in third and fourth places respectively.

Skua sp.   *Stercorarius sp.*

In addition to the specific records already listed, there have been a further thirteen records of unidentified skuas. Four of these were thought by their observers to have been Pomarines, namely the two birds that accompanied the one positively identified as a Pomarine Skua at Bittell in 1936, one at Draycote on November 13th 1982 which was believed to be that later seen in Buckinghamshire where it was positively identified as this species, one at Blithfield on December 2nd 1988 and another at Draycote Water on November 20th 1994. Of the remaining nine, five were thought to have probably been Arctic Skuas, one was simply recorded as a skua, whilst the rest were considered to have been either Arctic or Pomarine.

It should be noted that the identification features of immature skuas have only recently been fully clarified and it is likely that some birds were misidentified in the past. This applies particularly to 'late autumn' records of Arctic Skuas, which may in fact have been Pomarine.

Mediterranean Gull   *Larus melanocephalus*
Uncommon passage migrant and winter visitor.

The last twenty years have seen a complete transformation in the status of the Mediterranean Gull in the West Midlands and it is now well-established as a regular visitor.

The first record did not come until 1971, when an adult was at Draycote Water on July 6th, and even as recently as 1980 there had only been ten—all of the other nine in Staffordshire, where the first record was at Blithfield Reservoir on September 20th 1972 (*BWM*). This low level of occurrence continued until the mid-1980s, with just 14 birds in the seven years 1980-86. There then followed a decade of rapid growth that saw the average rise from two a year to around 40 a year. Since 1995/96, however, the rate of increase has noticeably slowed.

Almost 600 birds were recorded during 1979-2001, including the first county records for Worcestershire and the West Midlands—at Madeley Heath on February 26th 1985 and Walsall on February 13th 1986 respectively. The latter flew past a school window, disrupting the timetable for several minutes whilst a description was taken by a teacher!

Dean (1988) referred to the marked population increase in the Russian stronghold since

1970 and to colonisation and expansion in several European countries, and pointed out that Mediterranean Gulls often arrive concurrently with the large numbers of Black-headed Gulls from central and northern Europe that winter in Britain. Colour-ringing has indeed confirmed that some of the region's birds originate from Europe, but so far only from just across the English Channel, with six ringed as chicks between 1998 and 2001 subsequently being seen here—three from the Low Countries and three from Pas-de-Calais (France). Five of these made their way to Worcestershire—three of them within eight weeks of being ringed—and one to Belvide Reservoir. Evidence that some of these birds use the region as a stop-over point is provided by one of the Worcestershire birds that later moved further west to Cork (Eire). Birds are now breeding in Britain as well and one, ringed as a nestling at Orfordness (Suffolk), was seen at Belvide the following autumn.

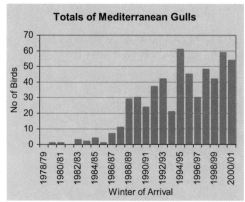

An examination of national data led Bourne (1970) to conclude there are three separate influxes, namely a post-breeding dispersal in July/August, a movement to regular winter quarters in October and a return to the breeding grounds in April. Dean (*op cit.*) went on to show that the post-breeding dispersal from July-September comprises mainly first-year birds, with adults appearing in November and December as they move to their secondary winter quarters and then returning during February. The January influx is assumed to relate to hard-weather movements, primarily by first-year birds. Subsequent records appear to reinforce this pattern, although in recent years there have been significantly more arrivals in August, January, March and April.

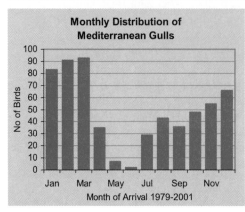

Interestingly, of those recorded during 1979-2001, most were either first-year birds

(39%) or adults (41%), with very few juveniles or second-year birds. The majority passed quickly through, but one or two made protracted stays, with the most notable being 83 days, in the West Midlands county from September 21st–December 12th 1992; 85 days, at Draycote Water from December 31st 1994-March 25th 1995; and 114 days, in the Middle Tame Valley from January 18th-May 10th 1992, by which time it was thought to be moribund.

Interestingly, after its early domination of records, Staffordshire, with 27% of birds, has now fallen behind both Warwickshire (39%) and Worcestershire (29%)—the remaining 5% having been in the West Midlands. For anyone seeking this species, the large evening gull roosts are best, with Draycote Water a must. This locality produced exactly a quarter of all the records during the current period, with the next best sites being Westwood Pool (9%); Belvide Reservoir (8%); Blithfield Reservoir, Chasewater and the Middle Tame Valley (7% each); and Bredon's Hardwick and Upton Warren (5% each). Draycote can also claim the largest concentration, with four birds in the roost on March 28th 2000, although an unsubstantiated claim was made of seven there in 1995.

One was an unlikely visitor to a garden in Hillmorton (Rugby) on December 16th 1993.

Laughing Gull *Larus atricilla*
Very rare vagrant. Three records.

There have now been three records of this rare Nearctic gull, as follows:

Regional Record Number	County Record Number		Year	Locality, Date and Notes
1	W Mid	1	1985	Edgbaston Reservoir: first-winter, January 15th-19th. *BB 80:541.*
2	Worcs	1	1996	Upton Warren: second-winter, August 26th to September 4th. *BB 90:483.*
3	W Mid	2	1997	Bartley Reservoir: adult, October 12th. *BB 91:478.*

Note: The last recorded date for the 1985 individual was given as January 18th in the *WMBC Annual Report* No 52, but the 19th in *British Birds*.

This species is locally common along the Atlantic coast of North America and has occurred in Britain nearly a hundred times (Rogers *et al*. 2004). The wide monthly spread of these three records is typical of this species, which nationally has been recorded in every month. This suggests that, having once crossed the Atlantic, birds then wander around the UK. (Dymond *et al*. 1989).

Franklin's Gull *Larus pipixcan*
Very rare vagrant. One record.

The first regional record of this vagrant gull from North America came in 2002.

Regional Record Number	County Record Number		Year	Locality, Date and Notes
1	Warks	1	2002	Draycote Water: adult, November 6th. *BB 96:574*

The same bird was present earlier just over the Warwickshire border at Stanford Reservoir, (Leicestershire/Northamptonshire) from November 3rd-5th. This remains a rare species in Britain, with just 41 records up to and including the above (Rogers *et al*. 2003).

Little Gull *Larus minutus*
Uncommon passage migrant and scarce winter visitor.

To see small flocks of delicate Little Gulls fluttering and dipping across a reservoir or battling into the teeth of a gale is one of the delights of birdwatching. They breed discontinuously from the Netherlands eastwards through Europe and into Asia and winter offshore around the coasts of western Europe and the Mediterranean.

It appears the migration pattern of the Little Gull might have changed over time as between 1952-1968 three-quarters occurred during August and the first half of September, whereas in the next decade this proportion had dropped to a quarter (*BWM*). During 1979-2001, it fell even further to 22%. This swing in the seasonal pattern has also been accompanied by a steady increase in numbers, which is probably linked to the population expansion that has occurred in Finland and the Baltic states (Hutchinson and Neath 1978). During 1969-78 almost 300 birds were reported—an average of 30 a year—whereas the period 1979-2001 produced around 1,500 at a rate of 65 a year. As with most migrants, numbers varied considerably, from just 23 in 1980 to 123 in 1989, probably due to weather patterns as the species is susceptible to being storm-driven. Seasonal variations are also quite marked, with the autumn of 1996, for example, bringing only six birds, whilst in Worcestershire it was less frequent than Mediterranean Gull for three successive years from 1995-97!

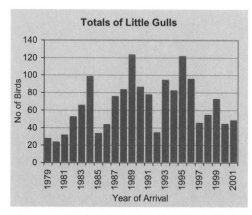

Totals of Little Gulls

Although there have been records in every month, this is essentially a passage bird, with the majority (50%) moving through during a concentrated spring passage in April and early May. The right weather conditions can sometimes result in a small influx, as on April 28th 1995 when a notable passage across southern England brought at least 55 (49 of them adults) to the region. The slightly weaker return movement during August and September accounts for 26% of birds, whilst a subsidiary passage in late October and early November produces a further 8% of birds. The former comprises mainly juveniles, while the latter tends to involve adults, which remain in the Baltic to moult before moving south and west

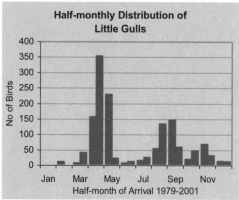

Half-monthly Distribution of Little Gulls

(*BWP*). The remainder are spread fairly evenly across the other months, with winter records often involving storm-driven birds, which at that time of year are often just offshore.

Of those birds specifically aged, 42% were adults—exactly the same figure as during 1969-78 (*BWM*)—while second-year birds made up only 4% of the total. There is a conspicuous peak of adults in April (and a less obvious one of second-year birds), while first-year birds are more evenly distributed between spring and autumn, but with September the best month. During 1986-2000 the best year for adults was 1995, whereas for first-year birds it was 1989 (A.R. Dean see www.deanar.btinternet.co.uk).

Little Gulls tend to appear haphazardly, particularly when they are grounded by heavy rain, but are generally seen at the main reservoirs and larger waters, with the four most frequented places being Draycote Water (17% of records), Belvide and Blithfield Reservoirs (14% each) and the Middle Tame Valley (13%). As a result, Staffordshire attracted most birds, with 43%, closely followed by Warwickshire with 40%, then Worcestershire with 13% and West Midlands with 4%. The largest spring flocks during 1979-2001 were 27 (26 adults and a first-year) at Chasewater on May 1st 1984 and 39 (36 adults, two second-summers and a first-summer) at Coton Pools on April 22nd 1987. The most in autumn were 26 (22 juveniles and four adults) at Draycote Water on September 12th 1993 and 20 (in parties of 12 and eight) at Belvide Reservoir on November 13th 1982. Interestingly, in a month when adults are normally in the majority, the latter comprised eight adults and twelve first-winter birds. Most birds pass through quite quickly, but two or three have lingered for as much as three weeks, with individuals at Blithfield Reservoir remaining for 23 and 24 days in 1982 and 1983 respectively. The longest stay, however, was made by a winter bird that roamed around north-east Worcestershire for 40 days, from January 18th to February 26th 1995.

Sabine's Gull   *Larus sabini*
Rare autumn passage migrant.

Prior to 1979 there had been just three records (*BWM*), but the period 1979-2001 produced a further eleven.

Regional Record Number	County Record Number		Year	Locality, Date and Notes
1	Warks	1	1883	Coleshill: immature, October 2nd.
2	Worcs	1	1948	Bittell Reservoir: adult, August 15th. *BB 42:125*
3	Staffs	1	1976	Blithfield Reservoir: adult, September 11th.
4	Warks	2	1981	Draycote Water: first-summer or early moulting adult, September 30th.
5	Staffs	2	1982	Belvide Reservoir: immature, October 1st.
6	Staffs	3	1983	Blithfield Reservoir: immature, September 25th.
7	Warks	3	1989	Draycote Water: juvenile, September 10th.
8	Staffs	4	1990	Blithfield Reservoir: adult, September 10th.
9	Worcs	2	1994	Upton Warren: juvenile, September 13th-14th. Same, Westwood Pool 15th.
10	Staffs	5	1995	Blithfield Reservoir: juvenile, September 30th.
11	Staffs	6	1996	Blithfield Reservoir: juvenile, October 6th-7th.
12	Worcs	3	1997	Wilden: juvenile, September 20th.
13	Worcs	4	1997	Trimpley Reservoir: juvenile, October 11th.
14	Staffs	7	2001	Westport Lake: juvenile, October 6th.

Apart from the adult at Bittell in August 1948, all records have fallen between September 10th and October 11th and eleven of the fourteen birds were juveniles or immatures. This is a classic pattern for this attractive little gull, since at this stormy time of year many are passing the western coasts of Britain as they leave their breeding grounds, which stretch from Greenland across Arctic North America to north-east Siberia, to winter at sea off the south-western coast of Africa. Inland occurrences frequently follow periods of strong westerly or south-westerly winds and often involve juvenile birds.

Bonaparte's Gull   *Larus philadelphia*
Very rare vagrant. Five records.

Although it was 1990 before this delightful little North American gull made its first appearance in the region, it wasted no time in returning and there have now been five records.

Regional Record Number	County Record Number	Year	Locality, Date and Notes
1	Warks 1	1990	Kenilworth: first-winter, March 10th-28th. Same, Draycote Water: four dates during March 18th-29th. *BB 84:475*
2	Staffs 1	1991	Westport Lake: first-winter, December 24th. *BB 86:489*
3	Warks 2	1992	Draycote Water: first-summer, May 24th. *BB 86:489*
4	Staffs 2	1994	Blithfield Reservoir: adult, October 4th-6th. *BB 88:518*
5	Staffs 3	1996	Blithfield Reservoir: first-winter, April 27th-30th. *BB 90:484*

This species seems to be occurring (or being detected) more often on this side of the Atlantic. Prior to 1958 there had been only 11 records, but a further 37 followed by 1985 and there have now been over a hundred British records (Rogers *et al.* 2004). The scatter of dates above, unusual for a Transatlantic vagrant but typical of this species (Dymond *et al.* 1989), suggests that such records may refer to wandering individuals that arrived in Britain sometime earlier.

Black-headed Gull   *Larus ridibundus*
Abundant passage migrant and winter visitor. Breeds frequently in Staffordshire and North Warwickshire, and rarely in Worcestershire.

Once an uncommon sight in the West Midlands, with even 150 considered notable in 1926, Black-headed Gulls have flourished since the 1940s and can now be seen in their hundreds almost anywhere from lowland meadows to upland pastures and from rural reservoirs to urban parks, sports fields and even gardens. Indeed it is our most abundant gull and on winter evenings continuous streams can be seen flying towards the huge gull roosts at reservoirs and gravel pits, where they make up three-quarters or more of the birds present (see A.R. Dean at www.deanar.btinternet.co.uk). Its widespread distribution was supported by the *Winter Atlas*, which showed it to be present in every 10-km square, except that covering the western-most part of the Teme valley.

Despite the massive increase in the number of birds that venture inland in search of food in winter, the Black-headed Gull remains an erratic breeding species, with colonies principally centred on two traditional areas. Several hundred pairs bred in the Meres and Mosses area of west Staffordshire, notably around Norbury and Shebdon, until the area was drained and enclosed around 1800. They were then rediscovered briefly at Doley Common (1969-73), until that site, too, was drained (*BWM*). This area nevertheless remains attractive to the species and a dozen or more pairs still nest sporadically at Aqualate Mere.

Colonisation of the Tame and Trent Valleys began at Curdworth Sewage Farm some years prior to 1913 (*BWM*), but this was not sustained and by 1942 the birds had all dispersed. Then a new colony was discovered in 1979 in the gravel pits at Elford. Within a couple of years this had grown to around 50 pairs and it eventually reached a maximum of 123 pairs in 1987, but by 1990 numbers had dropped back to around 50 pairs again. Birds then quickly spread to other parts of the Tame and Trent valleys, making this area the main regional stronghold with 50 pairs at Fisherwick in 1985; 36 pairs at Barton in 1988 and 100 there in 1994; and more recently 120 pairs at Branston in 2002.

However, the most significant move was into the Middle Tame Valley, where three pairs bred at Kingsbury Water Park in 1982—the first in Warwickshire for forty years—but it was 1992 before a colony became established here and the following year around 20 pairs bred. By 1995 some 50 pairs had moved northwards onto the new Dosthill Lake, which remained the main site for the next five years, reaching around 150 pairs in 1998 and 300 in 2000. In the spring of 2001, this colony was dispersed by jet spraying and many birds returned to Kingsbury, where an estimated 75-100 pairs bred—much to the detriment of the established ternery. To counteract this, the management regime has now been amended in an effort to dissuade the gulls from establishing their territories before the terns have returned in spring. Around 75 pairs also bred there in 2000 and again in 2002, whilst some pairs were back at Dosthill Lake in the latter year as well.

Elsewhere, the first breeding record for Worcestershire came from Wilden in 1970. During the current period there were several more sporadic breeding records around the region, including two more from Worcestershire where single pairs nested at Wilden again in 1981 and at Bredon's Hardwick in 1985, while a nesting attempt at Upton Warren in 2002 was abandoned. Currently the regional population is probably in the range 200-250 pairs, but it appears to be expanding although numbers are very variable.

The first post-breeding flocks begin to form in late-July, when juveniles disperse from their natal areas, their numbers swollen by immigrants from continental Europe, especially the Netherlands, Denmark, Fennoscandia and the Baltic States. Adults begin to arrive in August and numbers then steadily increase during the autumn to reach their maximum in December and January. By the end of February return passage is well underway and this accelerates in March, so that by April it is mainly only breeding birds that remain.

A major feature of the winter months are the enormous roosts that form at the main reservoirs, and especially at Draycote Water, where 80-100,000 were reported in the late 1970s. These huge numbers were the result of the reservoir being surrounded by landfill sites at that time, with several in Warwickshire (including the massive Packington site) and others across the borders in Leicestershire, Oxfordshire and Northamptonshire. The Control of Pollution Act, 1974, then introduced more rigorous measures to control pollution and vermin, including gulls, at landfill sites and since then these have become progressively more stringent. During the 1980s, there were indications that some roosts were declining and there were noticeably fewer birds at Draycote, with no gathering higher than 35-40,000 apart from 46,000 in 1982/83. Nevertheless, the count of 38,500 in January 1993 for the BTO Winter Gull Roost Survey was the second largest inland in Britain at the time. Weather is also a significant factor, with the larger gatherings tending to form on the coldest nights, when the sheer whiteness of the Draycote roost presents a daunting prospect guaranteed to make even the most enthusiastic gull fanatic think twice about embarking on a count. Between 15-25,000 of the birds feeding at Packington have, on occasions, also roosted at nearby Coton, Ladywalk and Shustoke Reservoir.

In Staffordshire, Blithfield Reservoir held 15-20,000 during the 1980s, followed by a peak of 26,200 in January 1993, but neither the Blithfield nor the Draycote roost has been comprehensively counted since. It is also thought that some recent counts at Draycote may have been under-estimates, as comparisons between the area of the roost here and those at Blithfield and Chasewater (where there around 10,000 birds) suggest a total of at least 25,000 (Dean *op cit.*). More regular

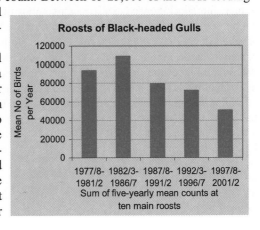

Roosts of Black-headed Gulls

Mean No of Birds per Year

Sum of five-yearly mean counts at ten main roosts

counting of the smaller roosts at Belvide Reservoir and Chasewater during the ten winters 1992/93-2001/2 showed numbers ranging from 3-6,000 (average 4,500) and 8-15,000 (average 11,000) respectively, but with no clear long-term trend. In Worcestershire the major roost at Westwood Pool ranged from 3-8,000 (average 5,500). In the region as a whole, the apparent downturn in the chart during 1997/8-2000/1 is therefore considered to be due to under-counting, or indeed the lack of counting, and there is no evidence to suggest wintering numbers have declined since the early 1990s.

During the day, flocks can frequently be seen following the plough, or scouring the pastures for earthworms and other soil invertebrates. They are especially numerous in the Severn and Avon Vales, Cotswold Fringe and Feldon areas of south Worcestershire and south-east Warwickshire, where they favour the old ridge-and-furrow pastures. Amongst the more impressive concentrations were 1,650 at Eckington on March 10th 1991, 2,500 at Priors Hardwick on December 4th 2000 and 10,000 at Napton on March 8th 1998. Such flocks are often drawn to feed on pastures after heavy rain has brought earthworms to the surface. This is especially so on the flood meadows, when inundations brought 8,000 to Longdon Marsh on February 5th 1995 and 10,000 to Upton-on-Severn in December 2000. Similar conditions in the Trent catchment, however, seem only to attract smaller numbers, with 1,500 at Rickerscote on September 18th 1994 more typical. Black-headed Gulls enjoy a wide diet, however, and many prefer to scavenge for food amongst the piles of rubbish at landfill sites. This habit, too, has resulted in some large gatherings, with 3,000 at both Judkins Quarry in 1990 and Queslett Tip in 1992, whilst Throckmorton Tip attracted 4,500 in February 1986. Less characteristically, eight hovering birds were seen to be deftly taking berries from some elder bushes at Kingsbury Water Park in 1987, whilst 500 were feeding on flying ants above Barnard's Green in 1988. Albinistic or leucistic birds are sometimes reported amidst such flocks.

Black-headed Gulls are often seen in built-up areas, with, for example, 900 on wasteland by the Black Country Route in October 2000 and a similar number roosting on the roof of a furniture store at the Festival Park, Hanley, in November 1998. More unusually, one alighted briefly on the pitch during a Birmingham City match at St Andrews in November 1996.

Ringing has provided much information about the origins of our wintering birds. Nestlings from colonies within the region disperse widely during the first few months after fledging, with juveniles being recovered in Dorset, Cornwall and many Welsh counties. At the same time, birds fledged in the southern counties of Hampshire, Kent and Essex and the northern counties of Lincolnshire, Yorkshire, Durham, Cumbria, Northumberland and the Shetlands arrive in the West Midlands. During the 1980s there were also sightings of two or three birds that had been dye-marked pink at Enderby Tip, near Leicester.

There is also a huge influx of juveniles fledged from continental breeding colonies. A high percentage of these recoveries are for birds ringed in Scandinavia, Russia and eastern European countries. Surprisingly a much smaller number have been recorded from western European colonies, but one example was a bird at Codsall in December 2000 that had been wing-tagged as a chick the previous June in the Netherlands. Many of these birds are subsequently recorded making return journeys to and from the Continent in later life. Birds ringed as adults show similar origins and destinations. Precise ages of seventeen and eighteen years are not unusual and movements of over 1,000 km are regular. Some birds have been recorded making colossal journeys of over 2,200 km to destinations in Finland and Russia.

Ring-billed Gull   *Larus delawarensis*
Rare vagrant.

Yet another North American Gull that waited a long time (1981) before first appearing in the region, but which has now been recorded on seventeen occasions, as listed opposite.

Regional Record Number	County Record Number		Year	Locality, Date and Notes
1	Staffs	1	1981	Westport Lake: second-winter, November 16th. *BB 77:531*
2	Worcs	1	1986	Throckmorton Tip: adult, March 2nd-5th. *BB 80:542*
3	Staffs	2	1987	Westport Lake: first-winter moulting to first-summer, various dates between March 14th-16th, 21st and 29th. *BB 81:564*
4	Warks	1	1987	Coton Pools: adult, December 20th. *BB 81:564*
5	Worcs	2	1989	Throckmorton: first-winter, February 16th-17th.
6	W Mid	1	1989	Queslett Tip: adult, March 8th and 15th.
7	Worcs	3	1989	Bredon's Hardwick: second-winter, November 21st.
8	Warks	2	1991	Draycote Water: second-summer, April 13th-21st.
9	W Mid	2	1996	Fens Pools: adult, January 3rd.
10	Worcs	4	1997	Bredon's Hardwick: adult, April 5th-12th.
11	Warks	3	1998	Draycote Water: second-summer or sub-adult, March 30th.
12	Staffs	3	1999	Chasewater: probable adult, February 14th.
13	Worcs	5	2002	Bredon's Hardwick: adult, March 31st (see next record).
14	Worcs	6	2002	Bredon's Hardwick: different adult, April 1st. (see also above). One of these stayed till April 4th and the other till April 7th.
15	Worcs	7	2002	Ryall GP: adult, April 3rd-21st. Presume same, Bredon's Hardwick April 11th-13th and 23rd.
16	Worcs	8	2002	Bredon's Hardwick: second-summer, April 7th and 13th.
17	Worcs	9	2002	Throckmorton Tip; adult, November 23rd.

Note: BBRC ceased to consider records of this species as from January 1st 1988.

All occurrences have been between November 16th and April 23rd, with the best months being March and April, with five birds in each—a pattern which accords well with that shown by Dymond *et al.* (1989). Of those precisely aged, five were adults, three were second-year birds and one a first-year. The Avon Valley in Worcestershire has provided most records, especially Bredon's Hardwick, which enjoyed an outstanding year in 2002.

This species went unseen, or at least unrecognised, in Britain until 1973, but was then, amazingly, detected 449 times in the next twelve years (Dymond *et al.* 1989). This dramatic increase was attributed to a population explosion in eastern America and better recognition in this country.

Common Gull   *Larus canus*
Common winter visitor and passage migrant, principally to the south and south-east of the region.

Despite its name, this is certainly not the commonest gull to visit the region. Indeed, a roost of 150 at Bartley Reservoir in February 1947 was described as exceptional, while *BWM* referred to a roost of similar size at Blithfield Reservoir in November 1963 as being the largest away from the much favoured Draycote Water. However, there are suggestions that the name derives from its habit of feeding on grasslands, or commons, and not from its abundance.

In winter Common Gulls certainly feed largely on earthworms, which they find most readily in well-drained, close cropped pastures (Vernon, 1970 and 1972) and there are large wintering populations in the adjoining counties of Northamptonshire, Oxfordshire, Gloucestershire and Cheshire. Within this region, they are most numerous amongst the limestone grasslands and old ridge-and-furrow pastures of the Cotswold Fringe, Severn and Avon valleys and Feldon areas in south Worcestershire and south-east Warwickshire. Some strong movements have been observed here, notably a hard-weather movement of 1,200 through Wormleighton in two days during December 2000, when 800 were also at Priors Marston. Many birds from this area join with those believed to be from the East Midlands to form the huge Draycote roost. Whenever flooding brings worms to the surface, large numbers of Common Gulls also congregate on the flood meadows along the lower Avon and Severn Valleys. Notable concentrations were 1,000 at Bredon's Hardwick in April 1989; 1,150 at Eckington in February 1998; 600 at Longdon Marsh in April 1998 and 1,100 at Upton-on-Severn in April 2001. During the *Winter Atlas* birds were found in 74% of 10-km squares, with the highest numbers in the areas mentioned above and also in the Needwood area around Blithfield Reservoir. Elsewhere they were widely, but sparsely, distributed.

Unfortunately, past counting of roosts has often been irregular, making it hard to discern trends, especially as numbers fluctuate considerably from year-to-year and season-to-season according to weather conditions. The roost counts that are available suggest that numbers increased during the 1980s, but then stabilised at a lower level during the 1990s. However, this broad assessment needs to be treated with extreme caution because of the overwhelming dominance of Draycote Water, which hosted over 80% of all recorded birds.

There have been records in every month, although most birds occur between late July and mid-May, with just a scatter of mainly first-summer birds noted outside this period. Although the first returning birds appear in late summer, numbers are very small and there is often a subsequent lull before the autumn build-up begins. Most migrant birds reach Britain by October (*Winter Atlas*), but it is usually November before many arrive here (*e.g.* 7,000 at Draycote in 1991) and maximum winter numbers are not attained, or at least recorded, until January. This suggests birds arrive further to the north or east, then later move southwards or westwards, perhaps in response to hard weather.

The larger winter counts usually concern birds roosting at the major reservoirs, with Draycote Water pre-eminent. In fact, over 90% of the region's birds roosted here during the decade 1992/3-2001/2.

Prior to that there were two exceptional roosts here, of 10,000 in March 1979 and 8,000 in March 1991, both of which were indicative of unusually heavy passages of birds that had presumably sought sanctuary further south and west during the preceding severe winter weather. In comparison, the average roost here is usually around 4,000. A roost of 1,000 also gathered at Ladywalk in February 1986, but counts from elsewhere have been insignificant by comparison, with the most at Blithfield Reservoir and Chasewater, both of which are noted for their gull roosts, being 190 in February 1991 and 304 in January 1996 respectively. In north Staffordshire, 170 on the fringes of the Moors during February 1984 and 210 at Tittesworth Reservoir in January 1995 were both good counts for that area.

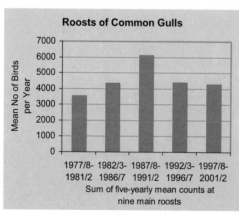

Roosts of Common Gulls

Mean No of Birds per Year

7000
6000
5000
4000
3000
2000
1000
0

1977/8- 1982/3- 1987/8- 1992/3- 1997/8-
1981/2 1986/7 1991/2 1996/7 2001/2

Sum of five-yearly mean counts at nine main roosts

Common Gulls are most numerous on spring passage in March and April, when about half of all birds occur. The majority are recorded in March, when firstly adult birds and then immatures create a strong north-easterly passage as they follow the lines of the Avon Valley and the Cotswold Fringe back towards their breeding grounds, or natal areas, in Fennoscandia, the Baltic States and Russia. Amongst the more notable examples of this movement were at least 1,300 passing through Broadway on various dates during April 1985, 460 flying north-eastwards through Bredon's Hardwick in seventy-five minutes on April 13th 1986 and 395 on Bredon Hill in March 1996. An indication of where our wintering birds come from and are returning to is provided by a nestling ring at Guldolmen, Norway, in July 1984 and found dead at Draycote Reservoir in March 1985, having made a journey of 1,082 km.

With their preference for feeding on grassland, Common Gulls are less inclined than the other species of gull to congregate at landfill sites, though 300 did gather at Throckmorton in February 1986. Within the conurbations and urban fringes, 150 were at Edgbaston Reservoir in January 1985, whilst 50 or more have roosted at Bartley Reservoir and a similar number have been seen more than once at Westport Lake, in the Potteries. Several individuals have also been reported visiting gardens, mostly during hard weather.

Lesser Black-backed Gull   *Larus fuscus*
Very common passage migrant and common winter visitor. Fairly common and increasing breeding species since 1986.

Once very scarce inland, with just 165 birds found wintering in the whole of England and Wales in 1953 (*Winter Atlas*), this is now the second commonest gull and can be seen in hundreds, if not thousands, around the region's reservoirs, gravel pits and landfill sites, or on farmland, flood meadows and playing fields.

Prior to the 1950s, the Lesser Black-backed Gull was a scarce passage migrant through the region, principally during August-November and to a lesser extent April and May, but with totals rarely reaching double figures. This was changed by the construction of two major reservoirs, at Blithfield and Draycote, which provided the safe roost sites that this species needs. Almost immediately modest winter roosts began to form and by the late 1960s 10,000 were roosting in the region. Within fifteen years this had increased to between 25-35,000, after which there was a slight decline to around 20,000 (*BWM*). The *Winter Atlas* recorded birds in 97% of 10-km squares, demonstrating just how widespread the species had become.

Birds rely heavily on landfill sites rather than farmland for their food, but not to the extent that Herring Gulls do, and it is thought that changing management practices, introduced at these sites since the Control of Pollution Act 1974, may have contributed to their decline. Even so numbers have remained large enough to dissuade people from counting the major roosts, particularly at Draycote Water, so information is sparse. However, ten main roosts were in existence throughout most of the period 1979-2001 and counts from these have been used to indicate the main trend in the wintering population. Numbers at these sites declined until they were back to around their 1960s level of 10,000 by the early 1980s. Allowing for sites not included and some possible under-counting, they have since recovered to something approaching 20,000, which is about the same as the last estimate in *BWM*.

The largest roost counts during the current period were 5,000 at Draycote Water (1992/3), 4,850 at Westwood Pool (1994/5), 4,500 at Belvide Reservoir (2000/1), 4,000 at Chasewater (1982/3 and 1992/3) and 3,000 at both Bartley Reservoir (1995/6) and Blithfield Reservoir

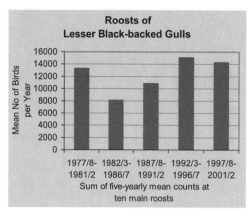

Roosts of
Lesser Black-backed Gulls

Mean No of Birds per Year

16000
14000
12000
10000
8000
6000
4000
2000
0

1977/8- 1982/3- 1987/8- 1992/3- 1997/8-
1981/2   1986/7   1991/2   1996/7   2001/2

Sum of five-yearly mean counts at
ten main roosts

(1999/2000)—all well below the all-time maxima of the 1970s, when 12,000 were recorded at Draycote, 10,000 at Kingsbury and 6,000 at Blithfield (*BWM*). Unusually, given the choice of reservoirs available, over 100 chose to roost in winter cereals at Park Lime Pits in the autumns of 1997 and 1999.

This species is an archetypal scavenger of landfill sites, where up to a thousand can sometimes be seen and a very impressive gathering of 7,000 was at Throckmorton in December 2001. Nevertheless it is also an opportunist feeder, with some resorting to tips only when needs must, such as in hard weather. For example, again at Throckmorton, the number feeding at the tip rose from 225 to 750 following a heavy overnight frost. At other times, substantial flocks do resort to fields, if only to loaf, preen and roost. In particular, they flock to feed on invertebrates brought to the surface by ploughing or flooding, with 2,500 on the flood meadows at Longdon Marsh on January 11th 1998.

The most significant change since *BWM* was published is that birds are now breeding in the region. The first reported instance was in 1986, when two pairs successfully nested in Worcester. The following year a pair raised two young in the centre of Birmingham and breeding has continued more or less continuously ever since, with both cities now having well-established colonies. For instance, 25 pairs were in Worcester in 2000 and eight nests were seen, while in Birmingham at least five nests were successful, with many more pairs present. From these initial beginnings, birds have spread to other areas too. In Birmingham, several pairs have colonised the Hockley area, an estimated 30 pairs were in the Bromford/Tyburn district in 2000 and smaller numbers have moved into the outer suburbs, using the flat roofs of tower blocks as nest sites. Preliminary results from the *BBCBB Atlas* showed birds in 43% of the tetrads during the breeding season. Breeding has also been confirmed in Kidderminster and Stourport, and on a gravel island at Bredon's Hardwick. Birds have possibly bred in Smethwick, too, and are suspected of having done so in Stratford-upon-Avon, whilst display has been observed at Wolverhampton. From the pattern of these records it is apparent that colonisation is taking place by birds coming into the region from the Bristol Channel. Indeed, colour-ringed birds from Bristol have been seen in June and July. Over 200 breeding pairs were reported in 2002 and it seems the true population must be at least 250-300 pairs. Moreover, judging from the ever-increasing number of summering records from all parts of the region, it seems set to further consolidate and spread. Similar colonisation in south-west England has created public concern due to the aggressive nature of nesting birds and means of dispersal are being investigated. This aspect may well become the focus of attention in this region too in due course.

The first arrivals from late July to September are mainly British birds, with several colour-ringed individuals from Bristol and others from the Ribble estuary and Walney Island recorded around this time. Continental migrants then begin to arrive from October onwards, with the main influx during November and December. After this numbers diminish markedly as many move on to Iberia and North Africa, while the flow of new arrivals gradually ceases. Spring passage seems to occur slightly earlier than in the past, with most birds passing through between mid-February and the end of March.

Foreign recoveries of birds ringed here during the winter have shown birds returning to breeding colonies in the Netherlands and Norway in the following or subsequent summers, whilst nestlings ringed in Norway have been recorded at Blithfield Reservoir and Chasewater in the following spring. A juvenile ringed in Worcester in August 1989 was recovered in the Netherlands in July 1994. Domestically, many birds ringed during the winter have been recorded travelling north to Lancashire, Cumbria and Scotland in the following or subsequent summers, while one travelled south-west to Cornwall. A remarkable record was for a nestling ringed in Cumbria in July 2000 and recorded at Chasewater in August 2002 after having visited Agidar in Morocco in 2001. More local movements were made by birds that were colour-marked in 1989 at the Stoke Orchard Landfill Site, near Cheltenham (Gloucestershire), and seen at Branston, Grimley, Throckmorton and Westwood in 1989, Blithfield (three) in 1990 and Bermuda (Nuneaton) in 1991. The oldest bird to be recorded was ringed at Droitwich Spa in January 1980 and recovered alive sixteen years later in Gloucester.

British Lesser Black-backed Gulls belong to the race *L. f. graellsii*, but a few migrants of the continental race *L. f. intermedius*, which breeds in the Netherlands, Denmark and southern Norway, are noted most years amongst the huge winter feeding and roosting flocks. Indeed, 3% of the 1,000 birds at Westport Lake on February 29th 1988 were attributed to this race, which very probably is often under-recorded.

'Baltic' Gull   *L. f. fuscus*

Between 1984-2001 there were also 33 published records involving 42 birds that showed characteristics of the Baltic Gull *L. f. fuscus*, which has decreasing breeding populations in northern Fennoscandinia and Russia and migrates overland to winter in east Africa (*BWP* and Wernham *et al.* 2002). However, field identification of this, the nominate race, is currently regarded as virtually impossible owing to the occurrence of small, very 'black-looking' individuals of the race *L. f. intermedius*. The state of moult can be a good, but not infallible guide, as *fuscus* moults at most the innermost two primaries before migration and completes its moult in the winter quarters. Unfortunately, it is now known that some *intermedius* (and *graellsii*) also suspend their moult. Nevertheless, a Lesser Black-backed Gull in active wing and tail moult in mid-autumn is certainly *not* nominate *fuscus*, and any claim of a putative *fuscus* must certainly include details of the state of moult (A.R. Dean, see deanar.btinternet.co.uk).

The status of *L. f. fuscus* on the British List is currently under review by the BOURC and its continued presence depends largely upon a single ringing recovery from Suffolk in 1981 and there are some identification doubts attached to this record (Piotrowski 2003). It is almost certain that none of the claims from the West Midlands includes adequate supporting details, including details of moult, and it must now be concluded that there are no substantiated records of this form from the region.

Herring Gull   *Larus argentatus*
Common winter visitor. Uncommon in summer and a scarce, but increasing, breeding species.

The Herring Gull, which is our familiar 'seagull', has been tempted to move inland from its traditional coastal haunts by the safe roost sites created by the building of large reservoirs and the abundance of food amongst the rubbish on landfill sites. If these two essentials can be found close to one another, as at Cannock Tip and Chasewater, then so much the better.

Prior to mid 1940s the species was a scarce migrant or storm-blown visitor to the region, with roosts of 250 at Belvide Reservoir in 1942 and 40 at Bartley Reservoir in 1944 regarded as noteworthy. In the mid-1960s around 5,000 were roosting in the region and by the early 1970s this figure had risen to 15,000. Numbers then began to decline, so that by the end of that decade there were 10,000-12,000 roosting birds (*BWM*). They nevertheless remained widespread and were recorded in 96% of 10-km squares during the *Winter Atlas* survey, being absent only from the Teme Valley.

The limited data seems to confirm the anecdotal evidence that the decline continued during the 1980s. This pattern was partially mirrored by the Lesser Black-backed Gull (*BWM*), but whereas the latter's numbers recovered during the 1990s, those of the Herring Gull stabilised at the lower level. The decline seems initially to have correlated with the introduction of a requirement for landfill sites to be regularly covered over, since when operational controls have been further tightened. Such changes are likely to have affected Herring Gulls most, since they rely more heavily on landfill sites for feeding than do other species of gull.

It would appear, however, that the decline has not been uniform. At Chasewater, where birds feed on the adjacent Cannock Tip during the day, the roost has generally changed little over time, with the maximum counts, in the same five-yearly periods as in the chart, being 2,500 in 1980/1, 3,000 in 1986/7, 2,700 in 1990/1, 2,000 in 1994/5 and 3,000 in 1998/9. However, a noticeable drop in numbers was reported whilst the tip was closed over the Christmas and New Year period in 1983/4. The roost at Westwood Pool has grown considerably, largely because of its proximity to the Throckmorton landfill site, where 500-700 birds regularly scavenge. On the other hand those at sites such as Belvide, Blithfield and Draycote have shown quite dramatic drops of over half or more. This could be partly due to insufficient counts as the upsurge of interest in gull identification appears to have been at the expense of counting and there are some large gaps in the data available for major roosts in recent years. The national gull census, which is carried out every ten years by the BTO, gives an invaluable indication of long term trends, but circumstances can change so quickly that regular annual counts over the winter months should be encouraged, initiated perhaps by the WMBC.

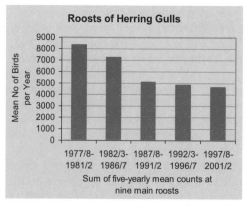

Roosts of Herring Gulls

Mean No of Birds per Year

9000
8000
7000
6000
5000
4000
3000
2000
1000
0

1977/8- 1982/3- 1987/8- 1992/3- 1997/8-
1981/2 1986/7 1991/2 1996/7 2001/2

Sum of five-yearly mean counts at nine main roosts

Notable counts at landfill sites were 900 adults at Bemersley in 1995 and 800 at Queslett in 1991. Herring Gulls more rarely feed on pastures and flood meadows than other gulls, but 800 gathered on fields at Great Wyrley in the winter of 1996, 200 did likewise at Kineton in September 2000 and 80 were on playing fields at Perry Hall in January 1998. Overall, the peak winter population probably ranges between 5,000 and 8,000.

The Herring Gull is primarily a winter visitor, with most occurring between November and February and rising to a peak in January—a month or two later than the Lesser Black-backed Gull. Small numbers can be found throughout the year, however, even in summer. Although most of the latter are immatures, as far back as 1977 an increasing number of adults were reported (*BWM*). This trend has grown over the past decade, most notably in the Severn and Avon Vales and Arden areas, with a pair summering at Earlswood, for example, for four successive years from 1996-99. Eventually, following failed breeding attempts on Worcestershire landfill sites, at Bromsgrove in 1969 and Throckmorton in 1993, at least one pair bred successfully in Worcester city from 1999 to 2001, with two or three pairs there in 2002. At the same time, birds have begun to accompany Lesser Black-backed Gulls into Birmingham, where two pairs bred in the city centre 2001 and at least six pairs were present in 2002. Currently the regional breeding population is thought to be between 5-15 pairs.

Many Herring Gulls have been colour-ringed or dyed and sightings of these tell us much about the origins of our birds. During the 1980s several individuals from County Durham appeared at various places in the region, one ringed at Hartlepool in 1979 was at Belvide Reservoir in January 1982 and other colour-ringed or wing-tagged birds from the Firth of Forth and Walney Island were noted in the region later in their year of ringing, in particular at Westport

Lake. At least some of these were ringed as nestlings, which later dispersed from their natal sites. Currently, birds from Bristol are now being seen at places such as Earlswood Lakes and Bartley and Frankley Reservoirs from June and July onwards. Evidence of return movements is provided by adults ringed here in the winter and recovered during the summer months in Lancashire, Sunderland and Scotland—presumably returning to breed in northern colonies. Other winter ringed birds have moved east into Lincolnshire and south into Surrey and Essex during the same period. Such records confirm that birds arrive in the West Midlands from all directions during the winter, with the most interesting being those of birds ringed here during the winter and recovered in either the following, or in subsequent, summers over 2,200 km away in their breeding colonies in Norway. One of these also demonstrates the longevity of this species, having been ringed at Coleshill in 1978 and found dead at Nordland, Norway, in February 1999, by which time it was at least 22 years old.

The Herring Gull is at the centre of a taxonomic conundrum that has caused great controversy in recent years. Two broad groups are recognised and representatives of each occur regularly in Britain. The northern *argentatus* group includes among others our British race *L. a. argenteus* along with the subtly different *L. a. argentatus* (Dean 1988), which breeds in Denmark, Scandinavia and the Kola peninsula, but winters in the UK including this region. Hume (1978) estimated 10% of the birds roosting at Chasewater to be *argentatus*. The second, southern group breeds from the Atlantic seaboard and islands of Iberia and NW Africa, east through the Mediterranean basin to the Black Sea and into Asia. Two forms of this southern group have been occurring with increasing frequency in recent years, both in Britain as a whole and in this region (Dean 2005). The Yellow-legged Gull *L. [a.] michahellis* breeds in the Mediterranean and the western parts of France, Iberia and NW Africa, with birds from the Atlantic islands (especially the Azores) frequently being differentiated under the name *atlantis*. The Caspian Gull *L. [a.] cachinnans* breeds from the Black Sea to eastern Kazakhstan, but has recently spread to the Moscow area, Germany and Poland.

Although this southern group is currently causing the greater taxonomic headache, the relationship between all the large 'white-headed' gulls is under review, aided by genetic studies that are beginning to supplement traditional field observations. Some authorities now consider the Yellow-legged Gull and Caspian Gull to be separate species, as we have here, although the BOU is adopting a cautious approach and has not yet accorded either full species status.

Ringing studies show a significant proportion of Herring Gulls wintering in Britain to be of the Scandinavian race *L. a. argentatus*, which arrive on their wintering grounds later than birds of our own race *L. a. argenteus*. The latter, which winter closer to their breeding grounds, arrive from August onwards whereas *L. a. argentatus* do not arrive in Britain before November. They then peak in January and disperse rapidly in February (Dean 1987 and www.deanar.btinternet.co.uk and also Coulson *et al.* 1984 and Stanley *et al.*1981). This pattern is very similar to the monthly distribution pattern for the West Midlands, showing that some of our wintering birds come from Scandinavia and Denmark, as is also demonstrated by the ringing recoveries from Norway mentioned earlier.

For the inexperienced birder, gulls can be very confusing. Not only are there so many ages and races to consider, but albinistic and leucistic birds are not unusual and hybrids remain an ever-present possibility. Typical of challenges to be faced was an individual at Kingswood and Chasewater from March 23rd-25th 1988, which was said to resemble Thayer's Gull, *L. a. thayeri*, but was possibly one of the '*thayeri*-type' of *L. a. argentatus* (described by Hume *op. cit.*) that occur in northern Norway. To add yet more complexity, there have been seven reports of individuals said to show some resemblance to 'omissus', a yellow-legged form of *L. a. argentatus* from the eastern Baltic, Finland and Russia. These were: Westport Lake, January 9th 1987; Westport Lake, January 12th 1988; Throckmorton, October 20th-22nd 1989; Throckmorton, December 15th-16th 1990 (trapped and ringed); Blithfield Reservoir, August 17th 1991; Throckmorton, November 15th 1991; and Throckmorton, August 30th 1992.

Yellow-legged Gull *Larus michahellis*
Frequent and increasing late summer, autumn and winter visitor.

The spread of the Yellow-legged Gull has been quite remarkable. It breeds in the Mediterranean region from Iberia to the Black Sea and was virtually unknown as a visitor to Britain thirty years ago. Since then it has become an ever increasing annual visitor, mainly to southern and eastern England between late-summer and spring, and birds now regularly feed at the region's landfill sites during the day and roost on our reservoirs and larger lakes at night.

The first white-headed, dark mantled, yellow legged bird to be detected in this region was at Chasewater (Staffordshire) in November 1973. After close scrutiny of the gull roost here in 1974/5 and 1975/6, Hume (1978) then described birds of this type, which he thought likely to be of Siberian, Mediterranean or perhaps hybrid origin and which we now know were almost certainly Yellow-legged Gulls. Other individuals were also noted at Blithfield Reservoir around this time (*BWM*), the first Warwickshire sighting was at Draycote Water in 1976 and more were reported from elsewhere in Britain (*Brit. Birds* 74:349-53).

The next reports from this region followed in 1981/2, since when birds have occurred in every winter. Initially numbers were very small, but in the late 1980s they increased fourfold, bringing the first records for the West Midlands and Worcestershire at Walsall in 1984 and Throckmorton in 1986 respectively. The population then appeared to stabilise during the early 1990s, but has increased so dramatically since that it is now impossible to determine exactly how many individuals are involved. At a very conservative estimate, over a hundred a year are now appearing and there have been at least 800 in total, with possibly as many as 1,200. Such imprecision arises because there is no way of knowing whether birds at a roost have also been counted at landfill sites, so double-counting cannot be eliminated. For a full review of this problem and a comprehensive analysis of the pattern of occurrences see Dean (2005).

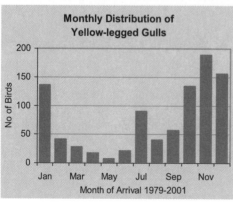

Birds arrive in two distinct phases. Firstly there is a small, but significant, influx in late July when the species makes a post-breeding moult migration northwards from its Mediterranean breeding grounds. This is then followed by the main arrival, which begins in October and continues through to January, after which numbers fall away rapidly. This pattern is somewhat unusual in that southern counties experience their greatest numbers in late summer and autumn after which numbers decline through the winter. It is possible that some birds from the south move up into the Midlands, but it might also be that our winter influx emanates from a different, discrete breeding population. The pattern is further complicated by the fact that occurrences vary even between counties within the region, with Warwickshire, for example, following the trend of southern counties, whilst Worcestershire, with the majority of birds (43%), sets the regional trend (Dean 2005). Here the roost at Westwood Pool and the tip at Throckmorton are the most favoured localities. Despite its southerly situation, Warwickshire has attracted only 23% of birds. Initially most were seen in the Middle Tame Valley, but numbers there have declined, whilst at Draycote they have increased and this is now the prime locality in the county. Most of Staffordshire's share of 25% of birds have been seen at the reservoir roosts, whilst the 9% in the West Midlands county have mostly been recorded at Bartley reservoir. Of those birds that were aged, the vast majority were adults (71%), with 6% in their fourth year, 10% third year, 8% second year and 5% first year. The largest gatherings were 16 at Draycote Water on January 8th 1998 and 11 at Westwood Pool in December 1997.

In 1999 an adult Yellow-legged Gull paired with a Lesser Black-backed Gull at Bredon's Hardwick and produced two young, but the two hybrid chicks resulting from this pairing failed to fledge.

Caspian Gull   *Larus cachinnans*
Rare winter visitor.

The Caspian Gull breeds from the Black Sea to eastern Kazakhstan, but has recently spread to the Moscow area, Germany and Poland. It is now widely recognised to be a separate species and up to the end of 2002 there had been thirteen accepted records as shown below:

Regional Record Number	County Record Number		Year	Locality, Date and Notes
1	Warks	1	1999	Draycote Water: adult, August 24th.
2	Warks	2	1999	Draycote Water: adult, November 28th.
3	Warks	3	2000	Draycote Water: second-summer, April 6th.
4	Warks	4	2000	Draycote Water: adult, September 4th.
5	W Mid	1	2000	Bartley Reservoir: second-winter, December 27th, also Frankley Reservoir same day.
6	Staffs	1	2001	Belvide Reservoir: first-winter, January 6th-13th.
7	Warks	5	2001	Lawford Heath Tip: adult, January 10th.
8	Staffs	2	2001	Belvide Reservoir: adult, January 14th.
9	Staffs	3	2001	Belvide Reservoir: second-winter, October 20th.
10	Worcs	1	2001	Throckmorton Tip: adult, November 25th.
11	Worcs	2	2002	Throckmorton Tip: fourth-winter, January 5th.
12	Worcs	3	2002	Lower Moor: adult, January 20th, also Throckmorton Tip same day.
13	Warks	6	2002	Kingsbury Water Park: second-winter, March 31st. Presume same, now in second-summer plumage April 17th.

Two adults at Belvide Reservoir on November 29th and December 5th 1992 were thought by the observer at the time to have been of the *cachinnans* race. However, this pre-dates the first accepted British records of the Caspian Gull, *L. [a.] cachinnans*, which came from Essex in 1995 (*Brit. Birds* 96:575-578). Another in 1997 at Westwood Pool also showed several characteristics which suggested *cachinnans*, but some features could not be discerned and the record has not been included above.

For further information see Dean (2002) and www.deanar.btinternet.co.uk and specifically for identification of Yellow-legged and Caspian Gulls, readers should refer to Garner (1997) and Garner *et al.* (1997).

Iceland Gull   *Larus glaucoides*
Scarce winter visitor.

Iceland Gulls are scarce visitors to the region, where they roost at the larger reservoirs and spend much of the day scavenging at landfill sites.

Despite its name, this is a Nearctic species that breeds in Greenland and Arctic Canada, but not in Iceland, where it is only a winter visitor. From here some move on to Britain. The trend towards regular inland occurrences only really began once other species of gulls had established roosts. The first to reach this region came in 1949 and then, after a scatter of records in the 1950s and 1960s, quickly established itself as a regular visitor, with around 70 in the ten years 1969-78 (*BWM*). At least 350 birds were then reported during 1979-2001, during which time the annual rate increased fivefold, from about five to twenty-five a year, before falling back again to about fifteen a year. These are conservative figures—exact numbers being hard to determine because of the high degree of turnover in birds at a relatively few sites. Despite birds seeming to frequently come and go, however, the occasional, clearly identifiable, individual demonstrates that they do have a strong site fidelity and will often remain in an area throughout the winter. Perhaps the best example of this is provided by an adult bird which has visited Draycote Water for eight successive winters, usually arriving in December and then being seen intermittently until early March (extreme dates November 24th and March 13th). Its longest stays were 93 days in 1998/9, from December 11th-March 13th, and 94 days in 2001/2, from November 24th-February 25th.

Always an exciting species to see, the arrival of the first Iceland Gulls is an eagerly awaited event. Although this sometimes occurs in November (with the earliest ever actually on October 30th, at Clayton in 1979), it is frequently not until around Christmas that the first birds appear. Numbers then reach a peak in January and early February, before falling away through March to leave only stragglers into April and perhaps early May, with the latest on May 3rd, at Chasewater in 1994. As with other gulls, birds are most numerous during spells of very cold weather.

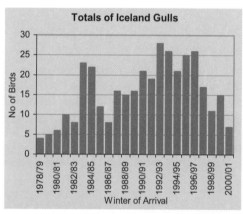

Given the direction from which Iceland Gulls come, most would be expected in Staffordshire, but the strength of that county's dominance (61% of all birds) is nonetheless surprising. Warwickshire's share of 27% is also substantial, whilst 5% in the West Midlands is about average, given its small size and highly urbanised nature. Worcestershire, with just 7% is clearly less attractive, principally because it lacks the large bodies of water required for roosting.

In the evenings, most birds join the thousands of other gulls that gather to form large roosts at the major reservoirs. Three sites have proved dominant, between them accommodating three-quarters of the birds that visited the region during 1979-2001. Chasewater especially, with 33% of all birds, developed a reputation as *the* place in the region to see this species. Many birds from here also feed on the nearby landfill site at Cannock during the day. The two other prime sites were Draycote Water, with 22% of birds, and Blithfield Reservoir with 19%. Elsewhere, the Middle Tame Valley and Westport Lake each held 6%, Westwood Pool and the nearby Throckmorton landfill site 4% and Belvide and Bartley Reservoirs 3% and 1% respectively.

Kumlien's Gull   *Larus glaucoides kumlieni*
Very rare winter visitor. Three records.

There have been three records of this western race of Iceland Gull, which breeds on Baffin Island and in north-west Quebec and winters from Labrador south to New England.

Regional Record Number	County Record Number	Year	Locality, Date and Notes
1	Staffs 1	1979	Westport Lake: first-winter, December 30th to January 12th 1980. *BB 90:484.*
2	Staffs 2	1999	Blithfield Reservoir: adult, February 14th.
3	Warks 1	2001	Draycote Water: adult, January 1st.

The first of these, at Westport Lake in 1979, was originally recorded as an Iceland Gull of the nominate race, but, on the evidence of photographs taken at the time, was subsequently accepted as being of the race *kumlieni*. This constituted only the second record for Britain, the first having been in Cornwall just a few months earlier, in March 1979.

Glaucous Gull   *Larus hyperboreus*
Scarce winter visitor.

Glaucous Gulls nest in the high Arctic, but move south as far as Britain for the winter, when a few can be found amongst the thousands of gulls that gather to roost on our reservoirs at night. During the day they mostly feed at the larger landfill sites, though very occasionally one is seen on a field.

Like Iceland Gulls, they have increased in number and some have moved inland since gull roosts became established. The first record for the region came in 1949—coincidentally just one month after the first Iceland Gull was seen, and at the same locality, Belvide Reservoir.

The Glaucous Gull soon became the commoner of the two species, with around 120 birds recorded in the decade 1969-78 (*cf.* 70 Iceland Gulls) (*BWM*). Throughout the 1980s numbers varied considerably from winter to winter, with 1984/5 producing just nine birds whereas in 1980/81, which was a good year for the species nationally (*Winter Atlas*), 34 were recorded. The long-term trend, however, remained fairly steady at between 20-25 a year. The winter of 1988/9 was particularly productive, with a record number of reports involving over 40 birds, though the widely spaced dates make it impossible to estimate numbers more precisely. Since 1990 numbers have steadily fallen and over the last five winters (1996/7-2000/1) they averaged roughly 12 a year, with Iceland Gull becoming the commoner species. The decline in fishing, with fewer trawlers for the birds to follow across to Britain, may be a contributory factor. Another could be that birds have not been forced so far south during the recent run of mild winters. The true explanation is probably much more complex, however, since Iceland Gulls continued to increase throughout much of this period and their numbers have only begun to decline during the last five years.

Glaucous Gulls tend to arrive slightly earlier than Iceland, reaching a peak from mid-December to mid-February, but with relatively fewer new birds in spring. The extreme dates

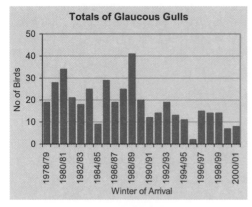

Totals of Glaucous Gulls

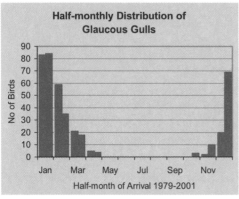

Half-monthly Distribution of Glaucous Gulls

remain those quoted in *BWM*, namely October 11th (1958 and 1970) and May 1st (1979).

Although most birds are seen singly, as many as four have appeared together twice— once feeding at Cannock landfill site on February 11th 1984 and once roosting at Chasewater in January 1986, whilst five were in the Blithfield roost on January 20th 1980. The latter included an adult that remained in the area for 85 days from December 16th 1979 to March 9th 1980—an unusually long stay. Of those specifically aged, 53% were first-year birds, 17% second-years, 7% third-years, 2% fourth-years and 21% adults.

The large gull roosts in Staffordshire made this the most attractive county during 1979-2001, with 56% of all birds. Warwickshire, with the enormous Draycote Water roost, came second, with 29%, whilst the landfill sites of the West Midlands raised that county's share to 9%—above Worcestershire with just 6%. As with Iceland Gull, Chasewater used to be known as *the* place to see this species and, indeed, this remained true over the period 1979-2001 as a whole, when 26% of the birds recorded in the region roosted there. Many of these could also be seen feeding at the nearby Cannock landfill site during the day. The Draycote Water roost attracted 20% overall, but in recent years has tended to produce more birds than Chasewater. The roost at Blithfield Reservoir has been almost as productive, holding 19% of birds. Thus two-thirds of the region's birds have been at just three sites. Elsewhere, other favoured localities, in descending order of importance, have been the Middle Tame Valley, Bartley Reservoir, Westport Lake and Belvide Reservoir.

The *Wintering Atlas* refers to hybrid Glaucous x Herring Gulls forming a high proportion of the breeding population in Iceland, so this is possibly the origin of the occasional bird of this pairing that is seen in the region.

Great Black-backed Gull   *Larus marinus*
Fairly common winter visitor, scarce in summer. Rare breeding species.

Being the most maritime of the large British gulls, it was perhaps to be expected that the Great Black-backed Gull would be the last to exploit the combination of safe roosts and feeding opportunities offered by our reservoirs and landfill sites.

BWM noted that parties in double figures were virtually unknown until 1970, but roosts up to 100 strong then developed over the next decade, at which time the wintering population was thought to be in the region of 400 birds. Based on roost counts, this increase then gradually accelerated throughout the 1980s to reach its maximum in 1990/1, by which time the five-yearly mean was almost 1,400 a year. Since then the population has remained stable at about this level. During the *Winter Atlas* period birds were found in 71% of 10-km squares.

The seasonal pattern is essentially that of a winter visitor, with the main influx beginning in November and continuing through December to a very pronounced peak in January. Thereafter birds move away quite quickly, with much reduced numbers in February and scarcely any by March. Summer records were once very rare, but recently more have been seen during May-July and, following the precedent set by Lesser Black-backed and Herring Gulls, a pair surprisingly bred at Bredon's Hardwick in 2001 and 2002, raising one and two chicks respectively. These are possibly the first breeding records for a truly landlocked county.

As with Lesser Black-backed and Herring Gulls, the location of this first breeding, in the Lower Avon Valley, points to the Severn Estuary as the most likely origin of the parents. The overwhelming majority of winter visitors, though, congregate in Staffordshire (70% of birds) and Warwickshire (24%), with barely any in Worcestershire (5%) and the West Midlands (1%). Whilst this is primarily due to the location of the major reservoirs, it also suggests that wintering birds probably arrive from Merseyside via the Cheshire gap, from the Wash, or from the Thames Estuary as well as the Severn. It is considered likely that a significant proportion are of Scandinavian origin (A. R. Dean www.deanar.btinternet.co.uk).

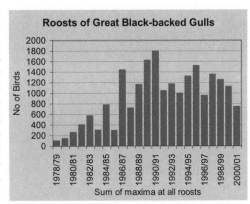

Roosts of Great Black-backed Gulls

No of Birds — Sum of maxima at all roosts (1978/79–2000/01)

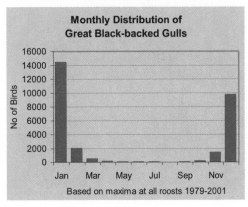

Monthly Distribution of Great Black-backed Gulls

No of Birds — Based on maxima at all roosts 1979-2001

The count for the BTO's Winter Gull Roost Survey in January 1993 showed 550 at Draycote Water, making this the largest inland roost for this species in Britain. During the five winters 1995/6-1999/00, however, the Chasewater roost was largest, averaging 505, whilst the average count at Draycote was only 174, although this was almost certainly under-recorded. The only other site to hold significant numbers is Blithfield Reservoir, where the last comprehensive count was 450 in 1994/5.

Kittiwake *Rissa tridactyla*
Uncommon passage migrant and storm-driven winter visitor.

Apart from a few brief months when Kittiwakes come ashore to breed, they spend most of their lives well out to sea, often crossing the Atlantic to feed on the fishing banks around Greenland and Newfoundland. Inland occurrences might therefore be regarded as unusual, except perhaps after severe gales. In fact, the BTO *Winter Atlas* states that the number of inland records is surprising and difficult to explain. However, Hume (1976) provided evidence of a definite spring passage

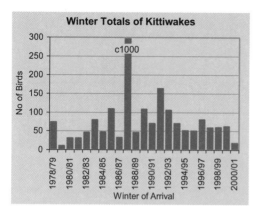

Winter Totals of Kittiwakes

c1000

No of Birds

Winter of Arrival

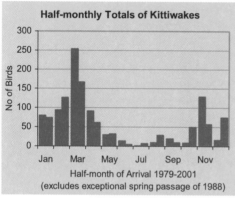

Half-monthly Totals of Kittiwakes

No of Birds

Half-month of Arrival 1979-2001
(excludes exceptional spring passage of 1988)

across the Midlands and this can sometimes be seen even in fine, calm weather, although many can pass overhead undetected in these ideal conditions. The largest numbers appear when weather fronts impede their progress.

BWM went on to identify three main movements, namely the significant spring passage mentioned above, which comprises mainly adults; a small influx of immature birds in August; and a further passage of adults in November and December, which frequently coincides with stormy weather. This pattern remained evident during 1979-2001, although even excluding the exceptional numbers of 1988, the spring passage was stronger and slightly earlier; the late-summer influx of juveniles was virtually non-existent, but it did bring the first-ever in July; and the late-autumn movement was weaker.

Overall, 2,400 birds were recorded during the current period, which, excluding those in spring 1988, represents an average of about 60 a year (*cf.* 20 a year in the 1970s). Up to 1978, 77% of all aged birds were adults (*BWM*), but during 1979-2001 this percentage rose to 84%. The latter accords well with the 88% and 82% quoted respectively in *BWM* for the spring and late autumn passages of adults. The overall difference must therefore result from the perplexing absence of juvenile birds in late-summer. One possible explanation for this is the recent poor breeding success of Kittiwakes in some areas, such as Shetland. Paradoxically, given the paucity of juvenile birds, the period 1979-2001 produced eight birds in July, whereas there were none during 1929-78.

The outstanding event of the current period has to be the exceptional spring passage of 1988, which brought around 1,000 birds to the region. Apart from the sheer numbers, this movement was unusual in that it occurred at three separate times. The first wave arrived on February 28th, with 30 at Sandwell Valley and a regional record of 200 at Blithfield Reservoir, and the last wave on March 27th, when 84 flew through Draycote Water at dusk. Sandwiched between these, the main influx occurred on March 12th-13th, when an active weather front, aligned north-west to south-east, remained stationary across the Midlands, effectively halting overland movement (Allsopp *et al.* 1988) and bringing around 500 birds to the region.

A smaller passage also coincided with a spell of cold, north-westerly winds around March 14th-16th 1992, when at least 100 arrived in Staffordshire. The majority of these were at Belvide Reservoir, where parties of 42, 12, ten and seven were recorded—the largest of these equalling the previous regional record of 42, which coincidentally was also at Belvide, on March 11th 1979. Later in 1979, a smaller influx produced 21 across the three larger counties on November 8th. There were also small 'wrecks' of storm-driven birds induced by strong westerly winds during January 10th-12th 1993 and again early in January 1998, when four days of strong south-westerly winds culminated in a severe gale. In addition to the flocks already mentioned, 40 were at Draycote Water on February 20th 1997 after a gale the previous day and 34 flew north over Sandwell Valley on November 3rd 1989.

With the bulk of the population wintering in the North Atlantic, it is strong north-westerly winds that bring most to the region, sweeping them into the Irish Sea and across the Cheshire Plain, from where they end up at the Staffordshire reservoirs. South-westerlies, on the other hand, tend to drive birds up the Bristol Channel and the Avon valley to Draycote Water. At times, Draycote also receives birds from the North Sea that are blown inland from the Wash by strong north-easterly winds. As a result, Staffordshire (55%) and Warwickshire (24%) have received most birds, with just 12% in Worcestershire and 9% in the West Midlands. The six most favoured sites have been Draycote Water (110 records), Westport Lake (93 records), Belvide Reservoir (92), Blithfield Reservoir (82), Chasewater (63) and Westwood Pool (48).

Sadly, at least a dozen birds were found oiled and a further 25-30 dead. One reason for this high mortality is that Kittiwakes apparently do not feed adequately at inland waters (*Winter Atlas*), so any arriving in a weak condition are likely to succumb quickly.

Gull-billed Tern   *Sterna nilotica*
Very rare vagrant. Five records.

Following four historical records, exactly ninety years elapsed before the fifth in 1989.

Regional Record Number	County Record Number		Year	Locality, Date and Notes
1	Worcs	1	Pre-1901	Cofton Reservoir: shot, date unknown , but presume nineteenth century.
2	Warks	1	1876	Wormleighton Reservoir: April 24th, shot.
3	W Mid	1	1896	Shirley: adult female, August 8th, shot.
4	Warks	2	1899	Coleshill: date unknown, shot.
5	Staffs	1	1989	Blithfield Reservoir: June 19th. *BB 83:467*

The bird at Blithfield was presumed to be the same as that seen at Burton Marsh, Cheshire, three days earlier (Rogers *et al.* 1990). The European population breeds in small, isolated colonies in Denmark, north Germany and Spain and winters off the West African coast and the Gulf of Guinea.

Caspian Tern   *Sterna caspia*
Rare passage migrant.

BWM listed seven records during 1968-79, since when there have been a further six sightings of this large, heavy-billed tern. All thirteen are listed below and overleaf.

Regional Record Number	County Record Number		Year	Locality, Date and Notes
1	Staffs	1	1968	Belvide Reservoir: July 20th. *BB 62:473*
2	Worcs	1	1971	Upton Warren: July 29th. *BB 65:337*
3	Staffs	2	1972	Blithfield Reservoir: July 16th. *BB 66:344*
4	Staffs	3	1973	Chasewater: October 14th. *BB 67:327*
5	Warks	1	1975	Bodymoor Heath: July 6th-11th. *BB 69:342*
6	Warks	2	1976	Draycote Water: June 23rd. *BB 70:427*

Regional Record Number	County Record Number		Year	Locality, Date and Notes
7	W Mid	1	1979	Sandwell Valley: July 25th. *BB 74:476*
8	Staffs	4	1984	Rocester (recorded as Alton in *BB*): April 26th. *BB 79:556*
9	Warks	3	1988	Seeswood Pool: May 8th. *BB 82:530*
10	Staffs	5	1988	Westport Lake: June 8th. *BB 82:530*
11	Staffs	6	1992	Belvide Reservoir: June 21st. *BB 87:532*
12	Warks Staffs	4 7	1993	Dosthill Lake: May 10th. *BB 87:532.* Same, briefly, gravel pits on Staffordshire side of county boundary.
13	Staffs	8	1999	Westport Lake: June 3rd. *BB 93:538*

The European population is isolated and declining, which is perhaps reflected by the records with six in the 1970s and three each in the 1980s and 1990s, but none since. Breeding is now confined to the Baltic coast, with birds wintering off the West African coast, as far south as the Gulf of Guinea. Twelve of the birds occurred between April 26th-July 29th—a typical period for this species—but the date of that at Chasewater on October 14th was unusual (Dymond *et al.* 1989).

The records also include three wandering individuals. The one at Seeswood Pool in 1988 was probably that seen at Spalding (Lincs) on May 5th, Rutland Water (Leics) on May 7th and Northwich (Cheshire) on May 8th (Rogers *et al.* 1989): the bird at Belvide in 1992 was probably that at Thornton Reservoir (Leics) the previous day: and the Dosthill bird in 1993 was probably that at Willington (Derbys) on May 11th, Lound (Notts) on May 12th and Goole (Humberside) on May 13th (Rogers *et al.* 1994 and 1995).

Sandwich Tern *Sterna sandvicensis*
Uncommon passage migrant.

Sandwich Terns nest in Britain at a relatively few traditional locations around the coast and winter off the West African coast. Each year some pass overland on their migration between the two and a few find their way to this region.

Steadily increasing numbers of Sandwich Terns were reported decade by decade during 1929-78, culminating in an average of six a year during the 1970s (*BWM*). In the early years

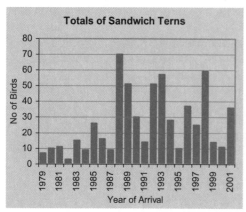

particularly, the growing number of bird-watchers must have had a significant influence on the figures, but there does seem to have been a genuine increase in the numbers passing through the region. During 1979-2001 this increase continued, with 600 birds being recorded at an average of 26 a year. However, the rate of growth was not uniform. Despite the customary year-by-year fluctuations, which ranged from three in 1982 to 70 in 1988, for most of the 1980s the average was no higher than 12 a year. Since then, although 1988 remains the best year ever, several others have approached the same level, bringing the current average up to 30 a year.

Sandwich Terns are the first of the terns to arrive back in Britain in spring and *BWM* gave the earliest and latest dates as April 3rd (1971) and early November (1877). During 1979-2001 there were seven March records—the first ever in that month—with the earliest on March 17th 1990, when three were at Lea Marston. The latest during this period was October 14th 1986, when three were at Chasewater and five at Larford. Comparing the monthly distributions for 1929-78 (see *BWM*) and 1979-2001 shows that the main arrival time has advanced slightly, from an even

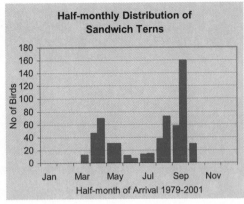

spread throughout April and May to a peak in April, whilst the autumn peak has moved backwards from early to late September. Whether this is in response to climate change is a matter for conjecture. Overall, the seasonal pattern was the same as that recorded in *BWM*, with 34% of records in April-May and 43% in August-September.

Most birds pass through very quickly, with phrases such as 'dropped in briefly' or 'stayed only a few minutes' frequently accompanying records. This makes it difficult to judge whether multiple arrivals on the same date are part of a broad movement or simply the same birds moving from one place to another. A typical example of this dilemma arose on September 25th 1988, when a flock of at least 40—the largest ever recorded in the region—flew into Draycote Water. Thirteen of these stayed to feed, but the rest flew off and the same day 28 birds were seen at Upton Warren, 33 miles to the west. These were presumed to have been those that left Draycote, although we shall never know for certain. Other large parties included 29, at Chasewater on August 22nd 1993, and 22, at both Lighthorne on August 8th 1988 and Belvide Reservoir on May 23rd 1989—the latter brought down by heavy rain.

The geographical spread shows 39% of birds occurred in Warwickshire, 34% in Staffordshire, 21% in Worcestershire and 6% in the West Midlands. Just four localities have dominated the records, namely Draycote Water (58 records, 163 birds), Chasewater (28 records, 67 birds), Blithfield Reservoir (28 records, 46 birds) and Belvide Reservoir (26 records, 59 birds).

Roseate Tern   *Sterna dougallii*
Rare passage migrant.

The Roseate Tern was described in *BWM* as probably the rarest breeding seabird in Britain and, with just over 70 pairs in 2002 (Ogilvie 2004), this remains true. The only other near colonies are in Eire and Brittany. Birds winter along the west African coast. Their rarity is reflected in the records in this region, with fourteen documented in *BWM* and only seven since.

Regional Record Number	County Record Number		Year	Locality, Date and Notes
1	Staffs	1	1941	Belvide Reservoir: nine, June 4th.
2	Staffs	2	1955	Blithfield Reservoir: May 7th.
3	Staffs	3	1955	Belvide Reservoir: May 28th.
4	Staffs	4	1957	Blithfield Reservoir: August 8th.

Regional Record Number	County Record Number		Year	Locality, Date and Notes
5	Warks	1	1959	Alvecote Pools: May 21st.
6	Warks	2	1965	Budbrooke Barracks: September 28th, found dying
7	Warks	3	1969	Draycote Water: May 4th.
8	Warks	4	1969	Bodymoor Heath: two, May 31st.
9	Staffs	5	1971	Belvide Reservoir: June 10th.
10	Worcs	1	1972	Westwood Pool: May 28th to June 1st.
11	Staffs	6	1972	Belvide Reservoir: June 24th.
12	Warks	5	1973	Coombe Abbey: August 31st.
13	Staffs	7	1974	Blithfield Reservoir: June 2nd.
14	Staffs	8	1980	Belvide Reservoir: May 7th-8th.
15	Staffs	9	1983	Belvide Reservoir: June 4th.
16	Warks	6	1987	Kingsbury WP: May 12th.
17	Warks	7	1993	Dosthill Lake: May 12th.
18	Worcs	2	1993	Eckington: May 19th-21st.
19	Worcs	3	1999	Upton Warren: May 8th.
20	Warks	8	2001	Kingsbury WP: adult, May 20th.
21	Warks	9	2002	Dosthill Lake: adult and immature, September 17th.

Seventeen of the above 21 records fell in spring, on dates ranging from May 4th-June 24th which reflects the late migration of this species. Of the other four, two occurred in August and two in September.

For such a rare bird, it is amazing to find that two of the above had been ringed—the 1965 individual at Budbrooke as a chick on Anglesey two years previously and the 1993 Eckington bird as a nestling four years previously in Wexford, Eire.

Common Tern   *Sterna hirundo*

Fairly common passage migrant. Uncommon or frequent as a breeding species, mainly in the Tame and Trent Valleys.

From its former status as a rare or scarce passage migrant, the Common Tern has now become a familiar summer sight at many of our reservoirs, lakes, gravel pits, rivers and canals.

This is largely due to the consolidation and growth of the incipient breeding colonies referred to in *BWM*. Originally a coastal breeding species, the heart of this expansion has been the flooded sand and gravel quarries of the Trent and Tame valleys. Birds initially spread up the Trent valley from the East Midlands, with the first breeding record at Branston as long ago as 1952. A small colony then persisted there until at least the early 1980s without ever expanding much beyond two or three pairs. One or two pairs also bred at Kingsbury Water Park between 1969 and 1974, but it was not until 1980, after two islands had been created especially to attract them to the Park, that regular breeding began. Work on the islands was finished in

March that year and, to everyone's surprise, three pairs raised four young that summer.

The following year about a dozen pairs raised 37 young and this colony has flourished ever since, increasing to between 30-40 pairs and raising 70-90 young several times, with a record 109 in 1999. However, 2002 was a poor breeding season with only 20-25 pairs, many of which deserted. For a time during 1994-97 a substantial part of the colony moved to Dosthill Lake, but once water skiing began there birds returned to the Water Park. Meanwhile, lower down the Tame and Trent valleys, birds began to nest at other gravel pits, such as Elford, Croxall and Barton, in the 1980s and at least 12 pairs were recorded there in 1988, with probably 10 pairs in 1994.

Away from the Trent and Tame Valleys, there have been an increasing number of sporadic, often unsuccessful, breeding attempts, including several in the heart of the Black Country at Sheepwash Urban Park and others at the WMBC's reserve at Belvide Reservoir. The only signs of birds becoming firmly established elsewhere, though, have come from Upton Warren, where nesting first occurred in 1991 and there are now four or five pairs, Brandon Marsh, where a pair first attempted to breed in 1995 and by 2002 there were 10-12 pairs and Marsh Lane, where the developing colony had grown to six pairs by 2002. The regional breeding population now is probably in the range of 50-75 pairs.

In an attempt to identify the main passage periods, the accompanying chart shows the monthly distribution of birds away from their breeding colonies during 1979-1992. Thereafter, breeding birds were so widespread that it became impossible to separate them from migrants. The chart reveals slightly fewer birds in spring (44%) and more in autumn (56%). This is the reverse of the balance found during 1969-78 (*BWM*) and presumably arises from the many young birds being produced by the expanding breeding population. A good indication of the increase in total numbers is provided by the average counts for 1969-78 and 1992-2001, which were approaching 200 and 700 a year respectively.

Birds usually begin to return from wintering in west Africa in early April, with the earliest on record being one at Bredon's Hardwick on March 29th 2001 and two at Draycote Water on March 30th 1999. Sometimes they are held back by poor weather, however, and in 1994 it was April 22nd before any appeared. Passage then gathers momentum later in the month, reaches its peak in the first-half of May, and then subsides by early June. Non-breeding birds and those from the breeding colonies then confuse the mid-summer pattern, but return movement commences in late-July, peaks in August and early September, then fades quickly so that most have left by October. Late birds are not unusual though, with over 100 having been noted in October, whilst the latest ever was at Draycote Water on November 8th 2001.

Weather has a significant bearing on passage numbers, determining both the course that birds follow and whether they fly straight over or drop down. As a result, figures are very variable, both between years and between seasons. Occasionally, as in 1988 and 2001, good numbers are recorded in both spring and autumn, but the opposite occurred in 1979 and 1989. Concentrated movements are also a feature. For example, a large southerly passage on August 30th 1985 brought 86 to Upton Warren, including groups of 15, 37 and 30, and at least 74 to Chasewater, including a flock of 60— which at that time was the largest recorded in the region. Similarly, strong passages involving between 200-220 birds occurred in 1990, during May 1st-3rd, and twice in 1992, during heavy rain and strong north-easterly winds on August 8th-9th and then again on September 11th (see also Black Tern). The latter included

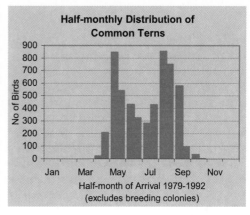

Half-monthly Distribution of Common Terns

No of Birds

Half-month of Arrival 1979-1992
(excludes breeding colonies)

flocks of 60 at Draycote Water—equalling the Chasewater record—and 45 at Bittell Reservoir. More usually, Common Terns tend to migrate in small parties, with groups up to 40 being seen quite frequently, but 50 or more very seldom, so 52 at Blithfield Reservoir in August 2001 was a notable flock. Typically, birds either pass straight through or remain only for a matter of hours before moving on.

With the bulk of the breeding pairs, Kingsbury Water Park is undoubtedly the best place to see this species, although Brandon Marsh, Marsh Lane and Upton Warren should also prove reliable. Away from these breeding sites, Blithfield Reservoir (64 records), Draycote Water (61 records), Belvide Reservoir (57 records) and Chasewater (52 records) have been most frequently visited. The overall distribution of birds between the counties during 1989-2001 was 34% in Warwickshire, 29% in Staffordshire, 22% in Worcestershire and 15% in the West Midlands.

Birds from the Kingsbury Water Park colony have provided some very interesting recoveries. Many have been colour-ringed and one of these, ringed as a chick in 1998, appeared at Upton Warren on July 10th 2001. Movements of over 120 km have also been made by a number of other juvenile birds as they regularly disperse each year into Merseyside and the open sea. There is also a tendency for birds from this colony to appear as adults at coastal sites in north-west England. Foreign recoveries include a nestling ringed in June 1998 that was recovered in Huelva, Spain, in September 2000 after making a journey of 1,750 km and another, ringed in June 1989, that was found dead the following December after making a journey of 4,476 km to Senegal. In total, four birds from Kingsbury Water Park have been recovered in Senegal, whilst a nestling ringed at Branston in July 1979 was recovered in December 1980 in Tena, Ghana, 5,235 km away.

Finally, a Common Tern fishing in a garden pond at Amington on May 5th 1986 provided a nice addition to the occupier's garden list!

Arctic Tern *Sterna paradisaea*
Frequent passage migrant in highly variable numbers.

The Arctic Tern is renowned for having the longest migration of any bird, travelling from the most northerly of its breeding grounds in the Arctic right to the very edge of the Antarctic ice cap and back again each year. This means it is not only the most travelled bird, but it experiences more hours of daylight than any other living creature. Much of these long migration flights are made at great altitude, sometimes overland, when birds are liable to be grounded by adverse weather conditions (Kramer 1995). It is in just such conditions that some find their way to our reservoirs and lakes, especially during the spring.

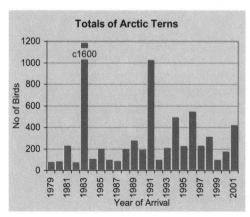

Such events are clearly unpredictable and because of this numbers fluctuate widely. For example, during 1969-78 the number of birds each year ranged from 46-565, with an average of 163 (*BWM*). This volatile pattern continued during 1979-2001, when totals ranged from 69 to about 1,600 and the average was 300 a year. However, even by these fluctuating standards, the 1,600 that occurred in 1983 and the 1,020 in 1991 were quite exceptional and if these years are excluded the range reduces to 69-538 and the average falls to 204 per annum. Despite increasing numerically, the Arctic Tern has lost ground compared with the Common Tern. During 1969-78, Common Terns were the more numerous, but only by 5%, whereas during 1979-2001 they were 40% more plentiful.

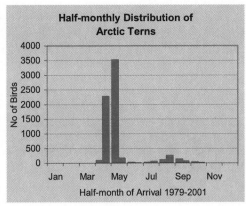

As well as being numerically very variable, Arctic Terns are also seasonally very biased, with 89% of birds occurring in spring. Even this passage is highly concentrated into a very short period of time between mid–April and mid–May, when birds are hurrying northwards or north-eastwards to reach their breeding grounds in Britain, Iceland and Scandinavia. Should they fly into a deep depression at this time, then the combination of strong winds and heavy rain is likely to force them down to ground, where they may choose to rest and feed before moving on.

This is exactly what happened in 1983, when a stationary front lying east-west across the region at the beginning of May resulted in the appearance of a phenomenal total of 1,350 on the 2nd, including 520 at Chasewater and 270 at Kingsbury Water Park. Similar circumstances prevailed again in 1991, but this time the movement was smaller and more spread, with good numbers on April 20th and 30th and between May 3rd-6th. Included in this passage were around 100 at Draycote Water on April 20th and May 5th. Also at the same locality there were 200 on April 23rd 1994. The earliest spring record to date was one at Edgbaston Reservoir on April 2nd 1989, but there were a further seven on dates during the first week of April, suggesting perhaps that the time of passage is advancing slightly.

Autumn passage, by comparison, is often miniscule, with 1995, for example, producing a mere six birds. What little movement there is normally peaks in late August, when the maximum recorded was 33 flying south-west over Netherton Hill on August 24th 1994. Most have left by mid-September, but one or two stragglers are sometimes noted as late as November, with the latest being that quoted in *BWM*, namely November 15th 1936 at Bittell Reservoir.

During 1988-2001, the most frequented locations by a long way were Draycote Water and the Middle Tame Valley, with 105 and 104 records respectively. Their dominance gave Warwickshire the largest share of birds, with 51%. In Staffordshire, Belvide and Blithfield Reservoirs each produced 77 records, whilst Chasewater had 55 and Westport Lake 21, giving that county 34% of birds. Although Worcestershire's share of birds was much less (just 9%), four sites did produce a significant number of records, namely Bittell Reservoir (48), Upton Warren (45), Westwood Pool (34) and Bredon's Hardwick (31). In the West Midlands, which had 6% of birds, Sandwell Valley proved to be best site with 29 records.

Sooty Tern   *Sterna fuscata*
Very rare vagrant. One historical record.

This incredulous record from way back in 1852 remains the only one.

Regional Record Number	County Record Number	Year	Locality, Date and Notes
1	Staffs 1	1852	R. Dove near Tutbury: unknown date, killed by a stone thrown by a boy.

The last British record of this species, which breeds on tropical and sub-tropical islands and around the Red Sea, was in 1989, bringing the total to 26 (Rogers *et al.* 1998). What makes the Staffordshire record unique is not so much the unusual manner in which the bird was obtained, but the fact that it was the first ever for Europe (*BWM*). The exact date was unrecorded and there is much confusion about the season, with Mosley (1863) referring to 'summer' and Whitlock (1893) to 'about October', while the *Zoologist* of December 20th 1852 said 'killed about four months ago'. Witherby *et al.* (1938-44) accepted the record and quoted October as the month, but the uncertainty over such details and the circumstances of the record as a whole have to raise doubts over its authenticity.

Little Tern *Sterna albifrons*
Scarce passage migrant.

A few of these delicate little birds pass through the region in spring and autumn, when they might be encountered at our reservoirs and gravel pits. Often they are seen being blown along by a brisk wind or hovering as they search for food.

During the 1980s Little Tern numbers increased steadily, with the five-yearly running mean rising from around 12 a year to a peak of almost 20 by 1994. Since then, numbers have fallen back to an average of 10 per annum or less. This correlates with a decline in the small population that breeds around the British coast, from 2,400 pairs around 1990 (*Breeding Atlas*) to an average of 1,600 pairs during 1997-2002 (Ogilvie *et al.* 2004).

There has been a significant shift in the seasonal pattern of Little Terns moving through the region. During 1929-78 there was a distinct autumn bias, with 61% of birds at this season compared to only 39% in spring (*BWM*), whereas 1979-2001 showed a noticeable bias in favour of spring (55%). The spring passage generally begins in the second half of April, with the two earliest records both coming from Staffordshire in 2001, when singles were at Chasewater on the 13th and Belvide Reservoir on the 15th. Movement then builds to a pronounced peak in early May, but then subsides quite quickly, although some late migrants continue into June when they can begin to mingle with the earliest returning birds. Return passage shows two high points, in the first halves of August and September respectively, after which movements rapidly decline, with very few lingering into October. As with the earliest records, the latest in the current period was also in 2001, when an adult was at Kingsbury from October 16th-18th, but the latest birds ever were three at Belvide Reservoir on October 30th 1954 (*BWM*).

Likewise the largest party ever was an old record of 12 at Brandon Marsh on August 30th 1963, with the two best during 1979-2001 both coming from Blithfield Reservoir, where eight were present on September 6th 1982 and nine immatures on September 13th 1986. Birds generally pass through either singly (51%) or in twos (26%). Most also move through quickly, with very few staying more

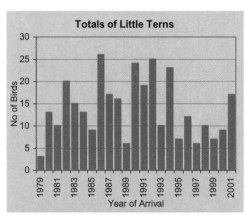

Totals of Little Terns

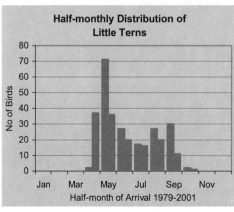

Half-monthly Distribution of Little Terns

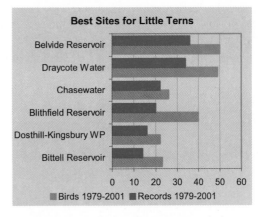

Best Sites for Little Terns

Belvide Reservoir
Draycote Water
Chasewater
Blithfield Reservoir
Dosthill-Kingsbury WP
Bittell Reservoir

0 10 20 30 40 50 60
■ Birds 1979-2001 ■ Records 1979-2001

than a day or two, and four days constituting the maximum stay during the current period.

The Staffordshire reservoirs, especially Belvide, have been the most favoured localities, and 45% of all birds were seen in this county. Warwickshire, thanks largely to Draycote Water, attracted 28% of birds, Worcestershire 23% and the West Midlands 4%.

Whiskered Tern *Chlidonias hybrida*
Very rare vagrant. Five records.

Only two more records have been added to the three documented in *BWM*.

Regional Record Number	County Record Number		Year	Locality, Date and Notes
1	Staffs	1	1969	Belvide Reservoir: April 27th. *BB 63:280.*
2	Staffs	2	1970	Blithfield Reservoir: May 10th. *BB 64:355.*
3	Warks	1	1976	Draycote Water: May 24th. Probably same, Kingsbury Water Park (then known as Bodymoor Heath gravel pits), May 25th. *BB 70:426.*
4	Warks	2	1987	Kingsbury Water Park: May 18th. *BB 81:568.*
5	Worcs	1	1994	Bredon's Hardwick: May 1st. *BB 88:522.*

Following current convention, the two sightings in 1976 are now treated as one record. All occurred in spring, between April 27th-May 24th, which is the typical time for overshooting migrants from southern Europe to appear. Whiskered Terns breed discontinuously from Iberia eastwards through southern and eastern Europe and into Asia and winter mainly in Africa.

Black Tern *Chlidonias niger*
Frequent passage migrant.

Small parties of Black Terns skimming across a reservoir or gravel pit, then dipping down to feed from the water's surface, are one of the delights of spring and autumn.

Their appearances are very erratic, however, with very few in some years and large numbers in others. For example, there were only 59 in 1995, but at least 2,300 in 1992, when strong passages occurred in both spring and autumn. 1990 was another good year, with almost 1,400. Excluding these two exceptional years, the average over 1979-2001 was 270 a year (*cf.*

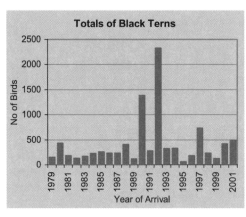

Totals of Black Terns

Year of Arrival

200 during 1969-78 *BWM*), whilst the inclusive total for the period was 9-10,000 birds in twenty-three years compared with just 5,000 in the fifty years 1929-78 (*BWM*).

The more concentrated of the two passages is in spring, when small influxes often arrive on warm, easterly or south-easterly winds. During the current period 48% of birds occurred at this season (*cf.* 47% 1929-78). The latter period, however, embraced a significant seasonal shift, from 56% in spring between 1929-68 to just 34% during the colder springs of 1969-78. Recently, there has been a tendency for birds to arrive earlier, with passage during the current period peaking in early May compared with late May during 1929-78. Even so, the earliest recorded date of April 10th, at Bredon's Hardwick in 1991, is only a day earlier than that given in *BWM*. By early June, all that remain are a few late stragglers.

The best spring passage occurred on May 2nd 1990, when an anticyclone centred over south-west Britain caused a massive overshoot of migrating terns that brought over 1,100 into the region. Movement occurred on a broad front, with the highest counts coming from Belvide Reservoir (220), Draycote Water (172), Blithfield Reservoir (148) and Coton Pools (112).

The return movement is more widely spread, beginning in late July, peaking in early September and lasting into early October. A few individuals even linger into November, with the latest ever being one that remained at Belvide Reservoir from November 16th-26th 1994. Other late birds were seen on November 12th, at Westwood Pool in 2001 and at Worcester in 1849—the latter record, of two that were shot, having been inadvertently omitted from *BWM*.

The most impressive autumn passage occurred on September 11th 1992—a day of strong westerly winds—when an incredible 1,952 were recorded (*cf.* just 2,000 in the entire decade 1969-78 *BWM*). Movement was again widely spread, with counts of 350 at Draycote Water, 300 at Blithfield Reservoir, 250 at Belvide Reservoir, 205 at Westwood Pool, 194 at Coton Pools and 100 at Bittell Reservoir and Earlswood Lakes—many shattering the counts of 1990 and establishing some new site records. These figures might include some duplication if birds moved from one place to another, but it is equally possible that others went through unnoticed as the passage continued throughout the day.

More typically though, Black Terns move in much smaller groups of up to 20 or so that seemingly appear from nowhere, stay a few hours and then just as mysteriously vanish again. Just occasionally one or two stay for a day or so, with records even up to a fortnight, while one spent 32 days at Upton Warren, from September 28th-October 29th 2000.

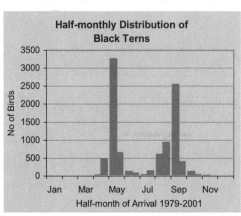

Half-monthly Distribution of Black Terns

Half-month of Arrival 1979-2001

Geographically, the majority of birds have passed through Warwickshire and Staffordshire (40% and 38% respectively), with Worcestershire (17%) and the West Midlands (5%) clearly less favoured. Obviously this reflects the locations of the larger bodies of waters, with Draycote Water having produced most records (14%); the Middle Tame Valley 13%; Blithfield Reservoir 8%; Belvide Reservoir and Upton Warren 7%; and Bittell Reservoir, Chasewater and Westwood Pool all around 5%.

White-winged Black Tern   *Chlidonias leucopterus*
Rare vagrant, usually in autumn.

During 1979-2001, the following 12 records were added to the 15 listed in *BWM*.

Regional Record Number	County Record Number		Year	Locality, Date and Notes
16	Warks	5	1981	Kingsbury Water Park: adult, June 27th. *BB 75:511.*
17	Warks	6	1982	Draycote Water: juvenile, September 18th. *BB 76:501-2.*
18	Warks	7	1983	Kingsbury Water Park: juvenile, August 21st. *BB 77:536-7.*
19	Warks	8	1983	Draycote Water: juvenile, September 24th. *BB 77:536-7.*
20	Staffs	8	1992	Belvide Reservoir: moulting adult, August 8th. *BB 86:493.*
21	Worcs	3	1992	Wilden: moulting adult, September 11th. Same later, Westwood Pool. *BB 86:493.*
22	Staffs	9	1992	Blithfield Reservoir: adult, September 11th. *BB 87:536.*
23	Warks	9	1996	Draycote Water: adult, July 26th. *BB 94:480.*
24	Staffs	10	1999	Belvide Reservoir: moulting adult, August 3rd. *BB 95:500.*
25	Worcs	4	2000	Nafford: juvenile, September 3rd. Same later, Bredon's Hardwick. *BB 94:480.*
26	Warks	10	2001	Draycote Water: adult, July 29th-31st. *BB 96:581.*
27	Warks	11	2001	Kingsbury Water Park: juvenile, August 26th. *BB 95:500.*

White-winged Black Terns breed from Hungary and Bulgaria eastwards into Asia and winter in Africa south of the Sahara. On migration a few join parties of Black Terns and are sometimes displaced westwards as far as Britain. In the region overall, there have now been four records in May, all prior to 1970, and one in June (1981). The remaining 22 all occurred during 'autumn' passage, with three in July, six in August and 13 in September. July 12th and September 28th were the extreme dates and 60% of the birds were juveniles.

Common Guillemot   (Guillemot)   *Uria aalge*
Very rare vagrant. Six records.

This is a common seabird, breeding around our coasts and wintering just offshore, but inland records are very rare and there have been none in this region to add those listed in *BWM*, the last of which was in 1980.

Regional Record Number	County Record Number		Year	Locality, Date and Notes
1	Staffs	1	1841	Near Stoke-on-Trent: date unknown.
2	Staffs	2	1889	Gailey Reservoir: June 28th., shot.
3	Staffs	3	1901	Gailey Reservoir: unknown date in June, shot.
4	Staffs	4	1920	Stone: adult male, May 19th., injured flying into telegraph wires.
5	W Mid	1	1976	Bartley Reservoir: December 16th., found freshly dead.
6	W Mid	2	1980	Wordsley: December 30th., taken to Dudley Zoo but later died.

The first acceptable record from Warwickshire is still awaited, Norris (1947) having doubted the specific identity of one that was reportedly shot from the roof of a thatched cottage sometime prior to 1904.

Three in the generally calm months of May and June are intriguing (see also Fulmar and Northern Gannet), since most inland occurrences normally involve storm-driven birds. Sadly most of the above birds came to an unfortunate end.

Razorbill   *Alca torda*
Very rare vagrant. Five records.

Although Razorbills breed around our coasts and winter offshore, inland records are extremely rare and in this region there have been none to add to the five documented in *BWM*, the last of which came in 1953.

Regional Record Number	County Record Number		Year	Locality, Date and Notes
1	W Mid	1	1890	Harborne: July 25th, found dead.
2	Warks	1	Pre 1904	Stratford-upon-Avon: unknown date, locally obtained specimens brought for preservation.
3	Warks	2	Pre 1904	Warwick: unknown date, locally obtained specimens brought for preservation.
4	W Mid	2	1912	Sandwell Golf Course: November 11th, found injured, later died. *BB 6:282*
5	Worcs	1	1953	Overbury: May 10th, found dead in rabbit trap.

All were either dead, or injured and died later. As with the Common Guillemot, records in May and July are interesting, since this is not normally a windy time of year. Strangely, there are no records for Staffordshire, whereas four of the six Common Guillemot records were from that county.

Little Auk   *Alle alle*
Rare wind-blown winter vagrant.

Precisely how many times this tiny seabird from the high Arctic has occurred is unknown, as several historical references are imprecise. *BWM* refers to 25-30, but could only fully document the lower figure, so the additional 22 during 1979-2001 (listed in the table opposite) brings the overall total to at least 47.

Little Auks winter widely across the northern North Sea, but spend most of their time well offshore (*Winter Atlas*). Being so small, they are particularly prone to being 'wrecked' during storms, hence the pitiful state in which so many were discovered. Such circumstances sometimes result in multiple occurrences inland. This happened immediately after bad weather had pushed many onshore on November 6th 1984, then again during December 7th-9th 1987 and September 21st 1991. The Chasewater bird in February 1983 was just one of a major wreck of auks nationwide that month. Not all

Regional Record Number	County Record Number		Year	Locality, Date and Notes
26	Staffs	11	1983	Chasewater: February 12th.
27	Staffs	12	1984	Tittensor: January 14th, found in garden. Ringed and released at Blithfield Reservoir the following day.
28	W Mid	5	1984	Bromford: November 5th, found dying beneath electricity pylon.
29	Staffs	13	1984	Blithfield Reservoir: November 6th, found alive.
30	Warks	6	1984	Bodymoor Heath: November 7th, picked up by farmer and taken to Drayton Manor Zoo, subsequently released at Draycote Water on 9th.
31	Staffs	14	1984	Amington: November 13th., picked up and later released at Alvecote Pools.
32	Worcs	7	1987	Chadbury: December 7th, found dead beneath overhead wires.
33	Worcs	8	1987	Malvern: December 7th, picked up alive, but died on way to coast next day.
34	Staffs	15	1987	Belvide Reservoir: December 9th, found freshly dead on ice.
35	Staffs	16	1988	Near Flash: February 10th, found on road and released at Tittesworth Reservoir.
36	Worcs	9	1988	White Ladies Aston: November 21st, found exhausted, died soon afterwards.
37	W Mid	6	1991	Near Sandwell Valley: January 6th, found exhausted, died next day.
38	Worcs	10	1991	Beckford: January 27th, found beneath wires, believed dead for about a week.
39	Warks	7	1991	Chadshunt: October 21st, died in captivity next day.
40	Staffs	17	1991	Westport Lake: October 21st.
41	Worcs	11	1993	Bredon: October 23rd, found exhausted, died soon afterwards.
42	Staffs	18	1994	Edingale: January 28th, on small garden pond.
43	Warks	8	1995	River Avon, Stratford-upon-Avon: November 2nd.
44	Staffs	19	1996	Great Haywood: October 26th-30th.
45	Worcs	12	1998	Wickhamford: November 7th, picked up alive, but died soon afterwards.
46	W Mid	7	1999	Wednesbury: early November, rescued from canal but died shortly afterwards.
47	Staffs	20	2001	Tittesworth Reservoir: two, November 9th, flew through to north.

appearances involve exhausted or dying birds, however, as the latest record of two flying north through Tittesworth Reservoir in 2001 testifies.

Puffin   (Atlantic Puffin)   *Fratercula arctica*
Rare vagrant.

Although Puffins are rare inland, there have been three more records since 1979, bringing the overall total to eleven that have been fully substantiated as shown in the table overleaf.

Apart from coming inshore to nest during April-July, Puffins spend their lives well out to sea in the North Atlantic, further from the safe havens of sheltered bays than Common Guillemots and Razorbills. This perhaps makes them more susceptible to being caught up in storms and being driven inland before they can get to the shelter of the coast. This might explain why there are more records than for Common Guillemot and Razorbill. As with other seabirds though, it is hard to explain the appearances of birds in June.

Regional Record Number	County Record Number		Year	Locality, Date and Notes
1	Staffs	1	unknown	Aqualate: date unknown, procured locally.
2	W Mid	1	c1880	Broad St., Birmingham: female, date unknown, picked up and found to have stomach full of rubber bands.
3	Worcs	1	1936	Near Hagley: mid-July, found exhausted, later died.
4	Warks	1	1953	Near Earlswood: February 1st, found alive but subsequently died.
5	Staffs	2	1963	Rugeley: adult, unknown day in June, picked up alive.
6	Worcs	2	1963	Redditch: immature, August 30th.
7	W Mid	2	1963	Bartley Reservoir: immature, October 18th.
8	Staffs	3	1967	Longdon: immature, November 4th.
9	Staffs	4	1983	Bignall End: adult, June 12th, walking up garden path, died two days later.
10	Warks	2	1984	Ratley: sub-adult in non-breeding plumage, unknown day in June, found in road, later died.
11	W Mid	3	1999	Near Sandwell Valley: early April, picked up by RSPCA and taken to their Cheshire seabird centre.

Pallas's Sandgrouse   *Syrrhaptes paradoxus*
Very rare vagrant. Eleven acceptable records prior to 1909.

There are eleven reasonably well documented records, though none of them appears in *The Handbook of British Birds* (Witherby *et al.* 1938). Of these, all but that in 1866 coincided with major irruptions into Europe (*BWP*), with eight of them in 1888 alone.

Regional Record Number	County Record Number		Year	Locality, Date and Notes
1	Staffs	1	1863	Eccleshall: c20, May 22nd, three shot.
2	Staffs	2	1866	Swinfen: date unknown, shot.
3	Worcs	1	1888	Near Littleton: male, May 18th.
4	W Mid	1	1888	Rough Hills: female, May 23rd, shot.
5	Warks	1	1888	Radway: June 22nd, shot
6	Warks	2	1888	Near Kineton: nine, July, one shot.
7	Staffs	3	1888	Ipstones: four, September, one male killed and another injured.
8	Worcs	2	1888	Cofton Hall Farm: five, December 28th, four shot.
9	Warks	3	1888	Stratford-upon-Avon: date unknown, shot locally.
10	Warks	4	1888	Edge Hill area: at least two, date unknown, shot and eaten.
11	Staffs	4	1908	Hamstall Ridware: December 18th.

This species appeared in Britain in at least twelve years between 1859 and 1909. Since then there have been just six records (seven birds) between 1964-1990 (Rogers *et al.* 1991). Its rarity here may be due to an eastwards retraction of its range in western Siberia (*BWP*).

Feral Pigeon   *Columba livia*
Very common resident in urban areas.

The true Rock Dove, the original ancestor of the Feral Pigeon, has suffered by man's domestication of the dove for centuries. It was kept in dovecotes for food, used for carrying messages or just competitive racing and developed into fancy varieties for showing. Captive birds escaped and bred with natural populations, so that now, in Britain, true Rock Doves can only be found in the remoter parts of Scotland. The plumages of Feral Pigeons vary considerably in colour and markings, but occasionally birds show all the characteristics of the true species, such as four at Doxey Marshes in September 2000.

Feral Pigeons are considered by most people to be tame birds, so few bother to submit records and this is a national as well as a regional problem when trying to establish population numbers and trends. The concentrations are often in city or town centres, where there is a ready supply of food provided either intentionally by people feeding them, or accidentally from the rubbish thrown away, especially these days with so many fast-food and take-away outlets. Because of the nuisance of droppings, which in particular foul seating areas and make wet pavements very slippery, steps have been taken in some centres to try and reduce numbers by discouraging the public from actively feeding birds, as the more they are fed the more frequently they breed. Authorities have also used physical deterrents in nesting areas, although this could just push the problem elsewhere.

During the period 1979-2001 there were no published records for eleven of the twenty-three years, and what few there were in the other years referred, more often than not, to just a few flocks at various locations. The largest flocks in this period were 275 in West Bromwich during December 1996 and 250 at Thicknall in 1983, again in December. The latter were with Stock Doves, but unfortunately the report does not say how many Stock Doves there were or what sort of habitat the birds were in. About half of all the reported flocks were specified as in town, city, and shopping centres, or other similar urban locations, with numbers ranging from about forty to the 275 mentioned above. Around 200 were also seen at the old Hams Hall Power Station in 1993 and the same number were at the nearby Whitacre Waterworks in both 1994 and 1996. Maybe the architecture of this particular building reminded the birds in some way of their ancestral home of rocky cliffs! Numbers at the Waterworks fell to only 50 during 1999, but had increased to 100 by 2000. These figures are the only indication of changes in populations, other than the occasional comment suggesting either no change in status, as was the case in the first two annual reports to mention them at all in 1981 and 1982, or some reduction in flock sizes at a particular site.

The *Breeding Atlas* shows birds in 91% of 10-km squares being most abundant in Birmingham, the Potteries, Redditch, Worcester and the Feldon area. Presumably the latter is influenced by Coventry as the first results from the Warwickshire Tetrad breeding survey suggest that very few birds breed in the county away from the larger towns and industrial sites (*WMBC Annual Report* 2002). The *Winter Atlas* shows an even wider distribution with a 97% coverage and birds being scarcest in the Dales. The BBS data shows regional numbers to be very erratic during the period 1994-2002, but little change in the national trend or in the overall regional population. Due to the inadequate data, no attempt has been made to assess the regional population.

Stock Dove   *Columba oenas*
Very common resident.

Stock Doves commonly nest in 'stocks', or tree stumps, from which they derive their name (Buczacki 2002). They are most likely to be found along the edges of mature woods, in land-

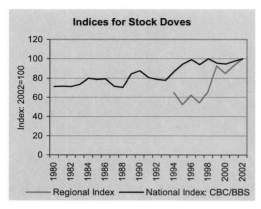

Indices for Stock Doves

Index: 2002=100

—— Regional Index   —— National Index: CBC/BBS

scaped parkland or along well-timbered hedgerows, where they nest in holes in the old trees. However, they are very adaptable and will also use holes in buildings. Some good populations can also be found in the region's urban environments.

It is included on the *Amber Alert List* as a species of medium conservation concern because Britain holds a high proportion (at least 20%) of the European population (Gregory *et al.* 2002). Following a decline perhaps due to poisoning by chemicals, numbers here recovered once the ban on organochlorine seed dressings was introduced in the 1960s (*Migration Atlas*). This set back apart, modern farming practices do not yet seem to have posed any problems for this species (Mead 2000). Its status here now seems reasonably secure, although it has been suggested that a lack of suitable nest holes in old trees and buildings might be limiting numbers. Certainly its willingness to use nest-boxes where these are provided, or to occupy boxes intended for owls, might suggest a lack of natural nest sites.

The West Midlands region, with its many landscaped parklands and well-timbered hedgerows is an important area for Stock Doves. Both the *Winter* and *Breeding Atlases*, showed birds to be present in every 10-km square at densities at or above average. Indeed, densities in the Avon Valley, Feldon, Cotswold Fringe and Meres and Mosses areas were particularly high and preliminary survey work shows 80% of the tetrads in Warwickshire to be occupied. Birds are also widespread in the West Midlands conurbation, occurring in just over half of all tetrads, again often at high densities. Teagle (1978) said that Edgbaston Park, Castle Hill (Dudley) and Warley Park suited the Stock Dove's requirements and a CBC in the woodland of Mons Hill, Dudley, during 1992-1998 revealed a mean density of 24.9 pairs per km^2 (range 16.2-38.5) compared to the national average for woodland of 4.2 pairs per km^2. During 1999-2002 the density there rose still further to virtually 50 per km^2. However, these concentrations involve relatively few birds in a very small area (13 ha.). On the broader expanse of the Malvern Hills numbers inexplicably fell from 32 pairs in 1989 to 20 the following year, but they have since recovered and generally there have been between 25-30 pairs.

Densities on the region's farmland CBC plots were also high, at nearly twice the national average. The BBS also confirms Warwickshire and the West Midlands county as the regional strongholds, with densities some 20% above the regional average. Conversely, Staffordshire has the fewest birds, with a density 30% below average. Extrapolating from all the available data, it seems likely that the current regional population is around 10,000-13,000 territories, or possibly even higher, compared with the 5,000-10,000 pairs suggested in *BWM*. Such an increase is in line with the national CBC/BBS index, which rose by 40% during 1980-2002.

Outside the breeding season, flocks of Stock Doves gather around good food sources, such as stubbles and weedy fields. They are never as numerous as Wood Pigeons, however, and three-quarters of the reported flocks contained less than 100 birds. Of the bigger gatherings, several reached 200 and the largest were 500 at Longdon Marsh in January 1981 and 700 at Fenny Compton in November 2001.

British Stock Doves are generally sedentary and the movement of one, ringed as a nestling at Evesham back in 1933 and recovered in the following November at Landes, France (*BWM*), remains one of only four BTO recoveries to show a movement in excess of 200 km (*Migration Atlas*). Of these, one was a movement within Britain, two were recovered in France and one in Spain. Stock Doves from Fennoscandia and eastern Europe are migratory, with many wintering in Iberia, but there is no evidence of these birds passing through the region.

Wood Pigeon   (Woodpigeon)   *Columba palumbus*
Abundant resident and winter visitor.

Wood Pigeons are ubiquitous birds, familiar to almost everyone and liable to occur in almost any situation, including our cities and larger towns. However, they are usually most numerous where arable crops predominate, especially oilseed rape. Indeed, they are widely regarded as a major pest in such areas, where large winter flocks cause serious damage to crops. Breeding can occur at any time of year, although display is mostly noted in early spring. After the breeding season, some birds, especially juveniles, may move into more favourable feeding areas, but otherwise this is largely a sedentary species.

Numbers are regulated by the availability of food in winter, when the natural harvest of weed-seeds, nuts and berries is insufficient to sustain the population. During the 1950s and 1960s, this led to huge flocks descending on fields of brassicas and clover, where they caused farmers considerable economic loss. Just how many there were can be gauged from the fact that 110,000 were shot on eight large vegetable farms in the Vale of Evesham during the severe 1962/3 winter (*BWM*). Birds would feed in sown cereals until December and then turn to clover leys for the rest of the winter. But the switch to winter-sown cereals and the conversion of grass to arable land, coupled with the widespread use of herbicides, led to a decline in the population. Then the introduction of oilseed rape in the 1970s plugged the gap left by the absence of clover and numbers have since recovered. Both the *Wintering* and *Breeding Atlases* showed them to be present in every 10-km square and generally very abundant, except on the higher ground of north Staffordshire where densities are noticeably lower during the winter.

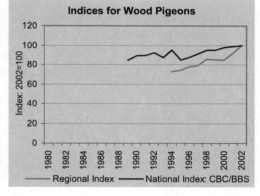

Estimating the population is far from easy as birdwatchers generally pay scant attention to this species. Even the CBC data is sparse, especially at the regional level. The situation is further compounded by the protracted breeding season, which means that birds could be nesting at any time of year (Murton 1965).

The BBS is more informative. Regionally, it shows the Wood Pigeon to be the second most recorded bird, after the Common Starling, although it must be remembered that both of these species are conspicuous and therefore more likely to be counted than, say, the Wren. It also shows there are fewest birds in Staffordshire, where the density is 20% below the regional average, and most in Warwickshire, where the density is 20% above average. Nationally, the CBC/BBS index increased by around 20% during 1989-2002. Based on these trends, there are probably now between 110,000-160,000 territories in the region (*cf.* 77,000-385,000 in *BWM*).

Birds flock together during the short, cold days of winter, when food is scarce. Gatherings build up during November and December and reach their peak in January, when the greatest number of large flocks are seen. During the current period, two-thirds of all reported flocks contained less than 1,000 birds, with most having between 400-600. However, there were also some larger concentrations, notably 3,000 in the Fenny Compton-Wormleighton area in 1997, 3,800 at the Coombes Valley in 1992, 4,000 in the Coombes Valley-Churnet Valley area in 1997, 5,000 in a sprout field at Holt Heath in 1981 and the same number at Ettington in 1983. These are all comparable in size to the largest flocks mentioned in *BWM*, suggesting little change in the wintering population.

Considering the respective size of each county, the number of flocks reported was fairly evenly distributed, with 29% in Staffordshire, 26% in both Warwickshire and Worcestershire and 19% in the West Midlands. However, there were noticeable differences in flock sizes, with the smallest being in Worcestershire and the West Midlands, where only 20% comprised more than 1,000 birds. In Staffordshire the proportion was a third and in Warwickshire just over a half. Indeed, a third of the flocks in the latter county were between 1,000-1,500 birds.

Wood Pigeons roost communally in woodland and counts reveal that these can vary enormously in size from just 200 or 300 birds to several thousand. Most reports have come from the region's arable stronghold in the Dunsmore and Feldon areas, where the largest concentration was 2,200 at Chesterton Wood in 1994. Elsewhere, 2,000 roosted at Fullmoor Wood in 1980 and 3,000 at Cheswick Green in 1999, while the largest roost has been in the heart of the Black Country, at Saltwells Wood, where up to 3,000 have been regularly reported and a record 3,150 assembled in 1993.

The region's wintering population is probably swollen by immigrants from elsewhere in Britain, but there is little evidence that continental birds come here and the *Migration Atlas* concludes that very few foreign birds reach these shores. Ringing recoveries during the current period show only local movements of between four and seven kilometres, apart from a modest one of 24 km made by a bird ringed as a pullus at Loxley in August 1977 and recovered in January 1982 at Banbury, Oxfordshire. *BWM*, however, mentions recoveries from Cornwall, Cumbria, Kent and France.

Collared Dove   *Streptopelia decaocto*
Very common resident.

Collared Doves are now such familiar garden birds that it is easy to take them for granted. Yet the speed with which this species spread across Europe was one of the twentieth century's most amazing ornithological events. From a slender foothold in the south-east of the Continent at the beginning of the century, the westwards expansion was so rapid that within fifty years the first birds had reached Britain. Here they bred for the first time in 1955, in Norfolk. The first breeding records for this region quickly followed—near Kings Bromley and at Worcester in 1961—and there are now few areas where they cannot be found. Away from the urban parks and gardens, birds feed mostly on spilt cereal grain around storage barns and silos, so they are more likely to be encountered around farmyards than in the open countryside.

Both the *Winter* and *Breeding Atlases* confirmed their presence in every 10-km square except those covering the moors of north Staffordshire. They also show the density of birds to have been at, or above, the national average across most of the region. Data from the national CBC/BBS suggests the population increased by around 50% during 1980-2002, but the regional sample was too small to indicate any clear trend. However, the regional BBS suggests stable rather than increasing numbers.

Analysis of BBS data for 1994-2002 also reveals that the density of birds in the West Midlands county was twice that of the neighbouring shires. This reflects the Collared Dove's preference for urban parks, cemeteries and large suburban gardens with ornamental conifers such as cypress and, of course, well-stocked feeders. Of the shire counties, the density in Staffordshire was around 25% lower than that in Warwickshire and Worcestershire. Currently there are probably between 10,000-25,000 territories, which is similar to the 15,000-25,000 estimated in *BWM*.

Indices for Collared Doves
Index: 2002=100
Regional Index ——— National Index: CBC/BBS

Breeding occurs throughout the year and there have been several references to eggs or fledglings being seen in winter, including a pair with one young during the severe weather of January 1982. However, numbers vary markedly from year-to-year. For instance, on a CBC plot at Mons Hill they fluctuated between one and seven pairs between 1992-2002, while in 1996 they were said to have been down by 50% at Highgate Common. Perhaps the best illustration of such fluctuations is provided by a BBS plot at Tibberton, where there were 10 pairs in 1998, six in 1999 and 16 in 2000.

Hudson (1965) said that spring was the peak time for dispersal in Britain and *BWM* refers to a small, but distinct, passage at that season. There is no documented evidence of such a passage having occurred during 1979-2001, but it may have gone unnoticed amongst the greater number of birds now present. In fact the only recent reference to any noticeable movement came in 1996 when, following a poor breeding season across the south of the region, there was an influx into south-east Warwickshire during November.

Flocks of Collared Doves are a regular feature from late-summer through to early winter and they usually reach their maximum size in August or during November and December. Gatherings up to 50 are quite common and three-figure totals were reported on at least 30 occasions during 1979-2001—over half of them in Worcestershire. Warwickshire, on the other hand, seldom attracts flocks much above 50, so one of 225 at Wolston in October 1993 was especially noteworthy. In Worcestershire the largest gathering was 300 at Bredon's Hardwick in December 1993, but Staffordshire—despite having the lowest overall density of birds— attracted 300 at Hatherton in November 1993 and 300-400 at Cheslyn Hay in August 1988. Such gatherings have occurred around a variety of food sources ranging from grain stores and silos to the breweries in Burton-on-Trent. There is less scope for large flocks to form within the West Midlands county, so 84 on a factory roof at Aldridge was unusual. More typical of the reports from this area are small groups in suburban gardens, the most notable of which was a sequence from a south Walsall garden, where between 22-39 were noted every winter from 1991/2-1996/7. The largest flock mentioned in *BWM* was one of 350 in 1975.

Turtle Dove   *Streptopelia turtur*
Frequent or fairly common summer visitor and passage migrant, mainly to the southern parts of Warwickshire and Worcestershire.

In *BWM* the Turtle Dove was described as a fairly common bird of arable farmland with tall hedges, spinneys and coppices for nest sites. Whilst its preferred habitat remains the same, it has sadly been lost in many areas and numbers are now much reduced almost everywhere. Birds also need open, weedy ground where they can forage for seeds and this has become much scarcer with modern farming practices. As a result, many of the surviving pairs are now to be found feeding in the rough margins around gravel pits and nesting in the tall hedges along canals and railway lines.

Indeed, the national population has declined by more than half in the last twenty-five years, placing the species on the *Red Alert* list of Birds of Conservation Concern (Gregory *et al.* 2002). In terms of distribution, the *Breeding Atlases* showed birds to be present during 1988-91 in 74% of 10-km squares compared with 96% during 1968-72. These figures largely reflect a retreat away from Staffordshire, north Warwickshire and north-west Worcestershire that left the majority of occupied squares (90%) south-east of a line from Tamworth to Malvern.

Since then the range has contracted still further. There were no breeding records at all from Staffordshire in either 2000 or 2001, although two pairs were discovered on Cannock Chase during 2002 compared with 10 there in 1997. Elsewhere, reports during 1997-2001 were very few away from the favoured areas of the Severn and Avon Vales, the Cotswold Fringe and the Feldon and Dunsmore districts. Moreover the density has reduced too, with birds more

sparsely spread even within these areas and records coming from little more than 50-60 sites a year. Small populations of four or five pairs still remain at a few favoured localities, notably Kingsbury-Dosthill-Drayton Bassett in the Middle Tame Valley; the DM Kineton army camp; and the Grimley-Holt, Lower Moor and Ryall areas of Worcestershire.

The hills and commons of the Malverns perhaps provide the best evidence of the extent of the decline. Here, where the habitat has changed very little, there were a dozen pairs until 1988, but within five years this had reduced to four. A similar sharp decline, again in the early 1990s, was recorded at the DM Kineton army camp, where numbers fell from 22 in 1989 to four in 1993. Likewise, in central and southern Warwickshire, eighteen sites which had held birds since 1992 were resurveyed in 2000, but not a bird was found. Preliminary survey results from the Warwickshire Tetrad Atlas revealed birds in only 23% of tetrads, whilst the complementary survey of Birmingham and the Black Country found birds in just 2% of tetrads.

The CBC/BBS index fell by more than 80% nationally between 1980 and 2002, mostly in the late 1980s after the 1984 drought in the Sahel. Locally the population is now too small to give a representative sample, but it seems the main decline in the region came slightly later, in the early 1990s. Even the numbers recorded by the more broadly based BBS survey are so small that the trend is erratic, but they do confirm that the highest numbers are in Warwickshire and the West Midlands county. It should be noted that whilst Solihull and Coventry are in the West Midlands county, they are included in the Warwickshire Tetrad survey and not that for Birmingham and the Black Country. Against this background any population estimate is suspect, but a very tentative range of 200-500 territories is suggested, though even this might be optimistic. This compares with an estimate of 5,000-7,500 pairs in *BWM*.

The Turtle Dove is our only migratory dove, spending the winter in the Sahel zone of Africa. Over sixty-four years the average date for the first birds to arrive was April 24th, with the earliest at Draycote Water on April 1st 1995. Such passage as there is these days then follows in late April, with the main arrival in May or even early June. Birds leave again during August

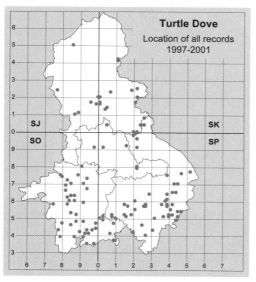

and September, with the average date for last birds, again over sixty-four years, being September 29th. An extremely late bird at Ladywalk on November 11th 1972 (*BWM*) was the latest to be recorded. Turtle Doves mainly migrate at night, but a few parties used to be seen during the day travelling in small groups. For example, 50 flew over Bentley in May 1988 and the following year parties of 21, 25 and 32 were seen in south Worcestershire between late June and mid-September. Nowadays, it is rare to find more than half-a-dozen together and most groups probably comprise locally bred families rather than passage birds. Up to a dozen have been seen at favoured haunts such as Kingsbury Water Park and Ryall, with 23 at the latter locality on August 22nd 1999 the largest count since the collapse of the early 1990s.

Problems seem to confront the Turtle Dove at every stage of its life. In its breeding areas it is faced with the loss of tall hedges in which to nest and the virtual elimination by herbicides of the arable weed seeds on which it feeds. In its wintering grounds the habitat has been degraded by successive droughts as well as by man's activities and on migration it is a favoured quarry of hunters, especially on the Continent. Birds know no international boundaries and there can be few better examples of the need for concerted action. Unless there is a dramatic reversal in its fortune, the soft, purring song of a Turtle Dove may soon be nothing but a distant memory and this species must be a prime candidate for inclusion in future Local Biodiversity Action Plans across the region.

Rose-ringed Parakeet (Ring-necked Parakeet) *Psittacula krameri*
Scarce feral visitor which has bred.

Only scant attention was paid to this species until it was admitted to the *British List* in 1983. Prior to then most records were considered to have related to escaped cage-birds—the species being popular with aviculturists. Records have been included in the *WMBC Annual Reports* since 1975 and the circumstances of the earliest sightings tended to support this view as they mostly came from places within or close to Birmingham and Black Country area, or from Stafford. The first records away from major settlements involved individuals at Belvide Reservoir in 1978 and at Wombourne in 1979.

There were reports in eighteen of the twenty-three years 1979-2001 involving 78 birds—an average of about three a year, with a maximum of 19 in 1998. During that time the species slowly became more frequent and widespread, with an average of five a year since 1989 and records in every year except 1995. These records were widely scattered across the region, but were thinnest around the periphery and absent from north Staffordshire apart from one at Stanton Dale. The greatest concentration remains around Stafford, Birmingham and the Black Country, particularly the Walsall area which produced the only breeding record so far when an escaped pair bred in a hollow tree near Pelsall back in 1975.

Most records have been of single individuals, many of them simply noted flying over, but two have been seen together on half-a-dozen occasions and three were recorded twice in 1998—at Clayhanger on August 31st and Stanton Dale on September 5th. The latter record was well away from any others and in a very rural situation, raising speculation as to the birds' origins. Birds have been recorded in every month, but most are seen during August to November. In particular, the numbers in the peak months of August and November have been double those of any month outside this period. Several have stayed around for a month or so, but the only indications of birds taking up residence came from Stafford in 1992, when one was said to have been present for over a year, and from Coombe Abbey, where one was seen intermittently from November 1992 to March 1995.

Their close association with human habitation is shown by the fact that 42% have been seen within the West Midlands county. Elsewhere, Warwickshire has had 28%, Worcestershire 15% and Staffordshire 14%. The slight bias towards the south and east of the region, which are the areas closest to the species' west London stronghold, may be significant. Although birds quickly discovered garden feeders, with the first report of one plundering peanuts coming in 1975, there have been surprisingly few reports of this behaviour since.

The recent run of mild winters should have enabled the Rose-ringed Parakeet to establish a firm foothold, but its vulnerability to hard weather is perhaps shown by the one at Coombe Abbey (see above), which survived almost three winters, only to succumb to a heavy snowfall in early March 1995. The widely scattered distribution of single birds, but with no recent evidence either of breeding or communal roosting, perhaps suggests a limited number of wandering individuals rather than immigration from elsewhere.

Common Cuckoo (Cuckoo)   *Cuculus canorus*
Fairly common, but declining, summer resident.

Everyone knows the Common Cuckoo's call, but few other than keen birdwatchers have ever seen one. Its distribution depends on that of its host species and its favourite food of hairy cat-erpillars. In this region the hosts are usually Dunnocks, Reed Warblers and Meadow Pipits. Between them these species cover the whole region, so the Common Cuckoo has a widespread distribution that includes the higher moors, though it does tend to avoid urban areas.

The first Common Cuckoo is one of the most eagerly awaited sounds of spring, though many very early reports are probably due to the inexperienced, but over exuberant, being mis-lead by the 'coo-coo' call of the Collared Dove. Over sixty-four years the average date of first arrivals was April 10th, with the earliest ever at Tibberton on March 8th 1990, which was an exceptional year for early migrants generally. Male birds are the first to arrive from Africa, with the more secretive females following about a week later (Wyllie 1981).

The *Breeding Atlas* shows birds to have been present in every 10-km square except that covering central Birmingham. Abundance levels were above average in the Teme and Severn valleys and the Cotswold and Feldon areas, but mostly about average elsewhere.

Nationally the CBC/BBS index declined by 31% during 1974-79, sufficient to warrant in-clusion on the *Amber Alert* list of Species of Conservation Concern (Gregory *et al.* 2002). Re-

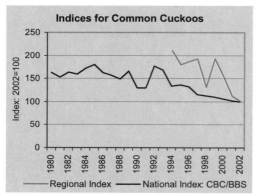

gionally the CBC index was too erratic to de-termine a clear trend, so only the BBS index is shown in the chart. Though fluctuating widely, this follows the downward trend of the national index, but with an even steeper fall that has seen it halve since the inception of the BBS in 1994.

The generally low density, combined with the male's habit of roaming across territories, makes this a hard species to census, but sev-eral reports have referred to declining num-bers or a scarcity of birds. A healthy popula-tion of 21-25 calling males on the Malvern Hills and Commons during 1986-89 suddenly collapsed to just 15 in 1990 and 12 in 1995. At other sites declines have been followed by a recovery, with an average of 21 a year at the DM Kineton army camp in the early 1990s, and a peak of 24 in 1995, dropping to just 10 in 1996. A hesitant recovery then saw numbers return to 21 by 2000. A similar, but smaller, collapse occurred on the North Staffordshire Moors, where numbers fell from 19 pairs in 1985 to 14 in 1992, but quickly recovered to 19 again by 1996 (McKnight et al. 1996). In Staffordshire, recent declines have left the majority of records emanating from the northern moors and Cannock Chase. The current regional population may be at the lower end of the range 2,000-3,000 pairs, which is half that suggested in *BWM*. This decline accords well with the 40% fall in the national CBC/BBS index during 1980-2002.

Common Cuckoos are most numerous where there are concentrations of their host species, such as the moors and heaths where Meadow Pipits are abundant, or reedbeds with colonies of Reed Warblers. Across much of the general countryside, though, it is the Dunnock in the hedgerows that acts as the primary host. In Britain as a whole these three species accounted for around 80% of breeding records 1939-71 (Glue and Morgan 1972). During 1979-2001 there were ten reports of Common Cuckoos in Reed Warbler nests and eight in Dunnock's nests, but surprisingly only one in a Meadow Pipit's, presumably because fewer people study them so closely on the heaths and moors. Other hosts included Yellow Wagtail, Sedge War-bler, Common Whitethroat, Common Starling and Reed Bunting—with one nest each—but strangely not Pied Wagtail which is often a victim. Interestingly, one was raised by a pair of Dunnocks in a Fradley garden in 1985.

Females of the rare 'hepatic' phase (rufous coloured) were reported on about ten occasions during 1979-2001. This is a not infrequently occurring colour abnormality in some species, especially adult female cuckoos (Richards 1980).

Small gatherings of Common Cuckoos sometimes occur in spring, with the most during the current period being eight at Brandon Marsh in 1995. The record, though, was an exceptional 30 at Packington on May 21st 1972 (*BWM*). Although birds tend to avoid urban areas, they are not averse to visiting urban oases and possibly even bred at Sandwell Valley and Sutton Park in 1988. They have also been reported more than once in the Netherton Hill-Mushroom Green area, but as numbers have fallen, so reports from these urban oases have dwindled away.

Males continue to call throughout May and into June, but towards the end of the latter month they begin their return journeys to south-east Africa for the winter. Females follow shortly afterwards, in July, leaving their voracious offspring to be fed by their foster parents. At Redditch in 1987, the combined efforts of a Robin, Great Tit and Dunnock were deployed in fulfilling the insatiable appetite of a hungry youngster. Most young birds embark on their first long migration south during August and September, with the average last date over sixty-three years being September 9th. The latest record during the current period was on October 2nd 1997 at Corley, though the latest ever was that mentioned in *BWM* on October 11th 1975 at Belvide Reservoir.

Barn Owl   *Tyto alba*
Frequent, but much declined resident.

Years ago the ghostly white shape of a Barn Owl could often be seen as it quartered a patch of rough ground or drifted slowly along a hedgerow in the twilight. Today birds are seen much less frequently, though thankfully there are signs that the population is recovering. As its name implies, this is very much the farmland owl, nesting in old barns, derelict buildings and holes in freestanding trees and hunting across fields and wastes, or along hedges and ditches. In winter it often hunts in broad daylight, especially during very cold or snowy weather. Small mammals are the main prey, particularly voles whose well-known population cycles govern the number of owls.

Numbers dropped during the last century as agricultural intensification removed rough grazing pastures, while pesticides reduced prey and poisoned birds. Later, nest sites were also lost through barns being converted into dwellings or commercial buildings. During the *Winter Atlas*, birds were recorded in 65% of 10-km squares, but few squares held more than one or two birds and they were notably absent from north Staffordshire, presumably because they move to lower ground at this season. The *Breeding Atlas* showed the species to have a number of strongholds nationally, but the West Midlands was not one of these. Indeed, by the time of the *Atlas,* birds were only recorded here in 42% of 10-km squares compared with 84% in the first BTO *Atlas* twenty years earlier.

Barn Owls have a high mortality rate in very cold weather and the bitter winters of 1979 and 1982 certainly reduced numbers, especially in Staffordshire, and no doubt contributed to the rapid contraction in range. Numbers seemingly reached their lowest level in 1982, but then began to recover after 1987, with minor set-backs again following spells of hard weather in the winters of 1991/2 and 1996/7. Conversely, the recent run of milder winters has extended the breeding season at both ends, aiding productivity and hence recovery (Glue 2003).

The accompanying map shows the distribution of all Barn Owl records during 1997-2001. From this, clear clusters are apparent along the main river valleys, especially the Dove and Churnet, the Trent and Tame and the Severn and Teme. Birds are less evident along the Avon

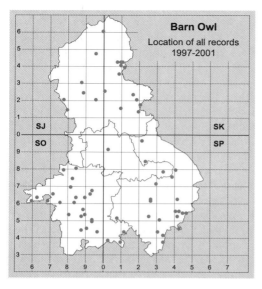

Barn Owl

Location of all records
1997-2001

valley, but there is a noticeable concentration in the Feldon area.

Preliminary results from the two tetrad surveys suggest that this owl may be present in as many as 15-20% of tetrads. However, this includes the high concentration in the Feldon area and J.J. Bowley *pers. comm.* estimates 45-50 pairs for Warwickshire as a whole. The RBBP included estimates of 45 pairs for Warwickshire, 40 for Staffordshire and three for Worcestershire in its 2002 report (Ogilvie *et al*. 2004). The latter figure has to be an underestimate, however, and on the basis of the accompanying map the true figure must be at least similar to those for the other two main counties. Together with the preliminary results of the *tetrad atlases*, it seems likely the current regional population lies in the range of 120-170 pairs compared to the 800 pairs suggested in *BWM*. This accords well with the most recent estimate of 4,000 pairs for the British breeding population (Toms *et al*. 2001).

There are several references to releases, escapes and birds of dubious origin in the region and there can be little doubt that some of these have aided the current recovery, although the 1990 *WMBC Bird Report* stated there was no evidence of released birds colonising traditional sites. The first releases to be mentioned were in the mid-1980s, at places such as Whitmore, Meerbrook and Consall. More recently, the WMBC has joined with the Hawk and Owl Trust and the Environment Agency in a scheme entitled Operation Riverside Link, which aims to provide continuous habitat corridors for Barn Owls. During 2001 and 2002 a total of 28 nest-boxes were erected in two phases, around 20 of them in the WMBC area, mostly in Staffordshire. Eight were put along the River Mease between Croxall and Netherseal, part of which is in Staffordshire; two along the Trent between Wychnor and Yoxall; four on the Tame from Croxall to Tamworth; and three on the Anker between Polesworth and Atherstone. Two boxes were also erected at Belvide and one at Ladywalk. It is still early days, but some have already been used by Barn Owls, with one or two successful broods in 2002 and 2003.

Pellets produced by a roosting bird at Dosthill during January and February showed that field voles made up 84% of the diet by weight, whilst bank voles and common shrews contributed 8% each and there were negligible remains of pygmy shrew and wood mouse. An indication of how successful Barn Owls are at catching prey is given by a bird which, during an hour's observation in 1981, made 14 successful kills in 21 attempts. Unfortunately roadside verges are favourite hunting grounds, even along motorways, and all too often these prove to be a fatal attraction. Seven found dead along roads within a mile radius of Ettington in 2000 and another picked up from the M5 at Bredon in 1986 serve to highlight what has become a major threat to the species. Indeed, 79% of the recoveries of birds ringed as pulli show them dying within eighteen months, chiefly as a result of collisions with traffic.

Barn Owls are normally extremely sedentary and one found dead near Upton Warren had travelled no further than 12 km (7.5 miles) from Redditch, where it had been ringed as a nestling the previous year. Such a short movement from its natal site is typical, with 54% of the recoveries of birds ringed as pulli being within 50 km and a further 23% between 50-100 km, while the remainder travelled over 100 km. However, a bird ringed in Warwickshire in August 1976 was found dead beside the A14 at Stowmarket (Suffolk) two years later. It had travelled at least 150 km, which represents one of the longest known movements of a British-reared

Barn Owl (Piotrowski 2003). Continental birds are more inclined to disperse in winter and a Dutch ringed bird was picked up injured at Broadway in November 1997, whilst a dark-breasted bird of the continental race *T. a. guttata* occurred at Lichfield on February 2nd 1985.

Among the more unusual records were one which competed with Carrion Crows at a roadside kill in broad daylight and another which flew through an open bedroom window at 03.00 hrs and sat on a dressing table!

Little Owl   *Athene noctua*
Fairly common resident.

The squat shape of a Little Owl is unmistakable as it emerges at dusk to perch on a branch or post. Its preference is for open countryside with plenty of hedgerows and mature, freestanding trees, together with small copses, orchards and parklands. Birds feed largely on beetles and earthworms and frequently use holes in veteran trees and old pollards for nesting and roosting.

From a series of widespread releases in the late-nineteenth century, the Little Owl soon became established throughout lowland Britain. Colonisation was initially quick, but expansion then slowed as persecution by gamekeepers, pesticide poisoning and hard winters all provided temporary set backs. More recently, agricultural change has caused some withdrawal from arable intensive areas, due to reductions in prey and the loss of nest sites and perches.

Nevertheless, this is a widespread owl, absent only from the most heavily built-up parts of the West Midlands conurbation. Birds were recorded in 90% of 10-km squares in both the *Winter* and *Breeding Atlases* and were most abundant in the Avon Valley, Feldon and Churnet Valley areas.

Little Owls are affected by weather and prey availability and as a consequence their numbers can be very erratic. In particular, the CBC shows that numbers nationally have fluctuated in three-to-five year cycles, which may reflect the population cycles of the small rodents on which they prey (Gibbons *et al.* 1993). However, the long-term national trend over 1980-2002 showed a decline of almost 40%. Unfortunately the regional CBC sample size is too small to compute a comparable regional index, but anecdotal evidence points to some declines.

The species was said to have decreased over the last ten years in the Stour Valley and north Worcestershire, for example, while in south-east Warwickshire declines were attributed to the loss of old trees. Certainly the species suffered here and in south Worcestershire from the denudation of the countryside that followed the outbreak of Dutch elm disease in the 1970s. Most regional data, however, relate to the adverse effects of cold weather. For example, 19 were reported dead or dying in north-east Staffordshire during the cold spell in 1986, while there were about 10 pairs at Fenny Compton in 1995, but only five pairs in the same area the next year following a hard winter. There have also been several examples of birds coming into gardens in hard weather, including one that killed a Fieldfare in a garden at Kingstanding in 1982 and returned to feed on it several times during the day. On the other hand, the warmer weather of recent years, especially in autumn, will have helped the survival of late broods.

The population was put in *BWM* as 750 pairs, but possibly in excess of 1,000. Current data from the national CBC/BBS would suggest a significantly lower population, but the *Breeding Atlas* does show many parts of the

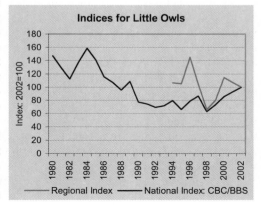

Indices for Little Owls

Regional Index — National Index: CBC/BBS

Owls

317

region to have an above average abundance of Little Owls and preliminary results from the two *Tetrad Atlas* surveys tend to confirm this. It seems probable, therefore, that the current population is in the range of 500-1,000 pairs.

Little Owls are sedentary and only local movements of two to eight kilometres have been recorded through ringing recoveries.

Tawny Owl   *Strix aluco*
Fairly common resident.

Best known by its drawn-out, quavering 'hoot' and sharp 'kwik' calls, the Tawny Owl is strictly nocturnal and very seldom encountered during the day. Courtship feeding begins early in the year and birds are often heard calling to each other during January and February, especially on calm, frosty nights. Although essentially a bird of broad-leaved woodland, it does venture into other well-treed habitats and is increasingly appearing in parks and gardens in suburban and even urban situations. It favours mature woods with old trees that have cavities suitable for nesting, such as parkland trees, but also readily uses tunnel-type nest-boxes. In winter it also ventures into coniferous woods and farmland areas. Although rodents are major prey items, the diet is broader than that of other owls and includes birds as well as mammals, so numbers depend less on the vole populations. Birds are highly sedentary and movements of any distance are unusual.

As with all nocturnal species, the Tawny Owl tends to be under-recorded. *BWM* noted that it was widespread and the *Winter Atlas* showed it to be present in 99% of 10-km squares, whilst the *Breeding Atlas* recorded it in 97%. The latter also showed it to be most abundant in the Dales, Churnet Valley, Wyre Forest, Teme Valley and Dunsmore and Feldon areas, whilst the 2001 *WMBC Report* said it was present in most mature woods in Worcestershire.

The sparseness of records, however, means less is known about the population level. Nationally, the CBC/BBS fell by about 33% during 1980-2002. Regionally the data were too few to compute a long-term index, but the larger BBS sample suggests the regional population increased significantly at a time when the national population was still falling. This is one of very few instances where the regional and national trends appear to have markedly diverged, but the time scale is very short and we would urge caution in drawing any firm conclusions from this. It might, however, be worthy of further study. Certainly the little quantitative data that is available points to stable populations in this region, as instanced by generally four pairs at Packington Park during 1986-91 and a constant seven or eight pairs at Coombes Valley from 1990-99. Judged by calling birds, there were an estimated 16 pairs on Cannock Chase in 2002, mostly in the coniferous plantations. Based on all available data, including the preliminary results from the *Tetrad Atlas* surveys, the regional population seems likely to be between 500-750 pairs (*cf.* 1,500-15,000 in *BWM*). However, it should be noted that the national densities on which this population range is based were derived from a year in which owl numbers were down, due to the low populations of small mammals (Gibbons *et al.* 1993), so the true figure is probably towards the upper end of this range. Even though it is definitely under recorded, it is not as common as it used to be.

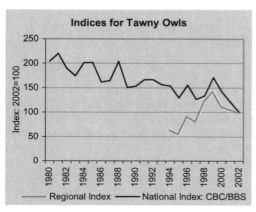

It is nestlings that are mostly ringed and recoveries show a high mortality in the post-fledging period, with 42% of records showing birds dying within the first eighteen months of their lives. Most of these arise from traffic strikes within 10 km of their natal sites. Our longest known movement is of a bird ringed as a nestling at Haresfield Hill (Glos) in May 1994 and recovered as a freshly dead road casualty in March 1995 at Lydiate Ash, 67 km to the north.

On the WMBC's reserves, birds have made good use of nest-boxes at Harborne and Lady-walk. Amongst one or two reports of early nesting, the most interesting concerned a pair at Coventry in 1992 that had four young on January 1st, implying egg laying on an incredibly early date sometime in October. Other noteworthy reports include an exceptional count of 28 birds at Coombes Valley in 1995, several road casualties in Warwickshire in 1997 and a bird that unusually was hunting in broad daylight at Church Eaton during the late-December freeze of 2001. Finally, a grey-phased bird, which was paired with a typical brown one, was reported from Park Hall in 1990.

Long-eared Owl   *Asio otus*
Uncommon and rather erratic winter visitor and scarce resident.

The Long-eared Owl is mostly found in conifer plantations, copses or patches of dense scrub that adjoin rough grassland or moorland with a high population of small mammals. It is strictly nocturnal and generally only seen if you chance across a daytime roost. Then you suddenly become aware of two 'ear tufts' projecting from a shape pressed against a tree trunk, or two orange eyes staring out from the middle of a dense thicket, often of hawthorn or willow. Birds are most numerous in winter, when immigrants arrive from their continental breeding grounds. Numbers vary considerably from year-to-year according to the population cycles of the voles which form their main prey, with more birds arriving after good vole years.

BWM said Long-eared Owls had always been scarce and local in Warwickshire and Worcestershire, but more numerous and widespread in Staffordshire and as a breeding species this is still true. The best indication that birds have bred is often the 'squeaky gate' calls of hungry youngsters begging for food. Breeding was recorded somewhere in the region in every year from 1979-2001, except for 1980, and was confirmed by fieldwork for the *Breeding Atlas* in three 10-km squares, with birds also present in a further two squares. Gribble (2000) says it occurs regularly on Cannock Chase and the moors, and also at Coombes Valley and Park Hall. (However, it would seem not all observers have sent their records to the WMBC).

He also says pairs favour conifer plantations, but in the moorlands they use old Carrion Crow and Magpie nests in scrub. During the moors survey of 1985, three pairs were recorded in old Magpies' nests and Waterhouse (1985) said these appeared to be part of a larger population on the lower farmland. However, no further details were given and there have been no records from this lower farmland area since then. Numbers on the moors and at Coombes Valley have remained fairly stable, but surveys on Cannock Chase have shown a steady increase, from one pair in 1992, to two in 1997 and at least three, possibly four or five, in 2002. There are also signs that the small population at Park Hall may be increasing, with one pair reported in 1996, but three pairs in 2002.

Elsewhere, breeding was confirmed in single years at four other sites in Staffordshire, one site in Warwickshire and one in the West Midlands. Breeding season records also came from a further site in the West Midlands, three or four more sites in Warwickshire and one in Worcestershire. Across the region as a whole, there were breeding season reports from 25-35 sites during 1979-2001, with between one and eight pairs a year and an average of three. However, taking into account the increased numbers in 2002 mentioned above, the regional population could be between 5-15 pairs, which is within the range of 3-20 pairs estimated in *BWM*.

Winter visitors from the Continent arrive in late October and early November and leave again in March. An unprecedented influx occurred during the 1975/6 winter, when at least 30 came into the region, with no less than 14 roosting at Ufton Hill (*BWM*). This seemed to mark a change in status, with records subsequently becoming more frequent and a similar influx in 1991/2 brought 45-50 into the region. During the winter most birds are located at their communal daytime roosts. Typically these contain up to half-a-dozen birds and some are used on a regular basis. For example, there has been a roost at Park Hall since at least 1985, with numbers ranging from just a single bird in 1987/8 to 12 the following winter. Another regular roosting area is the Tame Valley, particularly around Kingsbury, where up to four separate sites have been used and there were 12-16 birds in 1991/2. Sites used less regularly include Chasewater, where the maximum has been four birds; Sandwell Valley, which has been in intermittent use since at least 1987 and where the maximum was six in 1996; and Brandon Marsh, where small numbers were recorded in just over half of the years. At least five were at the latter locality in 1996/7, with unconfirmed claims of up to three times that number. Smaller numbers have been quite widely reported elsewhere, but often only in one or two winters, though Belvide Reservoir and a site in north Warwickshire were visited more frequently. Birds were also present at a site near Kineton for three winters, with a maximum of seven in 1988/9 and 14 were reported from a north Warwickshire locality in 1996/7. The largest reported roost was one of 17 or 18 birds near Stratford-upon-Avon in the autumn of 1991. Although this was said to be a regular site, no subsequent reports have been received.

In *BWM* it was stated that birds usually form a greater part of the diet than in other owl species, with Wood Lark, Meadow Pipit and Whinchat amongst the recorded prey. During the current period, however, pellet analysis from a roost at Bittell in 1987 showed the diet to consist almost exclusively of field voles, while, at Kingsbury in 2000, field voles made up at least 80% of the diet. A roosting bird at Holt in 1995 also had a dead vole hanging from its talons. A bird ringed at Stanford, Leicestershire, in February 1982 was caught 26 km away, at Nuneaton, in the following April. This was the most significant ringing recovery during the current period, but *BWM* contains an interesting record of one ringed at Hopwas in February 1973, which was recovered in the Czech Republic in May 1976.

Short-eared Owl   *Asio flammeus*
Uncommon winter visitor in variable numbers. Scarce and erratic breeding species.

Although an uncommon bird in the region, the Short-eared Owl is diurnal, so the chances of seeing one hunting in broad daylight are greater than with most other owls. A few pairs nest on the moorlands of north Staffordshire, but the species is better known as a winter visitor, when birds can be seen hunting across areas of rank grassland around gravel pits and reservoirs and across commons. They are less often seen on heaths or farmland. As with most owls,

numbers vary considerably from year-to-year according to the availability of prey. This is especially true of winter immigrants, whose numbers are governed by the three-to-four yearly cycles in the lemming populations on their Fennoscandian breeding grounds. These fluctuations are evident from the chart.

Short-eared Owls nest on extensive tracts of open ground that have high populations of small mammals, such as the moorland mosaic of north Staffordshire. Indeed, the small breeding population here—the most southerly in the Pennines—is especially important and this is one of three species that led to the area being designated as a SPA.

As in many parts of Britain, peak numbers were reached in the 1970s, when plantations such as that at Gib Torr were at their most suitable. At that time counts revealed a possible five pairs in 1971 and eight in 1977 (*BWM*). Birds were also recorded at five sites in 1979 and four the next year, but since then numbers have characteristically fluctuated in accordance with their food supply, with none some years but two or three the next. The *Breeding Atlas* shows confirmed breeding in two 10-km squares, while the RSPB Moors Surveys recorded none in 1985 but two pairs in 1992 and 1996 (Waterhouse 1985, Brindley *et al.* 1992 and McKnight *et al.* 1996).

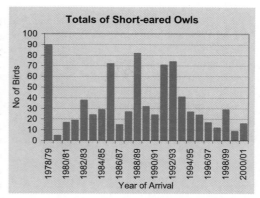

A pair bred successfully at Perton in 1974, but none have nested away from the moors since. However, display was note by a pair at Sandwell Valley in the spring of 1986, while in 1989 two that remained at Doxey Marshes from March to the end of the year were joined by a third bird on the unusual date of July 29th. It seems therefore that the regional population is only two or three pairs.

In winter, birds are more widely spread and the *Winter Atlas* recorded their presence in 38% of 10-km squares, including the moors where at least some birds are resident. The vast majority of birds at this season have been seen along the Middle Tame Valley, especially at Lea Marston, Coton, Kingsbury Water Park, Dosthill and Drayton Bassett. As a consequence, Staffordshire (39% of birds) and Warwickshire (35%) have been the dominant counties, with Worcestershire (16%) and the West Midlands (10%) relatively unimportant. Winter immigrants come from as far away as Fennoscandia and begin to arrive in September, although the main influx occurs in October and November. Some pass through to other areas and there is often a small return passage in March and April. Others remain for the winter, especially on the moors and in the Middle Tame Valley.

Apart from a roost of fifteen birds way back in 1895, no party greater than seven is mentioned in *BWM*. In comparison, during the current period there were six at Yoxall in 1993, eight at Berry Hill in 1988, 11 in the Middle Tame Valley during the winter of 1991/2 and up to 15 there in 1985/6.

Tengmalm's Owl   *Aegolius funereus*
Very rare vagrant. One old record

Details of this record from over a hundred years ago, as set out in *BWM*, are given overleaf.

Regional Record Number	County Record Number	Year	Locality, Date and Notes
1	Worcs 1	1901	Wolverley: November 17th, captured and taken into care.

"According to J.W. Lloyd writing in *The Field*, a bird of this species was caught in a pole trap at Wolverley (Worcestershire) on November 17th 1901. The bird was kept alive until February 25th 1902, when it was identified and subsequently cared for by the writer. The record was not included in *The Handbook of British Birds*, although four others of these Scandinavian vagrants appeared in eastern Britain during the autumn of the above occurrence. The record coincided with the first records in the district of the Little Owl, when a 'similar' bird to the above was shot little more than one kilometre away at Blakeshall on December 16th 1901. That this Little Owl was seen and identified as such by Lloyd adds credence to the correct identification of the Tengmalm's Owl."

Without further information there is no reason to change the above assessment.

European Nightjar   (Nightjar)   *Caprimulgus europaeus*
Uncommon to frequent, but very local summer resident, mainly on Cannock Chase. Rare passage migrant.

The 'churring' song of a European Nightjar drifting across a heath is one of the pleasures of a balmy summer's evening. Although still a bird of its traditional heathland haunts, changing management has often made this habitat less suitable and many pairs now nest in the clear fell areas of forestry plantations. Birds are nocturnal, roosting by day on the ground or horizontally along a branch and emerging at dusk to hunt moths and other night-flying insects.

This enigmatic bird declined dramatically in Britain throughout much of the last century, often due to loss of habitat through the afforestation of heathland. Pairs require bare ground for nesting, so reduced grazing and better control of heathland fires also contributed to this decline. However, they readily nest amongst the dead litter left by felling operations and are now utilising the clear fell areas on Cannock Chase as the old plantations are harvested.

Cannock Chase has traditionally been the regional stronghold. Local foresters said birds were common here between the two world wars, when large parts were being planted with conifers, and it was estimated that 50-60 pairs bred in those areas at that time, with a similar number on the then more extensive heathland (Craddock and Dedicoat 2001). Thus the total population was 100-120 pairs. Elsewhere, the species was also locally common and fairly widespread until the 1930s, with many breeding on the northern moorlands and others in lowland woods (*BWM*). However, with the cessation of coppicing many of these former haunts gradually became unsuitable and it was then that birds began to colonise the young conifer plantations on the Chase and in the Wyre Forest. Later afforestation at Bagot's Park, Enville and on the Hanchurch Hills, also attracted up to 15 pairs, but by the 1970s they had become unsuitable and the only populations away from Cannock Chase were two or three pairs at Kinver Edge, with an occasional pair at Highgate Common and in the Kidderminster area (*BWM*).

The WMBC has regularly monitored the population on Cannock Chase (Craddock and Lawson 1980, Baskerville 1992, Harbird and Gribble 1997, Craddock and Dedicoat 2001 and Bennett 2002) and the table below shows the number of 'churring' males or pairs recorded.

Numbers of European Nightjars on Cannock Chase									
Year	*1918-39*	*1950s*	*1976*	*1981*	*1989*	*1992*	*1997*	*2000*	*2002*
Churring males or pairs	100-120	60+	21-25	31	24-26	28-33	38	55	75

Note: The 2002 survey covered a larger area than those of previous years.

The BTO's national census of 1981 (Gribble 1983) seems to have occurred around the time of a turning point in the fortunes of the European Nightjar, as a repeat survey ten years later found 50% more 'churring' males. On Cannock Chase numbers reached their lowest levels in the late-1970s and 1980s, since when there has been a substantial increase. This has been largely due to the areas of clear fell now being created by forestry operations, but also to the heathland management being undertaken by Staffordshire County Council under the lottery funded *Saving Cannock Chase* project. This project involves clearing extensive areas of invasive bracken and trees so that heather can be restored. It also includes special management measures for European Nightjars and Wood Larks and the WMBC was asked to carry out baseline surveys in 2000 so that the success of these measures could be monitored. The Staffordshire Local Biodiversity Action Plan also includes a species action plan for European Nightjar which aims to increase the population to 50 pairs by 2005 and 70 pairs by 2015. That these targets appear to have been achieved already leaves no room for complacency, however, as the high population in clear-fell to six year old plantations can only be sustained through sympathetic forestry operations (Craddock and Dedicoat 2001).

This is generally a late summer visitor and, whilst five birds have appeared in April, with the earliest on the 20th at Burton Hastings in 1952, very few are reported before mid-May. Over fifty-eight years the average date for first birds was May 16th. Departure depends very much on the weather during the breeding season. For example, in 2002 'churring' and feeding activity was noted into early September 2002, indicating that some birds were attempting second or replacement broods (Bennett 2002). Normally most birds would have left for their winter quarters in eastern and southern Africa by this time, with the average last date over thirty-eight years being August 22nd and the latest being on September 23rd, at Byrkley Park in 1998, and 24th, at Burton-on-Trent in 1908.

In other parts of Britain radio-tracking has shown that birds will feed over farmland well away from their breeding sites and this has been recorded twice in this region, namely once about half-a-mile (800m) off the Chase at Springslade Pool in 1990 and then again when a bird was hawking over Trentside meadows at 22.00 hrs in 2001. Coincidentally, both occurrences were on July 19th.

Away from the Chase, one or two 'churring' males were recorded annually at Kinver Edge until 1986, but not since. Other casual records from Staffordshire presumably referred to passage birds. Elsewhere occurrences have been sporadic. In Warwickshire, after seventeen blank years, there were reports from Binton in 1988, Seeswood Pool in 1989, Dunchurch in 2000 and Long Lawford and Ryton Wood in 2001. The geographical proximity and closeness in time of the latter three perhaps hint at the intriguing possibility of an, as yet undiscovered, recolonisation of the county. A 'churring' male also held territory in the south of the county in 2003 (J.J. Bowley *pers. comm.*). The Kinver birds also crossed the boundary into Worcestershire on occasions, whilst that county also produced records of birds in or near to suitable breeding habitat at Bewdley in 1981 and Hartlebury Common in 1986. Others were also reported from Trench Wood and the Worcestershire Beacon in 1995, Defford in 1996 and the Wyre Forest in 1998, where a male 'churred' for four days in May. The last records from the West Midlands county came in 1979, when single birds were at Meriden and Sutton Park.

White-throated Needletail   *Hirundapus caudacutus*
Very rare vagrant. One record.

This was surely one of the least likely species to occur in the region.

Regional Record Number	County Record Number	Year	Locality, Date and Notes
1	Staffs 1	1991	Blithfield Reservoir: June 1st. *BB 85:533*

This was the ninth British record of this rare vagrant which breeds from western Siberia to Japan and winters in Australia. Its timing was typical though, as six of the eight previous ones fell between May 26th and June 20th. There were two other British records that year, at Maidstone (Kent) on May 26th and Noss (Shetland) from June 11th-14th. It is possible that the same individual was involved in all three records (Rogers *et al.* 1992).

Common Swift (Swift) *Apus apus*
Common summer resident and passage migrant.

The return of the first Common Swifts from Africa in late April is a sure sign that summer is coming. Apart from when they are at the nest, these most aerial of birds spend virtually their entire lives on the wing and they are a common sight over our towns and cities as well as villages and open countryside. On calm, warm days they can be so high as to be lost from view as they feed on swarms of insects. But in overcast, wet or windy conditions insects are forced down and birds can then be seen swooping just a few feet above the ground as they feed across meadows and open water. They breed colonially at traditional sites, where their piercing screams are a feature of warm summer evenings. Nests are usually in old buildings, either in the roof beneath the eaves or in small cracks in the walls. Tall buildings, such as church towers, are favoured because they give sufficient height for birds to drop from the nest and gather speed before flying off.

Common Swifts have a reputation for punctuality and over sixty-six years the average date for the first birds to arrive was April 22nd, with the main passage then following in May. During the last ten years, however, the average date has advanced by three days, perhaps in response to climate change. In 2001 there were record numbers of flocks totalling over 1,500 birds in April. The earliest ever was on April 10th 1961. Conversely, the latest arrival was in 1981, when the exceptional cold spell of late April held birds back and none appeared until May 3rd. Spring also brings the biggest concentrations of birds, especially during thundery weather or heavy rain. For example, 1,200 congregated at Dosthill during a thunderstorm on May 26th 1993.

The *Breeding Atlas* showed birds to be present in every 10-km square, with probable breeding in 92% of them. The *Atlas* notes that there is no reliable, quantitative estimate of numbers nationally and that there was no good evidence to suggest numbers had changed significantly since the 1968-72 *Atlas*. Neither is there any CBC data to indicate the long-term trend since, whilst the BBS data is conflicting as it shows a 30% decline nationally, but a 40% increase regionally during 1994-2002. However, most of the latter change occurred during 2000-2, so it is too early to say whether this represents a real difference, but the *Breeding Atlas* does indicate a generally high abundance level almost everywhere in this region. A population range of 2,500-3,500 therefore seems most appropriate and this embraces the 3,000 pairs suggested in *BWM*. Generally there is little information on colonies, but at Fenny Compton numbers increased from 30 nests in 1997 to 45 in 1999, when numbers at Brandon Marsh were also said to be the highest for several years.

Aerial insects are plentiful in warm, dry weather, but scarce when it is windy and wet. So Common Swifts are very sensitive to weather conditions and will travel long distances to feed. Indeed, radar studies have shown they travel up to a hundred miles (160 km) to feed on swarms that gather at the intersection of cold and warm fronts (Flegg 1981). This explains why large flocks, frequently accompanied by hirundines, suddenly appear over water in poor weather. Individual birds in such flocks can face several hazards. Many fall prey to hunting Hobbies, while for two years running several feeding close to the ground at Blithfield Reservoir were killed by traffic on the causeway. On the first occasion, 17 were found dead during drizzle and a cold south-easterly wind on June 2nd 1991, while the second occasion resulted in ten fatalities during heavy rain on June 5th 1992.

In the period 1979-2001 some three hundred flocks of fifty or more birds were reported. Of these, just over 220 contained up to 1,000 birds and 65 comprised between 1,000-2,500. There were also seven flocks of 3,000 and one of 5,000—the latter at Blithfield on May 16th 1991. This equalled the second largest flock to be recorded, which was also at Blithfield, on June 10th 1978, but both were surpassed by the 10,000 that gathered at Draycote Water on May 17th 1975 (*BWM*).

Common Swifts spend a relatively short time at their breeding colonies and by late July the first birds are beginning to move south again. The main departure then normally takes place in August. When food is scarce, however, the young go into a torpid state in order to survive and this can delay fledging by as much as two weeks. This was well illustrated in 1985 when, following a wet summer, there were three records of young still being fed in September. Such late breeding affects the timing of migration and spreads the passage. A few late birds such as these occur most years, so the average date for last birds, again over sixty-six years, is September 26th. Even later stragglers are by no means unusual and there have been November records in seven years, with the latest being those mentioned in *BWM* on the 24th, at Tettenhall in 1978, and 28th, at Westlands in 1976.

Birds have been recorded feeding on swarms of ladybirds, blackflies and flying ants, whilst around 25 were noted taking cabbage-stem flea beetles flying from a trailer full of oilseed rape. Care needs to be taken in identifying any unusual swift, as partial albino birds, sometimes resembling other species, have been reported several times. One such bird visited Belvide Reservoir for five years running.

Recoveries of Common Swifts show them to be long-lived, with records of birds between six and thirteen years old. Since none were ringed as nestlings, these represent minimum ages. Interestingly, virtually three-quarters of recovered birds had been ringed here previously, which may indicate a tendency towards site fidelity. Of the remainder, birds ringed in the region moved south to Hampshire and north to Lancashire, Yorkshire, Cheshire and Scotland. Conversely, birds ringed in Lancashire, Yorkshire, Derbyshire, Nottinghamshire, Leicestershire, Hertfordshire and Essex were recovered here. Just 6% of recoveries came from abroad and these showed movements to Spain, Denmark and Africa, with a bird from Solihull making a tremendous journey of 8,000 km to Malawi.

Alpine Swift   *Apus melba*
Very rare vagrant. Seven records.

Following the first record, documented in *BWM*, there were a further six up to 2003. Birds have now been seen in all four counties, with Worcestershire the most frequently visited.

Regional Record Number	County Record Number		Year	Locality, Date and Notes
1	Worcs	1	1973	Upton Warren: May 6th. *BB 67:329*
2	W Mid	1	1988	Rowley Regis: March 16th, found exhausted. *BB 83:471*
3	Worcs	2	1992	Upton Warren: May 24th. *BB 88:526*
4	Worcs	3	1994	Lower Moor, near Pershore: April 24th. *BB 89:511*
5	Staffs	1	1996	Belvide Reservoir: July 14th. *BB 90:490*
6	Worcs	4	1997	Cookley: April 28th. *BB 91:497*
7	Warks	1	2003	Merevale: August 3rd. *BB 97:589*

Alpine Swifts breed discontinuously from north-west Africa and Iberia, through southern Europe as far north as the Alps and eastwards to north Pakistan. The winter range is assumed to be in the Afrotropics or west India. The species is a fairly regular overshooting migrant into Britain between April and October, with peaks during May, early June and late September (Dymond *et al.* 1989). The March bird, though not unprecedented, was unusually early.

Common Kingfisher   (Kingfisher)   *Alcedo atthis*
Fairly common resident.

The glimpse of brilliant blue as a Common Kingfisher flashes past is always a highlight in any day's birdwatching. With patience they can be seen along most unpolluted rivers, streams and canals as well as at lakes, reservoirs and gravel pits. They excavate nest holes in sandy banks, particularly where there is overhanging vegetation to provide cover and convenient perches. Small, still waters are generally preferred, but these are often the first to freeze, so in cold weather birds may be forced onto the swifter rivers and larger reservoirs.

BWM noted that hard winters and polluted waters were the Common Kingfisher's worst enemies. Since then, the recent run of mild winters has aided population survival, while the water quality of the region's rivers has greatly improved. One consequence of the latter is that there have been few recent instances of birds nesting along polluted watercourses, but travelling elsewhere to find clean waters in which to fish. Common Kingfishers can even be found today in a number of urban situations, notably along the River Cole through Birmingham, the Sowe through Coventry and the Fowlea Brook in Stoke-on-Trent.

The *Breeding Atlas* showed birds in 91% of 10-km squares, with a high level of abundance that suggests the region is something of a stronghold for the species. The *Winter Atlas* recorded them in 94% of squares, confirming that most waters are occupied throughout the year. Although the distribution is wide, birds do avoid the faster-flowing stretches found on some of the northern and western streams. There are several pairs along the Dales rivers, however, where in dry periods they often feed on fish trapped along the shallow reaches after the main river has disappeared underground. In the west, a comprehensive survey of the River Teme in 1979 found 5-10 territories along 51 km, but this was immediately following a very cold winter and the carrying capacity was thought to be three times that level (*BWM*).

Although numbers were severely depleted by the hard winters of 1979 and 1982, they were quickly replenished. However, the recovery after the 1995/6 winter appeared to be slower, even though the weather was less severe. Despite these occasional set backs, there is little evidence to suggest any significant change in numbers. Nationally, the WBS index declined by around 20% during 1980-2002, mostly as a result of the 1982 winter. Based on the number of records received, the regional population has closely followed the fluctuations in the national WBS trend, but if anything, there may have been some increase in numbers. As mentioned above, two possible reasons for this are the milder winters and the extra habitat resulting from the reduction in polluted waterways, of which the West Midlands had a large share.

Population figures are highly variable. The latest estimates given by the RBBP show 14 pairs in the West Midlands and 18 in Worcestershire, both in 2000, and four pairs in Staffordshire and 80 pairs in Warwickshire in 2002 (Ogilvie *et al.* 2002 and 2004). However, the Staffordshire and Worcestershire figures can hardly be a true representation. The higher figures for Warwickshire and the West Midlands reflect the more thorough survey work being undertaken for the two *Tetrad Atlases* and there is no reason to suppose similar surveys in Staffordshire and Worcestershire would not produce the same result. Indeed, the county recorder for Warwickshire more than doubled his estimate of the county's population between 2001 and 2002 on the strength of the information coming in. On this basis, the population is probably towards the lower end of the range 200-500 pairs (*cf.* 200-350 estimated in *BWM*).

Evidence of birds spreading into urban areas is growing. One was recently seen along the River Stour in the centre of Kidderminster, which a few years ago would have been unthinkable and by 2002 there was evidence of breeding birds at Sandwell Valley, Sheepwash Urban Park, Walsall Arboretum and possibly Smestow Valley. Their widespread distribution is confirmed by the *tetrad atlas* work, which shows birds in almost the same percentage of tetrads in the West Midlands county as in Warwickshire. In the last few years one or two have also visited garden ponds, with an instance of one seen catching a goldfish. Most reports from rural parts simply state that birds are thinly, but widely, distributed. However, some idea of numbers can be gauged from the fact that 14 were ringed at Brandon Marsh during 1992. An unusual affect of cold weather came during the freeze of 1981/2, when one had to be rescued after it was found frozen to the metal fence on which it had perched.

A number of movements between 30 and 60 km have been recorded for this species, with birds ringed in Warwickshire moving to Gloucestershire and Northamptonshire and others ringed in Staffordshire moving to Shropshire and Cheshire. Birds ringed in Derbyshire and Shropshire have also been recorded in Staffordshire and Warwickshire respectively. The longest movement on record is for a juvenile ringed in August 1981 at Hackenthorpe, South Yorkshire, and found dead in November of the same year after moving 108 km to Coventry.

European Bee-eater   (Bee-eater)   *Merops apiaster*
Very rare vagrant. Four records.

Unfortunately there have been no further records of this stunning species to add to the four listed in *BWM* and repeated below.

Regional Record Number	County Record Number		Year	Locality, Date and Notes
1	Warks	1	1886	Red Hill: pair, female shot May 29th. (contained 5 eggs), male shot June 2nd.
2	W Mid	1	1955	Minworth: May 14th.
3	Worcs	1	1955	Kidderminster: two, September 2nd.
4	Worcs	2	1970	Redditch: September 22nd-27th. *BB 64:357*

European Bee-eaters breed from Iberia, southern France and north-west Africa eastwards to Kashmir and Kazakhstan and winter south of the Sahara. All of the above records conform to the general pattern of vagrancy, which falls between April and October, but shows a pronounced peak in May and early June (Dymond *et al*. 1989). September sightings are fairly scarce, however, so for half of the above to have occurred in that month is unusual. With only four records ever, it is also surprising that two (three birds) occurred in the same year.

European Roller   (Roller)   *Coracias garrulus*
Very rare vagrant. Two old records.

The following two records, listed in *BWM*, remain the only ones.

Regional Record Number	County Record Number		Year	Locality, Date and Notes
1	Staffs	1	1856-1863	Berkeley: Unknown date.
2	Staffs	2	1908	Patshull Hall: Unknown date in June, shot.

Smith (1938) gives the first record as at Berkeley, which presumably refers to Byrkley. European Rollers are numerous in north-west Africa and Spain, declining in eastern Europe and more common from Turkey into Asia. Most winter in east Africa. Records are few for inland counties, but in recent years have averaged about one a year in Britain as a whole.

Hoopoe   *Upupa epops*
Rare passage migrant or winter visitor.

Although a rare visitor to the region, the Hoopoe has a sufficiently distinctive and exotic appearance to be noticeable even to the inexperienced and its habit of feeding on garden lawns means that it is often reported by non-birdwatchers.

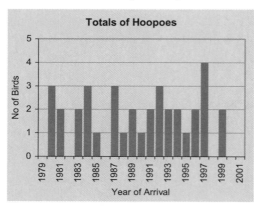

The first record, back in 1830, was followed by a further 22 up to 1933. After a thirteen year gap, there were a further 58 between 1947-1978, of which 44 occurred after 1957— a rate of almost two a year, but with a record five birds in 1968. Occurrences since then have fallen and during 1979-2001 only 36 birds were recorded. Although none were seen in 2000 and 2001, two appeared in 2002.

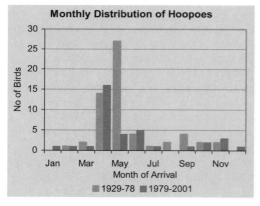

Hoopoes breed in north Africa, much of southern Europe and eastwards across Asia, and winter mostly south of the Sahara. Spring is therefore the usual time for them to appear in Britain, when southerly winds and cloudy conditions cause them to overshoot their intended destinations. During the *BWM* period 76% of birds arrived at this season, with 58% in May. The spring dominance (72% of birds) continued during the current period, but the timing noticeably advanced to a peak in April, when 58% of the spring birds were seen.

Autumn passage was very meagre during 1979-2001, but occasional birds continued to appear in winter, with November records from Cherington in 1983, Droitwich in 1985 and Honeybourne in 1991; a December bird at Wood End (Fillongley) in 1995; one at Offenham Cross in January 1989 and one at King's Norton in February 1984. Two birds were seen together at Whitmore in 1830 and Sutton Coldfield in 1956, but all records during 1979-2001 were of single individuals. Worcestershire, with 38% of records, has attracted most birds, followed by Warwickshire with 26%, Staffordshire 21% and the West Midlands 15%. No locality has been especially favoured.

Wryneck   *Jynx torquilla*
Scarce passage migrant. Last bred in 1941.

The Wryneck was once considered a common summer visitor to the region and was known as the 'Cuckoo's marrow' or 'Cuckoo's mate' because its arrival so often coincided with that of the Common Cuckoo. Its demise as a breeding species was documented in *BWM*, with the last known instance of nesting being at Malvern in 1941. Since then it has been mainly a rare passage migrant, usually in autumn. Like the Hoopoe, it often turns up in gardens, where it feeds avidly on ants.

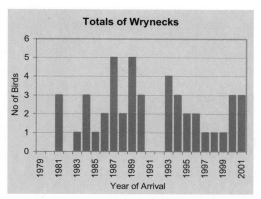

As the breeding population dwindled away, so records became ever fewer and the years 1942-1954 produced only eight birds. Thereafter occurrences appear to have increased, no doubt due as much to more observation as to more birds. The period 1955-1978 produced 31 birds, but that included eight in 1976—which is still the record for a single year. On the other hand, one year in three was blank. During 1979-2001 records increased slightly, with 45 birds, or virtually two a year. There were five birds in 1987 and 1989, with the former producing an exceptional three in April. Since then, there were six in 2002.

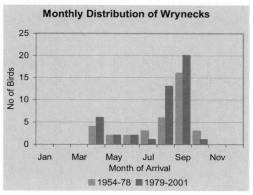

The monthly distribution during the current period was very similar to that from 1954-78, with the vast majority of birds arriving in August and September (61% and 73% respectively). Conversely the main spring passage months of April and May accounted for only 17% and 18% respectively, with the peak in late April. In autumn most occurred between mid-August and mid-September.

Since breeding ceased in 1941, all records have been of single birds. Most of those arriving in autumn are presumed to be Scandinavian migrants making their way south to winter in Africa, particularly as arrivals often seem to coincide with 'falls' on the East Coast. However, the geographical distribution shows that 58% of the records during 1979-2001 came from Worcestershire, which is the most south-westerly county. The remaining birds were shared more or less equally between the three other counties, with 16% in Staffordshire and 13% each in Warwickshire and the West Midlands.

Several records have come from the former breeding strongholds around Malvern and in the Vale of Evesham, suggesting perhaps that something about these areas is especially attractive to the species. Maybe it is the remaining orchards, or an abundance of ants, although these insects are usually most prolific in acidic grasslands and those in the Vale of Evesham are mostly calcareous. In 1990 a singing male even stayed at Broadway from June 1st to August 24th, so perhaps re-colonisation will occur some day.

Green Woodpecker   *Picus viridis*
Fairly common resident.

The Green Woodpecker is the largest and most conspicuous of our three native woodpeckers. It is also the least arboreal, inhabiting heaths, parklands, commons, orchards, gardens and well-timbered farmland as well as broad-leaved woodland. Drumming is rare, but the ringing laugh, or 'yaffle', often attracts attention before the bird breaks cover and shows its green body and yellow rump as it flies away with a deeply undulating flight. Birds habitually feed on open ground, where they mostly take ants, but also beetles, caterpillars and flies (Cramp *et al.* 1974-94). The species is sedentary, with birds remaining on their territories throughout the winter, while immatures disperse only a short distance. Indeed, ringing has shown only local movements of between one and six kilometres.

The distribution was described in *BWM* as widespread and this was confirmed by both the *Winter* and *Breeding Atlases*, which indicated the presence of birds in 95% of 10-km squares. They are most abundant across the south of the region, particularly in the Malvern Hills and Teme Valley, the Severn and Avon Vales and the Dunsmore and Feldon areas, where ants thrive on the closely-cropped sheep pastures. The old, species-rich grasslands and pastures of ridge-and-furrow are often most favoured. Rabbits, too, help to keep swards short and their recovery has doubtless been beneficial to both ants and woodpeckers.

Counts from the favoured Malvern area show fluctuating numbers, with 29 pairs in 1988, 16 in 1992 and 27 in 1995, plus a further seven on Castlemorton Common in the latter year. In contrast, numbers at DM Kineton steadily increased from nine in 1995 to 12 in 1997 and 14 in 1999, whilst a survey undertaken by the Banbury Ornithological Society in 1988 showed this to be the commonest woodpecker in south-east Warwickshire, with 118 sightings (*cf.* 93 for Great Spotted Woodpecker). A similar number of sightings was recorded again in 1992.

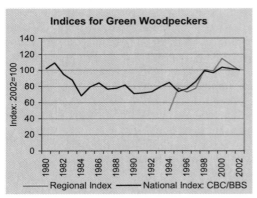

On the other hand, in 1987 it was said to be the scarcest woodpecker in Needwood, which has never been a favoured area despite its abundance of trees. In north Staffordshire, the Dales and moorland fringe provide much suitable habitat and counts of 15 and 14 came from here in 1990 and 1993 respectively. The county's prime site, however, has always been Cannock Chase and birds were recorded here at 20 sites in 1983, 33 in 1997 and 53 in 2002 (Bennett *et al.* 2002). These figures are not strictly comparable, since the 1983 survey was less comprehensive, whilst that of 1997 began too late to catch the early display in March and April. Even so, they do tend to suggest that numbers increased in the late 1990s. As shown by the chart, this view is also supported by the national CBC/BBS which, after a decline in the early 1980s, saw numbers recover in the late 1990s. The regional BBS data show a similar trend, but the CBC sample is too small to indicate the long-term trend.

As Green Woodpeckers feed on the ground, they are susceptible to prolonged spells of frost or deep snow, when they are unable to reach soil invertebrates. The very cold spells in 1978/9 and 1981/2 caused a set back that lasted four years, but the recent run of mild winters has aided the recovery mentioned above. Preliminary results from the *Tetrad Atlases* suggest birds are present in just under half of the urban tetrads and around three-quarters of the rural ones. Taking everything into consideration, the current regional population is probably between 1,000-2,000 pairs compared to the 750-1,500 pairs estimated in *BWM*.

Since the mid 1980s birds have increasingly been visiting suburban as well as rural gardens, where the closely mown lawns frequently house colonies of ants. Woodpeckers are seldom seen in numbers and reports of seven together, at Happy Valley in October 1987 and Sandwell Valley in September 1996, probably referred to family parties. The largest reported group was one of ten at Ufton Hill in 1975 (*BWM*). On first consideration, this might seem an unlikely species to fall victim to raptors, but one succumbed to a Eurasian Sparrowhawk after a long struggle at Ladywalk in 1987, whilst at Apedale in 2001 another was mortally wounded when it landed in a tree with a Eurasian Sparrowhawk sitting in it.

Great Spotted Woodpecker   *Dendrocopos major*
Fairly common to common resident.

Wherever there are mature trees, Great Spotted Woodpeckers can be found, whether in woods, copses, parks, orchards, hedgerows or gardens. Although broad-leaved woodland is their preferred habitat, they also frequent conifers, but tend to avoid dense plantations. Birds commonly occur within urban areas and often visit garden bird feeders. From late February into May the characteristic sound of drumming reverberates through the woodland, announcing the birds' presence. At other times their sharp 'tchick, tchick' call is diagnostic. British birds are largely sedentary, with ringing showing movements of only one to six kilometres, but the northern European populations make occasional irruptive movements, although there is no evidence of any having reached this region.

Records suggest this is the most widespread and numerous of our woodpeckers, even though at times it appears to be out-numbered by the more conspicuous Green Woodpecker. It was found in every 10-km square during survey work for the *Winter Atlas* and in 99% during the *Breeding Atlas*. The levels of abundance were well above average almost everywhere, except the uplands of north Staffordshire, the tree-less, open parts of Feldon and the Severn and Avon Vales and the core of the conurbation. Surveys for the *Tetrad Atlases* show that even in urban areas it occurs in almost 60% of squares, including parts of Edgbaston very close to the centre of Birmingham, whilst in rural districts three-quarters of all tetrads are occupied. The regional CBC sample was too small to draw conclusions, but nationally the index doubled at the time of Dutch elm disease (Marchant *et al.* 1990). Lack (1986) predicted numbers would decline once the disease completed its cycle, but unlike the Lesser Spotted Woodpecker, this species seemed to maintain its strength throughout the 1980s and then to increase again with the milder winters of the 1990s. Indeed, the BBS implies the regional population may have more than doubled since 1994—a faster rate of growth than has occurred nationally—and other local records support this. All available national and regional data point to a population of 2,000-3,000 pairs compared with the 700-1,500 suggested in *BWM*. Such an increase is broadly in line with the long-term change indicated by the national CBC/BBS index.

Cannock Chase is one of very few areas where thorough censuses have been carried out and these showed birds at 28 sites in 1983, 43 in 1997 and 51 in 2002. However, Bennett (2002) thought the 1997 count an under-estimate and considered the population to be probably stable at around 50 pairs. Counts from the Malverns during 1986-94 ranged from 10-20 pairs, with a general increase over the period of 40%, while at Coombes Valley during the 1990s numbers fluctuated between three and five pairs.

Although less affected by cold weather than Green Woodpeckers, birds are more inclined to venture into gardens at such times in search of food and there was a noticeable upsurge in records during both the 1981/2 and 1985/6 winters. Having acquired the taste, this habit now seems to have become the norm, irrespective of the weather, and one was taken from a Denstone garden by a Eurasian Sparrowhawk in 1998. Conversely, milder winters have encouraged earlier nesting and, at Church Pool Covert in 1992, drumming was heard on the exceptionally early date of December 27th. Although known as the architect of the forest because it creates nest-holes that other species use, Great Spotted Woodpeckers can at the same time be ruthless destroyers of nest-boxes.

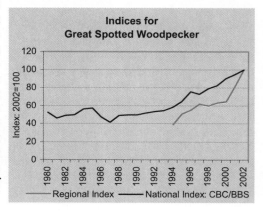

Indices for
Great Spotted Woodpecker

Index: 2002=100

——— Regional Index ——— National Index: CBC/BBS

Lesser Spotted Woodpecker   *Dendrocopos minor*
Frequent to fairly common resident.

The Lesser Spotted Woodpecker mostly favours deciduous woods, old orchards, parks and gardens, but can also be found in well-timbered hedgerows and streamside alders and willows. About the size of a House Sparrow, it is the smallest, scarcest and most elusive of our three resident woodpeckers and always a prized bird to see. Birds feed high in the canopy on beetles, spiders and various larvae and are largely sedentary, but in wintertime they roam more widely and often attach themselves to roving tit flocks. On mild days from February onwards the 'kee-kee-kee' calls and weak drumming may betray their presence, but even so, seeing them is still a challenge.

The species is on the *Red Alert* list of Species of Conservation Concern (Gregory *et al.* 2002), having declined nationally by 73% during 1974-1999. Within this region, the BTOs first breeding atlas survey (1968-72), which coincided with the outbreak of Dutch Elm disease, showed birds to be present in 57% of 10-km squares (Sharrock 1976). The disease quickly spread across the region, but was especially rife in the Severn and Avon valleys and the Dunsmore and Feldon areas. The elm was known as the 'Warwickshire weed' in that county and all were killed, denuding the area of a third of its hedgerow trees (WCC 1978). The abundance of beetles and larvae in and beneath the bark of dying trees provided plenty of food for birds and the Lesser Spotted Woodpecker was one species that quickly took advantage. The beetle infestation peaked around 1975 and breeding season records of this woodpecker in the years immediately following almost trebled (*BWM*). By the time of the *Winter Atlas* in the early 1980s, birds were present in 81% of 10-km squares. There is little comparative data on numbers, but the range expansion was presumably accompanied by an increase in density and the population was probably at its peak about this time.

There was then a marked decline as firstly the hard winters of 1978/9 and 1981/2 took their toll and then the felling of dead trees removed both the food source and nest sites (Osborne 1982). Fortunately, the region's other trees escaped the worst of the devastation inflicted by the 'Great Storm' of 1987, but by 1988-91, when the *Breeding Atlas* was carried out, this woodpecker's range had contracted somewhat, with only 73% of 10-km squares occupied. Declines were also regularly reported throughout the 1980s, particularly from Worcestershire, which, along with Staffordshire, was the stronghold at that time. The felling of dead elms and competition from Great Spotted Woodpeckers were both blamed, but again there was little quantitative data for this elusive species.

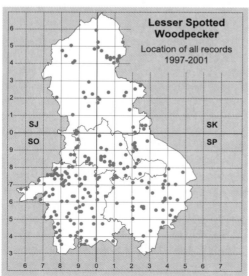

Lesser Spotted
Woodpecker

Location of all records
1997-2001

The *Breeding Atlas* shows an absence of birds on the high ground of the Moors and Dales and from much of the conurbation, where one flying over Spaghetti Junction in 1981 was most unusual. However, they are present in many leafy suburbs and sometimes frequent gardens and feeding stations. Occasional birds have been seen at the WMBC's Harborne reserve. The *Breeding Atlas* showed abundance to be greatest in the Churnet Valley, Needwood, Wyre Forest and Malvern areas—a distribution largely reflected on the distribution map of records for 1997-2001. This also shows the species to be most widespread in Worcestershire, but, away from the Churnet Valley and Cannock Chase, Staffordshire now appears to be less important. Surveys on Cannock Chase suggest a stable population, with three territories in both 1997 and 2002 (Bennett *et al.* 2002).

Although the species has declined nationally, reports from this region have been erratic, with no clear long-term trend. Despite being widely distributed, Lesser Spotted Woodpeckers are spread very thinly indeed, with the preliminary results from the *Tetrad Atlas* surveys showing them to be present in only 10-15% of tetrads. The regional population seems likely to be in the range 200-300 pairs compared to the estimate of 500-1,000 pairs in *BWM*. Such a decline is broadly in line with the national trend.

An unusual series of events concerned two or three juvenile birds, along with five Great Spotted Woodpeckers, which were taken into the Hollywood Animal Rescue Centre during May and June 2000. Only one Great Spotted Woodpecker had been brought in during the previous fifteen years, so quite what caused this influx in casualties is unclear, but heavy rain, hailstorms and the use of pesticides were thought to be likely causes.

Wood Lark   (Woodlark)   *Lullula arborea*
Resident until the 1960s, then a rare visitor and now an uncommon, but increasing, breeding species.

This splendid songster is primarily a bird of heaths and forestry plantations, where it nests amongst patches of rank grass and forages for food amongst bare ground or short, sparse vegetation. It especially favours areas that have been clear felled and has recently established a thriving population in such areas on Cannock Chase. Elsewhere it remains a rare and casual visitor.

In the nineteenth century the Wood Lark was more widespread, but by the 1930s its range had contracted to the point where half the records came from the Clent, Lickey and Malvern Hills, the Lenches and the heaths around Kidderminster, especially those in the Enville-Kinver area which for many years remained the species' stronghold (*BWM*). Birds were noted annually until 1965, but from then until 1992 there were only eleven records involving 14 birds. These included one singing on Cannock Chase in 1979 that prompted the comment in *BWM* that it "raises hopes that the species might one day breed again".

This was indeed prophetic, as in 1994 a pair was discovered on Cannock Chase and birds have been recorded there in every year since. Little information has been published on definite breeding, but seven pairs were found during the national census in 1997. The apparent decline thereafter was certainly due to less intensive fieldwork, particularly during 2001 when access restrictions curtailed visits, as in 2002 a thorough survey by the WMBC located 26 singing males—all bar one in clear-fell areas (Bennett *et al.* 2002). Again full details have not been published, but it is known that young fledged and almost certainly some pairs had second broods. This colonisation followed a general increase in Britain that saw the population grow more than six-fold between the 1986 and 1997 censuses, with a noticeable northerly spread. (Ogilvie *et al.* 1999).

Away from Cannock Chase, there were just eleven records during the current period, at

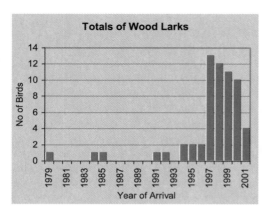

Totals of Wood Larks

Chasewater (1984), Edgbaston Reservoir (1985), Sheepwalks (1991), Trench Wood (1992), Clayhanger and Blakeshall (1997), Westport Lake (1998 and 2001), Valley Park (1998), Codsall (1999) and Wormleighton Reservoir (2001). Of these, eight occurred between January and early April and three in October or November.

Given the current national trend, it is hoped birds will eventually spread into other parts of the region. Elsewhere in Britain some have moved into low-intensity farmland, golf courses, orchards, coppiced woodland and even old coal mines (Ogilvie *et al. op.cit.*).

Sky Lark   (Skylark)   *Alauda arvensis*
Very common, though much declined, resident, passage migrant and winter visitor.

Time was when a singing Sky Lark could be virtually guaranteed on any summertime visit to the open countryside. Until the early 1980s birds were common on hillsides, heaths, moors, grasslands, commons and especially large arable fields. After about 1980, however, they began to decline. In winter small flocks resort to stubbles to feed on cereal grain, weed seeds and vegetable matter.

The Sky Lark is widely distributed across the region, with the *Winter Atlas* showing birds in every 10-km square and the *Breeding Atlas* in 99%. However, its abundance was below average everywhere except along the Cotswold Fringe to the south-east of the region. Moreover, whilst the range remains unaltered, numbers have fallen still further since the atlases were compiled as the chart shows.

The decline in Britain has been well publicised. The CBC/BBS show numbers fell by 55% during 1974-99, resulting in its inclusion on the *Red Alert List* of Species of Conservation Concern (Gregory *et al*. 2002), with some 40% of this decline occurring in the period 1980-2002. Birds have a preference for grass leys under five-years old (O'Connor and Shrubb 1986) and it seems a reduction in young leys, combined with a shift from spring to autumn sown cereals, seriously diminished the food resource available for feeding chicks. Autumn sowing also reduced the area of stubbles needed to sustain birds over the winter.

The regional index suggests an even faster rate of decline, though because of the small

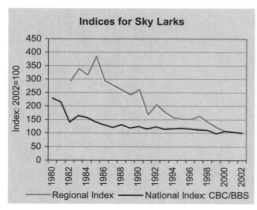

sample it is less reliable (the 1980 and 1981 values have been omitted for this reason). Both the regional BBS data and the preliminary *Tetrad Atlas* results suggest a regional population of 20,000-25,000 pairs compared with the 40,000-75,000 estimated in *BWM*.

Unlike most species there are several examples of breeding densities at different times, although most refer to atypical habitats. For instance, *BWM* quoted several examples that averaged 11.7 pairs per km^2 on farmland, 55 pairs per km^2 on the heathland of Cannock Chase and an exceptional 40-80 pairs per km^2 at the National Vegetable Research Station,

Wellesbourne, which was believed to be one of the highest densities in Britain. During the current period, farmland counts averaged only 6.4 pairs per km², but there were 10 pairs per km² on the grassland of a disused quarry site and four pairs in 6 ha of young forestry—an average of 67 pairs per km²—though this is only a transient habitat. This gives a measure of the decline on farmland, but several decreases have also been well documented in other habitats. At Alvecote Pools there were 10-12 pairs from 1979-84, but within two years numbers had halved, whilst on the heathland of Sherbrook Valley they fell from 49 pairs in 1967 to 38 in 2002. Part of the Malvern Hills held 17 pairs in 1989, but only six in 1995 and three in 1996 and at the DM Kineton army camp there was a dramatic collapse from a norm of 65-70 singing males until 1995 to just 34 in 1996, although here numbers had almost recovered again by 2000, when there were 63. Many of these figures make depressing reading, but on a more positive note numerous pairs have taken advantage of set-aside and there were some reports from Warwickshire of increases in 2000. Even better, the restored open-cast colliery sites at Bateswood and the Bleak House / Cuckoo Bank area have become strongholds for the species, with 30 and 173 territories respectively reported in 2002.

Diurnal passage is reported annually from mid-October to early November as birds cross the region on a broad front to destinations further south and west, perhaps even reaching Iberia. Many pass over urban areas as exemplified by 300 heading westwards at Woodshire's Green, Coventry, on November 4th 1993, although back in 1988 one observer from Birmingham commented on the lack of large movements over the city at that time compared with the peaks of 100 per hour he noted thirty years earlier. In rural districts, 150 over Belvide Reservoir in two hours on October 19th 1989 and 100 an hour moving south-westwards over Wilden on October 10th 1993 were typical, but the heaviest passage is usually along the Cotswolds Fringe in south-east Warwickshire. Here up to 200 per hour are regularly noted and an especially strong movement during October 8th-10th 1995 peaked at 400 per hour moving over Fenny Compton on the 9th. Comparing these with counts of 300 through Upton Warren in fifteen minutes in 1967 and 1,500 along the Tame Valley in two hours in 1951 (*BWM*) again gives some idea of the general decline in numbers. Return passage, though smaller than that in autumn, occurs from late February to early April (*BWP*), but surprisingly there have been few records of this in recent years.

Apart from their migrations, Sky Larks also make hard weather movements, with 1,500 heading south over Bittell Reservoir on January 27th 1996 the largest in recent times. However, *BWM* records that 5,000 passed over Sheriff's Lench in an hour in December 1962. Again such movements have also been observed over the conurbation, with 148 noted in 90 minutes over Netherton Hill on February 7th 1996. Other weather related behaviour involved one that resorted to feeding in an Alrewas garden during the 1982 freeze, 100 that gathered at Lower Kempsey after flooding in 1992 and six that continued to sing at Upton-on-Severn even though the devastating floods on Good Friday in 1998 had left their territories under several feet of water.

Those birds that remain through the winter gather in flocks around good food sources, but as these have become progressively scarcer so flocks have dwindled. It is generally presumed that continental immigrants may help to swell numbers at this time, but there is no evidence to say whether this occurs in this region. In *BWM* it was said flocks seldom exceeded 200 birds in October and November, but that such numbers were not unusual in the colder days from December to February, with 500 seen twice and a maximum of 600 at Bartley on the same day as the massive hard weather movement mentioned above at Sheriff's Lench. During the current period the mean flock size has been around 100 from October through to February and only 13% reached 200 or more. However, there were four of 500 or more, with the largest being 2,000 at Holt in January 1979 and 850 at Defford in December 2000. It is noticeable that the largest of these two flocks came at the beginning of the current period, with the more recent one being less than half its size.

Shore Lark   (Horned Lark)   *Eremophila alpestris*
Rare passage migrant and winter visitor.

There were three records prior to 1979 (*BWM*), since when there have been a further twelve.

Regional Record Number	County Record Number		Year	Locality, Date and Notes
1	Staffs	1	1879	Enville: female, December 9th, shot.
2	Worcs	1	1920	Malvern Hills: January 14th. *BB 1921*
3	Staffs	2	1972	Blithfield Reservoir: November 11th-12th.
4	Worcs	2	1987	North Hill: March 31st to April 18th.
5	Warks	1	1990	Coton Pools: October 17th.
6	Staffs	3	1990	Chasewater: October 28th.
7	Staffs	4	1992	Blithfield Reservoir: October 28th.
8	Warks	2	1994	Draycote Water: October 24th.
9	Worcs	3	1996	Upton Warren: three, October 15th.
10	Worcs	4	1996	Worcestershire Beacon: male, November 1st.
11	Worcs	5	1996	Caunsall: male, November 14th.
12	Staffs	5	1996	Tittesworth Reservoir: male, November 20th to December 8th.
13	Staffs	6	1996	Chasewater: male, December 14th to March 16th, 1997.
14	W Mid	1	1997	Billesley Common: January 2nd-11th.
15	Staffs	7	2001	Chasewater: adult December 9th. Relocated January 4th-5th, 2002.

Shore Larks breed in Fennoscandia and winter in small numbers around British coasts, chiefly on the east, but are rare inland. Two features stand out from the above records. Firstly, there is the unexpected upsurge since 1987, with birds in seven out of fifteen years. Secondly, there was an exceptional influx in 1996, which brought five records including a party of three that dropped into Upton Warren and fed for a couple of hours. Most arrived in autumn, with nine records between October 15th and November 20th, which is when birds typically reach Britain. The three December and two January records probably relate to birds that had come into the country in the previous autumn and were either wandering around or were displaced by bad weather, whilst that in March may well have been a bird that had wintered further west and was on its way back to its arctic breeding grounds.

Almost half the records came from Staffordshire, mainly from the reservoirs and especially from Chasewater, whilst in Worcestershire the bare summits of the Malvern Hills have attracted passage birds on more than one occasion.

Sand Martin   *Riparia riparia*
Fairly common, though much declined, summer resident and passage migrant.

Sand Martins breed in colonies, excavating nest-holes along river banks and in the faces of sand and gravel quarries. A few pairs take advantage of artificial sites, such as drainage pipes, and in parts of Britain whole colonies have occupied the holes in specially constructed nesting walls. Similar walls at Brandon Marsh and Sheepwash Urban Park, however, have had little or no success. Birds are most numerous on migration, with feeding flocks a frequent sight in spring over gravel pits and reservoirs, especially in poor weather. The return passage is less evident, but small groups are again seen over water, or perhaps sitting on telephone wires, as they move leisurely south. Numbers are only a fraction of what they were forty years ago and the species is now on the *Amber Alert List* (Gregory *et al.* 2002).

Sand Martins are one of the earliest of our summer visitors to return from Africa, with the first birds arriving on average on March 20th (based on sixty-five years observations). In recent years they have been arriving particularly early, with records in 1990 from Sandwell Valley and Belvide and Blithfield Reservoirs on February 24th being the earliest ever. That spring was an exceptional one for early migrants, but nevertheless the average first arrival date over the decade 1992-2001 was March 10th—ten days earlier than the long-term average. The volume of March arrivals has also been a feature of recent times, with around a thousand birds in 1989 and over 1,500 in 2000, with the latter including 950 at Shustoke Reservoir on the 29th. Numbers quickly build up with the main arrival in April, when flocks up to 200 strong are regularly seen at gravel pits and reservoirs, while up to 700 have recently roosted in the reed-bed at Ladywalk. Larger numbers are not unusual and 1,300 were at Draycote Water on April 22nd 2001. The three largest recorded spring flocks, however, were all of 1,500 at Belvide Reservoir, in 1947, 1961 and 1968 (*BWM*).

Sand Martins suffered an horrendous population crash of around three-quarters in the early 1970s as a result of a severe drought on their wintering grounds in the Sahel region of west Africa during 1968/9 (Gibbons *et al.* 1993) from which they never fully recovered. This was followed by a another severe drought in 1983/4 that caused a further decline (Gibbons *et al. op. cit.*). It is well known that annual numbers fluctuate enormously and data from the BBS (both national and local) and the national WBS confirm this. However, these data series have not been running long enough to indicate a long-term trend. Adverse conditions on the wintering grounds continue to affect survival rates and they are further compounded by changes here, with quarries and sometimes river banks changing from one year to the next and poor weather early in the season restricting pairs to a single brood. As a consequence birds have to be opportunists, nesting wherever conditions are right in that particular year. The capricious nature of colonies is well demonstrated by that at Beckford, which *BWM* mentions as being the largest with 265 nests in 1977. In 1988 the number of nests was identical, but in between times it had fallen as low as 20, whilst subsequently the site was said to be abandoned in 1991 but 10 pairs were present again in 1999. Numbers at other established colonies such as Cornets End, Grimley and Meriden (see *WMBC Annual Report* 54:141) have shown similar fluctuations. River banks are less liable to change, but on rivers such as the Tame rising storm-water quickly destroys nests and young. In 1995 this happened just prior to fledging, leaving the distressed adults hovering above their flooded nest holes. Several riverbank holes have also been dug out and predation by mink is suspected.

As a consequence, there is little reliable information on which to base a population estimate. The *Breeding Atlas* showed birds in 64% of 10-km squares, with abundance greatest along the Severn and Teme valleys and more especially along the Blythe, Tame and Trent where sand and gravel workings proliferate. Back in the 1970s the Teme was probably the most important river, with over 300 nests, but no comprehensive counts have been received since. Taking account of all available data, and the fluctuations in population, the regional population is probably between 1,000-2,000 pairs (*cf.* 2,000-4,000 estimated in *BWM*).

Around the mid 1980s, there was a significant shift in the seasonal distribution of Sand Martins. Prior to that time the bulk of birds had always occurred in autumn (88% during 1979-85), whereas since then spring has been the dominant season (85% during 1986-2001). This shift has arisen not so much from a stronger spring passage as from the dearth of an autumn one. Indeed, the Worcestershire recorder astutely observed that in autumn "they seem to trickle away before anyone notices." Some birds begin drifting south in early July, but most leave during late August and early September, just ahead of the Barn Swallows and House Martins. Records over 65 years show the average date for last birds to be October 10th, but the average during 1992-2001 was four days later. The latest ever was at Belvide Reservoir on November 13th 1977 (*BWM*).

Few autumn gatherings now exceed 200 birds and most are less than 100. The highest count during the current period was 1,200, at Kingsbury Water Park back in 1979, whilst 500 at nearby Dosthill in 2001 was the best in recent times. In contrast, *BWM* said concentrations of 1,000 or more could be seen and 3,000 were recorded twice. Visible migration and roosts display similar declines. Movements today seldom consists of anything larger than a group of 50 birds, whereas the heaviest passage mentioned in *BWM* was 2,500 in an hour, at Blithfield Reservoir on August 28th 1962. Time was when many departing birds would have joined with Barn Swallows in forming large reedbed roosts. For example, *BWM* refers to several roosts of 2,000, one of 3,000 and a record 4,000 at Two Gates on July 27th 1951. In comparison, the current period has produced two roosts of 300 and one of 500—on August 30th 1982 at Two Gates again. Such comparisons highlight just how drastic the Sand Martin decline has been.

Ringing recoveries reveal an influx during July to September of birds ringed earlier in the season in Cheshire, Cumbria and other northerly counties. One ringed in central Scotland in July 1980 was caught at Stubbers Green in August of the same year, having completed just 418 km of its long journey south to Africa. A considerable number of our birds initially move south to Icklesham, in West Sussex, where they join with thousands of others from elsewhere in the country before setting off south through France and Iberia to West Africa, whilst others are recorded passing through Icklesham again on their way back to the region in spring. A number of these small hirundines have also been re-caught as they travel along their migration route to and from the region. Birds ringed here have been recorded in France, the Netherlands and Spain, while birds ringed in those countries have been recorded in this region during the same or following years. No fewer than five birds have moved between the West Midlands and the Parc National de Djoudj in Senegal—a distance of 4,223 km, whilst another from here was recorded in Algeria, 2,077 km from its ringing site. The longest movement on record, however, was made by a bird ringed at Cannock in May 1989 and recovered in April 1990 in Koumpentoum, Senegal—a staggering movement of 4,441 km.

Barn Swallow   (Swallow)   *Hirundo rustica*
Very common, though declined, summer resident and passage migrant.

Said to be the harbinger of spring, the Barn Swallow is a familiar bird to many. Time was when virtually every farm had an attendant pair and birds could be seen swooping low across arable crops and cattle pastures alike. They nest in barns, stalls, outbuildings, porches, open sheds and garages. Whilst birds are commonest on lowland farmland, they also occur sparingly within urban areas wherever there are open fields for feeding. Though not strictly colonial, pairs often nest in loose groups and they have a strong site fidelity, returning to nest at the same site year after year. The species is now on the *Amber List* because of its unfavourable conservation status in Europe (Gregory *et al.* 2002).

Each spring the return of the first birds is always eagerly awaited and over sixty-six years the average date for this has been March 30th, with the earliest ever at Broad Green on February 7th 1997. These early migrants are very vulnerable to adverse weather and the exceptionally late snowfall in April 1981 forced many to rest on the shoreline at Rudyard Reservoir. As with most migrants, birds have been arriving earlier in recent years and during the decade 1992-2001 the average date of first arrivals was March 20th. April and May then bring the main influx, when large flocks can be seen feeding over reservoirs, lakes and gravel pits. *BWM* said heavy movements and large concentrations were unusual at this season, but during the current period flocks averaged 200 and reached a thousand on four occasions, including a maximum of 1,500, at Blithfield Reservoir on May 2nd 1983.

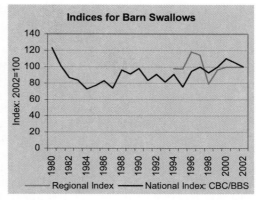

Barn Swallows are extremely widespread and were recorded in every 10-km square during the *Breeding Atlas*. Abundance was greatest in the Meres and Mosses and parts of Arden, Dunsmore and Feldon—all areas with dairy or cattle farms. The national CBC/BBS index declined sharply in the early 1980s, reaching its lowest point in 1984, but has since shown some recovery. This decline was doubtless due in part to their being fewer flies and nest sites as a result of intensive livestock rearing in modern buildings. Moeller (1989) also found that the amount of winter rainfall in South Africa had a marked effect on numbers in the following summer, with poorer breeding success and higher mortality after a dry winter.

Regionally the data are too few to compile a long-term index, but the BBS has broadly followed the national trend, whilst earlier reports, such as low numbers in the years immediately after 1984 and a 30% decline at Timberhonger in 1993, suggest the regional trend has mirrored the national one. Surveys in Warwickshire during 2000 located 98 birds on sixteen farms and other surveys in the south of that county indicated densities of 3-6 pairs per km², which is above the national average shown in the *Breeding Atlas*. However, numbers are known to fluctuate between one area and another and between one year and the next and some observers have reported declines. Indeed, at the National Trust property at Baddesley Clinton there were at least nine pairs in the mid-1990s, but only one pair by the beginning of this century. Weighing up the available information, the breeding population is probably in the range 10,000-20,000 compared with the 7,000-12,000 estimated in *BWM*, which on refection was probably an under-estimate.

Although a few individuals may leave as early as late July, significant passage is seldom noted until late August and most birds leave in September or early October, when many gather at communal roosts. This used to bring huge concentrations to reedbeds, such as those at Bedworth Slough, Brandon Marsh, Doxey Marshes, Ford Green and Two Gates, with the last named having a record 50,000 in 1950 (*BWM*). Such gatherings persisted through much of the 1980s, especially at Ford Green where the roost averaged 13,000 during 1979-90 and reached 30,000 in 1984. Thereafter it disappeared, although 6-8,000 roosted at nearby Chell Heath in 1997. Large numbers also roosted at Doxey Marshes from 1983-90, again with a maximum of 30,000, this time in 1988. Brandon Marsh consistently held a smaller roost until about 1990, whilst Betley Mere did so throughout the 1990s. Often these roosts were attended by one or two Hobbies, or on occasions a whole family. Since around 1990 many Barn Swallows have switched to roosting in newer, taller crops, notably maize, which means they have more choice of sites. As a result the mean size of roosts in reedbeds has fallen from 5,500 during 1979-1990 to barely 1,000 since.

Autumn passage frequently consists of birds moving in small groups of 50 or less. The largest movements in recent times involved 1,500 along a broad front across the Vale of Evesham on September 24th 1999 and 1,820 passing south through Belvide Reservoir in five and a half hours on September 17th 1998, but the heaviest passage ever was one of 5,000 in half-an-hour at Wilnecote in 1951(*BWM*). Whilst most have gone by mid-October, the final departures can be surprisingly late, with the average date of last birds over sixty-six years being November 3rd. Even later individuals were reported from Sherbourne on December 7th 1968, Shenstone until December 23rd in 1967 and Selly Oak on December 24th 1935 (*BWM*). So

January is the only month without a record and the gap between the extreme dates of the earliest and latest ever is a mere 44 days.

Examples of productivity include a pair at Abbots Bromley that raised thirteen young from three broods, whilst at Denstone 42 young were reared from four nests. An unusual occurrence concerned a pair which nested in an occupied bedroom at Malvern in 1981. Two birds resembling the race *H. r. savignii* were reported from Packington Great Pool on April 20th 1997.

The Barn Swallow is a transglobal migrant that has provided many examples of ringed birds making huge movements to and from their wintering quarters in South Africa. For instance, birds ringed here have been recovered in Spain, Algeria, Morocco (seven), Zaire and as far as the Cape of Good Hope in South Africa, with the following being the two longest recorded movements. Firstly, a bird ringed as a nestling in North Littleton in June 1998 was found dead in March 1999 at Kweperfontein Farm near Ceres in Cape Province, South Africa, 9,726 km from its ringing site. Secondly, another ringed as a nestling near Sudbury in July 1991 was recovered alive and well in March 1992 in Skinnerspruit, near Pretoria in Transvaal—a journey of 9,210 km.

Ringing has also shown a considerable interchange of birds between the region and adjacent counties and with counties further north and south. In particular, there are a number of migratory movements to and from the south coast, with birds interchanging with Dorset, Sussex and Essex. An interesting pair of recoveries involves an adult male and female ringed as a pair at their nest site at Weatheroak on August 1st 1990 and both recovered in June of the following year at the same site—an excellent example of both site and partner fidelity.

Red-rumped Swallow   *Hirundo daurica*
Very rare vagrant. Three records.

Following the first record documented in *BWM*, there have now been two more.

Regional Record Number	County Record Number		Year	Locality, Date and Notes
1	Warks	1	1972	Draycote Water: May 27th. *BB 66:346*
2	Worcs	1	1992	Upton Warren: May 1st-2nd. *BB 86:502*
3	Worcs	2	2001	Westwood Pool: April 17th. *BB 95:503*

Red-rumped Swallows breed widely in north-west Africa, Iberia and the eastern Mediterranean and are thought to winter in Africa north of the equator. With over 400 British records they are clearly fairly regular overshooting spring migrants and most appear in the second half of April or May, as indeed did the three above (Dymond *et al.* 1989, Rogers *et al.* 2004).

House Martin   *Delichon urbicum*
Common to very common summer resident and passage migrant.

The House Martin, like the House Sparrow, has a close affinity with man, building its mud nests under the eaves of houses, often in small colonies. Unlike Common Swifts and Barn Swallows, which have a strong preference for old buildings, this species is also quick to utilise new properties. Indeed, it often moves in during their construction, when most building sites provide a ready supply of mud. Specially designed nest-boxes are also utilised, giving the birds a head start, which may enable them to raise an extra brood. Although they breed mainly in towns and villages, many can also be found on isolated farms and other buildings. Apart from suitable nest sites, the House Martin's other need is for an abundance of aerial insects, which it finds most readily in sheltered, sunny situations. Birds feed in the airspace between the low-flying Barn Swallow and the higher flying Common Swift.

Normally the first House Martins arrive from their sub-Saharan wintering grounds about a week after the first Barn Swallows and over sixty-six years the average date for the first birds to appear was April 6th, but during 1992-2001 it was March 25th. The recent earlier arrivals of the three species of hirundine has been remarkably consistent and strongly resembles the changes in global and local temperatures (see page 20). The earliest ever arrival also occurred during this period—on March 15th 1997 at Brandon Marsh. When they first arrive birds frequently feed over water and large concentrations gather at reservoirs and gravel pits, especially in cool or wet weather when insects are flying low. Passage peaks in May and extends into early June, during which time parties up to 200 are widely reported and the heaviest movements noted were 1,000 at Belvide Reservoir on May 19th 1990 and 2,000 moving northwards through Sandwell Valley on May 7th 1997—the latter characteristically during squally showers.

House Martins are widespread and birds were recorded in every 10-km square during the *Breeding Atlas*, with breeding confirmed everywhere except the core of the Black Country. Densities were highest in the western parts of the region, where dairying and livestock are more widespread, and lowest in arable intensive areas and on the higher ground of north Staffordshire, where flying insects are less plentiful. Although birds nest within a mile or two of the centre of Birmingham, preliminary data from the *Tetrad Atlases* show they are less widespread in urban areas, breeding in around a quarter of tetrads compared to a half in rural districts. *BWM* said it was thought likely that nesting occurred on the limestone crags of the Dales, but there have been no records of this happening during the current period. Nor have there been any records of the large colony that used to nest on Hanchurch water tower.

Opinions on numbers vary, with some observers reporting stable numbers, while others mentioned drastic declines, such as 50% at Lichfield in 1992 and 90% in eight years at Evesham. On a long-term basis, numbers at Shustoke in 1995 were said to be 50% down compared to twenty years previously. Surprisingly though, there has been no quantitative monitoring of colonies to verify or refute such statements. Nationally, the CBC index was highly volatile during 1989-2002, with a very marked drop in 1991, but curiously this was one year when no-one mentioned any local declines. Overall, however, the index showed no significant change. The current population is probably towards the upper end of the range 8,000-16,000 pairs compared to the 15,000-23,000 estimated in *BWM*.

Autumn passage begins in July, but reaches a pronounced peak in September. As in spring, it is often most evident in poor weather, when birds gather over water as instanced by 1,000-2,000 feeding at Blithfield Reservoir in 1983. Flocks up to 400 are widely reported at this season, with the most notable during the current period being 2,000, at Blithfield Reservoir on September 8th 1984 and Draycote Water on September 10th 2001, and a record 2,500 along the River Severn between Trimpley Reservoir and Arley on September 28th 1982. Good numbers are also recorded away from water, with 1,643 over Kinver Edge on September 28th 1991, 402 moving through Lutley Wedge in ninety minutes on September 17th 1999 and 450 an hour moving south-west over Fenny Compton on September 19th 2000. The largest movement during the current period occurred on September 12th 1998, when 2,160 passed southwestwards over Needwood, but the most intensive passage occurred on September 18th 1951, when 4,000 passed over Wilnecote in two hours (*BWM*). An unusually late passage occurred between October 1st-3rd 1999, with 250 at Upton Warren and 300 at Draycote Water on the 1st; 195 at Chasewater and 360 moving west through Belvide Reservoir in five hours on the 2nd; and 400 at Blithfield Reservoir and 500 at Alvecote Pools on the 3rd. Whilst such numbers are exceptional in October, individual birds are commonly reported much later still. Indeed, some linger very late, so the average last date is November 1st (again over sixty-six years), with the latest on December 5th, at Wolverhampton back in 1962 (*BWM*).

Communal roosting is rarely mentioned, but 50 roosted at Doxey Marshes and 60 at Minworth in September 1983, while 100 did so at Packington Hall in August 1991. Two records of interest involved about 40 that were taking insects blown from sycamore trees by a strong wind and up to 50 that, over a couple days, flew around and settled briefly in a cherry tree, where they were seen to peck at leaves and appeared to be feeding, presumably on insects. In another incident, at Shustoke Reservoir, some were pursued by Pied Wagtails and one was knocked into the water where it drowned after being repeatedly mobbed by three wagtails, flying in turn from the nearby bank.

Compared to the other hirundine species, very small numbers of House Martins are ringed. There are several records of birds that were ringed in Kent and Sussex during the autumn and recovered in the region during the following and subsequent years, while one of particular interest involved a bird ringed as a juvenile on Copeland Island, County Down in Northern Ireland, in September 1995 and recovered 312 km away at Uttoxeter in May 1996. The longest recorded movement was made by a bird caught at Bilbrook Sewage Works in September 1992 and recovered in the following month on Jerba Island, Tunisia—a distance of 2,338 km from the ringing site.

Richard's Pipit *Anthus novaeseelandiae*
Rare vagrant.

The current period has produced a further six records to add to the four in *BWM*, but appearances of this rare pipit remain erratic.

Regional Record Number	County Record Number		Year	Locality, Date and Notes
1	Staffs	1	1887	Near Hednesford: adult male, October 21st, taken.
2	Staffs	2	1963	Blithfield Reservoir: April 8th. *BB 57:275*
3	Worcs	1	1967	Upton Warren: October 7th. *BB 61:353*
4	Staffs	3	1967	Blithfield Reservoir: one, October 15th, two on 29th and three November 5th. *BB 61:353* (Treated as one record by both BB and BWM)
5	Staffs	4	1993	Mow Cop: March 14th to April 3rd, feeding mainly in Cheshire but making occasionally forays into Staffs.
6	Staffs	5	1994	Westport Lake: October 13th.
7	Staffs	6	1994	Barton GP: two, October 23rd, one of these also in Derbyshire.
8	W Mid	1	1994	Bartley Reservoir: November 4th.
9	Warks	1	2001	Ilmington Downs: October 17th.
10	Staffs	7	2002	Black Bank, Newcastle-under-Lyme: first-winter, October 5th-6th.

Note: BBRC finally ceased to consider records of this species from January 1st 1983, having previously removed it from consideration during 1971-5.

The migratory race of Richard's Pipit breeds from western Siberia into Asia and winters with local races in the Indian sub-continent and south-east Asia. Despite coming from so far away, it is a regular autumn visitor to Britain. Large influxes in 1967 and 1994 both resulted in four birds reaching the region. The latter year brought 300 birds to Britain, being twice as many as in the previous best autumn of 1968 (when none reached this region). Two occurred in March and April respectively, when birds are rare (Dymond *et al*. 1989). Otherwise all were between October 5th and November 5th. The records also show a noticeable bias towards Staffordshire. More birdwatchers and a better appreciation of the identification characteristics, especially the distinctive call, have undoubtedly contributed to the increase in records.

Tawny Pipit *Anthus campestris*
Very rare vagrant. One record.

The only record is that listed in *BWM* from over fifty years ago.

Regional Record Number	County Record Number	Year	Locality, Date and Notes
1	Staffs 1	1953	Tutbury: December 29th.

The Tawny Pipit breeds in north Africa, Iberia, Italy and eastern Europe through to Asia, with a patchy distribution in west and central Europe as well. Birds winter in the Sahel zone of sub-Saharan Africa. Although it is a regular migrant to Britain in autumn, December records are incredibly rare, as are inland ones (Dymond *et al*. 1989).

Tree Pipit *Anthus trivialis*
Fairly common, though declining, summer resident and passage migrant, becoming increasingly restricted to the north and west of the region.

Tree Pipits need bare or sparsely vegetated ground for feeding and tall song posts from which to launch their distinctive song flights. These requirements are best met on heaths and hillsides with scattered trees, or in young forestry plantations. They also frequent the edges and glades of sessile oakwoods, where the field and shrub layers are sparse, but they are rarely found beneath a closed canopy. Its exacting needs make the species somewhat nomadic, occupying areas of forestry whilst the trees are young, but disappearing once the canopy closes over.

Birds return early from their wintering grounds in tropical Africa. Indeed, in 1967 one was at Alvecote as early as March 14th 1967, which at the time was the third earliest ever recorded in Britain (Hudson 1973). There were also March records in seven out of thirteen years during 1988-2001, although the average arrival date was April 3rd. Over the longer time-span of sixty-two years the average date for the first birds to return was April 7th. Passage then continues until early May, but nowadays it is so weak as to be virtually non-existent, with seven at Sandwell Valley in 1986 the most reported. In comparison, *BWM* cites an exceptional passage in 1967 that brought 25 to Blithfield Reservoir and 50 to Belvide Reservoir.

The *Breeding Atlas* recorded birds in 60% of 10-km squares, principally in the north and west of the region. Densities were below average everywhere, but reached their highest in the Dales and Moors of north Staffordshire, the Churnet Valley, Cannock Chase, Wyre Forest and Malvern areas. Nationally, the CBC/BBS index rose steadily until 1987, dropped sharply over the next five years and has since fluctuated markedly. Overall it fell by 75% between 1975 and 1999 and the species is now included on the *Amber Alert List* (Gregory *et al.* 2002). Locally, declines were first mentioned in the 1950s (*BWM*), but in recent times these have become more apparent, even in traditional areas. This is possibly due to subtle changes in habitat as a result of less grazing and heather management.

The average number of territories on the Malverns, for example, almost halved from 62 during 1986-88 to 35 during 1991-93, while a full count in 1995 revealed a further drop to 23 (Parr 1987-96). A long-term decline was also evident at Coombes Valley, where there were 20 pairs in 1977, 14 pairs during 1989-91 and then a collapse to just three or four pairs seven years later. One or two pairs still survive on Bredon Hill, the Clent Hills and in Sutton Park, but the last report from the Lickeys was in 1995. In Warwickshire the only hint of breeding since 1994 was a pair at a traditional site in 1997 and an unpaired singing male in 2000, but none are now thought to breed.

The strongest population now appears to be on Cannock Chase, where comprehensive surveys in 1992, 1997 and 2002 revealed 95, 179 and at least 119 territories respectively. Numbers have increased significantly in young coniferous plantations and clear-felled areas with peripheral broad-leaved trees. Indeed, many of the unprecedented 1997 total were in the clear-fell areas that were then available at Beaudesert. Woodland glades and the edges abutting heathland have also been favoured and the declines recorded on the dry heaths may possibly be because the felling of invasive pines has removed song posts (Bennett *et al.* 2002). Although only casual counts are available for the Wyre Forest, these support the warden's view that numbers are holding up (*pers. comm.*), with birds again taking advantage of clear-fell areas and woodland glades.

Estimating the regional population is difficult because the West Midlands is on the edge of prime Tree Pipit habitat, so national densities will almost certainly be inapplicable. Unfortunately the *tetrad atlases* do not help either, as so far these show hardly any breeding attempts. As a best estimate, the current population is probably between 1,000-1,500 pairs and possibly towards the lower end of this range. The estimate in *BWM* was 1,500-1,800 pairs.

This unobtrusive species often slips away unnoticed on its autumn migration south during August and September and, apart from a movement of 200 in the Sherbrook Valley on September 7th 1979, the maximum count in the current period was a mere eight, at Sandwell Valley in 1990. Sixty-years of data show an average date for last birds of September 21st, with the latest ever at Wormleighton on October 16th 2001.

Sadly our only ringing record is for an adult ringed at Kinver Edge on June 23rd 1989 and killed by a cat the very next day only five kilometres away at Wollaston.

Meadow Pipit *Anthus pratensis*

Common resident, though local in lowland districts. Widespread and common on passage, fairly common in winter.

In summer Meadow Pipits are most widespread and numerous across the northern moors, the limestone plateau of the Dales and hills such as the Malverns. A few can also be found at lower altitudes, where they nest on heaths, commons and rough grassland, especially around past industrial workings. Many pairs act as involuntary hosts to the Common Cuckoo. Most birds go south to Iberia for the winter, but some remain in the region, moving to lower ground where they may be joined by immigrants from northern Europe. Here they often form small flocks as they feed amongst rough grassland, derelict land, quarries and around reservoir margins. Occasionally birds forage among damp pastures or on newly drilled fields.

During the *Winter Atlas* birds were recorded in 99% of 10-km squares, but they were most numerous in the Black Country and the Potteries, where there is plenty of rough grassland. The *Breeding Atlas* showed a more restricted distribution, with birds in 75% of squares, but at densities well below average everywhere except on the northern moors, where this is the commonest species. They were most widespread in Staffordshire, but were absent from large parts of Arden and the Severn and Avon Vales, where drainage and the loss of permanent pastures contributed to their withdrawal.

Estimating numbers is complex because of the differences between upland and lowland densities and there is insufficient information to compile a regional population index. The combined results from two CBC plots in the Dales suggest around one pair per km^2, while another survey of a moorland estate (Yalden 1979) indicated a density of 2.1 pairs per km^2, when scaled down in accordance with the 1979-2002 change in the CBC/BBS index. Overall it appears that numbers have fallen, but with little consistent monitoring it is hard to know by how much. On the Malverns, for instance 40-80 pairs were recorded in the late 1980s, but only partial counts have been made since, whilst the Clent Hills held 40 pairs in 1946 (*BWM*) and 20 in 1978, but, with bracken invading the grassland, numbers had fallen to two pairs by 2002. At Doxey Marshes, where numbers fell from 12 pairs in 1984 to just one or two in the 1990s, the decline was attributed to increased public pressure. On the other hand Lighthorne Quarry experienced a steady increase from two pairs in 1993 to 15 pairs in 2001. Taking account of all available information, the regional population, of which at least half is in north Staffordshire, is perhaps in the range 4,500-6,000 pairs (*cf.* 8,000-12,000 pairs estimated in *BWM*). Such a decline would accord with the trend suggested by the national CBC/BBS index that justifies its inclusion on the *Amber List* of Species of Conservation Concern (Gregory *et al.* 2002).

To many people, Meadow Pipits are better known as passage migrants, although numbers are perhaps smaller now than in years gone by. The spring movement has become progressively earlier and is now concentrated into March and early April, when small groups move northwards to their upland breeding territories. At this time the average flock size is just over 80 and groups up to 150 are not usual. The largest parties at this season during the current period were 350 at Draycote Water in March 31st 1996, 500 near Meerbrook on the same day in 1991 and 1,000 at Blithfield Reservoir on March 20th 1993. In comparison, the most recorded in *BWM* was a movement of 800 through Belvide Reservoir on April 4th 1958.

Small groups begin to drift away from the moors in late July, but the main passage through the lowlands occurs in September and October, when some significant numbers are recorded. Again *BWM* says parties up to 250 were regularly noted, with a maximum of 600 in October 1959. During the current period autumn flocks were generally larger than those in spring, with an average size of 100 and several up to 300. The only larger one, however, was 500 at Tittesworth Reservoir on September 26th 1993. Some heavy, concentrated movements have been noted in recent years, especially during the three days September 29th-October 1st 2000, when the daily movements through Westport Lake were 167 in three and a half hours, 141 in two hours and 122 respectively. The same passage was also evident in south Warwickshire, where there were corresponding counts of 200 flying south-westwards in an hour, 340 south-east in an hour and 150 south respectively. The latter area also experienced strong movements in 2001, with counts of 290, 265 and 315 moving south-westwards

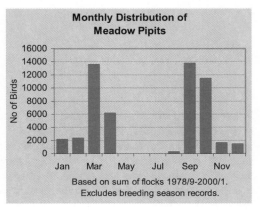

Monthly Distribution of Meadow Pipits

Based on sum of flocks 1978/9-2000/1.
Excludes breeding season records.

in one hour periods on October 3rd, 4th and 9th respectively. Despite the apparent decline in numbers, these passages compare favourably with those recorded in *BWM*.

Wintering flocks averaged around 50 birds, with the largest being 150 at Sandwell Valley in January 1985 and 200 at Blithfield Reservoir in December 1989. Roosts of 40 or more have been reported on five occasions, with the largest being 105 in heather on Gun Hill in September 1987 and 250-300 on the Malvern Hills in September 1996.

Red-throated Pipit   *Anthus cervinus*
Very rare vagrant. One record.

Rather characteristically, this bird was first identified by its distinctive call. It was then seen by a few observers during its brief stay.

Regional Record Number	County Record Number	Year	Locality, Date and Notes
1	Warks 1	1994	Near Lawford Heath tip: October 22nd-23rd. *BB 88:530*

Red-throated Pipits breed in Arctic Fennoscandia and Russia and winter mainly in sub-Saharan Africa. They are annual, if scarce, visitors to Britain, principally to eastern and southern coastal counties. Inland occurrences are rare, but October is a typical month for birds to appear (Dymond *et al.* 1989).

Rock Pipit   *Anthus petrosus*
Uncommon passage migrant and rare winter visitor.

Although it is a common bird in Britain, the Rock Pipit is almost exclusively coastal and inland occurrences are fairly unusual. Small, but noticeable passages through the region are nevertheless noted each autumn and, to a lesser extent, in spring. At such times birds pause to feed around the margins of reservoirs, gravel pits or other wetlands and one or two individuals occasionally over-winter. Until 1985 Rock and Water Pipits were considered to be races of the same species.

British birds are generally sedentary, but do disperse locally, often along river valleys. The nearest breeding areas to this region are the North Wales coast, the Severn estuary and the East Coast north of the Humber estuary and it seems likely that many of those reaching here do so along the Severn and Trent. The first regional record came in 1948, after which appearances became annual and numbers increased to between 13 and 30 individuals a year from 1970 (*BWM*). Occurrences continued at much the same level through most of the 1980s, with an average of 21 each winter. Since then the average has increased to 33 and 1995/6 was the best winter with 53 individuals. Recently, however, there has been a downturn.

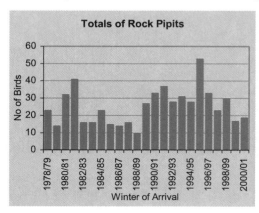

The autumn dispersal from breeding areas is clearly shown by the heavy concentration during September-November, with 77% of birds occurring at this time including 58% in October alone. In contrast the spring passage is quite small, with a peak in March.

During the current period most birds were seen in Staffordshire (40%), followed by Warwickshire (29%), Worcestershire (18%) and the West Midlands (13%). Sites holding at least 5% of birds were Draycote Water (12%), Blithfield Reservoir (10%), Belvide Reservoir (8%), Chasewater (6%) and Sandwell Valley and Westport Lake (5% each). Up to four together have been seen a number of times, Draycote has attracted five birds on four occasions, Belvide six in 1989 and Blithfield eight in 1981. Some 30 birds were recorded during the December-February period, but the only instances of complete over-wintering came

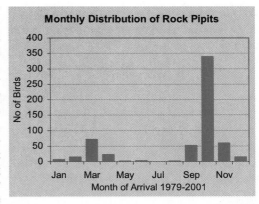

from Blithfield Reservoir in four consecutive seasons from 1987/8-1990/1, with the longest stay being from October 8th 1989 to March 23rd 1990. Unseasonable records include one in May, two in June and one in August.

Scandinavian Rock Pipit   *Anthus petrosus littoralis*
Rare passage migrant.

As well as the resident British race *A. p. petrosus*, birds showing the characteristics of the migratory Fennoscandia race *A. p. littoralis* have also been reported, especially during spring.

Regional Record Number	County Record Number		Year	Locality, Date and Notes
1	Staffs	1	1975	Chasewater: April 9th.
2	Staffs	2	1977	Belvide Reservoir: March 13th.
3	Staffs	3	1987	Chasewater: March 13th-26th.
4	W Mid	1	1987	Sandwell Valley: two, April 3rd-5th, at Forge Mill Pool.
5	Staffs	4	1990	Chasewater: March 20th.
6	Staffs	5	1990	Crossplains: October 12th.
7	Worcs	1	1993	Bittell Reservoir: October 21st.
8	Worcs	2	1993	Upton Warren: November 8th.
9	Warks	1	1994	Draycote Water: March 27th.
10	W Mid	2	1996	Sandwell Valley: March 19th-26th.
11	Staffs	6	1996	Belvide Reservoir: two, March 26th.
12	Worcs	3	1997	Holt: March 8th.
13	Warks	2	1998	Coton: March 14th.
14	Staffs	7	1998	Chasewater: March 14th.
15	Warks	3	1999	Draycote Water: March 24th.

Of the fifteen records, twelve were in spring, between March 8th and April 9th, and three in autumn, between October 12th and November 8th. Virtually all were seen around wetlands, especially reservoirs, with Chasewater particularly favoured.

Water Pipit   *Anthus spinoletta*
Scarce passage migrant and winter visitor.

Water and Rock Pipits used to be regarded as races of a single species and the BOU only considered them to be separate species as recently as 1985. The Water Pipit breeds in the mountains of mainland Europe, but descends to lower ground, usually in damp situations, during the winter. Many records refer to passage birds in spring and autumn. Most are seen around reservoirs, gravel pits and other aquatic habitats, with some wintering at a few select localities.

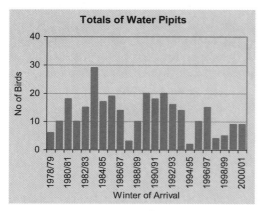

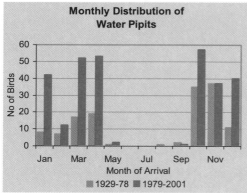

The first regional sighting in 1919 was then followed by a series of records during the 1920s-1940s, mainly from Bittell, Bartley and Belvide Reservoirs, including several from the late Horace Alexander. *BWM* mentions 123 birds between 1934-78, of which 88 came during 1968/9-1978/9. Numbers continued to grow in the early 1980s, but then wavered before declining again in the late 1990s. In all, 1979-2001 produced almost 300 birds, or around thirteen a year. Interestingly the seasonal pattern has shifted, with 26% of birds occurring in spring (March-April) and 52% in autumn (October-November) during 1929-78, whereas 35% came in spring and only 32% in autumn during the current period.

Water Pipits visit a few favoured sites most winters, but after a few years they sometimes desert them for no apparent reason. *BWM* documented 33 records from Bittell Reservoir and 14 from Chasewater, but during the current period there were none from Bittell and only six from Chasewater. Instead, Wilden was the most frequented site with 35 records between 1979-95, but birds ceased to visit here after the sugar beet factory closed. The Middle Tame Valley then became the place to see this species, with 30 records from Coton during 1981-95 and 23 from the Dosthill area during 1984-2001. Other favoured sites, with their number of records, have included Upton Warren (16), Ladywalk (12), Belvide Reservoir (11) and Blithfield Reservoir and Kingsbury Water Park (eight each). The species' site fidelity has strongly influenced the geographical spread, with 42% of birds in Warwickshire (including the Dosthill complex) and 38% in Worcestershire, whereas Staffordshire attracted only 18% and the West Midlands just 3%. Most records are of lone birds, but two have been seen together on several occasions, up to five were in the Dosthill area during the 1996/7 winter, seven were at Coton in 1982 and Wilden held a record 12 in February and March 1984.

Yellow Wagtail   *Motacilla flava*
Fairly common, but declining, summer resident and passage migrant.

Traditionally Yellow Wagtails are associated with damp, cattle grazed, tussocky pastures and marshy wetlands along river valleys. With land drainage and fewer dairy herds in the fields, however, many have adapted to nesting in cereals, beans and oilseed rape.

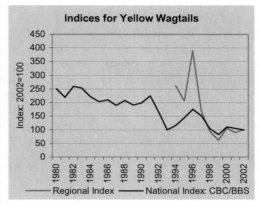

This is one of the earlier summer residents to return from wintering in sub-Saharan Africa, with the first brilliant yellow males often arriving in late March. The earliest ever was at Cofton on March 20th 1966, whilst the average date for first birds over 63 years was April 4th. During 1992-2001, however, the average advanced to March 31st. The main spring passage then occurs in the second half of April and in May. When they first arrive birds often form feeding flocks, with groups up to 50 or so frequently noted around reservoirs, gravel pits and sewage works. Even counts of a 100 or more were by no means unusual throughout the 1980s, but numbers have slumped since and the most reported in recent years were 75 in 1997 and 90 in 1998, both at Draycote Water in April. The largest spring flock during 1979-2001 was 200 at Draycote Water on April 28th 1985, which equalled the maximum mentioned in *BWM*, but the only report of a spring roost was 60 at Shustoke in May 1996.

Birds were found in 87% of 10-km squares during the *Breeding Atlas*, with the highest densities in Feldon and the lower Trent and Tame valley areas. Abundance levels elsewhere were below the national average, however, as this species tends to be retreating south-eastwards. It relies heavily on flies and spiders for food and has undoubtedly suffered from the drainage of riverside meadows, fewer cattle, the use of insecticides and the conversion of grasslands to arable cultivation. It also favours spring-sown cereals, but finds that autumn sowing produces too dense a crop for nesting (Gribble 2000).

The national CBC/BBS index shows a decline of about 60% between 1980-2002, much of it during the 1990s, and the species is now on the *Amber List* of Birds of Conservation Concern (Gregory *et al.* 2002). Regionally the data sample is too small to indicate a long-term trend, but the regional BBS has closely followed the national index since 1997, though before then it was highly erratic. Some measure of the local decline can be gleaned from the average

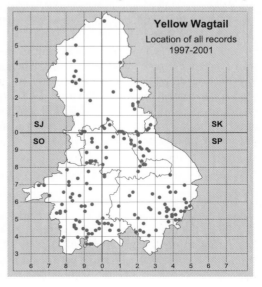

size of reported flocks, which fell by 80% during the current period, with a dramatic drop of 60% between 1991 and 1993 (*cf.* National CBC/BBS index on chart). Since then numbers have failed to recover and the population is now probably towards the lower end of the range 400-1,000 territories compared with 1,500-2,000 pairs estimated in *BWM*. The adjacent map shows the location of all records during 1997-2001, including passage birds.

In 1982 the BTO's Waders of Wet Meadows survey located 70 pairs in Staffordshire, but recent casual counts show that only a fraction of these remain. As with many farmland species, the Feldon area of south-east Warwickshire seems to have become the Yellow Wagtail's regional stronghold, but even here numbers have fallen markedly. For instance, breeding pairs were found in at least sixteen

349

contiguous parishes in 1996, with 28 pairs in 941 ha at Fenny Compton. Of these, 20 pairs nested in field beans and the remainder in wheat and set-aside. The same area held 26 pairs the following year, but only 15 pairs in 1998 and 11-15 subsequently, whilst there were five pairs in a nearby km^2 between Gaydon and Upper Kingston in 1998.

BWM remarked upon birds nesting in growing crops, including, in order of preference, potatoes, beans and oilseed rape. There have since been further reports of breeding in fields of rape, beans and potatoes as well as in maize and the usual cereal crops, whilst some were seen feeding in sugar beet. An instance of birds venturing into strange habitats came from the heart of Birmingham, where two were at the old Snow Hill station in September 1983.

During the current period 46% of birds were recorded in spring and only 51% in autumn, when the population should be enlarged by a high proportion of juvenile birds. This suggests that the Yellow Wagtail is having poor breeding success. Indeed, post-breeding numbers were reported as being particularly low in 1991, birds were exceptionally scarce in the following spring and, after a short revival, numbers have remained very low since—again reflecting the national pattern shown on the chart.

Evening roosts in reeds and other tall emergent vegetation were once a feature of late August and September and an estimated 1,000 gathered at Doxey Marshes in 1970 and 1972 (*BWM*). Although such roosts continued to be reported during the early years of the current period, numbers were typically no higher than 50 or 60, except for 200 at Grimley in 1981 and the same number at Doxey Marshes in September 1983. The only report of any roost since the mid-1980s was 50 near Wormleighton Reservoir in September 1996. Flocks, too, are now much diminished in size. There were 220 at Ladywalk on September 16th 1979 (*cf.* a maximum of 250 mentioned in *BWM*), but the last three-figure flock was 120 at Blithfield Reservoir in September 1995 and now even groups of 20-30 have become noteworthy. Most birds leave between mid-August and the end of September and the heaviest recorded passage was 1,000 in an hour moving SW or SSE over Wilnecote on August 22nd 1950 (*BWM*). In recent years more than fifty have been unusual. Over 63 years the average departure date of last birds was October 12th, but a few have lingered into early November, with the latest ever on the 23rd, at Brandon Marsh in 1986.

Ringing shows our birds have a marked tendency to move initially to the southern counties on their way to Africa, with recoveries from Devon, Dorset, Wiltshire and Hampshire, often within a few days of having being ringed here in July, August and September. Other recoveries show movements into France and Portugal, whilst the longest recorded movement was one of 2,792 km, made by an adult female that was ringed at Stubbers Green in July 1981 and shot in Morocco in February 1983.

Our British Yellow Wagtails belong to the race *M. f. flavissima*, but a number of other races also occur here, most as vagrants. The geographical ranges of these races often overlap, however, leading to racial hybrids and their identification is further complicated by the normal variations in plumage and by the presence of unusually pale birds (*BWP*). Often only breeding males are separable in the field (*BWP*) and even then extreme caution is needed as there is much variation in head patterns and colour. Records of birds showing the characteristics of other races are set out below.

Blue-headed Wagtail   *Motacilla flava flava*
Rare passage migrant, mainly in spring.

The commonest of the other races to occur is the Blue-headed Wagtail, *M. f. flava*, which breeds on the near Continent and occurs regularly in small numbers, usually as an overshooting spring migrant. Apart from 1975 and 1994, this race has been recorded annually in the region since 1963, with generally between one and six each year except for 1996, when there may have been as many as 20 individuals (allowing for some duplication in records), and

1997, when eight were reported. Seventy percent of reported birds were males, with the
remainder generally described by experienced
observers as just 'female types'. Over a hundred individuals were recorded during the current period, of which 95% occurred in spring,
with the vast majority in late April or early
May. Two mixed pairings were of interest. At
Needwood Airfield in 1986 one of five pairs
comprised a male Yellow Wagtail (*flavissima*)
and a female Blue-headed Wagtail (*flava*),
while at nearby Blithfield Reservoir in 1990 a
male *flava* paired with a female *flavissima* and
was seen carrying food. The only late summer
and autumn reports involved an adult male at
Fenny Compton on August 31st 1999, a juvenile at Holt from August 28th-29th 2000 and
one of unspecified age and sex at Draycote
Water on September 13th and 21st 1988.

As might be expected of a southern migrant, most occurred in Worcestershire (40%)
and Warwickshire (32%), with 21% in Staffordshire and 7% in the West Midlands. The
most productive localities, in descending order, were Bredon's Hardwick, Draycote Water, Blithfield Reservoir, Upton Warren and
Grimley.

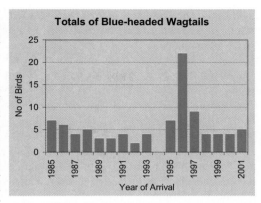

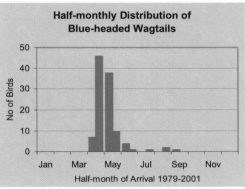

Spanish Wagtail   *Motacilla flava iberiae*
Very rare vagrant. Three records.

Birds showing characteristics of the Iberian race were recorded as follows:

Regional Record Number	County Record Number		Year	Locality, Date and Notes
1	Worcs	1	1981	Wilden: male, June 11th to July 8th.
2	Worcs	2	1982	Wilden: male, May 9th-28th.
3	Staffs	1	1993	Tittesworth Reservoir: male, May 16th.

Grey-headed Wagtail   *Motacilla flava thunbergi*
Very rare vagrant. One record.

A very dark-headed bird was eventually determined to have been of this race, which breeds
from Fennoscandia eastwards into Siberia.

Regional Record Number	County Record Number		Year	Locality, Date and Notes
1	W Mid	1	1996	Sandwell Valley: male, April 18th-19th.

Citrine Wagtail *Motacilla citreola*
Very rare vagrant. One record.

This bird was one of three to be reported in Britain during May 1997.

Regional Record Number	County Record Number	Year	Locality, Date and Notes
1	Warks 1	1997	Brandon Marsh: female, May 18th. *BB 92:588*

The Citrine Wagtail expanded its breeding range westwards from central Asia into Belarus and the Baltic countries during the twentieth century (Rogers *et al.* 2004). As it did so, British records increased, but it nevertheless remains very rare inland. Birds winter in the Indian sub-continent and south-east Asia.

Grey Wagtail *Motacilla cinerea*
Fairly common resident, passage migrant and winter visitor.

This is very much the wagtail of fast-flowing, upland streams and rivers, although it can also be found around weirs on more sluggish watercourses and at locks along the canals, even well within urban areas. On passage and in winter it is more widespread, when it also visits sewage and water treatment works, reservoirs and even gardens.

The *Winter Atlas* showed birds to be present in 95% of 10-km squares, whilst the *Breeding Atlas* showed a more restricted range embracing just 81%. Abundance was highest along the streams and rivers of the Dales and Moors and along the River Teme, but birds were absent during the breeding season from the Dunsmore area, much of Arden and the lower reaches of the main rivers. Recently, however, it has been spreading more into lowland situations.

In Staffordshire, the limestone dales are the stronghold, but there are good populations along the gritstone streams of the moors and also on the Churnet and its tributaries. In Worcestershire, birds are most numerous west of the Severn, especially along tributaries such as the Teme and the Dowles and Leigh Brooks, but they also occur along the Stour and its tributaries. The more sluggish Warwickshire rivers are less suited to its needs, but a few pairs inhabit the headwaters of the Alne, Arrow and Stour and several pairs nest on the flights of canal locks that drop down from the Midland Plateau into the Avon Valley. Overall numbers are increasing in the county and it probably now breeds in most 10-km squares (J. J. Bowley *pers. comm.*). Within the West Midlands county breeding has been confirmed in 40% of tetrads (K. Clements *pers. comm.*), including some heavily urbanised situations. Singing birds were heard at the old Snow Hill station, Birmingham, in 1985 and in Coventry city centre in 1991, while a pair bred in Stourbridge town centre in 1989 and two pairs did so in central Birmingham in 1993. Breeding also occurs regularly along the many canals in the county.

In prime habitat, 15 were counted along 11 km of the River Dove in April 1976, 25 birds were found along 57 km of the River Teme during August and September 1979 (*BWM*) and 10 pairs were found along approximately 3 km of the Churnet valley between Froghall

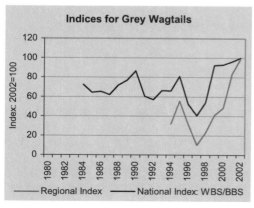

Indices for Grey Wagtails

and Consallforge in 1986. The population is hard to assess, as birds are thinly spread along waterways that are often inaccessible. Moreover counts are understandably related to the length of watercourse rather than to area, but data on the total lengths of suitable rivers, streams and canals is not available. Numbers fluctuate markedly, but the WBS index showed a long-term decline of 41% during 1975-99, which was sufficient to place the species on the *Amber Alert List* (Gregory *et al.* 2002). However, much of that decline occurred during 1975-82, a period that included two particularly hard winters in 1979 and 1982. Grey Wagtails are especially vulnerable in cold weather and it is noticeable that the BBS dropped dramatically after the cold, snowy spells of 1995/6 and 1996/7. Since then it has recovered rapidly with the run of milder winters. Overall, the national index rose by almost 40% between 1984 and 2002 and this would suggest a regional population towards the lower end of the range 500-1,000 pairs (*cf.* 400-600 pairs suggested in *BWM*).

The two most regularly monitored stretches of water are Coombes Valley and the Dowles Brook through the Wyre Forest, where the populations have had contrasting fortunes. Each began with four pairs after the hard winter in 1982, but numbers had halved by 1988 and 1989 respectively and they remained at that level until 1994. Since then there has been no change at Coombes Valley, but numbers along the Dowles Brook have gradually increased to around half-a-dozen pairs.

Small movements can sometimes be seen in autumn, when birds disperse more widely as they move from higher to lower ground for the winter. For instance, a total of 40 were observed flying generally southwards over Wyken Slough between September 1st and November 8th 1993 and 36 did likewise between July 17th and November 1st 1994, mainly during late September and October. The peak movements in these two years involved just seven and six birds. An excellent example of a bird moving south for the winter is given by one ringed as a nestling in the Grampian region of Scotland in May 1979 and found 497 km away, in Sutton Park in the following September. Birds also gather outside the breeding season to roost, with the most noted being eight at Belvide Reservoir in October 1989 and 15 in recesses in the dam at Bittell Reservoir on August 19th 1995.

This species is the least gregarious of the wagtails and even outside the breeding season birds are mostly solitary, with some establishing winter territories. However, loose groups of six or seven, perhaps family parties, are sometimes noted in autumn, with the most during the current period being eight at Smestow Valley, Wolverhampton, on September 26th 1993. A good feeding area can draw more birds and a record 17 gathered at Whittington Sewage Farm in December 1971 (*BWM*). At one time birds were only rarely reported visiting garden ponds, usually in hard weather, but such behaviour has become more frequent and is now no longer confined to hard weather. They are also now more regular in town and city centres, where they frequent shopping centres and are sometimes seen attacking their own reflections in the wing mirrors of parked cars.

Pied Wagtail *Motacilla alba*
Very common resident, summer resident, passage migrant and winter visitor.

The Pied Wagtail occurs in a wide range of habitats, both urban and rural, but tends to prefer open country and is often found near water. Mixed farming suits it best and intensively farmed, arable areas are avoided. A confiding bird, it often nests in buildings, on machinery or in drystone walls and forages for insects on roads, roofs and around pedestrian shopping precincts in town and city centres. In winter loose flocks feed on playing fields and lawns, or around reservoirs and sewage or water treatment filter-beds. Birds also roost communally in winter, often using factory buildings or trees near street lights for warmth. The regional population is largely sedentary, but upland birds do move down to lower ground for the winter and

in extremely severe weather some may emigrate to the Continent. More northerly populations also migrate, leading to noticeable spring and autumn passages.

The species is widespread and was recorded in every 10-km square during both *Atlas* surveys, with an average abundance during the breeding season, but a slightly above average one in winter. Cold weather invariably takes its toll and the aftermath of the severe winter of 1981/2 is clearly evident in the indices. The small sample on which the regional index is based makes it very variable, but, without the benefit of an ameliorating maritime influence, the lower night-time temperatures experienced here do seem to deplete numbers, as shown by the cold snaps in 1993/4 and 1996/7. Nationally the CBC/BBS increased by around 25% from 1980-2002. Locally there is little information on densities, but the current population is probably in the range 10,000-17,000 pairs compared with an estimated 6,000-12,000 pairs in *BWM*.

Passage is not always evident, but 57 at Draycote Water on March 15th 1987 were probably moving through, while later in the year an extraordinary 529 at Sheepwash Urban Park during heavy rain on October 27th almost certainly included many passage birds.

Recoveries of birds ringed in the region during October show southerly movements, with birds moving to Somerset and France by the following January. Similarly, a juvenile female ringed in Aberdeen in August 1982 had moved 494 km south into the West Midlands by the following October. Recoveries also show birds ringed in Worcestershire in October moving over 500 km north in the following year to their breeding grounds in Aberdeen and the Highland region of Scotland. *BWM* mentioned locally bred birds being recovered in the region and in Portugal (one), which points to some being residents and others summer visitors.

In winter, birds roost communally in a variety of safe, warm situations ranging from reedbeds at Brandon Marsh, Doxey Marshes, Ford Green and Upton Warren to trees under street lights in Birmingham city centre and buildings such as the Manders Shopping Centre and Goodyear tyre factory in Wolverhampton. Others have roosted in tall heather, in shrubbery on traffic islands, in warehouses and around supermarkets, for instance at Sainsbury's in Leamington where there were 500 in October 2000. Among the more interesting examples were 200 roosting in greenhouses at Holt in 1980, up to 300 roosting in an enclosed courtyard warmed by extractor fans at the Shire Hall, Warwick, in 1983 and 1984 and around 400 at Stoke-on-Trent railway station in October 1994. The largest roosts during the current period were 1,000

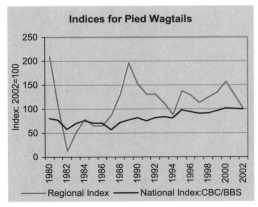

Indices for Pied Wagtails

Index: 2002=100

— Regional Index   —— National Index:CBC/BBS

in reedmace at Grimley in September and October 1982, 1,000 in ornamental trees by Wolverhampton Civic Centre in 1997, 1,200 in Worcester city centre in 1997, with 1,000 there again in 2001, and a record 2,200 in willows alongside the main A500 road in Stoke-on-Trent on October 17th 1993.

Additionally, loose gatherings up to 100 strong can be found at good feeding sites, with larger parties of 200 by no means unusual. The largest counts during the current period were 400 at Tividale in October 1985 and at Oldington the next month and 700 at Dunstall Park in February 1992 and January 1993. As with Grey Wagtails, there have also been several reports of birds attacking their own images in the wing-mirrors of vehicles, including 10 that did so on a van parked at the Strensham services on the M5 in 1983.

Our native Pied Wagtail belongs to the race *M. a. yarrellii*, but the continental White Wagtail of the nominate race *M. a. alba* is also a regular, if uncommon, visitor to the region.

White Wagtail   *Motacilla alba alba*
Uncommon passage migrant, mainly in spring.

White Wagtails appear annually on passage in the region, often in company with Yellow Wagtails. Spring is the usual time for them to visit our reservoirs, gravel pits and other wetlands and during the current period an overwhelming 98% of birds were reported at this season—an identical percentage to that for 1929-78 (*BWM*). Passage mainly takes place between late March and early May and during the current period the extreme dates were March 10th at Whittington SF in 1981 and June 20th at Sandwell Valley in 1987. *BWM*, however, quotes records on March 6th 1966 and June 21st 1975. Peak movement occurs in the second half of April, when 60% of birds pass through. Annual totals increased steadily from 20-30 a year during the 1970s to 33 in 1979 and then much more rapidly through the 1980s to a maximum of 152 in 1989. After this they fell to around 60 a year during the first half of the 1990s, since when they have varied between 50-125 a year. Parties up to 20 have been reported several times, but the two largest were 31 at Wasperton on April 23rd 1989 and a 'fall' of 36 at Draycote Water that were grounded by heavy rain on April 25th 1997.

Surprisingly few are reported in autumn, perhaps because at that time they are less easily separated from juvenile Pied Wagtails. In fact only 42 birds were reported at this time and these included a party of 12 adults and first-winter birds at Draycote Water on September 10th 1995—the only time that more than two have been seen together at this season. Interestingly, *BWM* mentions two winter records—at Belvide Reservoir on January 7th 1935 and Leamington Spa in 1975—and a female, paired to a male Pied Wagtail, at a nest in Malvern in 1973.

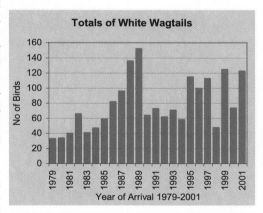

The distribution between the counties, given their respective sizes, was fairly even during the current period, with 33% in Staffordshire, 31% in Warwickshire, 23% in Worcestershire and 13% in the West Midlands. With records from over 120 localities, it is apparent that White Wagtails might turn up almost anywhere, although they generally have a clear affinity with wetlands. The sites that produced most records during the current period, in descending order, were Upton Warren, Draycote Water, Blithfield Reservoir, Belvide Reservoir and Sandwell Valley. It could, however, be that these are the places most visited by birdwatchers and not necessarily because they are more attractive to the birds than smaller, less visited areas.

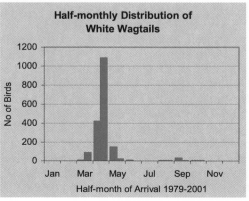

Waxwing   (Bohemian Waxwing)   *Bombycilla garrulus*
Erratic and usually rare winter visitor, but occasionally numerous in invasion years.

Waxwings are regular winter migrants to western Europe from their breeding grounds in Fennoscandia and Siberia and some reach Britain every year. Their first landfall is usually in the north or east, where they feed avidly on berries, especially those of *Sorbus spp.* such as rowan. They are nomadic and periodically irrupt in such huge numbers that trees and shrubs are quickly stripped, forcing them to move further south and west in search of new food sources. It is in such years that most are recorded in this region. As well as rowan berries, hips, haws and mistletoe are also taken, as are the berries of ornamental trees and shrubs. Indeed, most birds these days are seen feeding on exotic trees and shrubs planted in urban situations such as roadside verges, supermarket car parks, the surrounds of public buildings and private gardens.

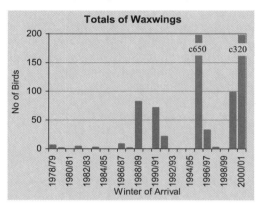

The chart shows quite clearly how numbers vary from winter to winter, with none at all in nine winters, whilst around 650 were reported in 1995/6 and 320 in 2000/1. After two good winters, there were none in 2001/2. An even bigger invasion occurred in 1965/6, when up to 750 were recorded   (*BWM*). The risk of double counting cannot be eliminated during these major influxes, however, as flocks are very mobile.

The major invasions also strongly influence the monthly distribution of arrivals. That of 1965/6 began very early, with the first birds on November 8th, and peaked in December when flocks up to 50 strong were seen. By that time birds were widespread and some stayed until April (*BWM*). In contrast, the first bird of the 1995/6 winter was not seen until January 18th and it was mid-February before the larger flocks formed, with 129 at Brereton on the 18th rising to a regional record of 150 in early March. Birds also stayed late, with over 50 still present at Willenhall in mid-April. In 2000/1 the first birds appeared in late December, but it was February and March when the largest numbers were recorded, including a flock of 89 at Newcastle College on March 24th.

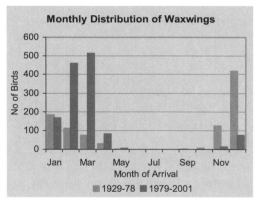

The earliest and latest birds are those mentioned in *BWM,* at Moseley on September 22nd 1971 and Selly Oak on May 14th 1979 respectively, but the earliest during the current period was at Whittington on November 3rd 1988, while the latest since that in 1979 was at Kingsbury Water Park on May 11th 2001. Although most are seen for just one or two days, if their food supply subsists they may stay for some considerable time, with one remaining in the Sutton Coldfield area for three months in 1992, from January 21st to April 16th.

As mentioned earlier, birds tend to move southwards through the country and to have a penchant for urban areas. Both are reflected in the county distribution for the current period, which shows 57% of birds in Staffordshire and 31% in the West Midlands county, but only 8% and 4% respectively in Warwickshire and Worcestershire. Birds also seem to be attracted to specific areas, with several records from the Newcastle-under-Lyme district and the settlements around the edge of Cannock Chase, such as Brereton, Bridgtown, Rugeley and Staf-ford—the latter perhaps because birds are initially attracted to the Chase. In the West Mid-lands, they quite often appear in the Monkspath and Shirley areas. The pattern of birds return-ing to traditional areas, even after an absence of several years, maybe suggests that the older ones can remember where to find the best sources of food.

Dipper   *Cinclus cinclus*
Frequent resident in north Staffordshire and north-west Worcestershire. Rare else-where.

A bobbing Dipper, perched midstream on a boulder, typifies an upland stream. Truly an aquatic bird, it is best known for its fascinating habit of swimming and walking under water to feed. In this region, it is confined to the swift, boulder strewn streams and rivers of north Staf-fordshire and north-west Worcestershire. There it feeds in gravelly shallows and nests in over-hanging banks or beneath bridges, culverts or weirs. Food consists mainly of mayfly nymphs and caddis fly larvae during the breeding season, but at other times fish such as bullheads are taken more often (Ormerod and Tyler 1986, 1987). Provided there is a way into the water, Dippers can even feed under ice, so severe winters affect them less than they do Common Kingfishers and Grey Wagtails.

Numbers are highest along the rivers and streams flowing over base-rich rocks, such as those of the Dales, the Teme catchment and some tributaries of the Severn, notably the Dow-les Brook. These watercourses are richer in invertebrate and fish life than those of the acidic gritstone moors, although the Dane catchment does hold reasonable numbers as it escaped the widespread afforestation that contributed to acidification elsewhere. At times of drought, or when rivers are in spate, birds will move up or down stream to find suitable feeding areas, but otherwise they are highly territorial, even in winter. Indeed, they nest very early and on low-land rivers, such as the Teme, begin to sing and pair in January if the weather is mild, although those at higher altitudes or on acidic streams tend to breed later.

During fieldwork for the *Winter Atlas* they were recorded in 23% of 10-km squares, whilst the *Breeding Atlas* revealed a similar distribution with birds in 25% of squares. Nationally, the WBS shows an increase during the early 1980s followed by a decline later in the decade, since when numbers have been more or less stable. Overall, numbers appear to have changed little during 1980-2002, either nationally or regionally, and the current population is probably still the same as that estimated in *BWM*, namely 100-150 pairs.

A survey in Worcestershire in 1982 found 47 pairs, mainly in the Severn and Teme catch-ments, whilst 27 nests were found along the tributaries of the Severn, Teme and Rea in 1984. The county's best monitored population is that along the Dowles Brook in the Wyre Forest, where numbers varied from two to five pairs during the current period. Elsewhere, six to eight pairs were recently seen along the River Rea, but casual reports from the Teme reveal no more than three pairs. A post-breeding survey along 57 km of this river in 1979, however, produced 29 birds, which would suggest around half-a-dozen pairs. With limited feeding shallows along the Teme, tributary streams are important components of most territories, which may lead to under-recording as many of them are inaccessible. Birds have also been noted fairly regularly in the headwaters of the Stour and its tributaries, with several records from Wombourne and Sling Pool and possible breeding at the latter site in 1979. They have even penetrated into and through the Black Country, with possible breeding at Lutley Gutter in 1985 and confirmed nesting within the West Midlands County in 1986 and 1997 at least. Breeding along the Leigh Brook was fairly regular too, until the stream was polluted by run off from agricultural fertilis-ers, but a recent record from The Knapp in 1997 gives hope of a return.

Staffordshire has been less well monitored, but there are usually one to three pairs at

Coombes Valley and numbers along the Churnet Valley as a whole are good. Again tributary streams form an integral part of many territories, with birds travelling as far upstream as Stanley Pool and Deep Hayes Country Park. They are also regularly seen at Tittesworth Reservoir. Casual counts consistently show high populations along the Dales rivers, especially the Dove above its confluence with the Churnet. Seven, including four in song, were noted along a 5 km stretch between Milldale and Dovedale in January 1983, with four to six territories along the same stretch in 1995. Good numbers also occur along the Manifold, but surprisingly few are reported from the Hamps. On the moors, the Dane and its tributaries provide a number of consistently used nest sites, particularly at Bearda, Danebridge, Three Shires Head and along the Black Brook. Occasional records from Biddulph, Greenway Bank CP and Knypersley Reservoir hint at a small, isolated population along the headwaters of the Trent as well.

The region is on the periphery of the Dipper's range, however, and birds have withdrawn from some sub-optimal areas. At least one pair used to breed in the headwaters of the Warwickshire Stour until 1979, but the last record from here was a single bird near the regular Burmington nest site in 1981. A small population existed just over the border in Oxfordshire at that time, but it too is apparently now extinct (Hay *et al.* 2002). Likewise, the *Breeding Atlas* included a record from the Warwickshire–Worcestershire border, but there have been no subsequent reports from the Alne or Arrow catchments, where breeding had been recorded in the past. However, one was found 'miles from any stream' on a road leading to Bittell Reservoir on July 7th 1997. This and two other July records, at Calf Heath and Kineton, suggest that juvenile dispersal might occur around this time. Otherwise, away from the regular breeding areas, birds were recorded at Cannock Chase, the Potteries, Stafford, Stone and Weston Park in Staffordshire; Baginton and Stoneleigh in Warwickshire; Sandwell Valley in the West Midlands; and Bredon Hill and Upton Warren in Worcestershire.

Black-bellied Dipper   *Cinclus cinclus cinclus*
Very rare vagrant. Two records.

British Dippers belong to the race *C. c. gularis* and are sedentary, but there have been two records of the migratory nominate race from Scandinavia.

Regional Record Number	County Record Number	Year	Locality, Date and Notes
1	Warks 1	1993	Weddington: mid-November to March 26th 1994.
2	Warks 2	1996	Near Shustoke Reservoir: October 6th, on River Bourne

Wren   *Troglodytes troglodytes*
Abundant resident.

The diminutive Wren is generally widespread and plentiful throughout the region, but it suffers greatly during cold weather when numbers plummet. Despite its abundance, it might easily be overlooked were it not for its loud song, since it forages unobtrusively amongst dense undergrowth. Birds are very adaptable, occurring in almost every habitat with scrubby vegetation, although densities are lower on the moors and in the towns and cities. They prefer broadleaved and mixed woodland with a dense shrub layer, but also occur widely in rank vegetation alongside watercourses. Hedgerows, however, appear to be a secondary habitat. Calls and song can be heard throughout the year, as birds defend territories even in winter, although they do come together at this season to roost communally.

The *Winter* and *Breeding Atlases* both show that birds were present in every 10-km square, but at lower densities on the moors and in the arable intensive areas of the Lichfield district, the Feldon and the lower Severn and Avon valleys. The BBS data suggest that densities might be as much as 30% lower in Stafford-shire than in Worcestershire, which enjoys the ameliorating influence of the Gulf Stream and where numbers seem to recover more quickly.

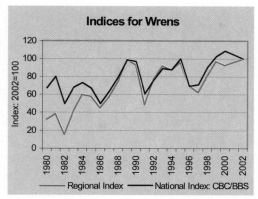

Winter temperatures are the biggest deter-minant of breeding numbers (Marchant *et al.* 1990) and the indices show how numbers drop dramatically after spells of very cold weather, such as those in 1982, 1986, 1991, 1996 and 1997. Since 1986 the similarity between the regional and national indices has been quite remarkable. Prior to then, the pattern was the same, but recovery from the severe winters of 1978/9 and 1981/2, together with the blizzards and ice storms of late April 1981, clearly took longer in this region than it did nationally. Mor-talities were presumably higher here because of the region's pronounced diurnal temperature range and the frequency of extremely cold nights. Temperatures during February 1982, for instance, dropped as low as –20°C. Between these set backs, numbers recovered well and they are now between one third and two thirds higher than in 1980.

Few sites have been consistently monitored for any length of time, but at Coombes Valley numbers doubled within a year from a low point of 38 pairs in 1986 and then rose to around 100 a year throughout the 1990s, with an exceptional 168 in 1995. Park Lime Pits also experi-enced an increase, from nine pairs in 1989 to 30 pairs by 2000, but at Shortwood Roughs num-bers fluctuated more or less in line with the indices shown in the chart. The most dramatic ex-ample of the effects of heavy frosts was at Fradley Wood, where the severe weather of early 1979 reduced the population from 46 pairs to three. Examples of density, in addition to those of the CBC, came from a variety of habitats, all of them in Warwickshire and the West Mid-lands county. These ranged from 9-30 pairs per km^2 with an average of 20 per km^2 on farm-land and 150 per km^2 in an area of mixed woodland. Taken together, data from the *Breeding Atlas* and the CBC/BBS index suggest a current population for the region of between 200,000-300,000 territories compared with the 130-230,000 pairs estimated in *BWM*. This suggests the Wren could be the region's most numerous bird.

Among the more unusual records, a pair bred in the centre of Birmingham, at Lancaster Circus, in 1991 and another nested amongst the fuchsias in a hanging basket despite regular watering. Few roosts have been reported, but six were in a House Martin's nest in 1987 and 30 roosted in a small patch of weeds at Strensham in 1989.

During the current period there have been two long distance movements suggesting south-erly movements to winter quarters. The first involved a juvenile, ringed in October 1981 at Sutton Coldfield, and found dead the following January 136 km away at Reading (Berkshire). The second was a movement of 175 km made by an adult ringed in Droitwich Spa in July 1985 and found dead the following February in Poole (Dorset).

Dunnock   (Hedge Accentor or Hedge Sparrow)   *Prunella modularis*
Abundant resident.

The Dunnock is an unobtrusive, but very widespread bird that is commonly found in rural and urban gardens, parks, hedgerows, heaths, scrub and woods. It nests in hedges and dense, low undergrowth and is one of the three main hosts of the Common Cuckoo, along with the

Meadow Pipit and the Reed Warbler. Outside the breeding season birds are largely shy and solitary, spending much of their time feeding on the ground under cover of thick vegetation or beneath garden bird tables. They are also very sedentary.

Birds were recorded in every 10-km square during both *Atlas* periods. Abundance levels were generally above average except where hedges are sparse, such as in the arable strongholds and the uplands of north Staffordshire where they are replaced by drystone walls.

The species has an unusually complex social structure, with males and females holding independent territories. Those of the males are generally the larger and hence overlap those of two or more females, but they may be occupied by two cock birds. As a result, every permutation of polygamy is practised, so estimating the population is fraught with difficulty.

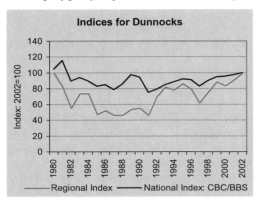

Nationally the CBC/BBS index declined between the mid-1970s and the late 1980s, but has since shown some recovery. Nevertheless, the Dunnock is included on the *Amber List* of Species of Conservation Concern (Gregory *et al*. 2002). Regionally the decline of the early 1980s was more severe as the population was heavily depleted by the bitterly cold winters of 1978/9 and 1981/2. The Dunnock took longer to recover from this set back than the Wren and it was the early 1990s before numbers really began to climb again. Overall, however, neither index shows any significant change between 1980 and 2002 and the current population is probably in the range of 60,000-90,000 territories. By way of comparison, the population estimate in *BWM* was 70,000-120,000 'pairs'.

Numbers at some sites have shown reasonable stability, with six or seven pairs consistently at Alvecote Pools during 1984-96 and generally 14-17 pairs at Old Hills Common from 1989-95, but just six in 1990. Coombes Valley, too, had a stable population of 10-12 pairs from 1989-99 apart from 17 in 1998. However, numbers here had earlier dropped from 19 pairs to just nine after the 1982 winter. Apart from the CBC plots, other examples of density came from farmland in Warwickshire and the West Midlands county, where the number of territories per km^2 ranged from 5-15 with an average of 12, which is slightly below the CBC level.

As remarked in *BWM*, this is a much ringed, but highly immobile species, with most movements being less than 5 km. The only distant recoveries were of a bird ringed at Alcester in December 1967 and recovered at Malton (North Yorkshire) the following April (*BWM*) and what was virtually an opposite movement of 174 km by one ringed at Hornsea (Humberside) in September 1987 and recovered in Tamworth the following February. Evidence of eruptive behaviour was observed at Wyken Slough on September 26th 1993, when a party of six circled high into the air before flying off to the west and similar behaviour was again seen here in the next two years. The *Migration Atlas* shows some movements between the East Coast and Scandinavia and two pale birds resembling continental forms were reported from Crossplains on November 10th 1990, so perhaps some of our Dunnocks are more mobile than we thought. There have been two records of birds acting as foster parents to Common Cuckoos.

Alpine Accentor *Prunella collaris*
Very rare vagrant. One record.

The record opposite is mentioned in *The Handbook* (Witherby *et al*. 1938), but neither Tomes (1904) nor Norris (1947) were able to obtain definite data (*BWM*).

Regional Record Number	County Record Number		Year	Locality, Date and Notes
1	Warks	1	Pre 1904	Near Ettington: date unknown, shot. *Witherby et al. 1938*

Alpine Accentors breed in the high mountain ranges from north-west Africa and Spain, through central Europe and the Balkans to Greece and into Asia. In winter most descend below the snowline and some disperse to lowland situations. However, with less than fifty records (Rogers *et al.* 2003), it is certainly a national rarity with very few inland occurrences.

Robin   *Erithacus rubecula*
Abundant resident.

The confiding habits of the perky Robin have endeared it to man and it has been voted our national bird. Although familiar in our gardens, town parks and hedgerows, it is primarily a bird of woods, especially those with plenty of shrubs and undergrowth. Our British Robins belong to the race *E. r. melophilus* and most are sedentary and highly territorial throughout the year.

Both *Atlases* show they occurred in every 10-km square, generally at well above average levels of abundance. However, Robins need the cover of trees and bushes and so are more sparsely distributed across the higher, more open country of north Staffordshire and parts of the Cotswolds, where drystone walls replace hedges. They may also be absent from some intensively developed inner city areas, although even there, open areas such as churchyards and cemeteries usually support a pair or two.

The CBC/BBS data show clearly how the Robin's population fluctuates from year-to-year, both nationally and regionally. Often the short-term declines correlate with colder winters, especially when these occur back-to-back as during 1980-82, 1990-92 and, to a lesser degree, 1995-97. Robins suffered greatly during the very severe weather of 1982, when overnight temperatures plummeted to –20°C, and it took several years for the population to recover. The BBS survey also shows that densities are a third higher in Worcestershire than Staffordshire and this, too, could be due to climatic differences stemming from altitude and the effect of the Gulf Stream.

Nevertheless, the underlying regional trend has closely followed the national one, with the steady increase in population since 1986 no doubt assisted by the run of generally mild winters. The long-term trend over the past twenty years suggests that both the national and regional populations increased by about a third. The CBC also suggests that regional densities are around the national average of 22 pairs per km². Other surveys revealed widely varying densities. During the 1990s, for instance, the woodland at Coombes Valley held an average of 66 pairs per km², whilst on farmland in south Warwickshire densities ranged from 5-24 pairs per km². Taking all available data into consideration, a regional population in the range 140-170,000 seems most likely, compared with the 90-120,000 suggested in *BWM*.

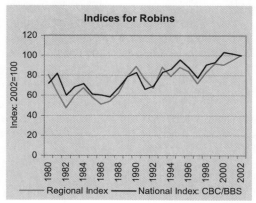

Many defend territories around garden feeding stations and several have now mastered the skill of feeding from suspended nut-feeders. Others have been reported singing at night during the winter—especially in the vicinity of street lights—when local residents

have often mistaken them for Common Nightingales! Again at night, one flew around a Brier-
ley Hill warehouse in 1993, setting off the security alarms. Some unusually large concentrations were reported in 1995, with 40 at Ladywalk, 45 at Smestow Valley and up to 50 feeding
on fire scorched areas. Exceptionally for such a territorial species, nine were at the Brocton
Field feeding station on February 10th 1999, where they were uncharacteristically said to be
'quite friendly to one another'. A month later, however, they were 'not so tolerant'. Another
exceptional report concerned a juvenile caught by a cat at Fordhouses on February 19th 1989,
which indicated eggs having been laid around mid-January, while in 2001 a brood in a Harbury garden was fed in the nest for two days by a pair of Blackbirds whose own young had
been predated.

Although most Robins are resident, some make local seasonal moves, forsaking the bleak
high ground in winter for the more sheltered lowlands, as instanced at Coombes Valley where
they moved out in the cold weather of 1982. Some also leave the countryside to winter in urban parks and gardens, where it is usually warmer and bird tables provide a reliable source of
food. Others make longer journeys as shown by an influx at Ladywalk in late-September 1998
that coincided with large arrivals on the East Coast and may have involved continental birds.
A bird showing characteristics of the nominate continental race *E. r. rubecula* was seen at
Jackson's Bank on February 21st 1987, whilst one or more individuals resembling this form
were reported from Crossplains on several dates in 1990. Two ringing recoveries during the
current period also demonstrated movements to and from the Continent, with one, ringed at
Sutton Park in April 1983, moving 394 km to the Netherlands by October of the same year
and the other, ringed as a juvenile in Poland in September 1982, found dead in Solihull in November 1983 after a huge movement of 1,214 km. A juvenile, ringed in Cumbria in August
1989, was recovered the following month in Stafford, but movements otherwise are normally
between one and five kilometres, with most recovered birds being victims of domestic cats.

Common Nightingale   (Rufous/ Nightingale)   *Luscinia megarhynchos*
*Uncommon and declining summer resident, increasingly confined to the southern
parts of Warwickshire and Worcestershire.*

The Common Nightingale is justly renowned
for the richness of its magnificent song. This
is delivered both by day and night, but is most
frequent around dusk and dawn. But for its
song, it would go largely unnoticed as it forages on the ground, or low down in thick
vegetation, and rarely comes into open situations. Birds prefer coppiced woodland with a
rich ground flora, especially pedunculate oakwoods, but they also nest on commons with
dense thickets of thorn scrub. The range
within Britain has contracted markedly and it is now on the *Amber List* of Species of Conservation Concern (Gregory *et al*. 2002).

The West Midlands has always been on the edge of this species' range and over the years it
has steadily retreated south-eastwards. In *BWM* it was said to have formerly been more widespread and numerous. In the early twentieth century it was breeding as far north as Uttoxeter.
Fifty years later it could still be found to the west of Stafford (Norris 1951), but by 1962 the
only nesting in Staffordshire was in the Enville district (Lord and Blake 1962). Even this was
irregular and the final bird was seen there in 1981, whilst the last report from the West Midlands county was of a bird in song at Meriden in 1979. By this time Worcestershire was the

regional stronghold, with probably half-a-dozen pairs in most of the cluster of small woods centred on Himbleton and twice as many in some. The largest single concentration, though, was at Wappenbury Wood in Warwickshire, where up to 18 were in song in 1976 (*BWM*).

The first BTO Atlas (Sharrock 1976) showed birds in 44% of 10-km squares, virtually all of them south of a line from Kidderminster through Solihull to Coventry. By the time of the *Breeding Atlas* twenty years later this had halved to 22% and the range had moved south to a line from Worcester, through Redditch to south of Rugby. Today no more than a few pairs linger on in the southern parts of Warwickshire and more especially Worcestershire.

The BTO Census in 1980 revealed 99 singing birds, of which 23 were in Warwickshire and the rest in Worcestershire. This total was 41% down on that just four years earlier. By the next census in 1999 numbers had fallen by a further 41%, to just 58 singing males—10 of them in Warwickshire. The reasons for this decline are almost certainly complex, but two things are evident. Firstly, the progressive retreat south-eastwards is so clearly demarcated geographically that factors going beyond the region, such as climatic change, must be implicated. Secondly, within the region, the way the population moves from site to site each year suggests that habitat change is a significant factor. In the past, the widespread coppicing of lowland woods provided a stable habitat, with the open canopy and dense understorey that the ground feeding Common Nightingale requires. Now that coppicing has virtually ceased, this stability has been lost and birds have to wander more widely in search of suitable sites.

Trench Wood is an excellent example of this. Cleared and closely replanted with hardwoods, it was very reminiscent of coppice growth during the 1980s and at that time it usually held 8-12 singing Common Nightingales, with a WoWT survey in 1990 recording a maximum of 14. However, once the trees were tall enough to shade out the ground flora, the population quickly declined and the last birds to be reported here were two singing males in 1994. Similar rises and falls have been documented at other sites, but over different time periods, which confirms that habitat changes, rather than other environmental factors, are responsible. Examples, mostly involving a maximum of three singing birds, include Wappenbury Wood, where the last singing bird was recorded in 1984, Goosehill Wood, where a population of eight in 1980 had fallen to one by 1986, Yeald Wood (1981-93), Wellesbourne Wood (1985-91), Bascote Locks (1986-93), Ripple (1990-98) and Bowshott Wood (1993-99).

Numbers have been more variable on commons and other similar sites. At Old Hills Common, for example, one or two birds sang in most years from 1982 to 1998, but with four in 1994 and 1995, whereas at the DM Kineton army camp there were five to seven singing birds between 1993-1997, none the next year, but two or three subsequently.

Today's strongholds appear to be at Langdale Wood in Worcestershire, where numbers peaked at 10 singing males in 1998 and 1999, and DM Kineton and the Stretton-on-Fosse area in the extreme south of Warwickshire, where there are perhaps three or four pairs at each. Small numbers also occur regularly at Strensham, where unusually a pair was watched feeding young in 2000 and a family party of three was later seen. There are also a few more isolated pairs, but overall the population now is probably as low as 10-30 pairs (*cf.* 150-200 pairs estimated in *BWM*) and if this southerly retraction continues the species seems doomed to become extinct within the region in the not too distant future. There were two ringing recoveries during the current period, both involving adults. One, ringed at Hardwick Wood (Northamptonshire) in May 1980, was at Sale Green in May 1982, while the other, ringed at Gadbury Bank in May 1988, was recovered just two kilometres away in June 1996, giving an age of at least eight years.

Occasional birds are reported on passage, usually from well-watched sites such as Bittell Reservoir, Draycote Water and Upton Warren. Some isolated occurrences have also been recorded well to the north of the breeding range, with individuals at Belvide Reservoir on April 24th 1988 and Alvecote Pools on May 1st 1999. The biggest surprise was one that sang in the Churnet Valley in 1981, which was the most northerly record for a quarter of a century.

Bluethroat   *Luscinia svecica*
Very rare vagrant. Seven records.

The current period brought five more Bluethroats to add to the two shown in *BWM*.

Regional Record Number	County Record Number		Year	Locality, Date and Notes
1	W Mid	1	c1837-41	Near Birmingham: unknown date, killed.
2	Worcs	1	1944	Arley: second week in April. *BB 38:155*
3	Worcs	2	1981	Upton Warren: May 24th.
4	W Mid	2	1985	Longbridge: male, May 14th.
5	Staffs	1	1988	Knotbury: male, May 17th.
6	Staffs	2	1994	Tittesworth Reservoir: male, May 22nd.
7	Warks	1	1995	Brandon Marsh: September 9th.

All were birds of the Red-spotted form *L. s. svecica* that breeds in Scandinavia and Siberia and winters in the Mediterranean and sub-Saharan Africa. Of the dated records, five occurred in spring and one in September—all fairly typical times for this species to arrive in Britain.

Black Redstart   *Phoenicurus ochrurus*
Scarce summer resident, passage migrant and winter visitor.

The West Midlands is a national stronghold for the Black Redstart—an urban speciality that breeds amongst the region's older industrial complexes and redevelopment sites. Data from the RBBP suggest that between 1986 and 2000 the region held around 6% of the UK population. However, not all records appear to have been submitted to the Panel, especially for 1986-88 and 1998, when the region possibly held as much as 15% of the national population.

Although nesting was first confirmed at Birmingham University in 1943, colonisation was slow and it was 1958 before breeding became a regular occurrence. City centre bomb sites were the first to be colonised. Then, as the redevelopment of inner city areas produced extensive areas of cleared land during the 1960s and 1970s, birds moved out into the neighbouring industrial areas. Since 1979 numbers have fluctuated widely, largely in relation to the available habitat, with the peak during 1985-89 when the region's manufacturing base collapsed, leaving plenty of large industrial buildings empty and derelict. However, undercounting also contributes to the fluctuations, as some territories are small and easily missed. Also many are in large installations, such as gas works and power stations, to which access cannot always be gained.

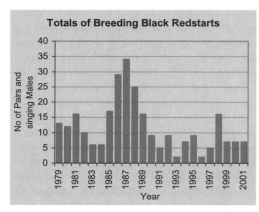

In the West Midlands, most territories include large, derelict buildings for nesting, tall structures for song posts and areas of bare or sparsely vegetated ground, tall herbs and scrub to provide food and shelter. It can take several years for disused sites to reach this stage of dereliction, so there is often a time lag between an industrial complex closing and Black Redstarts moving in. Since the 1990s, it has been Government policy to steer development towards these derelict, or 'brownfield', sites and few now remain vacant long enough to provide suitable territories, which partly explains the fall in numbers. However, more intensive monitoring for the BBCBBS produced a sharp rise in 1998, whilst in 2002 up to five breeding pairs and possibly another five singing males were recorded. It seems likely, therefore, that the current regional population is 5-15 pairs, which is much the same as that shown in *BWM*.

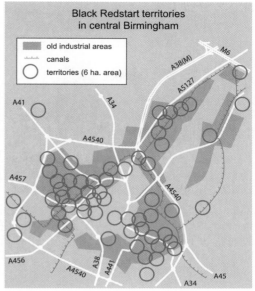

The map shows all Black Redstart territories within central Birmingham between 1958-2001. Most were near canals and at one time it was thought the distribution depended on the presence of water. This now looks to have been a coincidence of the industries that congregated alongside the canals abandoning waterside buildings when they switched to rail and road transport. In later years colonisation followed the abandonment of old railway stations, sidings, gasworks and power stations. Indeed, from 1974-92 the old Snow Hill Station was the most favoured site and from here birds spread along three axes that followed the city's traditional industrial corridors running north-west through the Jewellery Quarter to Hockley; north-east to Aston, Nechells and Saltley; and south-east along Digbeth to Bordesley.

Considering how much suitable habitat is available, there have been surprisingly few records from the Black Country, where the only regularly used sites were Ocker Hill power station (1978-89) and the Albright and Wilson works at Oldbury (1986-95). Sporadic nesting also occurred at Coseley and Smethwick in 1987, Deepfields and Smethwick in 1988, Wolverhampton in 1999 and possibly Tividale between 1985 and 1989. Breeding also occurred in Coventry during the 1970s, but has not been sustained since.

In the Potteries sporadic nesting occurred in Stoke-on-Trent and possibly at Hanley in 1988 and Etruria in 2000, while breeding season records came from Burslem (1987) and Newcastle-under-Lyme (1998). Elsewhere in Staffordshire, pairs bred at the power stations at Meaford (1976 and 1988) and Rugeley (1986-95) and also at Rocester (1985 and 1986). In Warwickshire, birds nested regularly at Hams Hall power station (1974-84), the nearby Coleshill gasworks (1978-82) and at Rugby (1985). Worcestershire has never been colonised, but in 2001 a male held territory in Kidderminster and breeding possibly occurred near Droitwich Spa.

In this region a high proportion of males are brown/grey and clutch size is small. This suggests it is immature birds that are breeding and a study by WMBC members during 1987-91 (Winsper 1991) showed that only one successful breeding bird returned to the same site in subsequent years, whereas several youngsters came back to their natal areas. It seems that experienced birds move on, leaving vacated territories to their offspring. However, plumage differences also showed that brown/grey males could be up to two years old, implying that some birds may have been incorrectly aged in the past. Although birds arrived from mid-April, it was another month before territories were finally secured. On arrival, males defended a territory of approximately six hectares, but then retracted into a smaller area once a nest site had been chosen. Vacated song-posts were then taken over by unpaired birds, invoking a response from former residents and adding to the difficulty of counting. Once the clutch was complete, full song ceased, but resumed again a day or two after the young had left the nest. In the in-

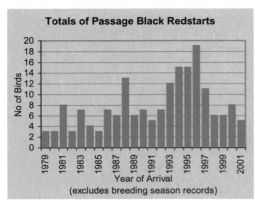

Totals of Passage Black Redstarts

Year of Arrival
(excludes breeding season records)

terim, only brief snatches were heard, whereas unmated males sang from May until July.

The Black Redstart is also a scarce passage migrant and winter visitor. Numbers gradually increased throughout the 1980s and climbed sharply in the mid-1990s, but have since fallen back. Spring passage mostly occurs between March and May, with a strong peak in April, whilst the smaller autumn passage takes place mainly in October and November. Thereafter records steadily reduce and during the current period there were only four in February—all in Worcestershire. One bird over-wintered at its breeding site in 1988/9. The records also show a slight southerly bias, with 32% in both Warwickshire and Worcestershire and 18% each in Staffordshire and the West Midlands. Passage birds can occur almost anywhere, but the hills of the Cotswolds (including Bredon Hill) and the Malverns are often favoured. One thing is certain, it will be the changing face of Birmingham that will dictate the fortunes of this fascinating urban gem in the future.

Common Redstart   *Phoenicurus phoenicurus*
Fairly common, though localised and much decreased, summer resident in Staffordshire and Worcestershire. Widespread on passage.

Sessile oakwoods in the hilly country of west Worcestershire, Cannock Chase and the uplands of north Staffordshire provide summer homes for most of the region's Common Redstarts. Here they join with Wood Warblers and Pied Flycatchers to form a characteristic bird community. Ashwoods are also freely used in the Dales and a few pairs nest in hillside scrub, dry-stone walls and exceptionally in old hedgerows or pollarded willows in lowland situations. Nest-boxes are also used, especially at Coombes Valley and in the Wyre Forest. In winter they migrate to the Sahel region of Africa.

Birds used to be more widespread, with the first BTO Breeding Atlas (Sharrock 1976) confirming their presence across much of the Arden, Dunsmore and Feldon districts of Warwickshire and east Worcestershire. The range then contracted north-westwards during the 1970s and 1980s, so by the time of the next *Breeding Atlas* during 1988-91 they were only present in 48% of 10-km squares. Breeding was confirmed in nearly every square in Staffordshire and in the Wyre Forest and Teme Valley areas of Worcestershire, but not in the other two counties. Moreover, the level of abundance was below average everywhere, except in the Churnet Valley and the Dales. This pattern accords with the *Breeding Atlas*, which states that it appears to be increasing where it was already abundant, but decreasing at the periphery of its range. Winstanley *et al.* (1974) linked these declines to the severe drought in the Sahel region, which had such a disastrous effect on Sand Martins and Common Whitethroats in 1969.

The CBC Index fell dramatically between 1965 and 1973, but then rose steadily until the mid 1990s, with a further drought in the winter of 1983/4 seemingly having no significant impact. Between 1980 and 2002 the index increased by almost a quarter, but regionally even the BBS sample was too small to give a reliable indication of local trends. The West Midlands lies on the fringe of the Common Redstart's range, which here contracted still further during this period as birds withdrew from lowland parts of Staffordshire. To base a regional population on national densities would therefore result in too high an estimate. Unfortunately neither of the embryonic *Tetrad Atlases* covers the species' breeding range within the region.

Mean Counts of Common Redstarts at Selected Sites									
	Pre 1969	1969-1973	1974-1978	1979-1983	1984-1988	1989-1993	1994-1998	1999-2002	
Bredon Hill				2	6	6	2	7	
Cannock Chase					25	27	35	17	
Clent Hills			2	5	1		3	4	No records 1985-94
Coombes Valley	30	19	35	35	17	32	38	12	
Malvern Hills					26	27	31 (13)	(6)	(Midsummer Hill only)
Sutton Park	40			10	3				Probably last bred 1986
Wyre Forest	18	6	5	6	7	7	12	6	

Note: Based on all available counts: some sites were counted only once in five years.

Moreover, as the table shows, local data is somewhat at variance with the CBC Index, as numbers dropped dramatically at some sites following the 1983/4 drought. Coombes Valley, for example, saw numbers fall from 36 pairs in 1983 to five in 1984, but they recovered within four years. Sites with smaller populations were less fortunate, however, as they never recovered and 1986 saw the last breeding records for Bentley Park, where there had previously been two or three pairs, and Sutton Park, where thirty years before there had been 40 pairs. Recently there have been signs that the species might be attempting to re-colonise Warwickshire. A pair bred at Priors Hardwick in 1999 and since then summer sightings have increased, with two singing males along the Cotswold Fringe and two breeding pairs in riverside willows in 2003 (J. J. Bowley *pers. comm.*).

Unfortunately there are few comprehensive pre-1969 counts, but what information is available suggests numbers at least halved in the late 1960s and early 1970s, which would be in line with the CBC. The residual population then consolidated in the those areas of prime habitat, such as the Wyre Forest and Coombes Valley, and withdrew from the smaller, sub-optimal sites. Prime habitat also exists in the Brocton Coppice-Sherbrook Valley area of Cannock Chase and it is a pity there were no comprehensive surveys here prior to 1987 to compare with those since. These revealed 25 singing males in that year, 27 in 1992, 35 in 1997 and 17 in 2002. The cause of the recent decline is not known, but rather worryingly it is also reflected in counts from Coombes Valley, Midsummer Hill and the Wyre Forest. Some of the mean counts for 1999-2002 were based on a single year, however, and the BBS Index did not fall significantly over this period, so it will be interesting to see what happens in the future. Little information is available on density, apart from Coombes Valley, where there are 35-45 pairs per km^2, and the Dales, where there were 10 pairs per km^2 along the Hamps Valley downstream of Waterhouses in 2002. Intuitively, from the data available, the current population might be in the range 800-1,200 pairs compared to the 1,200-2,500 estimated in *BWM*. The Common Redstart is included on the *Amber List* of Species of Conservation Concern because it has an unfavourable conservation status in Europe (Gregory *et al.* 2002).

Common Redstarts arrive fairly early in spring, with the earliest being on March 30th 1983 at Solihull Lodge. There have also been five records of arrivals on March 31st, whilst the average date for first birds over sixty-four years was April 10th and for the decade 1992-2001 April 7th. Passage is then noted between mid-April and mid-May, particularly around reservoirs, as birds move through the region on their way to their breeding grounds further north and west. Roughly a third of passage birds are seen in spring, mostly in small numbers.

After the breeding season, birds are noted at a variety of localities between July and September as they make their way steadily south again. The average date for the last birds over sixty-three years was September 26th, with the latest on November 4th 1988 at Blithfield Reservoir. At this time small parties up six are not unusual and groups of 10 were seen at Sandwell Valley in 1989, Walton Hill in 1997 and Bredon Hill in 1998, while the most seen was 11 at Sandwell Valley on September 6th 1996. Passage birds might appear almost anywhere, even in suburban gardens, but thick thorn hedges are a favoured haunt. At times, the arrival of birds in autumn coincides with 'falls' on the East Coast and it could be that some of our passage birds originate from Scandinavia, although there is no definite proof of this.

Whinchat   *Saxicola rubetra*
Uncommon or frequent, but much declined, summer resident, now mainly in north Staffordshire. Widespread on passage.

The habitat requirements of this little chat are hard to define. Formerly widespread, it is now virtually confined to the northern moorlands, where it frequents scrubby farmland and nests in bracken, tussocky grass, tall weeds or even mowing grass and young forestry. Tall herbaceous plants, drystone walls and fences are also used as song posts. Birds feed mainly on insects which are taken from grasses and flowering plants, especially umbellifers.

Whinchats are summer visitors that spend the winter in sub-Saharan Africa. The earliest bird to return was seen at Middleton on April 10th 1998 and over sixty-four years the average date for the first birds to arrive was April 22nd, but during 1992-2001 it was four days earlier. Just over a quarter of birds (27%) were recorded in spring, when passage peaks in late April and early May. At this season birds might be seen anywhere where there is rough ground with rank grasses and tall herbs. Most are usually found around the margins of reservoirs and gravel pits, but that probably reflects where the birdwatchers are as much as the birds.

Early authors described the Whinchat as widespread and common, although Smith (1938) remarked that owing to the cultivation of former wastes it was scarcer than formerly in many districts. Since then numbers have continued to fall and its range has contracted considerably. Habitat change is largely to blame, with land drainage, early cutting for silage and the use of herbicides all driving birds out of lowland situations in particular. Tidying up urban wasteland and reclaiming post-industrial sites have robbed it of much suitable habitat, too, especially in the Potteries and the West Midland conurbation. Birds are also susceptible to human disturbance, so increased recreational activity in remote areas must have contributed to the decline.

The 1980s saw breeding end at many sites. In Warwickshire, for instance, regular nesting ceased at Kingsbury Water Park in 1984, Brandon Marsh in 1986 and the Ladywalk-Hams Hall area in 1988. In Worcestershire breeding occurred at Wilden until about 1984 and Stourvale Marsh until 1985; and in the West Midlands County at Sandwell Valley until 1982, Tividale until 1985 and Sutton Park until 1988. There have been no subsequent breeding records from the latter county. In Staffordshire, breeding ceased at Chasewater in 1983, Doxey Marshes in 1986 and on Cannock Chase in 1988.

The *Breeding Atlas* shows birds were present in 35% of 10-km squares during 1988-91, embracing Cannock Chase, several sites across the lowland Staffordshire, the Feldon district and the Severn valley. Since then, the range has contracted still further. In Warwickshire, birds bred fairly regularly at the DM Kineton army camp until 1996, but thereafter only sporadic singing males have been noted in the county, while in Worcestershire a female was seen feeding a juvenile at Malvern in 1991 and a party of nine, including juveniles, at Strensham in July 1998 raised the possibility of local breeding. In Staffordshire, two pairs reappeared on Cannock Chase in 1992 and sporadic, isolated breeding has occurred elsewhere since, but otherwise all subsequent records have come from the moors. Here numbers seemed to be holding up reasonably well, with the RSPB surveys revealing 51 pairs across 83 km^2 in 1985, 41 pairs in 1992 and 52 in 1996. Indeed, McKnight *et al.* (1996) said that this was the only passerine to have enjoyed a stable, if not increasing population in the area since the previous surveys and noted that along with the Northern Wheatear it does not depend on wet ground or hay meadows. Casual reports suggest there may have been declines since then, however, and the BBS shows that 1996 was a peak year nationally, with numbers subsequently falling by 40%.

Even in Staffordshire it is doubtful whether breeding occurs in more than half-a-dozen 10-km squares, or 8% of the regional total. Given the paucity of records away from the moors, the current regional population cannot be put any higher than 30-70 pairs and is probably towards the lower end of that range—a catastrophic decline from the 250-400 pairs estimated in *BWM*.

Birds begin to leave their breeding territories in July and passage is then noted from August through to early October at similar localities to those in spring. Numbers are higher at this season (70% of birds), with small parties up to ten sometimes noted. The largest groups recorded in the region were 20, at Castlemorton Common on September 8th 1988 and in the Sandwell Valley on September 6th 1996, and 21 on September 2nd 1987, again at Sandwell Valley. Over sixty years the average date for last birds was October 10th, but there have been eleven November records and two in December, with the latest on the 19th at Doxey Marshes in 1984. During the current period, Staffordshire, despite having the main breeding population, surprisingly only attracted 19% of passage birds compared with 29% in Warwickshire, 27% in Worcestershire, where Upton Warren is the best place to see this species, and 25% in the West Midlands. Unusual records concerned a male Whinchat and a female Common Stonechat carrying food to the same nest in Sutton Park in 1979, though whether this was a hybrid pairing is unknown. Another male sang in central Birmingham on May 20th 1986.

Common Stonechat (Stonechat) *Saxicola torquatus*
Uncommon resident, but frequent passage migrant and winter visitor.

Lowland heaths and commons with gorse, heather and rough grass are the most likely places to find the Common Stonechat. Less common than its name implies, it breeds on the Malvern Hills, on Cannock Chase and sparingly on the moors of north Staffordshire. It feeds on bare, or sparsely vegetated, ground and uses tall herbs as song posts and perches from which to drop onto prey. Some are sedentary in mild winters, but juveniles disperse in autumn and birds from further north move south for the winter, creating a significant autumn influx. Many of these pass through the region, but others remain for the winter around waste ground, rough grassland and the fringes of gravel pits, reservoirs and marshy areas.

Birds are very vulnerable to prolonged frosts and for a long time attempts to colonise the region were thwarted by periodic hard winters. Sporadic nesting occurred for many years (*BWM*), but only with the recent run of milder winters has it become regular. The *Breeding Atlas* confirmed the presence of birds in just 13% of 10-km squares covering the Malverns, parts of the Potteries and Churnet Valley, an outlying site in north-east Warwickshire and Cannock Chase, but the latter area was the only one where breeding was confirmed. Abundance levels were well below average everywhere, which was to be expected as this is primarily a species of western coasts, where winter survival is made easier by the milder climate.

There are now at least six pairs on the Malvern hills and commons (20 singing males in 2001), a dozen on Cannock Chase and three or four on the northern moors. Birds have also bred occasionally in Sutton Park and possibly at one or two other localities on rare occasions. This suggests a total population in the range of 20-30 pairs compared with the 3-10 pairs estimated in *BWM*, but the loss and fragmentation of heathland may hamper further expansion.

From September to March Common Stonechats are more widespread and numerous. During the *Winter Atlas* they were recorded in 19% of 10-km squares. Cannock Chase again held the largest number of birds, but ones or twos were seen on the heaths in Sutton Park, around

Kidderminster and in parts of Birmingham and the Black Country—all situations where they are likely to be encountered today. Numbers begin to increase during September, but the main passage occurs in October and November, when 44% of birds are recorded. Many pair and establish territories which they then defend throughout the winter, but others move on and the number of fresh arrivals gradually wanes during December and January. A smaller return passage (22% of birds) is then evident during February and March. Wintering numbers vary each year, but a widespread influx in the autumn of 2001 brought 160 individuals to 41 sites in Worcestershire (including 18 at Bishampton Vale Pool), around 60 to 10 or so sites in the West Midlands and 50 to eighteen sites in Warwickshire. Apart from 15 at Cuckoo Bank, surprisingly few were reported from Staffordshire, but in the following year a remarkable 26 were seen in Sherbrook Valley, Cannock Chase, on October 6th. By way of comparison, *BWM* recorded flocks of 30 at Perton in the 1975/6 winter and 50 at Malvern on October 28th 1938.

Outside the breeding season, Worcestershire was the most visited county, with 33% of records. The other counties each attracted similar shares, with 24% in Staffordshire, 22% in the West Midlands and 21% in Warwickshire. The high percentage in the West Midlands is due to the extent of suitable habitat compared to Warwickshire. Even taking into consideration the greater numbers of observers, there has been a significant increase in the number of winter records, with at least twice as many in the 1990s as in the 1980s. Two birds that were colour-ringed as nestlings in Cumbria have been sighted in the region. The first was ringed in May 1994 and seen at Brandon Marsh in February 1995, while the second, ringed in May 1999, was at Belvide Reservoir in the following September—both having travelled 280 km.

Northern Wheatear   (Wheatear)   *Oenanthe oenanthe*
Frequent, but possibly declining, summer visitor, mainly to north Staffordshire. Fairly common and widespread on passage. One winter record.

Northern Wheatears are summer residents in upland Britain. Small numbers breed in the north of Staffordshire and on the Malvern Hills, but the species is better known as a passage migrant, when it flits across arable fields, the short swards of upland sheep pastures or around the sparsely vegetated surrounds to reservoirs, gravel pits and derelict industrial sites. Within urban areas birds pause to feed on the short turf of golf courses, playing fields and parks. Most nest in rabbit burrows, drystone walls or under rocks and scree and numbers have increased with the recovery of the rabbit population following myxomatosis.

A true precursor of spring, this is often the first species to return each year from its sub-Saharan and east African winter quarters, although few come as early as those at Offchurch on February 23rd 1968 and Blithfield Reservoir on February 25th 1998. There were February records in two other years as well, but the average date for first arrivals over sixty-three years was March 19th. During 1992-2001, though, it was eight days earlier. Indeed, spring passage, which with 70% of birds is much stronger than that in autumn, is becoming earlier and significant numbers of birds arrived in March in 1995, 1996 and 1999. Even so, April still remains the peak month. Passage then continues into early May, when a few larger, brighter birds of the Greenland race *O. o. leucorhoa* sometimes occur. Numbers of Northern Wheatears vary from year to year, but parties up to 25 are quite often seen and the most recorded during the current period were 30, at Bredon Hill on May 1st 1997 and Draycote Water on April 23rd 1999, 31 at Blackbank Hill on April 26th 1997 and 35 at Sandwell Valley on April 23rd 1983.

The *Breeding Atlas* recorded birds in 38% of 10-km squares, but several of these must have referred to passage birds. Confirmed breeding was confined to just five squares (6%), all of them in north Staffordshire. There, surveys of the 83 km^2 of moorland by the RSPB showed an increase from 57 pairs in 1985 to 94 pairs in 1992, but then a decline to 68 pairs by 1996 (McKnight *et al*. 1996). Interestingly, this overall increase has been accompanied by a change in distribution, with fewer west of the A53, where recreation pressures on areas such as the Roaches are very intense, and more to the east, where the recovery in the rabbit population is thought to have increased the extent of suitable habitat. In the Dales, two pairs bred at Calton in 1981, up to three pairs have been reported in recent years at nearby Musden Low and six birds were in Stanton Dale in 1998. Otherwise little is known about the population here, but Frost (1978) observed that in neighbouring Derbyshire it was higher on the Carboniferous limestone than on the Millstone grit and *BWM* says this was the impression gained in Staffordshire as well. It would be interesting to know whether this is still the case. In Worcestershire, the species retains its tenuous hold on the Malvern Hills. Breeding there was very sporadic throughout the 1980s, but since 1991 one or two pairs have nested in most years.

In the past breeding was more widespread and *BWM* mentions nesting in the Kinver and Enville area. During the current period sporadic breeding was recorded in the West Midlands, on Dudley Golf Course in 1979 and Turners Hill in 1984 and 1985 (two pairs); in Warwickshire at a site near Meriden in 1986; and in Worcestershire on Bredon Hill in 1987. There have also been half a dozen reports of possible breeding in the region away from established sites. In *BWM* the regional population was estimated as 200-250 pairs, but without more knowledge of the situation in the Dales it can now only be put at 80-200 pairs.

Return passage begins in July with the dispersal of juvenile birds, which can sometimes lead to false suspicions of local breeding. The peak movement then occurs between the middle of August and the end of September, although a few individuals remain later. Over sixty-four years the average date of the last recorded birds was October 17th, with the latest at Mount Segg on December 6th-7th 1994. Even with juvenile birds to swell the population, numbers in autumn rarely approach those of spring and groups seldom exceed a dozen birds. *BWM* mentioned concentrations of 30 and 50 at this season, but during the current period none has reached 20. The only ringing recovery was of an adult female, ringed at Brandon Marsh on September 6th 1981, and recovered in Khouribga, Morocco, just twenty days later. An interesting report mentioned in *BWM* concerns a bird on the Malvern Hills on the unusual date of January 29th in 1967, which means there have been records in every month of the year.

Greenland Wheatear   *Oenanthe oenanthe leucorhoa*
Rare or scarce passage migrant.

A few birds showing the characteristics of this race, which breeds in north-east Canada, Greenland and Iceland, are noted most years and *BWM* referred to birds trapped and identified in 1957 and 1958 as evidence of its occurrence.

There were records in eighteen of the twenty-three years during the current period. Most involved just one or two birds, but there were six on Bredon Hill on May 6th 1996. The best year was 1999, with eight records involving 14 birds. Spring was the dominant season, with 92% of birds occurring between April 6th and June 6th—57% in May alone. The few autumn records were spread between July 28th and November 11th.

Desert Wheatear   *Oenanthe deserti*
Very rare vagrant. One record.

A surprising discovery, although a bare gravel pit was an appropriate place for one to appear.

Regional Record Number	County Record Number	Year	Locality, Date and Notes
1	Staffs 1	1996	Barton GP: first-winter male, November 23rd-30th. *BB 90:496*

Desert Wheatears breed in the arid regions of north Africa, the Middle East and Asia. Some north African birds remain resident, but many winter further south in the Sahara and Sahel regions. With less than a hundred records (Rogers *et al.* 2004), this is a rare visitor to Britain, but four arrived in the country during that November and December. This was perhaps only the fourth record from well inland, the last being in Herefordshire in November 1994.

White's Thrush   *Zoothera dauma*
Very rare vagrant. Two historical records.

The only records are two from the nineteenth century mentioned in *BWM*.

Regional Record Number	County Record Number	Year	Locality, Date and Notes
1	Warks 1	1859	Near Welford-on-Avon: January 6th-26th, shot on latter date.
2	Warks 2	1895	Near Packington: unknown date in autumn, shot.

White's Thrush breeds in central and southern Siberia and winters in southern Asia. There have been just over fifty British records.

Ring Ouzel   *Turdus torquatus*
Scarce, and declining, summer resident on the North Staffordshire Moors. Uncommon passage migrant. Very rare in winter.

A few pairs of Ring Ouzels breed amongst the rocky outcrops and steep-sided valleys, or cloughs, of the North Staffordshire Moors, where they search the upland pastures for earthworms and other soil invertebrates. After breeding, small parties, or family groups, gather to feed on rowan berries and bilberries. The best chance of seeing this species in the region now, however, is to visit the Worcestershire hills during its migration times.

Ring Ouzels winter in mountainous areas around the Mediterranean basis, including the Pyrenees and the Atlas mountains of north Africa. The journey back to their upland breeding grounds is thus relative short and they return early in spring, with the first ones frequently being back on their territories before March is out. The earliest was a passage bird at Broadway on March 12th 1987, whilst over forty-four years the average date for first arrivals was March 30th. Spring migration is the stronger, accounting for almost 60% of birds, with 80% of these in April, but some movement continues into early May. Although migrants might occur anywhere, they regularly stop to refuel on the Malverns, Bredon and Clent Hills. Totals vary, but since the mid-1980s they have generally numbered between 20 and 40 birds. In 1987 strong passages at both seasons resulted in an exceptional total of at least 90.

There are historical breeding accounts from Warwickshire in 1848 and Worcestershire, on the Malverns, in 1849, 1877 and 1887 as well as evidence of a wider distribution in Staffordshire (*BWM*), but all breeding records since then have come from the northern moors. The species is very much in decline in Britain and is included on the *Red Alert List* of Species of Conservation Concern (Gregory *et al.* 2002).

During the *Breeding Atlas* it was recorded in the three 10-km squares that cover the higher moors of north Staffordshire. Here numbers have fluctuated widely. Lord and Munns (1970) estimated between 3-20 pairs and this was endorsed in *BWM*. During the first RSPB census in 1985, however, an incredible 61 pairs were found. This was probably an exceptionally good year, but even so it

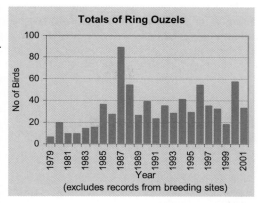

Totals of Ring Ouzels

(excludes records from breeding sites)

was disappointing when subsequent surveys found only 18 pairs in 1992 and just five in 1996. Since then five pairs were reported again in 1997, four in 1998 and 1999, two in 2000, just two males in 2001 and six males and a female in 2002, but without proof of breeding. This suggests the current population is below six pairs and the future prospects for this thrush look decidedly bleak. The reasons for its decline are complex, but probably include drier land as a result of lower rainfall and improved drainage, over-stocking, competition from Blackbirds and high recreational pressures, especially on the once favoured Roaches where successful nesting occurred only occasionally in the 1990s (Gribble 2000).

By late July birds become elusive as they disperse more widely to moult and search for food. Berries are important at this time and small groups often gather to feed on rowans. Return migration, which accounts for 40% of birds, begins in September and continues through to the end of October. The average date for last birds over thirty-eight years was October 26th, with the latest at Beaconwood on November 30th 1980. As most British birds leave during September, it is possible that some of the later migrants are wind-drifted Scandinavian birds moving south, but there is no conclusive evidence of this. As in spring, birds again visit the same stop-over points on their journeys south, with the elder and rowan berries in the Happy Valley of the Malverns often favoured. Parties of a dozen or so sometimes gather on the hills and 15 have twice been seen, on September 28th 1980 and again on September 25th 1987.

During the current period half of all passage birds were seen on the Malvern Hills, with 9% on the Clent Hills and 5% each at Bredon Hill and Sandwell Valley. There were also four winter records, all of males, with one at Kidderminster from January 27th to February 2nd 1990 and three during the hard weather of 1995/6, when one visited a Kenilworth garden from December 29th to January 12th, one was at Corley from January 24th to April 6th and another at Birlingham on January 24th. The latter three were part of a national influx of over 20 individuals that accompanied a huge arrival of winter thrushes. A mid-summer record from Alvechurch on July 12th 1985 was also unusual.

Blackbird   *Turdus merula*
Abundant resident, passage migrant and winter visitor.

Almost everyone knows and recognises the Blackbird, which can be found in all parts of the region from the highest moors to the city squares of central Birmingham. First and foremost a bird of woodland, over the last couple of centuries it has adapted to live in virtually every natural and man-made environment, but it is most abundant along hedgerows and in suburban parks and gardens. On the moors it inhabits similar areas to the Ring Ouzel, often nesting beneath rocks, or in heather and tussocks of rush. In autumn the population increases substantially as continental birds arrive to spend the winter here. For much of the year birds forage through the leaf litter of the woodland floor and hedge bottom in search of earthworms, but in autumn they feed on haws and other berries as well as windfall apples.

Nationally the population expanded during the first half of the twentieth century, surpassing the Song Thrush as the commonest thrush in about 1930 (Sharrock 1976), but it then stabilised in the middle of the last century (Gibbons *et al*. 1993). Regionally both the *Winter* and *Breeding Atlases* confirmed the presence of birds in every 10-km square with high levels of abundance almost everywhere except for the higher moors. There is no evidence to suggest any more recent change to this widespread and abundant distribution and the BBS shows it now outnumbers the declining Song Thrush by six to one.

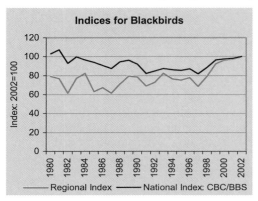

The national CBC/BBS index gradually fell through the 1980s, but it has recovered since 1997 and so shows little long-term change during 1980-2002. Regionally the recent pattern was very similar, but the 1980s were more variable. Overall there could have been an increase of around a quarter between 1980 and 2002. The chart shows that hard winters have less effect on Blackbirds than other thrushes. On the other hand, this species is more likely to fall victim to Magpies, cats and traffic. The BBS shows densities in the West Midlands county to be a third higher than those in the shires and taking account of this the current regional population could be 160,000-240,000 pairs. Allowing for an increase in line with the regional index between 1980 and 2002, this is slightly above the range of 120,000-160,000 pairs estimated in *BWM*.

Breeding information from individual sites shows conflicting trends. Numbers at Alvecote Pools remained steady at 10-12 pairs from 1986-98, whereas at Doxey Marshes they halved from 23 pairs a year during 1984-90 to 11 pairs a year from 1997 to 2000. The larger populations at Coombes Valley and the DM Kineton camp were more variable. The former ranged from 28-64 pairs during the 1990s, with an average of 41, while the latter fluctuated between 67-121 pairs during 1993-2000, with an average of 96 pairs a year, which was a slight improvement on the average of 83 a year prior to 1993. Information on densities during the current period, additional to that from the CBC plots, ranged from about 40 territories per km^2 in woodland at Coombes Valley and the Piccadilly-Wood End area to between 10-25 pairs per km^2 on farmland in central and south Warwickshire.

Our resident birds are mostly sedentary, although those on the moors generally move to lower ground in the winter. A few, usually juveniles, move south for the winter, but they are replaced by very many more from the Continent. The latter begin to arrive at the end of September, but the main influx comes from late October to mid-November. Arrivals after this derive mostly from hard weather movements. Resident birds defend territories throughout the year, except during severe weather when feeding becomes paramount. Indeed, they often nest early and pairs feeding juveniles or with well grown in the nest were noted twice on January 24th, in 1988 and 1999 and coincidentally both times at Stratford-upon-Avon. Migrant birds are more sociable and often form loose feeding flocks up to 50 strong. Sometimes these merge into larger gatherings later in winter. For example, 105 were at Brocton Field on November 29th 1983 and 145 at Fenny Compton on December 27th 2000, whilst the favoured Smestow Valley held 250 on November 10th 1991. There was also a spectacular movement in south Warwickshire on October 28th 2001, when hundreds were grounded at dawn following heavy overnight rain including 250 at Wormleighton alone. These immigrants begin their return to the Continent in late February, with the main passage during the first half of March.

Ringing recoveries prior to the 1980s indicate that winter migrants originate from Fenno-scandia, Germany and the Low Countries and this is confirmed by more recent data. Recoveries of birds ringed in the region during the winter show that 16% moved to the Netherlands or Germany during the following or subsequent summers, while 84% went to Denmark, Norway, Sweden and Finland. Most other movements were local within the West Midlands. Some birds have also been recorded moving south in winter, with an adult female, ringed in Worcestershire in November 1997, killed by a cat in Buckinghamshire the following February. Others have moved inland from the coast and it is interesting to speculate whether these are continental or British birds. For instance, a juvenile male ringed in Kent on October 1st 1983 was retrapped at Brandon Marsh 22 days later, while another bird from Kent, ringed in November 1986, was found dead in Staffordshire on December 14th in the same year. Another interesting recovery relates to a bird ringed in Worcestershire in January 1987 and found dead in March 1989 on the Rolf A Oil Platform, 589 km away, out at sea.

Dusky Thrush   *Turdus naumanni*
Very rare vagrant. One record.

This exciting find was only the sixth British record of this rare Siberian vagrant and the second inland, the previous one having been in Nottinghamshire in 1905 (Rogers *et al.* 1980).

Regional Record Number	County Record Number	Year	Locality, Date and Notes
1	Worcs 1	1979	Majors Green: February 17th-18th, 27th-28th and March 18th-19th and 23rd. *BB 73:521*

Clearly forced well west of its normal range by the bitterly cold winter of 1978/9, it made periodic visits to a garden at Majors Green, near Shirley, during the coldest spells, where it fed on windfall apples and apple peelings in a compost heap. Majors Green is in Worcestershire, but *Brit. Birds* erroneously recorded this bird as being at Shirley, West Midlands.

Dark-throated Thrush   *Turdus ruficollis*
Very rare vagrant. Two records.

This species has two distinct races, but both records were of the Black-throated form, *T. r. atrogularis*, which breeds in western Siberia and Khazakstan and winters from the Middle East eastwards.

Regional Record Number	County Record Number	Year	Locality, Date and Notes
1	Staffs 1	1978	North Staffordshire, locality withheld: first-winter male, November 26th, trapped and ringed at roost. *BB 72:535*
2	Worcs 1	1996	Webheath: first-winter male, January 17th to February 18th. *BB 90:497*

Only the ringers were able to enjoy the first of these—which was only the ninth British record—but the second delighted many as it fed in paddocks and on pyracantha berries in the front gardens of an adjoining housing estate in Redditch. It was one of an unprecedented influx of four to arrive in Britain with a large hard weather movement of thrushes early in 1996.

Fieldfare   *Turdus pilaris*

Very common passage migrant and winter visitor. Bred North Staffordshire Moors
1974-77, 1980 and 1985.

Large flocks of this thrush are a familiar part of the winter country scene. Upon arrival, most birds feast on hedgerow berries, particularly haws, or on windfall apples in orchards and gardens. Once they have depleted these food sources, they scour the grasslands for earthworms, which by this time, in floodplains at least, have usually been brought closer to the surface by rising water tables. Permanent pastures, especially old ridge-and-furrow, are mostly favoured as these provide optimum feeding conditions at all but the very driest and wettest times. Fieldfares are highly gregarious and habitually mix with other thrushes and Common Starlings.

Birds occasionally appear very early, but a flock of 150 at Spetchley on July 7th 1983 was most remarkable. Eleven were also seen near Leamington Spa on August 12th 1944 (*BWM*), one was at Alvecote Pools on August 19th 1980 and September arrivals have been recorded many times. Indeed during the 1960s and 1970s the average date for first birds was September 19th, but since then it has slipped backwards again and over sixty-five years it has been October 1st. From mid-month onwards, immigration then gradually increases to reach a peak in November. Thereafter, new arrivals to the region are usually birds displaced from elsewhere in Britain by severe frosts, heavy snow or lack of food. For example, a large hard weather movement took place in January 1984 ahead of the blizzards that swept across northern England.

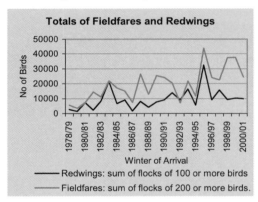

Totals of Fieldfares and Redwings

No of Birds

Winter of Arrival

—— Redwings: sum of flocks of 100 or more birds
—— Fieldfares: sum of flocks of 200 or more birds.

Numbers vary considerably depending on food supply and weather, but Fieldfares invariably out-number Redwings. Given mild weather and a good berry crop in Scandinavia, as in 1995, few appear here before November, but if the opposite happens, they come earlier. Some move straight through to winter further south or west, but others remain until food runs out or conditions become too harsh. For instance the region was virtually vacated during the severe cold of 1981/2 and February 1986, although birds quickly returned once a thaw set in. Numbers were also low in the 1986/7, 1988/9 and 1994/5 winters when there were few berries. However, a good late spring passage was recorded on the moors. Conversely, in 1995/6, very cold weather elsewhere brought record numbers here, with huge flocks at many places. Heavy passage is quite often recorded in autumn, with movements of 400-500 an hour not unusual. In 1998 a huge, widespread movement between November 6th-8th included 2,600 at Priors Hardwick, 1,100 at Fenny Compton, 1,000 at Chasewater, 900 at Belvide Reservoir and flocks of 500 at several localities in Worcestershire.

Birds are normally widespread and were recorded in every 10-km square during the *Winter Atlas*. They especially favour the rich crop of haws on the hedges and scrub of the Churnet Valley and its tributaries; the enclosure landscapes of the Feldon area, where the hawthorn hedges and old ridge-and-furrow pastures provide ideal feeding conditions; and the apple orchards in the Vale of Evesham and the Teme Valley. Impressive concentrations in these areas included 4,500 in the Vale of Evesham and 5,200 in Coombes Valley during the autumn of 1990; 4,500 in hawthorns along one kilometre of the Oxford Canal between Fenny Compton and Wormleighton in 1999; and 3,000-7,000 feeding on un-harvested dessert apples in an orchard at Suckley during the winter of 2001/2 (Brown and Skeates 2003). None, however, can match the 15,000 at Coombes Valley in the autumn of 1973 (*BWM*). Other notable counts were 4,000-5,000 at Crowle in March 1984 and 4,000 at Sandwell Valley in January 1986, whilst 1,100 feeding in a rape field at Wormleighton in 2000 were unusual. Of those flocks containing 200 or more birds, 20% exceeded 1,000, but 40% held less than 350. Birds are normally shy, but hard weather sometimes drives them into gardens and 30 feasted on apples at Weeping Cross in 1997. They normally roost in conifers, woods with a dense understorey, or in scrub and the largest concentrations during the current period were 5,500 at Yeald Wood in January 1985 and 2,000 at Pelsall Wood Common in December 1989 (*cf.* 25,000 at Brandon Marsh in March 1977 *BWM*). Overall, during the current period, 39% of birds were in Warwickshire, 28% in Staffordshire, 27% in Worcestershire and 6% in the West Midlands county.

Birds begin to leave for their breeding grounds in late February and numbers increase during March as the return passage gets into full swing. Most have gone by the end of April, although in 1981 many were held back by the ice storm late in that month. One or two often stay into May, but a flock of 150 at Ladywalk on May 8th 1993 was unusually large. The average date for the last birds to depart over sixty-four years was May 3rd, whilst the latest to be recorded were on the 25th—at Sandwell Valley in 1987 and Ryton Wood in 2000.

Until recently Fieldfares were the wintering thrush least ringed in the region, but recoveries from the 1960s and 1970s indicated that over-wintering birds originated mainly from Fennoscandia and Ukraine. Birds recently ringed here in December and January confirm the former, with breeding season recoveries from Sipoo (Finland), Telemark (Norway) and Varmland (Sweden). There is also a record of a bird ringed in Sweden in May 2001, which was recovered at Suckley the following December. However, there are no recent recoveries to support the Russian connection.

Fieldfares breed widely across Fennoscandia and central Europe through to Siberia, but they have also been spreading westwards and began to nest in Britain in the 1960s. Colonisation has been fitful, however, with less than 10 pairs a year of which no more than two definitely breed (Ogilvie *et al.* 2003). The species' breeding history in this region was little more than a brief flirtation, when one or two pairs nested annually in north Staffordshire from 1974-77. Single pairs also bred in 1980 and 1985 (Waterhouse 1985), a bird appeared to hold territory in 1987 and a pair plus a single individual were present in 1988—the latter records presumably being those shown in the *Breeding Atlas*. Intriguingly, one was watched carrying food to a nest in a garden near Belvide during May 1996.

Song Thrush   *Turdus philomelos*
Much declined, though still abundant, resident, passage migrant and winter visitor.

During the breeding season the Song Thrush announces its presence through the repeated phrases of its highly distinctive, but variable song, which is often strongest at dusk. Birds occur in a wide range of habitats including woods, heaths, fields, hedges, parks and gardens. Earthworms are their preferred food, but caterpillars are also taken during the breeding season as are berries in autumn. Snails, which are their best known food, are most important in very dry or frosty conditions, when other foods become hard to access.

Though nowhere as numerous as the Blackbird, the Song Thrush is equally widely distributed and it was recorded in every 10-km square in both the *Winter* and the *Breeding Atlases*. Its density was mostly about average, but birds were more abundant in the Severn and Avon valleys, which generally enjoy milder winters than the rest of the region. This is confirmed by the BBS, which shows the highest densities in Worcestershire and Warwickshire.

Since the mid-1970s numbers have declined to such an extent that the Song Thrush is now on the *Red Alert List* of Species of Conservation Concern (Gregory *et al.* 2002). The decline between 1974 and 1999 was 53%, but much of this occurred during the cold weather of the late 1970s and early 1980s. During 1980-2002 the CBC/BBS index fell nationally by around 20%. The regional index needs to be interpreted with care as it is based on a small sample, but

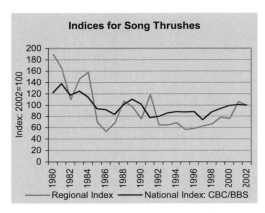

Indices for Song Thrushes

Index: 2002=100

200
180
160
140
120
100
80
60
40
20
0

1980 1982 1984 1986 1988 1990 1992 1994 1996 1998 2000 2002

——— Regional Index ——— National Index: CBC/BBS

it does show the greater impact that hard winters have away from the ameliorating effect of the sea. As a consequence numbers fell dramatically during the early 1980s and apparently reached their lowest point after prolonged cold spells in the winter of 1985/86, when food became especially hard to find in the frozen ground.

The situation has been compounded by the loss of hedgerows and permanent grassland and the change to autumn sowing, which means there is less tilled ground to provide food at critical times. The propensity for long, dry spells, which cause even ditches to dry out, and the increased use of molluscicides, especially in gardens, have also doubtless contributed to the decline. Indeed, it is no coincidence that numbers have begun to recover in this region with the recent run of mild, wet winters. Overall, the regional population probably halved during 1980-2002, leaving the current level towards the lower end of the range 25,000-40,000 pairs compared with the 30,000-75,000 estimated in *BWM.*

Apart from the CBC plots, few sites were monitored during the 1980s, but in the 1990s there were declines between the first and second halves of the decade of 21% at Coombes Valley, 30% at Smestow Valley and 35% at the DM Kineton army camp. On Castlemorton Common numbers fell from 35 pairs in 1994 to just six in 1995. Illustrations of density away from the CBC plots ranged from 2-15 pairs per km^2 in three areas of south Warwickshire to 5 per km^2 in the Tardebigge area and 8-15 pairs per km^2 in the woodlands of the Piccadilly-Wood End area and Coombes Valley respectively. In winter, systematic walks by WMBC members revealed a ratio of seven Blackbirds to every Song Thrush (*cf.* ratio of 6:1 shown by BBS).

Many of our Song Thrushes move further south or west for the winter. This is illustrated by a bird ringed at Brandon Marsh in May 1984 that was recorded in Glamorgan in January 1985, one ringed at Coombe Abbey in May 1981 and recovered in Cornwall in January 1985 and another ringed at Fillongley in November 1987 and shot in France in December 1990. There was also one winter movement from Tamworth to Lincolnshire, but apart from these few recoveries, all others show only local movements within the West Midlands. However, hard weather movements are sometimes made during the winter in response to any bad weather.

Just as some of our birds leave in autumn, so an influx arrives from Scandinavia and the Low Countries. This movement spans the period mid-September to early November, but it mainly occurs during late September and early October. Some birds pass through the region, perhaps to return again the following spring, but others remain here for the winter. The numbers involved are smaller than those of Blackbirds, but groups up to 30 are by no means unusual and the larger gatherings reached 140 at Fenny Compton on October 28th 2001 and 300 at Ladywalk on November 16th 1980. Those native birds that left for the winter then return in March, whilst the winter visitors leave in April. Spring passage is barely noticeable, however, although 70 were seen at Tatenhill on March 6th 1983. Our British Song Thrushes belong to the race *T. p. clarkei,* but an unknown proportion of our winter visitors may belong to the nominate race *T. p. philomelos,* which breeds in Fennoscandia, central and eastern Europe. It is thought that some Scandinavian birds of this nominate race winter in Britain, but Wernham *et al.* (2002) found only one ringing recovery to support this. Nevertheless, birds showing the characteristics of this race were reported as follows: Happy Valley on October 10th 1992; Marsh Lane, five, on October 3rd 1997; Harborne NR on October 9th and December 9th 1997; and Happy Valley, two, on September 19th 1998. Most recently, up to 20 were seen on a farm near Shipston-on-Stour in the early months of 2002 (Warren 2004).

Redwing   *Turdus iliacus*

Very common passage migrant and winter visitor.

Redwings, like Fieldfares, are winter visitors to the region. Most herald from Fennoscandia or Iceland, but some may come from countries around the Baltic or even as far away as Russia. Being the smallest of our thrushes, they are the most vulnerable in cold weather and so are even more nomadic, moving progressively further south and west as winter advances, frosts sharpen and nature's larder of fruits empties. In mild weather their habits are much the same as those of Fieldfares, with which they frequently consort in large, mixed flocks to feed firstly on hedgerow berries and later on earthworms in old pastures. During heavy frosts, however, they show a greater inclination to emulate Blackbirds by foraging amongst the leaf litter on the woodland floor. They also come more readily into gardens.

Generally Redwings come about a week earlier than Fieldfares. The earliest to be recorded was on August 18th, at Bartley Reservoir in 1980, but over sixty-six years the first birds arrived on average on September 26th. The main influx then comes towards the end of October and in early November, when nocturnal passage can often be detected by the high-pitched contact calls as parties pass overhead. In some years movements are very strong. For instance, 2,000 crossed over Dydon Wood in two hours on October 20th 1991 and 2,300 passed over Little Comberton in five hours on October 30th 1993. A concentrated passage between October 11th-13th 1997 saw 5,000 move through Coombes Valley during the three days, plus 850 through Park Lime Pits in two hours and 800 through Cookley in three hours on the 12th; and 590 through Fenny Compton in an hour on the 13th. Passage through Coombes Valley in October 1992 totalled 3,500 during the month. Although some birds move quickly on, others continue to arrive and maximum numbers are generally attained in December. From January onwards they often start to fall, with birds moving away once their food supply is exhausted.

Birds are usually widespread and during the *Winter Atlas* they occurred in every 10-km square. As with the more numerous Fieldfares, they tend to be most abundant in the Feldon, Avon Valley and Churnet Valley areas, while the first arrivals are often attracted to the rowans around the moorland fringes. Both numbers and timing vary considerably from winter to winter according to weather and food supply (see chart in Fieldfare). As with Fieldfares, Redwings time their departure from Scandinavia according to berry crops and weather conditions. Here, too, numbers vary according to food availability, with the bumper berry crop of 1983 attracting large numbers, whereas there were few birds in 1986, 1988 and 1994 when the crops were poor. Most also left the region during the bitter cold of 1978/9, 1981/2, and 1996/7, but there was a big influx in 1995/6 when birds came here to escape harder weather elsewhere.

Most feeding flocks contain 20-50 birds, but, of those numbering 100 or more, a half held less than 250 birds and only 20% consisted of 500 or more. The largest flocks during the current period were all in Worcestershire, with 3,000 at Crowle in March 1984 and at Tibberton in November 1993, and a very precise 5,072 at Defford on March 19th 1996. In comparison, the largest flock mentioned in *BWM* was 7,000 at Coombes Valley in the autumn of 1973. Some visit playing fields, large gardens and urban parks, where they feed on areas of mown grass, whilst in a cold spell a few may even be bold enough to come into suburban gardens to strip the berries from cotoneasters and other ornamental trees and shrubs. However, 70 in a garden at Acock's Green in 1996 were unusual. In even more built-up areas, up to 150 fed on berries near the Central Fire Station in Birmingham in 1990, while in 1997 some 200 did likewise in the town centre at Newcastle-under-Lyme and a similar number fed on a traffic island at Ladywood, Birmingham. During the current period as a whole, 32% of birds occurred in Worcestershire, 27% in Staffordshire, 24% in Warwickshire and 17% in the West Midlands county. Little information has been received on roosting birds, but 40 did so in reeds at Belvide Reservoir in 1994 and a regular roost at Maer in the 1980s peaked at 5,000 in 1982/3.

In late February numbers rise again as birds begin to move north-eastwards towards their breeding grounds. An illustration of the potential strength of movement comes from Coombes Valley, where 3,860 passed through during February 1992, but in recent springs passage has been less evident. The main exodus then occurs in March and most have gone by early April, although flocks up to 50 were present until mid-April in 2000. The average date for last departures over sixty-five years was April 19th, but a few stragglers are usually still about in May, when an occasional bird may be heard in full song. In 1978 one lingered at Edgbaston until May 30th and an injured bird was at Henley-in-Arden on June 12th 1971(*BWM*).

There is still no definite proof from ringing that Icelandic birds visit the region. However, recoveries have shown that birds from Fennoscandia and Russia do (*BWM*) and further evidence of the former is provided by a bird ringed in Finland in April 1981 and found dead in Warwickshire the following January, after making a journey of 1,691 km. They are often unfaithful to their wintering sites, but whether one ringed in Warwickshire in January 1980 and recovered in Portugal in January 1982 is an example of this, or whether it had been on its way to Portugal when it was originally ringed, is a matter of speculation. Likewise, one ringed in Staffordshire in December 1992 was also recovered in Portugal in January 1996. Perhaps another example of a change in wintering venue, just to show that Portugal is not the only alternative, is provided by a juvenile bird ringed in Staffordshire in November 1981 and recovered the following year in Kilkenny, Eire.

Mistle Thrush   *Turdus viscivorus*
Common resident.

Known as the storm cock from its habit of singing from the uppermost branches of a tree even in the teeth of a gale, the Mistle Thrush can be found right across the region from the city suburbs to remote rural areas and from the windswept uplands to the lush river valleys. Their favoured habitat is a blend of open woods, or countryside with scattered mature trees for song posts, and pastures for feeding. Parkland suits them admirably, whether it be a rural estate or an urban recreational area, some frequent large suburban gardens and many search for earthworms on playing fields and lawns. Nestlings are fed insects taken from trees and in autumn roving groups search for holly, mistletoe, rowan and yew berries. These groups then disperse, as individual adults or pairs select a particular source of fruit, which they then defend from all comers while the berries last. Most are sedentary, but first-year birds, especially females, migrate to other areas. Additionally, most individuals forsake the higher ground for more sheltered situations in winter.

Nationally there was a major spread of birds during the nineteenth and twentieth centuries and in this region most of the suitable habitat now appears to be occupied. Indeed, the Mistle Thrush's widespread distribution was confirmed by its presence in every 10-km square during both *Atlas* periods. Birds were most plentiful in those areas with plenty of woods and hedgerow trees, such as Arden, the Wyre Forest and the Churnet Valley. Interestingly, preliminary results from the survey work for the two *Tetrad Atlases* both show 75% of the tetrads to be occupied, whilst the BBS shows the density of Mistle Thrushes in the West Midlands to be higher than in any of the shire counties. One in Summer Row, Birmingham, in May 1990 shows they can even be found within inner city areas.

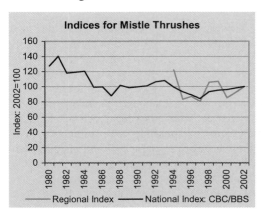

During the 1980s they declined sufficiently to warrant inclusion on the *Amber List* of Species of Conservation Concern (Gregory *et al.* 2002). Nationally the CBC/BBS fell by 20% during 1980-2002, as did the Song Thrush, but the regional sample was too small to determine a trend. Even the larger regional BBS sample shows marked fluctuations, although it does broadly reflect the national trend. The current population is probably in the range 6,000-9,000 pairs compared with the 7,500-15,000 suggested in *BWM*.

Mistle Thrushes have large territories, so they occur at low densities with on average little more than one pair per km^2. However, the woodland at Coombes Valley holds around 5 pairs per km^2, while a km^2 of mixed habitats at Ladbroke held 4 pairs in 1997. The prime habitat of the Malvern Hills held up to 35 pairs until 1991, but four years later there were just 19. Otherwise very little information is available.

From July to September flocks gather to feed on fruiting trees, areas of short grass or in orchards. On average these contain 25-30 birds, but gatherings up to 50 are not unusual and 82 were at Tittesworth Reservoir in July 1994, 90 were in Sandwell Valley in July 1992 and 100 were feeding on yew berries at Trentham Gardens in October 1979. Such flocks then disperse during October as birds begin to adopt their winter territories and very few remain by November. In comparison *BWM* referred to six flocks of 100 or more and one of 200.

All records for recently ringed birds show only local movements of 10 km to 15 km, but *BWM* mentioned two birds moving between here and northern England and one travelling to France. Unusually, calling birds were also heard amongst flocks of Redwings and Song Thrushes passing over Woodshires Green after dark on October 13th 1994.

Cetti's Warbler   *Cettia cetti*
Scarce resident, breeding only since 1993.

The loud, explosive song instantly betrays the presence of this otherwise secretive, nondescript warbler. A careful search may then reveal the bird skulking low in the midst of a dense patch of damp scrub. Brambles and sallows are often favoured and birds are seldom seen far away from reedbeds, to which they regularly resort in winter.

After spreading northwards through Europe, Cetti's Warblers began to colonise Britain in the 1960s and the first record in this region was an adult male at Edgbaston Park in 1975. Further records followed in 1977 and 1978, but birds remained scarce in the 1980s, with just six noted—three of them in 1988. In 1992, a singing male was ringed at Brandon Marsh and the following year a pair reared three young. Since then the species has become firmly established here and has probably bred annually ever since, with five singing males in 2003.

The other established population is at Upton Warren, where, after an isolated record in 1987, a singing male arrived in 1993 and stayed into the winter. The next year two pairs bred, since when breeding has again been an annual occurrence. Numbers here have stayed small, however, with generally two pairs at most, although there were possibly three singing males in 1999. A male, ringed here in 1997, was discovered the following year near Redditch, paired to an unringed female that was nest building, but both birds subsequently disappeared. This apart, there has been no suggestion of possible breeding elsewhere, although several singing birds have been heard, including three in the Middle Tame Valley—at Kingsbury Water Park in 1988 and 1998 and Middleton in 2000. Elsewhere, singles were recorded in spring and sum-

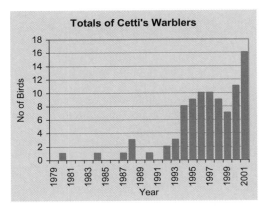

Totals of Cetti's Warblers

mer at Church Lench and Netherton in 1988, the Avon Valley (Worcs) in 1995 and Wilden in 2000; October dispersal was noted at Bittell and Wormleighton Reservoirs in 1999 and at Sandwell Valley in 2001; and winter reports came from Lower Moor in 1992/3, Ladywalk in 1995/6 and Oakley in 2001/2.

In the 1990s, twelve individuals ringed at Brandon Marsh yielded two recoveries. A juvenile male, ringed on July 28th 1993, was re-caught in Northampton on June 29th 1995 and an adult male, ringed on October 2nd 1994, was re-caught 28 days later after making a journey of 110 km to Cottam (Notts).

Grasshopper Warbler   *Locustella naevia*
Frequent, but much declined, summer resident and passage migrant.

The distinctive 'reeling' song coming from dense cover usually betrays the Grasshopper Warbler's presence, which otherwise might go undetected. When they first arrive in April, the males sing from exposed perches, but later on they 'reel' from within thick vegetation, when the ventriloquial effect of the song makes location difficult. Song is often heard at night. They prefer wet areas where the lush herbage, sedges and rushes are full of insects. With the drainage of wetlands, however, many have moved into the thick tangles of rank grass and bramble on dry heaths, commons and farm headlands. Even young plantations have been exploited, but the species is nomadic, moving on from any habitat once the vegetation becomes too tall.

The first Grasshopper Warblers do not normally arrive back from their winter quarters in tropical west Africa until April, with the 17th being the average date over sixty-four years of recording. During 1992-2001, however, the average date was four days earlier. An exceptionally early bird was at Kingsbury Water Park on March 25th 1990.

Numbers are notoriously variable, but generally show a substantial decline sufficient for inclusion on the *Red List* of Species of Conservation Concern (Gregory *et al.* 2002). In the late 1960s they were exceptionally high, ranging in this region from 120-160 a year, but then fell by at least a half to little more than 60 a year in the early 1970s (*BWM*). This fall has been attributed to changes at the wintering grounds, where areas were wet one year but parched the next, and it has been suggested that the fluctuating population may reflect its nomadic nature,

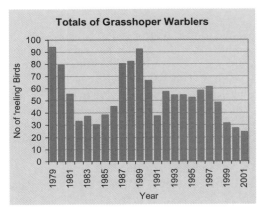

Totals of Grasshoper Warblers

with birds having no strong fidelity to either wintering or breeding areas (*Migration Atlas*). There was a recovery to around 100 a year in the late 1970s, but since then, apart from three good years in the late 1980s, there has been a long-term decline. This reached an all-time low of just 24 in 2001, but there have since been some early signs of a recovery.

The range has contracted too, with birds recorded in only 61% of 10-km squares during the *Breeding Atlas*—a third fewer than in the 1968-72 Atlas (Sharrock 1976). The losses were most evident in north-west Worcestershire, the Arden district, the Trent Valley and

Needwood area and the northern moors. Since then the range has contracted still further and the accompanying map shows just a thin scatter of records during 1997-2001, with clusters only along the chain of wetlands in the Middle Tame Valley, the Feldon area and the area west of the Lenches.

Preliminary results from both *Tetrad Atlases* show birds to be present in only 2-4% of tetrads, with the higher figure in Birmingham and the Black Country. The BBS reinforces this, suggesting that birds are slightly commoner in Staffordshire and the West Midlands than in the other two counties. However, it is often difficult to differentiate between migrant and territorial birds and it is possible the BBS counts include some passage birds. In Worcestershire, it was feared this warbler had been lost as a breeding species in 2000 and 2001, but at least three pairs bred in 2002.

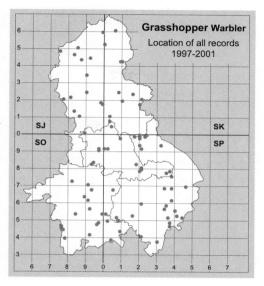

At its peak there were some impressive numbers, with up to ten at several sites, 17 'reeling' at Monkwood in 1979 (but none by 1984) and reports of birds spreading into oilseed rape and barley. By the early 1980s declines were widely reported and few sites held more than two or three birds. There was a strong passage in 1988, but by the mid-1990s numbers were low again and birds were only singing for a day or two, suggesting that many may have been on passage. Numbers at individual sites are too small to indicate long-term trends, but Brandon Marsh generally held an average of three 'reeling' males from 1965-98, whilst Sandwell Valley and Sutton Park have generally had one or two 'reeling birds'. At Castlemorton Common and Upton Warren numbers dwindled from as many as five in song in the late 1980s to just one in recent years, while on Cannock Chase numbers declined from four pairs in 1992, to two in 1997 and one in 2002. Allowing for fluctuating numbers and under-recording of what is probably our most inconspicuous bird, the population seems most likely to be between 50-150 pairs. Based on atlas densities at the time (Sharrock 1976), the estimate in *BWM* was 700 pairs. There is often a second song period in July, but after this birds make their way south largely unnoticed during August, with the 27th being the average date of last records over fifty-three years. The latest recorded was one at Dunstall Park on October 2nd 1999.

River Warbler   *Locustella fluviatilis*
Very rare vagrant. One record.

This was only the twenty-sixth British record of this species, which breeds from central and eastern Europe into Asia and winters in south-east Africa (Rogers *et al*. 1997).

Regional Record Number	County Record Number	Year	Locality, Date and Notes
1	Staffs 1	1996	Doxey Marshes: in song, June 20th to July 22nd *BB 90:499*.

The bird carried a bright metal ring, suggesting it had been ringed earlier in the year, but where remains a mystery since it was not re-trapped. Its appearance inland was perhaps made less unusual by one that had visited Greater Manchester the previous year.

Savi's Warbler   *Locustella luscinioides*
Rare vagrant.

The current period produced six further records to add to the six listed in *BWM*.

Regional Record Number	County Record Number		Year	Locality, Date and Notes
1	Warks	1	1968	Brandon Marsh: in song, April 21st. *BB 62:478*
2	Warks	2	1972	North Warks, locality withheld: in song, May 2nd to June 4th. *BB 66:347*
3	Warks	3	1976	North Warks, locality withheld: in song, July 14th-19th. *BB 70:433*
4	Warks	4	1977	North Warks, locality withheld: a pair and a second male in song on dates between April 24th and May 5th *BB 71:519*
5	Staffs	1	1977	Locality withheld: in song, June 6th to July 5th. *BB 72:536*
6	Warks	5	1978	North Warks, locality withheld: in song, May 3rd-21st. *BB 72:536*
7	Worcs	1	1985	Upton Warren: in song, May 11th-19th.
8	Warks	6	1989	Brandon Marsh: May 7th-16th, ringed. Later controlled Tring (Herts) July 14th.
9	Worcs	2	1992	Church Lench: in song, May 13th.
10	Worcs	3	1994	Upton Warren: in song, May 11th-12th.
11	Warks	7	1995	Brandon Marsh: in song, June 29th to July 12th.
12	Worcs	4	1999	Oakley: in song, May 2nd-19th.

Note: BBRC ceased to consider records of this species as from January 1st 1983.

Savi's Warblers breed discontinuously across much of western Europe and winter in east Africa. Almost all of the above conform to the general pattern for overshooting spring migrants, with ten of the records falling between April 21st-June 6th and, characteristically, nine involved singing males. The two records outside this period were also of singing birds, but these were not detected until late June and July respectively. Warwickshire and Worcestershire have a near monopoly of records.

Aquatic Warbler   *Acrocephalus paludicola*
Very rare vagrant. One record.

This secretive little warbler is difficult to see and many, such as this one, are only discovered when they turn up in a ringer's mist-net.

Regional Record Number	County Record Number		Year	Locality, Date and Notes
1	Worcs	1	1983	Oakley: juvenile, August 19th, trapped and ringed.

The Aquatic Warbler is much the rarest and most threatened migratory passerine in the Western Palearctic and is regarded as globally threatened due to its small world population and further projected declines (Tucker and Heath 1994). The breeding range stretches from Germany into European Russia, with most believed to be in Belarus. Birds migrate southwestwards in autumn to winter in west Africa (Rogers *et al.* 2004). August and September are the peak months for British records (Dymond *et al.* 1989).

Dunsmore and Feldon

The **Dunsmore and Feldon** landscape consists of flat or gently undulating countryside, with regularly-shaped fields enclosed by hawthorn hedges. Mixed farming still survives in many parts with the consequence that once common farmland birds, notably Tree Sparrows, are fairing better here than in most parts of the region. (*J.&G. Harrison*)

Fieldfares are visitors that come from Scandinavia to spend the winter here. Along with other thrushes, when they first arrive in autumn, large numbers descend on the hedgerows to feast on the hawthorn berries. Once the berries have been stripped they search the adjoining pastures for earthworms.

(*Mike Wilkes*)

The old **Feldon** pastures, especially those still showing the ridge-and-furrow pattern of Medieval strip farming, provide valuable winter feeding for thrushes, as well as Northern Lapwings, gulls and Common Starlings.

(*J.&G. Harrison*)

Dunsmore and Feldon

The pools, reedbeds and marshes of **Brandon Marsh,** the Warwickshire Wildlife Trust's head-quarters, are visited by a variety of waterfowl, waders and marshland birds and many rarities have occurred over the years. *(J. &G. Harrison)*

Sedge Warblers are just one of several warblers that regularly visit Brandon in the summer. As well as attracting the commoner warblers, the first regional records of Savi's, Great Reed and Barred Warblers also came from here. *(Mike Wilkes)*

The Severn-Trent's **Draycote Water** is one of the two best reservoirs in the region for birds. It is particularly noted for its wintering waterfowl, huge gull roost, passage waders and terns and for its long list of rarities. *(J.&G. Harrison)*

Over the years Draycote has proved the most consistent site for divers, with **Great Northern Divers** almost annual winter visitors. *(Keith Stone)*

Pectoral Sandpiper is just one of the rare Transatlantic waders to have occurred at Draycote. *(Keith Stone)*

The Cotswold Fringe

The long line of Jurassic hills—from Edge Hill to **Bredon Hill**—form a strong southern boundary to the region. Observations show that many migrant birds follow this line of hills, particularly during the autumn. *(J.&G. Harrison)*

Bredon Hill—an outlier of the main Cotswold scarp—is well known as a fairly regular stop-over point for migrant **Dotterel** in spring. *(Mike Lane)*

The Severn and Avon Vales

The broad, flat plain of the **Severn and Avon Vales** stretches away to the foothills of the Malverns and the Cotswolds.   (*J.&G. Harrison*)

Mute Swans are a feature of many towns along the Severn and Avon, but none more so than at Stratford-upon-Avon, where they have reputedly been present since Shakespeare's time at least.   (*J.&G. Harrison*)

The Severn and Avon Vales

The flashes at **Upton Warren**—a Worcestershire Wildlife Trust reserve—are a rare example of saline pools. They are very attractive to waders and great excitement was caused when Avocets bred here in 2003. *(J.&G. Harrison)*

Up to twenty **Green Sandpipers** are often present in late summer, making this the second best site in the region for this species. *(J.&G. Harrison)*

The Malvern Hills

The long ridge of the **Malvern Hills**, with its switchback outline of grassy summits standing above wooded slopes, forms a dominant feature within the region. The summits hold one or two pairs of breeding Northern Wheatears, whilst Snow Buntings are fairly regular passage visitors in autumn.

(J.&G. Harrison)

The **Common Stonechat** is a characteristic bird of the hills and adjacent commons, especially where there are patches of gorse. *(Mike Lane)*

The Teme Valley

The picturesque **Teme Valley** consists of undulating farmland surrounded by wooded scarp slopes. Its other characteristic features are the fast-flowing tributary streams, dingles, orchards, hop fields and oast houses.

(J.&G. Harrison)

Dippers occur along the fast running stretches of water where there are stony shallows. They are fascinating to watch walking under water as they search for food.

(M. Lane)

Some Birds in Decline

Corn Bunting (above), **Tree Sparrow** (bottom left) and **Grey Partridge** (bottom right) are all examples of farmland birds that have declined dramatically in recent decades—mainly due to changes in farming practices, but steps are now being taken to try and reverse these declines.
(all photos: Mike Wilkes)

More Birds in Decline

Sadly the **Spotted Flycatcher**, once a familiar summer visitor to our open woods, parks and gardens, is seen less often nowadays. (*Mike Lane*)

Northern Lapwing (bottom left) and **Common Snipe** (bottom right) are two of the breeding waders whose numbers have dropped in both the uplands and lowlands, largely due to the drainage of wet meadows. (*both photos: Mike Wilkes*)

Some Birds on the Increase

The spread of **Common Buzzards** across the region has been phenomenal and they are now commonplace in areas where twenty years ago they would have been a rare sight.

(Mike Wilkes)

The number of wintering **Blackcaps** has steadily increased, perhaps as a result of the recent run of milder winters. *(Mike Wilkes)*

Eurasian Nuthatches have also increased in recent years and now visit our gardens more frequently. *(Mike Wilkes)*

More Birds on the Increase

Huge flocks of diving duck, particularly **Common Pochards** and **Tufted Ducks**, are now a regular feature in the Middle Tame Valley at Coton Pools and Lea Marston. *(Mike Lane)*

The rapid increase in **Little Egrets** in Britain has been reflected in the number of sightings in this region since the early 1990s. *(Mike Lane)*

As they spread from the Continent, more and more **Yellow-legged Gulls** are now being discovered amongst the flocks of gulls at the region's waters. *(Mike Lane)*

Some Birds New to the Region

Amongst the birds new to the region since 1979 was this **Desert Wheatear** at Barton Gravel Pits, Staffordshire, in 1996.

(*Phill Ward*)

Staffordshire also claimed the first **Cattle Egret**, at Doxey Marshes in 1987, but this photograph shows the second bird, which was seen at Besford, Worcestershire, in 1993.

(*Phill Ward*)

The first **Bonaparte's Gull** in the region was discovered at Kenilworth, Warwickshire, in 1990. Since then there have been another four sightings of this rare visitor from North America.

(*Keith Warmington*)

Some Birds Rare or New to the Region

The first **Melodious Warbler** was at Newcastle-under-Lyme, Staffordshire, in 1996, but this picture shows one that was ringed at Brandon Marsh, Warwickshire, in 2000.

(Andy Hale)

Although not quite a new bird, this superb male **Woodchat Shrike**, at Sutton Park, West Midlands, in 1999, was the first in the region for over 100 years. *(Phill Ward)*

There have been just five records of the North American **Buff-breasted Sandpiper**, the first being in 1978.

(Phill Ward)

Each year, **Mute Swans** are carefully rounded up during their summer moult and herded into a pen ready for ringing.   (*J.&G. Harrison*)

Identification rings are attached and each bird is measured and weighed. The information gathered tells us the age and condition of every individual. That way we can monitor the health of the herd and get early warning of any harmful changes in the environment.

(*J.&G. Harrison*)

Ringing of Birds

The small, light metal alloy ring seen on this **Blackbird** (left) causes no discomfort to the bird.

Ringing migrant birds, such as the **Turtle Dove** here (centre left), tells us which routes they follow and where they spend the winter, or summer, when they are not in this country.

We know, for example, that **Barn Swallows** (bottom right) travel to southern Africa and back each year. Knowing this helps us to assess whether numbers are being affected by conditions at home or abroad, such as droughts in Africa.

Ringing also enables fairly plain birds, such as this **Meadow Pipit** (bottom left), to be closely studied and this can reveal characteristics that aid field identification.

(all photos: Bert Coleman)

Sedge Warbler *Acrocephalus schoenobaenus*

Fairly common to common, though declining, summer resident.

The first Sedge Warblers announce their arrival in mid-April by indulging in song flights or singing from a prominent bramble or thorn bush. They have a clear preference for wetlands and most are found around flooded gravel pits or along rivers and canals, but some occur well away from water, in dry scrub, bramble and fields of oilseed rape. There are signs that small sewage treatment works with reed filtration beds could become another useful habitat.

The species suffers very badly from the unpredictable rainfall in its west African wintering grounds and following the most severe drought of 1983 it is estimated that fewer than 5% of adults returned to their breeding territories (*Breeding Atlas*). Such events are very evident from the CBC/BBS Index, which shows repeated troughs, followed by brief recoveries, but little long-term change. Numbers at individual sites broadly follow these cycles, but their long-term trends often vary. For instance, the populations at Alvecote Pools and Upton Warren remained fairly stable during the current period, whereas that at Kingsbury Water Park fell by two-thirds after the 1991 collapse and seemingly failed to recover. Conversely, numbers at Doxey Marshes doubled to around 70 pairs, making this the most important site for Sedge Warblers in the region. Rivers have also been shown to be important,

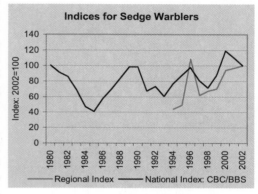

with at least 53 singing males counted along the Trent and some of its tributaries during the Waders of Wet Meadows Survey in Staffordshire in 1982, while 65 pairs were found in the lower Avon valley in 1988.

The range also contracted by a quarter between the 1968-72 and 1988-91 BTO *Atlases*, with birds disappearing from the Dales, the Teme Valley and the headwaters of the Warwickshire Stour—all hilly areas with fast-flowing streams and rivers, which afford sub-optimal habitat. Whilst birds were recorded in 73% of 10-km squares, it is clear from the *Breeding Atlas* that this region is on the edge of the Sedge Warbler's range in terms of density, so a slower recovery might be expected in a marginal area. Certainly the *Atlas* shows abundance levels to have been below average almost everywhere, with the highest levels along the lower reaches of the Severn, Avon and Trent where the riparian habitat is augmented by sand and gravel quarries. A population of 7,000-8,000 was suggested in *BWM*, but with few sites holding more than twenty pairs and precious little quantitative data from the rivers and canals, a conservative estimate now would be no higher than 2,000-4,000 pairs.

One at Upton Warren on March 29th 1998 was the earliest spring arrival, but the average date for first birds over sixty-four years was April 15th. However, the average during 1992-2001 was seven days earlier. Spring passage is the stronger of the two, with sizeable influxes in some years. For example, good numbers in 1996 brought at least 60 to Upton Warren on April 21st. Birds have also been recorded in gardens, some of them in song. The long migration back to sub-Saharan Africa begins in late July and reaches its height in mid-August. This return passage is less intense, with birds slipping quietly away in small groups. By late September most have left, with the 29th being the average date for last birds based on fifty-eight years of observation. The latest was at Doxey Marshes on November 5th 1988.

Birds ringed in the region during June and July have been re-caught in France during August of the same or following years, while others ringed in France and Belgium during July and August have been recovered in subsequent years in Warwickshire and Staffordshire.

385

Sedge Warblers provide some excellent examples of quite rapid migratory movements, with one ringed at Bedworth in August 1992 moving 239 km to Sandwich Bay (Kent) in two days, while another, ringed at Maer in August 1991 took just five days to travel 269 km to Dorset. Many of the recoveries show birds travelling to Icklesham (Sussex), where they congregate prior to crossing to the Continent. The longest recorded movements involved two adults, one ringed at Settat in Morocco, which travelled to Packington, and the other ringed in Chenec-Saint-Seurun-d'Uzet in France, which moved 780 km to Hams Hall.

Marsh Warbler   *Acrocephalus palustris*
Rare passage migrant. Formerly a summer resident.

The recent history of the Marsh Warbler in the West Midlands makes depressing reading. For many years the Lower Avon Valley in Worcestershire was the national stronghold of the species, holding three-quarters of the UK population (Sharrock, 1976). Because of the area's importance, the WoWT worked hard to secure the protection and appropriate management of some twenty riparian sites between Evesham and Tewkesbury, where this delightful songster nested amongst beds of nettle, meadowsweet, willowherb, osiers and other rank vegetation.

Early records provided little quantitative data, but a comprehensive survey in 1977 revealed 46 singing males. Allowing for some under-recording, this was taken to indicate a population of 50-60 breeding pairs. No changes in status were reported over the next four years and a second census in 1982 confirmed a stable population, with 45 singing males at eighteen sites. From this a maximum of 60-65 pairs was postulated. The next year numbers were similar, with 44 males at sixteen sites and there was nothing to portend the catastrophe about to befall. Within four years the population collapsed to just three breeding pairs and an unpaired male in 1987.

In the interim, ringing data provided a valuable insight into what was going wrong. Firstly, it showed more males returning than females. Then it revealed that, of those birds ringed in 1984, 48% of adults had returned, but only 14% of juveniles. With fewer females and young birds, the population had clearly become unsustainable. What ringing could not tell us was why the population had crashed in this way, but the cause was widely believed to lie beyond the breeding sites, possibly along the migration routes or in the wintering grounds.

By 1989 the sole record was of an unpaired male that had been colour-ringed there the previous year and it seemed that would be the end of the story. But surprisingly there was a twist in the tail, when six pairs returned to breed in 1990, raising 14 young, and four pairs in 1991, two of which were successful. Sadly, any optimism soon waned, as 1992 saw four males return, but only one female came to complete a breeding pair. The final proof of breeding came in 1993, when two pairs raised six young. Thereafter, returning males continued to search in vain for non-existent mates. Four sang in 1994 and again in 1995, when one paired with a female Reed Warbler, and two sang in 1996. The final chapter in this unhappy saga was the sad spectacle of a single male, originally ringed here in 1991, singing to attract a mate in 1997 and again in 1998. These were the final records.

Prior to the collapse of the core population in the Lower Avon Valley, sporadic breeding or singing birds were also noted at a few sites in Worcestershire beyond the normal breeding range. This occurred in 1978 (three sites with breeding at one), 1979, 1980, 1983 (two sites) and 1984. Following the crash, such occurrences were confined to singles singing in the south of the county in 1986, in Warwickshire in 1987 and 1992 and in the Lenches, where a bird previously ringed in the Avon Valley was discovered in 1995. The only record since the collapse was an overshooting migrant at Brandon Marsh on May 27th 2001. Paradoxically, whilst the Marsh Warbler was inexorably vanishing from the Lower Avon Valley, it was doing well in south-east England. It seems equally likely, therefore, that sightings at Sandwell Valley in 1982, Brandon Marsh in

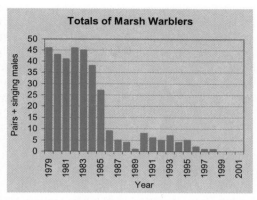

Totals of Marsh Warblers

Notes: 1. Figures vary slightly from those in the text, as the graph includes records from outside the Lower Avon Valley.
2. Assumes minimum of 40 territorial males in Lower Avon Valley during 1979-81, when no change in status was reported.

1987 and Doxey Marshes in 1996 were overshooting birds from the growing population in the south-east rather than from the traditional Worcestershire sites.

Despite the declining numbers, the region's Marsh Warblers still reflected the recent trend for summer migrants to arrive earlier, with one on May 15th 1993 the earliest on record. Otherwise the average date for first arrivals over forty-eight years was May 30th. Information on departures is very scanty, but most left during July or early August.

Records show Marsh Warblers have a high degree of site fidelity. A juvenile male ringed at Pershore in June 1985 was not seen again until it was re-trapped on the same site in May 1989. It then returned to this site for the next four years and it is possible that it also did so from 1986-88, but remained undetected. Another bird, ringed in July 1991 at Defford, was re-trapped at the same site in 1996 and 1997. The longest recorded movement was of a bird ringed at Defford as a nestling in August 1985 and found dead the following October 2,968 km away at Karpathos, Greece, confirming the south-easterly route taken to their wintering grounds in south-east Africa.

Reed Warbler   *Acrocephalus scirpaceus*
Fairly common to common summer resident.

True to its name, the Reed Warbler is very seldom found far from stands of common reed, although at times these may be very small. Because of this, it has a much more restricted range than the Sedge Warbler, but breeds in colonies in the reedbeds at places such as Aqualate, Brandon Marsh, Copmere, Ladywalk and Upton Warren. Many pairs also nest in the narrow strips of reed that fringe sluggish lowland rivers, abandoned canals and the margins of lakes and flooded gravel pits. More recently they have begun to nest in the reed filtration beds now being installed at small sewage treatment works.

This is one of the later summer migrants to return from wintering in Africa and very few are seen before May, even though the average date for the first birds to arrive, over sixty years, was April 25th. The earliest record came from Brandon Marsh on April 10th 1977.

The *Breeding Atlas* shows birds to have been present in 53% of 10-km squares, but their specialised habitat needs means they are very localised. For instance, the BBS suggests that Warwickshire and the West Midlands county have the highest densities in the region, yet preliminary results from the two *tetrad atlases* show only 20% of squares to be occupied in Warwickshire, whilst in Birmingham and the Black Country the figure is just 9%.

This is one of the hardest species to adequately census, since even counting singing males can be difficult at colonies in inaccessible reedbeds. Information is therefore sparse. However, Reed Warblers winter further south than Sedge Warblers, so they have been less affected by the unpredictable rainfall of the Sahel region and the CBC/BBS index rose by almost 40% between 1989-2002. Locally there were many reports of increases from the mid 1980s coupled with some declines. Based largely on singing males, *BWM* postulated 2,000-3,000 territories, but the current population may be slightly higher at 2,000-3,500 pairs.

At Alvecote Pools around six pairs were consistently reported during the current period (range 4-8), whilst the important Brandon Marsh colony averaged 40 pairs (range 30-50). Some colonies increased from the mid-1980s, with Belvide Reservoir growing from just one or two pairs to twelve, Doxey Marshes from around six to twelve and Upton Warren from around 10 to 25 pairs. Other notable counts included 44 territories along a 5 km stretch of the Droitwich Canal in 1987 increasing to 82 singing males in 1998, 60 pairs in the lower Avon valley in 1988 and 73 along a 10 km stretch of the Worcester and Birmingham Canal in 2001. Up to 15 pairs were also noted at Napton sewage works, with smaller numbers at several similar works in south Warwickshire, while one sang well away from water in a crop of oilseed rape at Harbury in 2001. Even more unusually, in June 1996 one sang for two days in a patch of scrub along Birmingham's inner ring road! During the course of a Constant Effort ringing programme at Betley Mere 178 were caught in one season in 1994, demonstrating just how many birds can use a single site.

Late July sees the start of the return passage, which then reaches its peak in the second half of August. Numbers thereafter quickly diminish and September 26th is the average date for last birds over fifty-four years of recording. Stragglers are not unusual, however, with the latest being at Betley Mere on October 31st 1988.

Reed Warblers illustrate well the migratory journeys made by our summer visitors. Many from all parts of the region make a southerly autumnal movement to the coast at Icklesham (Sussex), which features prominently as a staging post. In spring it is also a major point through which a lot of our Reed Warblers pass before dispersing to the West Midlands. The longest movement recorded involved an adult ringed in April 1993 in the Parc National du Djoudi, Senegal, and re-caught 4,218 km away, at Tixall in April 1995. Similarly an adult ringed at Chillington in August 1989 was found dead in the same park in Senegal in April 1992. Our oldest known Reed Warbler was ringed as a nestling at Brandon Marsh on June 20th 1990 and last re-trapped at the same site just six days short of nine years from when it was ringed. This individual also provides an excellent example of the site fidelity shown by many Reed Warblers, having nested in the same ditch on the marsh during its continuous breeding span of eight years. Site fidelity was also demonstrated by one that was caught in the same net at Whitacre Heath for seven consecutive years.

Great Reed Warbler   *Acrocephalus arundinaceus*
Very rare vagrant. Two records.

There have been no records to add to the two documented in *BWM*.

Regional Record Number	County Record Number		Year	Locality, Date and Notes
1	Warks	1	1977	Brandon Marsh: June 12th., trapped and ringed. *BB 71:520*
2	Warks	2	1979	Brandon Marsh: June 10th, trapped and ringed. *BB 73:523*

For two to be caught at the same locality within two years, and on dates just two days apart, is a remarkable coincidence. Great Reed Warblers breed discontinuously across much of the Continent and winter in sub-Saharan Africa. Most British records are of overshooting migrants in May and June (Dymond *et al*. 1989).

Icterine Warbler   *Hippolais icterina*
Very rare vagrant. Two records.

There have been two further records to add that listed in *BWM*.

Regional Record Number	County Record Number	Year	Locality, Date and Notes
1	Worcs 1	1942	Sheriffs Lench: in song, June 29th.
2	Staffs 1	1993	Belvide Reservoir: in song, July 10th.
3	Warks 1	1997	Napton Hill: August 25th.

Icterine Warblers are long distance migrants, breeding in Fennoscandia and from the Low Countries eastwards through Europe and wintering in southern Africa. They are scarce, though regular, migrants to Britain, mainly along the east and south coasts in autumn, but are much less numerous in spring. The three listed records are interesting in that inland occurrences are relatively rare, whilst late June and early July is extremely late for spring passage birds, most of which go through during May (Dymond *et al*. 1989).

Melodious Warbler   *Hippolais polyglotta*
Very rare vagrant. Two records.

After waiting so long to make its debut, two in fairly quick succession were unexpected.

Regional Record Number	County Record Number	Year	Locality, Date and Notes
1	Staffs 1	1996	Newcastle-under-Lyme: May 20th.
2	Warks 1	2000	Brandon Marsh: adult, June 3rd, trapped and ringed.

Melodious Warblers breed in Iberia, France and Italy and winter in west Africa. Whilst the vast majority are recorded in autumn, the above dates are typical for overshooting spring migrants to reach Britain and the Newcastle bird coincided with an unprecedented influx along the south coast.

Blackcap   *Sylvia atricapilla*
Very common to abundant summer resident. Frequent and increasing winter visitor.

The Blackcap's habitat preference is for deciduous woodland with a well developed shrub layer. In this regard its requirements are very similar to those of the Garden Warbler, but it is less fastidious and much more tolerant of a closed canopy. As a consequence, it has been less affected by the cessation of coppicing, which has allowed so many of the region's woods to grow into high forest. Birds also occur in a range of marginal habitats, including the scrub on former industrial and gravel extraction sites and urban parks.

The Blackcap is one of the twentieth century's avian successes, with both breeding and wintering numbers showing very marked increases. The *Breeding Atlas* shows they were present in every 10-km square and that breeding was indeed proved in all bar one. Abundance was highest along the Avon, Severn and Teme valleys in Worcestershire and lowest in central Staffordshire. This pattern is reinforced by the BBS, which shows densities to be highest in Worcestershire and the West Midlands county and lowest in Warwickshire and Staffordshire.

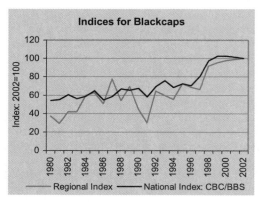

The national CBC/BBS index shows that the population almost doubled during 1980-2002, while the more exaggerated regional index suggests that locally it might have grown even more. Overall, the current regional population is probably in the range 20,000-30,000 pairs compared with the 7,000-13,000 estimated in *BWM*.

On the Malverns numbers increased from around 60 pairs in the late 1980s to 100 pairs in the early 1990s, while at Coombes Valley they rose more gradually from about a dozen pairs in the 1980s to almost twenty pairs in the late 1990s. There was also an increase at Sandwell Valley in the same period, but elsewhere numbers were more variable with no clear long-term trend. Interesting examples of density include 1.1 pairs per ha in the small-leaved lime coppice at Shrawley Wood in 1985, seven pairs in 14 ha at Packington Park in 1988, two pairs in 6 ha at Windmill Hill in 1990 and 10 in 100 ha of mixed habitat at Ladbroke in 1997.

The WMBC ceased recording arrival and departure dates in 1991 because it became impossible to distinguish migrants from an increasing number of wintering birds. Prior to then the average date for first arrivals, based on fifty-years of observation, was April 4th, whilst for departures, based on fifty-three years, it was October 10th. Loose gatherings up to 10 are frequently reported on autumn passage, with the largest being a 'fall' of 18 at Napton Hill in September 2000 and at least 25 at Wormleighton Reservoir on September 10th 1999. Most of our breeding Blackcaps are migratory, wintering around the western Mediterranean as evidenced by three ringing recoveries from Morocco and two from Algeria—each representing movements of over 1,000 km. One bird also moved from Staffordshire to Belgium, whilst domestic journeys saw movements from this region to Dorset, Berkshire, Sussex and Kent during July-September, and others coming here from Yorkshire during July and August. A bird ringed in Kent also arrived here in May.

Although there was a winter record back in 1930/1, the phenomenon of over-wintering really began in the late 1960s. It then gathered momentum in the 1970s and by the time of the *Winter Atlas* birds were recorded in 62% of 10-km squares. Since then numbers have increased still further, from just over 40 a year in the 1980s to some 120 a year in the 1990s. Ratcliffe (1999) undertook an informative study of wintering birds in Worcestershire. This is the most favoured county (38% of birds), followed by the West Midlands (31%), Warwickshire (17%) and Staffordshire (14%). These wintering birds are quite distinct from the breeding population and come from the near Continent (*Breeding Atlas*), but our only ringing recovery is of a young female, ringed in Hertfordshire in November 1999 and killed by a car in Nuneaton in January 2004. Numbers appear to build up quickly during October-December and peak in February. However, this is probably because they initially remain within the cover of shrubberies and woods, feeding on native fruits such as honeysuckle, but become more obvious as the winter progresses and they venture more into gardens to feed at bird tables, or on the berries of exotic shrubs such as cotoneaster, skimmia and viburnum.

Garden Warbler *Sylvia borin*
Fairly common to common summer resident.

The Garden Warbler has a beautiful, sustained contralto song, which it usually delivers from deep cover. Its preferred habitat is broad-leaved woodland with a dense, tall tangle of coppice growth, shrubs and ground cover beneath an open canopy. As a secondary habitat, it also resorts to dense patches of scrub on hillsides, commons and farmland.

At one time Garden Warblers were considered to outnumber Blackcaps (Smith 1938 and Norris 1947), but records show that during 1954-68 there was little difference between the two (*BWM*). Since then, the Blackcap has forged ahead to become clearly the more abundant. Habitat change is largely responsible, since the Blackcap is more tolerant of the closed canopies that have developed over so many broad-leaved woods since coppicing ceased. Competition between the two could also be a factor, as Blackcaps are the first to arrive on their territories and they may then exclude Garden Warblers from otherwise suitable sites (Garcia 1983).

The average date for the first birds to arrive from wintering in central or southern Africa, based on sixty-three years of records, was April 20th, with the main influx following in May. One at Tittesworth Reservoir on March 22nd 1998 was exceptionally early. Garden Warblers are quite widely distributed with records from 96% of 10-km squares shown in the *Breeding Atlas* and above average abundance levels in the meres and mosses area and the Churnet and lower Avon valleys.

Nationally the CBC/BBS index increased by 25% during 1980-2002, but this mostly occurred during the 1980s, for which time there is little comparable regional data. The BBS, however, highlights a divergence of trends, with the national index falling since 1997 whereas regionally it appears to have risen sharply since 1995. Local references to numbers being high in 1987 and low in 1994 indicate a degree of conformity to the national pattern at those times, but other reports of stable populations in the late 1990s from three Worcestershire sites at Dog Hanging Coppice,

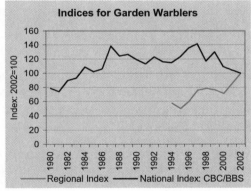

Indices for Garden Warblers

Long Bank and Shelfheld are at variance with both indices. Of the shire counties, the BBS shows the highest density to be in Staffordshire and the lowest in Warwickshire, where the species has probably declined through loss of habitat (J. J. Bowley *pers. comm.*). Preliminary results from the *Tetrad Atlases* show about a quarter of the urban tetrads to be occupied and just over a third of the rural ones. From this confusing picture the regional population is tentatively put at 2,000-5,000 pairs compared with the 2,000-4,000 pairs estimated in *BWM*.

Trends are best illustrated by counts from the Malverns and Coombes Valley. Comprehensive surveys at the former during 1986-95 showed numbers climbing from 61 pairs to a maximum of 115 in 1991, only to fall back again to 77 pairs. The pattern at Coombes Valley was similar during 1988-99, but with a different timing as numbers rose from 28 pairs to a peak of 44 in 1989 before settling back at an average of 20 pairs a year. An exceptional 20 pairs in 9 ha of small-leaved lime coppice at Shrawley Wood in 1985 emphasised the importance of this habitat, whilst five pairs in 8 ha of damp woodland at Packington in 1988 was well above average. Outside woodland, four or five pairs along one kilometre of the Oxford Canal at Fenny Compton in the late 1990s was also a high density.

Departure begins in late-July. Birds then gradually drift away during August, when small groups are sometimes seen, with the most reported during the current period being 15 at Brandon Marsh on August 9th 1998. The average date for last birds, calculated on sixty-two years of observation, was September 16th, but very late individuals were noted at Sutton Coldfield on November 19th 1992 and at Acton on November 22nd 1975.

The few recoveries of ringed birds show only local movements of 15 km and under, but there is one record of a long distance movement involving a bird ringed at Brandon Marsh in August 1988 and shot 5,172 km away, in Obudu, Nigeria, in March 1990, which indicates a south-westerly migration. The only other movement of note was a juvenile, ringed at Lea Marston in July 1986, and re-trapped the following month 258 km away at Dungeness (Kent).

Barred Warbler   *Sylvia nisoria*
Very rare vagrant. One record.

The only record is that documented in *BWM*.

Regional Record Number	County Record Number		Year	Locality, Date and Notes
1	Warks	1	1979	Brandon Marsh: adult male, June 3rd, trapped and ringed.

Barred Warblers breed from eastern Europe and the Balkans, through Russia and into Asia and winter in east Africa. They are scarce, but regular, visitors in autumn, mostly to counties along the east and south coasts. Spring records, however, are exceedingly rare as are those inland (Dymond *et al.* 1989). This bird was therefore exceptional on two counts.

Lesser Whitethroat   *Sylvia curruca*
Fairly common summer resident. Two winter records.

The Lesser Whitethroat is a bird of lowland farmland, especially where there are tall, thick hedges of hawthorn and blackthorn. Some also nest in the scrubby areas on commons and around abandoned gravel pits.

The first birds usually arrive in April, settle quickly into their territories and begin to nest straight away. Over sixty-four years the average date for first arrivals was April 21st, but during 1992-2001 it was five days earlier. The earliest to be recorded was at Kingsbury Water Park on April 3rd 1994.

During the *Breeding Atlas* birds were recorded in 92% of 10-km squares, but apart from the lower Avon valley and south-east Feldon areas, their abundance was slightly below average. Their absence from the high moors and central Birmingham was to be expected, but it is harder to understand why they were not recorded in a large part of Arden, where thick hedgerows are generally plentiful. Work for the two *tetrad atlases* has shown them to be present in a quarter of the tetrads covering Birmingham and the Black Country and slightly more than half of those in Warwickshire. Interestingly, the latter confirms the distribution of the *Breeding Atlas* by showing very few in Arden, but plenty in Feldon, where it is said to be the fourth commonest warbler after Common Whitethroat, Blackcap and Common Chiffchaff (J. J. Bowley *pers. comm.*).

Nationally the CBC/BBS index was very erratic during 1980-2002, but it did show an overall decline of around 40%. Much of this was due to loss of habitat through the mechanical trimming and grubbing up of hedges. Regionally the BBS sample is too small to show a trend, but, in terms of abundance, the *Breeding Atlas* shows the West Midlands to be on the fringe of the Lesser Whitethroat's range, so densities are probably below the national average. This suggests a current population in the range of 1,000-2,000 pairs, which is only half the 2,000-4,000 pairs estimated in *BWM*. This decrease accords well with the decline in the CBC/BBS index.

Apart from the CBC, evidence on local densities is scarce, but six territories in 85 ha of arable area around Shipston-on-Stour in 2000 was seven times the national average, indicating the excellent numbers still to be found in the Feldon and Cotswold fringe stronghold. In the former area there were good numbers at both Fenny Compton and the DM Kineton army camp, where, apart from the collapse in 1998, the average counts in recent years have been eight and 16 respectively. Elsewhere, seven pairs along 10 km of the Worcester and Birmingham canal demonstrate the value of the thick hedges that border many miles of canal. Site totals typically vary from one year to the next, but at places such as Belvide Reservoir, Ladywalk, the Malverns, Sandwell Valley and Upton Warren there has been little long-term change. This points to habitat loss in the wider countryside being the main cause of decline.

The only two ringing recoveries for the current period involved a juvenile ringed in July 1980 at Saddington Reservoir (Leicestershire) and found dead in August 1983 at Brandon Marsh and a first-year male ringed in September 1985 at Frampton-on-Severn (Glos) and retrapped in May 1986 at Malvern. However, the Lesser Whitethroat is known to have an unusual migration strategy, travelling south-eastwards via the eastern Mediterranean to winter in north-east and central Africa. Most birds start their journey between mid-August and late September, with September 22nd the average date for last birds over sixty-four years of records. During this period small parties up to ten may be observed working their way along hedgerows or through the bushes around gravel pits and reservoirs. Passage birds occasionally visit gardens and in 1997 individuals were even noted at Dartmouth Circus and St Chad's Circus in central Birmingham. In 2001, one lingered until October 22nd, in the Kingsbury area, whilst the first wintering birds—a nationally increasing phenomenon—were noted in a Stafford garden from November 25th into December 1999 and at Fens Pools in December 2001.

Common Whitethroat   (Whitethroat)   *Sylvia communis*
Very common to abundant summer resident.

Common Whitethroats occur throughout the region on heaths and commons, along hedgerows and in areas of scrub, young forestry and industrial wastes. They especially favour open areas with thickets of gorse, bramble and hawthorn. They forage and nest low down, so often utilise the low-trimmed hedges around arable fields that are unsuited to other hedgerow species.

The population collapsed during the winter of 1968/9 as a result of the prolonged drought in the Sahel region of Africa and three-quarters failed to return the following spring (Winstanley *et al*. 1974). *BWM* then charted the beginnings of a faltering recovery, which, despite further set-backs such as those of 1984 and 1991, has continued ever since. Even so, numbers have never reached their pre 1969 levels.

Although one was recorded on the incredibly early date of March 22nd, at Ladywalk in 1991, most birds do not arrive before mid-April and the average date for first arrivals over sixty-six years is April 14th. In common with most migrants, however, recent arrivals have tended to be earlier and the average advanced by five days during 1992-2001.

The Common Whitethroat is widely distributed and the *Breeding Atlas* recorded birds in 97% of 10-km squares, with only the northern moors and the centre of Birmingham uninhabited. Abundance was mostly average everywhere, but was greatest in the southern parts of Warwickshire and Worcestershire. Despite some exaggerated fluctuations resulting from the

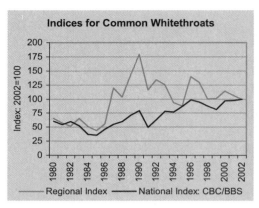

Indices for Common Whitethroats

Index: 2002=100

200
175
150
125
100
75
50
25
0

1980 1982 1984 1986 1988 1990 1992 1994 1996 1998 2000 2002

——— Regional Index ——— National Index: CBC/BBS

small sample size, the regional index broadly reflected the national trend during 1980-2002, showing an increase of around 60%. This suggests a regional population of 20,000-35,000 pairs (*cf.* 5,000-15,000 estimated in *BWM*).

The prime habitat on the hills and commons of the Malverns holds exceptional numbers and territory counts here during 1987-1995 averaged 112 and ranged from 100 in 1991, which was a poor year generally, to 175 during the peak year of 1990. Unfortunately only partial counts have been made here since. Good numbers also occur at the DM Kineton army camp, where numbers halved from 86 to 43 between 1992 and 1993, but then rose again to around 80 again during the next decade. An estimated 66 pairs were in the Middle Tame Valley in 1987, but there have been no further comprehensive counts of this area. Belvide Reservoir and Brandon Marsh generally hold 10-20 pairs, with their respective averages during 1992-2001 being 13 and 14, but otherwise few regularly monitored sites exceed ten pairs. There are several examples of density, mostly from Warwickshire and especially the Feldon district. These vary widely according to the different habitats, with six pairs along 1.6 km of woodland edge at Leek Wootton in 1989, six pairs in 7 ha of unmanaged meadowland at Haseley in 1999, nine in 100 ha of arable fields at Ladbroke in 2000 and nine pairs in 7 ha of young forestry at Upper Kingston in 2001. The latter year also produced 20 pairs along 1.5 km of the Oxford Canal at Fenny Compton, where surveys of the parish during 1996-99 revealed an average of five pairs per 100 ha. Within the West Midlands county birds use the canals and rivers to penetrate the urban core, where males have been heard in song at Aston, Deers Leap Wood at Edgbaston and Small Heath railway station.

Departure takes place during August and September, with September 30th the average date for last birds based on sixty-seven years of observation. Extremely late birds were recorded at Lower Smite Farm in 1998, when one fed on berries from November 21st-28th, and Draycote Water, where one was at the feeding station on November 30th 2001.

A bird ringed at Upton Warren in August 1996 and found dead there in July 2000 indicates site fidelity. Other recoveries give some indication of the route taken on migration, with two in Iberia mentioned in *BWM* and a further one since of a recently fledged bird that was ringed at Lea Marston in July 1980 and found dead 2,437 km away in Morocco in December 1981. *BWM* also includes an unusual record of a bird ringed in Nuneaton in June 1955 and found on the Gocree lightship, in the North Sea, on June 11th 1956.

Dartford Warbler   *Sylvia undata*
Very rare winter visitor. Seven records.

Two definite records were listed in *BWM*, the most recent of which was in 1914. Eighty-one years then passed before the next, but there have now been five in the space of seven years— all of them in Worcestershire.

Britain is at the northernmost extremity of the Dartford Warbler's range, where until recently it was largely confined to the lowland, gorse-clad heaths of Dorset, the New Forest and Surrey. It is particularly vulnerable to cold weather and mortality is heavy in hard winters. However, numbers are currently high following the recent run of mild winters and birds have begun to colonise, or re-colonise, other parts of the country. The recent records in this region reflect this spread, but so far all have been outside the breeding season. There is, however, a

Regional Record Number	County Record Number		Year	Locality, Date and Notes
1	Staffs	1	c1870	Cannock Chase: pair on unknown date, captured and taken with eggs.
2	Warks	1	1914	Yarningale Common: October 10th-11th.
3	Worcs	1	1995	Lickey Hills: first-winter, December 9th-31st.
4	Worcs	2	1997	Castlemorton Common: March 6th.
5	Worcs	3	1998	Devils Spittleful: in sub-song, February 14th-21st.
6	Worcs	4	1999	Malvern Hills: female, August 6th intermittently to January 1st 2000.
7	Worcs	5	2001	Bittell Reservoir: first-winter male, October 9th.

remarkable report of a male singing and holding territory on the Malvern Hills from May 24th to June 1st 1987 (Parr 1987). The precise location is not specified, but it may have been outside Worcestershire as the record does not appear in the *WMBC Report*. A possible sighting near Rugeley in 1915, quoted by Smith (1938) and mentioned in *BWM*, is not included in the above list. Whether any remnants of our much-fragmented heathland will ever attract the species to breed again, as they seemingly did on Cannock Chase around 1870, remains to be seen.

Arctic Warbler   *Phylloscopus borealis*
Very rare vagrant. One record.

This little gem was just reward for those who regularly watch their local patch and delighted many during its stay.

Regional Record Number	County Record Number		Year	Locality, Date and Notes
1	Staffs	1	1993	Blithfield Reservoir: September 8th-11th. *BB 87:558*

Arctic Warblers breed across the sub-arctic belt of northern Fennoscandia and Russia and winter in south-east Asia. They are rare visitors to Britain and this was the first to be recorded away from coasts and islands (Rogers *et al.* 1994).

Pallas's Leaf Warbler   *Phylloscopus proregulus*
Very rare vagrant. Four records.

Three more records to add to that in *BWM*, brings the total for this tiny jewel of a bird to four.

Regional Record Number	County Record Number		Year	Locality, Date and Notes
1	Staffs	1	1970	Weston-under-Lizard: November 8th, trapped and ringed. *BB 64:361*
2	Worcs	1	1987	Westwood Park: immature, November 17th. *BB 82:550*
3	Warks	1	1993	Kenilworth: October 4th, seen in garden.
4	Warks	2	2001	Wolford Wood: November 4th.

Note: BBRC ceased to consider records of this species from January 1st 1991.

Although breeding in south-central Siberia and wintering in the Himalayan foothills, south-east Asia and southern China, Pallas's Leaf Warblers are regular autumn visitors to Britain in small numbers. All of the above fell within the peak time for British records in October and early November (Dymond *et al.* 1989).

Yellow-browed Warbler   *Phylloscopus inornatus*
Very rare vagrant. Six records.

Half of the records have come from Worcestershire, with one in each of the other counties.

Regional Record Number	County Record Number		Year	Locality, Date and Notes
1	Worcs	1	1986	Upton Warren: juvenile, October 8th.
2	Worcs	2	1993	Happy Valley: October 10th.
3	Warks	1	1996	Napton Hill: juvenile, September 22nd-26th.
4	W Mid	1	1998	Valley Park: October 25th-26th.
5	Worcs	3	1999	North Hill: October 13th.
6	Staffs	1	2001	Westport Lake: September 29th.

Yellow-browed Warblers breed from Siberia southwards to north-west India and eastwards across Asia and winter in India and south-east Asia. They are regular autumn visitors to Britain, occurring mainly in eastern and southern coastal counties during late September and October (Dymond *et al.* 1989).

Hume's Warbler   (Hume's Leaf Warbler)   *Phylloscopus humei*
Very rare vagrant. One record.

This diminutive warbler was originally regarded as a race of Yellow-browed Warbler, *P. i. humei* and was then known as Hume's Yellow-browed Warbler. It was only accorded the status of a separate species by the BOURC in 1997.

Regional Record Number	County Record Number		Year	Locality, Date and Notes
1	Staffs	1	1994	Westport Lake: December 20th. *BB 91:508*

Hume's Warbler breeds from central Asia south to the north-western Himalayas and winters across the Indian sub-continent from Pakistan to Bangladesh. Birds usually arrive in Britain during the second half of October and November, so it is possible that this individual had arrived some time before it was seen at Westport Lake.

Dusky Warbler   *Phylloscopus fuscatus*
Very rare vagrant. One record.

This amazing record of a superb bird for an urban locality is detailed on the facing page.

Regional Record Number	County Record Number	Year	Locality, Date and Notes
1	W Mid 1	1996	Sheepwash Urban Park: November 16th-18th. *BB 90:502.*

Dusky Warblers breed in Siberia and winter in India, southern China and south-east Asia. Although a few reach Britain each autumn, they mostly occur along the East and South Coasts and this was the first to be recorded so far inland.

Although initially elusive, it was eventually seen by many observers and proved just how good this reclaimed Black Country wasteland has become.

Wood Warbler *Phylloscopus sibilatrix*
Frequent, though declining, summer resident, now mainly confined to the north and west of the region.

The Wood Warbler today is largely confined to the sessile oakwoods of west Worcestershire and north Staffordshire—a habitat it shares with the Common Redstart and Pied Flycatcher. Its song is a characteristic sibilant trill, the delivery of which sets the whole bird quivering. It prefers woods with a closed canopy, little or no shrub layer and sparse ground cover. At one time it could be found sparingly in beechwoods, but these now appear to have been forsaken.

The West Midlands is very much on the edge of the Wood Warblers range and there has been a notable contraction to the north and west. Sharrock (1976) shows that birds were present in 69% of 10-km squares, but by the time of the *Breeding Atlas* they were present in only 56% of squares, having withdrawn from east Warwickshire especially. Since then they have also deserted Arden and none now nest in Warwickshire. Over the period 1980-2002 the number of sites at which birds were recorded fell by 60%.

This contraction of range has been accompanied by a fall in numbers, although information to confirm this is scanty. Even nationally the species has been poorly monitored and its inclusion on the *Amber Alert List* is based on a dramatic decline of 43% revealed by the BBS over the very short time span of 1994-2000 (Gregory *et al.* 2002). This decline has since continued and over the period 1994-2002 the BBS index fell by 60%. The regional BBS index, although based on a very small sample, showed a comparative fall of 70%—worrying figures indeed. Overall it seems the region might hold only 50-150 singing males, mostly in north Staffordshire and west Worcestershire, compared with 100-200 estimated in *BWM*.

Serious declines first became evident in 1983. For instance, at least 80 singing males were reported from Worcestershire in 1982, but by the following year there were only 46, while in Staffordshire numbers at Coombes Valley fell by 56%. At this locality they quickly recovered and until 1999, at least, they remained fairly stable, but in the Wyre

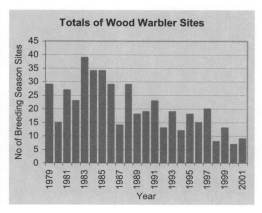

397

Forest they gradually declined still further and are now only a third of their former level. Both localities probably still hold around ten pairs, but comprehensive counts are lacking. During the BTO survey of 1984, 169 singing males were located in the nineteen 10-km squares covering Staffordshire, while WMBC surveys of Cannock Chase showed 13 singing males in 1983, 10 pairs in 1992, four in 1997 and seven territorial males in 2002 (Bennett *et al.* 2002). On the Malvern Hills numbers plummeted much later, from 30-40 pairs during the late 1980s to around 20 in the early 1990s. They then crashed completely to just three pairs in 1994 and none have been reported since 1997. Modest breeding populations on the Lickey Hills and in Sutton Park also faded away during the late 1980s and early 1990s and 1989 saw the last recorded nesting in Warwickshire, where small numbers had formerly bred at Bentley Park, Clowes Wood and Edge Hill.

Few are noted on passage as they return from their winter quarters in equatorial Africa, but the first birds are back on their breeding territories in April. The earliest to be recorded was on April 3rd, near Earlswood in 1967, and the average date for first birds over sixty-fours was April 21st, although many do not appear until May. Their departure is early and even less evident, with some leaving in late July and most during August. Over fifty-seven years the average date of the last birds seen was August 21st. An extremely late individual was at Kingstanding on October 5th 1986. A nestling ringed at West Malvern on June 17th 1985 and recaught at Wellington (Shropshire) in May 1986 is the only ringing recovery.

Common Chiffchaff   (Chiffchaff)   *Phylloscopus collybita*
Very common summer resident and uncommon winter visitor.

The Common Chiffchaff's onomatopoeic song, delivered from high in the woodland canopy, is a welcome sound in early spring. Although a few birds over-winter, the majority are summer visitors to the region that spend the winter around the Mediterranean or further south in Africa. They prefer tall trees and are most often found in mature deciduous woods and copses with a tall diverse understorey. Well-timbered hedgerows, heaths and even maturing forestry plantations are also used, although they dislike heavy shade. Wintering birds tend to seek warm, sheltered situations close to water.

Surveys for the *Breeding Atlas* found Common Chiffchaffs in 99% of 10-km squares, being absent only from the northern moors, where trees are few. Abundance levels were generally above average, reaching their highest levels in the south of the region. The BBS shows densities in Worcestershire to be twice those in other areas. Surveys for the two *Tetrad Atlases* have also shown birds to be quite widespread in urban areas, with records from 65% of tetrads compared with 88% in more rural parts.

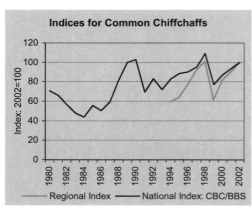

The CBC/BBS index shows considerable variation, with significant falls in the population in 1984, 1991, 1993 and 1999. Since 1997 the regional trend has closely followed the national pattern, but the data prior to that are too sparse to draw any conclusions. Nevertheless, along with Blackcap, this warbler seems to be doing very well. Overall, there was a 40% increase nationally between 1980-2002 and the regional population is now thought to be in the range 15,000-25,000 pairs compared with the 6,000-18,000 estimated in *BWM.* This increase has been greatly aided by the continued progression towards high forest of woods that once were coppiced.

The pattern at individual sites has been variable. On the hills and commons at Malvern, for instance the average number of pairs from 1988-95 was 120, but with a maximum of 163 in 1990 and a minimum of 89 the following year (*cf.* indices chart). However, at Coombes Valley numbers gradually doubled during 1990-98, from five pairs to eleven, whilst at the DM Kineton camp they ranged widely from 8-31 territories between 1993-2000. In comparison, numbers at wetland sites such as Alvecote Pools, Belvide Reservoir, Ladywalk, Sandwell Valley and Upton Warren remained relatively stable. Apart from the CBC plots, the only information on density comes from linear counts that showed 4 pairs per km along woodland edge at Wootton Wawen and 7 pairs per km along the Oxford Canal at Fenny Compton.

Because of the difficulty in separating migrants from wintering birds, the recording of first and last dates ceased in 1991. Prior to then, the average date for first arrivals, based on fifty-nine year's observations, was March 16th, although most do not arrive until the first half of April. The bulk of birds leave during September, with the average for the last departing ones, over fifty-six years, being October 16th. Seldom are more than a dozen noted together on spring passage, so 20 at Bredon's Hardwick on March 27th 1990 and at Castlemorton Common on March 25th 2000 were noteworthy, whilst 50 at Pendeford Mill on April 13th 1996 was an outstanding count. Larger groups are seen in autumn, with up to 25 quite often recorded and maxima of 44 at Castlemorton Common on September 9th 1995 and 50 in the nearby Happy Valley on August 24th 1989.

Although there are nineteenth century records of birds singing in February (Harthan 1946, Norris 1947), the extraordinary increase in wintering birds dates from the late 1970s. By the time of the *Winter Atlas* there were records from 26% of 10-km squares, although at this time less than ten birds a year were being reported. By the late 1990s this figure had risen to a little over 50 a year, with the two southern counties being most favoured. Most are seen along streams or around reservoirs and gravel pits. In colder weather, though, they frequently exploit the warmth of industrial installations, especially the filter beds and outfalls of small sewage treatment works where insects are plentiful. In harsh weather they may also visit gardens. Even so, survival is hard, with the percentage of birds increasing from 28% in November to a peak of 38% in December, but then fading away in the colder months to 21% in January and just 13% in February.

Most ringing recoveries show birds returning to the same, or relatively close, sites in subsequent years. Other recoveries reveal southerly movements, with two that were ringed in Worcestershire during the summer being re-trapped in Sussex the following September and one ringed in Warwickshire in September being re-caught the next month in Kent. In spring a bird ringed in Wiltshire in March 1986 was recovered in Stourport-on-Severn in May of that year. The three foreign recoveries during the current period involved a bird ringed at Bilbrook Sewage Works in August 1992 that had moved 2,340 km to Morocco by December; one ringed at Alfrick in July 1992 that by October had reached Renteria, Spain, 986 km away; and another ringed in Senegal in January 1993 that travelled 4,158 km to Storridge Common, where it was re-caught in the following July.

A bird that held territory for three consecutive springs at Fens Pools between 1992-94 was identified from its distinctive song as being of the then race *P. c. brehmii*, or 'Iberian' Chiffchaff (*WMBC Annual Reports* 60:146 and 61:144). This race has subsequently been recognised by the BOU as a separate species, known as the Iberian Chiffchaff *P. ibericus* and even retrospective records are now assessed by the BBRC. Up to 2004 eight British records had been accepted, all based on sound-recordings (Rogers *et al*. 2004), and unless this one is submitted to and accepted by the BBRC, this species cannot be admitted to the regional list.

In recent years, close scrutiny of wintering individuals, coupled with a better knowledge of the identification features, has also revealed a growing number of 'northern race' birds. Latterly several have been discovered at small sewage treatment works and outfalls. Around a dozen were not assigned to a specific race, or were considered to be intergrades, but those listed under the relevant headings below were recorded as showing the characteristics of the Scandinavian and Siberian races *P. c. abietinus* and *P. c. tristis* respectively. Hybrid Willow Warbler x Common Chiffchaff, showing mixed physical and vocal characteristics, were also reported in 1993, 1995 (three separate localities) and 2001 (two separate localities).

Scandinavian Chiffchaff   *Phylloscopus collybita abietinus*
Rare winter visitor.

This race breeds from Norway and Sweden eastwards into Russia and winters in the eastern Mediterranean, the Middle East and east Africa. All dated records fell between October 20th and March 30th, with six in December.

Regional Record Number	County Record Number		Year	Locality, Date and Notes
1	Staffs	1	1983	Chasewater: December 10th.
2	Staffs	2	1989	Westport Lake: December 19th to January 1st 1990
3	W Mid	1	1989	Meriden: unknown date.
4	W Mid	2	1991	Meriden: October 20th-26th.
5	W Mid	3	1991	Sheepwash Urban Park: December 11th.
6	Worcs	1	2000	Lower Moor: January 4th-30th.
7	Worcs	2	2000	Lower Moor: March 15th.
8	Worcs	3	2000	Upton Warren: November 9th.
9	Worcs	4	2000	Kempsey Sewage Treatment Works: December 2nd-28th, with two 26th-28th, three during January 2001, two in February and one till March 30th 2001.
10	Worcs	5	2000	Lower Moor: December 17th-27th, then two to March 2nd 2001.
11	Worcs	6	2001	Upton-on-Severn Sewage Treatment Works: two, February 17th.
12	Worcs	7	2001	Lower Moor: two, December 2nd, with one on 8th.

Siberian Chiffchaff   *Phylloscopus collybita tristis*
Rare winter visitor.

This race breeds from the Pechora basin and the Urals eastwards across Russia and winters from the Middle East to India. All records occurred during the period September 23rd-April 18th, with December and January the main months with four each.

Regional Record Number	County Record Number		Year	Locality, Date and Notes
1	Worcs	1	1928	Evesham: September 27th. *BB XXII:262*
2	Warks	1	1976	Draycote Water: October 1st.
3	Staffs	1	1983	Blithfield Reservoir: September 23rd.
4	Staffs	2	1989	Hollybush Lake: November 2nd-3rd.
5	Worcs	2	1992	Eckington: April 18th.

Regional Record Number	County Record Number		Year	Locality, Date and Notes
6	W Mid	1	1994	Sandwell Valley: November 7th.
7	Staffs	3	1996	Chasewater: December 1st.
8	Staffs	4	1998	Westport Lake: December 7th-26th.
9	Warks	2	2000	Draycote Water: January 2nd.
10	Worcs	3	2000	Lower Moor: three, January 2nd-4th, with two till March 12th and one till 19th.
11	Warks	3	2000	Ladywalk: January 27th.
12	Worcs	4	2000	Kempsey Sewage Treatment Works: December 17th to February 21st 2001.
13	Worcs	5	2000	Lower Moor: December 17th to March 2nd 2001.
14	Worcs	6	2002	Redditch: January 1st-2nd.
15	Staffs	5	2002	Westport Lake: March 22nd-23rd, relocated April 5th-17th.
16	Worcs	7	2002	Lower Moor: December 22nd-26th.

Willow Warbler   *Phylloscopus trochilus*
Very common to abundant, but declining, summer resident. One winter record.

The Willow Warbler was described in *BWM* as the commonest of our summer visitors, but that is certainly no longer the case. It is still very widespread and can be found right across the region in urban as well as rural situations and from lowland river valleys to the highest moors. It breeds wherever there are bushes and small trees, but prefers open situations, such as heaths, commons and the edges and clearings of mature woodland, rather than a closed canopy. Many pairs can be found in the scrub around the region's wetlands, where insects are abundant, while large gardens, hedgerows and young forestry act as secondary habitats.

Willow Warblers are amongst the earliest of our summer visitors to return from wintering in southern Africa, with one at Doxey Marshes on March 10th 1990 the earliest to be recorded. Sixty-six years of records show the average date for first birds to be March 27th, but in common with most migrants, arrivals have recently been getting earlier and the average date during 1992-2001 was three days earlier. Parties up to 30 are quite regularly reported in spring and the largest gatherings during the current period were 70 at Edgbaston Reservoir in April 1984 and 75 at Wormleighton Reservoir on April 19th 2000.

The *Breeding Atlas* indicates a widespread distribution, with birds present in every 10-km square and the highest densities in north-east Worcestershire and the Churnet Valley. This is reinforced by the preliminary results from the two *Tetrad Atlases*, both of which indicate the presence of birds in two-thirds of all tetrads, while the BBS confirms that densities in Staffordshire are almost twice as high as in the other counties.

Assessing numbers is exceedingly difficult. The national CBC/BBS recorded a decline of 31% during 1974-99—sufficient to warrant inclusion on the *Amber List* of Species of Conservation Concern (Gregory *et al.* 2002). Impressions are that local declines have been much greater, although opinions vary from area to area. Ignoring the unexplained peak in 1996, the regional BBS data points to a sharper decline than has occurred nationally, particularly since 1998. Prior to 1994, the regional data is too variable to be regarded as reliable, but it implies a significant decline, perhaps by as much as three-quarters. In comparison the national decline was only a third. The CBC data also shows regional densities for both woodland and farmland

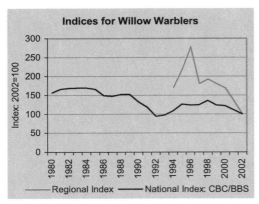

Indices for Willow Warblers

Index: 2002=100

———— Regional Index ———— National Index: CBC/BBS

to be only half of those nationally during the late 1990s. As a consequence, the regional population is probably at the lower end of the range 15,000-30,000 pairs, which is about half the 35,000-50,000 pairs suggested in *BWM*.

As a reminder of just how much fortunes have changed, counts from the Wyre Forest showed 61 singing Willow Warblers in 1982 compared with seven Common Chiffchaffs, while two years later the comparative figures were 39 and six. Today there is little difference in the ratio between the two, although Willow Warblers are much the scarcer in lowland areas. Indeed, until very recently it seemed little had changed in uplands areas, with the population reasonably stable at Coombes Valley where on average there were 125 pairs (range 108-134) during the 1990s. On the Malverns counts ranged from 326-436 during 1986-95, but with little long-term change. However, in 1999 numbers there were found to be 80% down in Happy Valley, although on Castlemorton Common there was no change. In the lowlands, there was a rapid decline at Trench Wood from 63 pairs to around eight as the hardwood plantations matured and it seems that many declines can probably be attributed to the widespread progression towards high forest. In the last few years, however, serious declines have also been reported from widely differing habitats, such as DM Kineton and Upton Warren, where numbers recently halved. Apart from the CBC, information on density is scant, but there were 23 pairs per km^2 in the Piccadilly-Wood End woods in 2000, 20 sang along 800m of Stanton Dale in 1999 and three pairs were in a km^2 at Chapel Green in 1998. A count of 120 singing males on Cannock Chase in 1997 indicates a strong population, but unfortunately there appear to be no other full counts for comparison.

Return passage gets underway in late July and peaks in the second half of August, when groups up to 40 can be seen. In August 1990 some 430 passed through Coombes Valley during the whole month, while a particularly strong passage in 1984 brought the largest autumn gatherings of the current period, with 60 at Westport Lake and 85 at Chasewater. In contrast to these, the highest count in recent years was only 45, at Napton Reservoir in 2001. Sixty-six years of observations have shown October 7th to be the average date for last birds, with the latest in Sandwell Valley on November 2nd 1989. However, one at Draycote Water on January 5th 2001 constitutes the first winter record for the region.

Birds ringed in the region and recovered during the same year show autumnal movements to the southern counties of Suffolk and Essex, while others have been re-caught in subsequent years in Dorset and Kent. Two summer ringed birds have also been recorded in more northerly counties in subsequent summers, with one ringed in Worcestershire in August 1991 and recovered in Strathclyde in June 1992 and another ringed in Staffordshire in August 1996 and recovered in North Yorkshire in May 1997.

There have also been four overseas recoveries. One ringed on April 24th 1999 in Cabrera, Spain, was killed by a cat at Yoxall on June 19th 2001; a bird ringed in the Channel Islands, on Sark, in April 1980 was at Little Aston in May 1981; a first-year male ringed at Betley Mere in August 1988 was recovered in Maisonneuve Vienne, France, in August 1989; and the longest recorded movement was one of 5,108 km made by a bird ringed at Sutton Coldfield in April 1982 and recovered in the Ivory Coast in January 1983.

One said to show the characteristics of the northern race, *P. t. acredula* was at Windmill Hill, Nuneaton, on April 30th 1996, whilst another displaying the characteristics of the Siberian race, *P. t. yakutensis*, visited a garden at Warndon on April 19th-20th 2000. However, there is a fine distinction between these two races and intergrades also occur.

Goldcrest   *Regulus regulus*
Very common resident and winter visitor.

Although the agile, hyper-active Goldcrest is our smallest bird, it is quite hardy and able to survive all but the worst winter weather. To do so it exploits its adaptation to life in coniferous trees, where there is less competition for food, and uses its small size and fine bill to probe between needles and take tiny insects that are inaccessible even to tits (*Winter Atlas*). Indeed, wherever there are conifers there are likely to be Goldcrests. Its range expanded greatly during the last century, when it quickly colonised the new plantations of pines, spruce and European larch. Although these are its preferred habitat, it also occurs in mixed woods, churchyard yews and the exotic cedars and cypress trees in many rural and suburban gardens. The mild winters of recent years have improved survival rates and the population is currently at a high level.

During the *Winter Atlas* period, birds were recorded in every 10-km square, whilst during the *Breeding Atlas* they were found in 92% of squares. Abundance was greatest in the Wyre Forest and Teme Valley areas of Worcestershire, where there is much suitable habitat and the climate is more equable than on the afforested, higher ground of Staffordshire. Indeed, the BBS suggests densities are four times higher in Worcestershire than in the other three counties. Preliminary results from the *tetrad atlases* show birds in 40% of urban squares and 60% of rural ones.

Many birds stay close to their breeding territories throughout the winter, but others readily join with roving tit flocks, when their search for food may take them into broad-leaved as well as coniferous woodland. The winter populations are expanded by continental immigrants.

The winters of the late 1970s and 1980s were marked by periodic cold spells and, despite its adaptations to winter survival, between 1974-1999 Goldcrest numbers fell by 55%. As a result it is included on the *Amber Alert List* (Gregory *et al.* 2002). The indices show quite clearly how the population plummets every time there is a cold snap, with the impacts in 1981/2,1985/6 and 1990/1 being especially severe. By feeding in trees, birds are less affected by snow, but they suffer during glazed frosts such as that of April 1981. The species has a high reproductive rate, however, so losses are quickly replenished and the

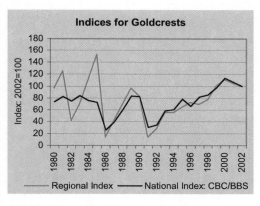

recent run of mild winters has brought a period of steady, continuous growth. Smoothing out these ups and downs, the national CBC/BBS index rose by 35% during 1980-2002 and the current population is probably in the range 10,000-20,000 pairs. The estimate in *BWM* was 3,000-13,000 pairs, made after an exceptionally hard winter.

There is very little information on regional trends, apart from Coombes Valley where numbers have recovered from just a single pair in 1991 to around 14 pairs. At the DM Kineton camp, the population during 1993-97 was relatively stable, except for a drop following the cold winter in 1996. Then, after a run of mild winters, by 2002 numbers increased by 45%. A transect survey of 29.6 km across the Needwood area in 1987 revealed 46 birds.

For such a tiny bird, Goldcrests can make phenomenal movements from eastern Europe and Fennoscandia (*Migration Atlas*). Our ringing recoveries, however, show only more modest journeys, with birds at Blithfield Reservoir in 1989 and 1996 moving over 100 km into Yorkshire and Merseyside respectively in subsequent years. Others, ringed in the Isle of Man in September 1981 and County Durham in October 1988, were recovered in Sutton Coldfield in January 1983 and February 1989, after making respective journeys of 257 km and 244 km.

The autumn influx begins in late September and is usually very evident, particularly during its height in late October and early November. Small 'falls', or groups, of 20-30 birds are noticeable at this time along with a few larger flocks up to 100, whilst the most reported during the current period were 130 in the Lickey Woods in November 1986 and 151 at Anson's Bank on October 7th 1984. The frequency and size of these flocks then reduces during December and January as many birds pass through the region to winter further south or west. A small, barely discernable return passage then occurs from mid-February to April, which may have accounted for an exceptional flock of 250 at Beaudesert in February 1986.

Although most birds prefer to winter in woods, some at least come into gardens, where they have learnt to feed from nut-bags, holders and fat balls. They are also very common winter visitors to the WMBC's urban reserve at Harborne. Among the less likely situations, a passage bird was seen at the top of the Telecom tower in Birmingham in October 1967 (*BWM*) and one was found dead inside a shop at the Merry Hill Centre in October 1998.

Firecrest   *Regulus ignicapilla*
Scarce passage migrant and winter visitor. Rare breeding species.

Brightly-coloured, but elusive, this immaculate little bird is now an annual visitor to the region, though it was formerly much scarcer. It is less tied to conifers than the Goldcrest and prefers mature, mixed woodland for breeding, typically with larch, spruce, beech, oak or holly. Outside the breeding season it tends to occur in sheltered woods or patches of scrub, especially along streams or around gravel pits. When feeding, birds move quickly from one tree to the next, searching less diligently than Goldcrests. Often they associate with roving tit flocks in winter.

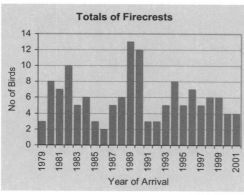

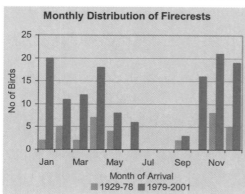

During 1950-64 there was only one record, but occurrences began to increase in the late 1960s and rose sharply during the 1970s (*BWM*). Even so, there were records from only three 10-km squares during the *Winter Atlas*. Instead there was a significant increase in spring records and, following the first recorded nesting in Britain in 1962, several were seen in suitable breeding habitat in Staffordshire and Worcestershire during 1972-75. These culminated in the first positive breeding in 1975, when there were three or four pairs in the Lickey Woods (*BWM*). The prospects for colonisation looked promising, but following a national set-back in 1976, nesting has been very sporadic since. The *Breeding Atlas* showed confirmed breeding in one 10-km square, which was presumably that reported from west Worcestershire in 1988 and at least one pair bred in Warwickshire for the first time in 2002. Birds probably holding territories were also seen in the Wyre Forest in 1981 and 1982, west Staffordshire in 1981 and north Worcestershire in 1989.

Numbers increased rapidly in the 1970s, since when the average has been around six a year. They are heavily depleted in cold weather, however, and nationally the number of pairs closely mirrored the index for Goldcrest, with steep falls after hard winters, but a strong growth during the recent run of mild winters (Ogilvie *et al.* 2004).

In this region at least, this recent growth has not been reflected by an increase in wintering totals, suggesting that most of our wintering birds come from the Continent. Support for this view comes from the fact that virtually all of the birds ringed during the current period, which has averaged one a year, were caught in winter (R. Skeates *pers. comm.*).

Most birds were reported between October and January, or in April, suggesting many are passage migrants, but some at least attempt to over-winter. Those seen in December and January may well have arrived earlier and remained undetected. Outside the breeding season most records were of single birds, but two were seen together on eleven occasions and three were at Kingsbury on January 17th 1991. During the current period 36% of birds occurred in Worcestershire, 24% in Staffordshire, 22% in the West Midlands county and 18% in Warwickshire.

Spotted Flycatcher   *Muscicapa striata*
Fairly common, though much declined, summer resident.

It is always a pleasure to watch this endearing, yet unobtrusive little bird as it perches on a prominent vantage point ready to make sudden sorties after passing insects. Although it is catholic in its choice of habitats, it tends to favour the edges and rides of broad-leaved woodland, parkland, orchards and large gardens with plenty of insects. It is no stranger to urban areas, where it often breeds in churchyards or town parks. Nests are frequently concealed behind climbers on walls, often close to habitation, and open-fronted nest-boxes are freely used.

Spotted Flycatchers are one of the last summer visitors to return from their wintering grounds in southern Africa. The earliest recorded migrant was at Draycote Water on April 13th 2001, but the average date over sixty-four years for the first birds to return was May 2nd. Birds usually arrive singly or in pairs and are scarcely noticed until they are back on their breeding territories.

The *Breeding Atlas* confirmed its widespread distribution, with birds recorded in every 10-km square and breeding actually confirmed in all but one. They were most abundant in the Wyre Forest, Teme Valley and Arden districts, where small woods, parklands and well-timbered hedgerows abound. Numerically, however, the species has been in serious trouble since the 1960s and, with a population decline of 75% during 1974-99, it is included on the *Red List* of Species of Conservation Concern (Gregory *et al.* 2002). As implied by its name, it feeds largely on flying insects and the widespread use of insecticides, coupled with the recent lack of warm springs, have almost certainly contributed to its decline. Recent surveys for the two *tetrad atlases* show it to be present in around 10% of urban squares and 30% of rural ones, while the BBS indicates that densities are highest in Staffordshire and Worcestershire.

The serious plight of the Spotted Flycatcher is clearly evident from the national CBC/BBS index, which fell by 85% during 1980-2002. Regionally the CBC sample is too small to show a trend, but the BBS suggests that the regional decline may have been even sharper. This would certainly accord with recent reports, which are a catalogue of woe. Taking account of all information, the popula-

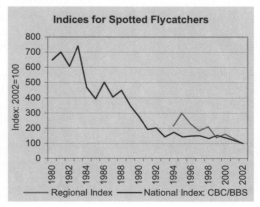

Indices for Spotted Flycatchers

405

tion may now be as low as 300-600 pairs compared with the 2,000-5,000 estimated in *BWM*.

In the southern parts of Warwickshire and Worcestershire the species is still locally common in villages with a blend of large, shady gardens, churchyards and farm buildings. There is an especially strong population in the gardens around Bredon Hill, which the villagers are carefully nurturing with the encouragement of a local enthusiast, John Clarke. In 2002 there were 40 pairs and, with 50 nests located, this suggests that some had double broods. Most nests were in upturned coconut shells, behind wisteria and Virginia creeper, or in yews (J. Clarke *pers. comm.*). In contrast, only one territory was found along the Dowles Brook, where ten years previously there were seven. At Coombes Valley, however, numbers remained fairly stable at around five pairs from 1989-99 as indeed they did at Farnborough Park and Fenny Compton from 1996-2001. At most other sites, numbers are now too small to show any clear trend, but several observers have highlighted poor breeding success due to the predation of eggs and young. According to *BWP,* flies, bees and ants are the main prey, but two observers referred to birds taking peacock butterflies, with one counting 96 pairs of wings beneath a buddleia bush at Packington in 1992! Maybe the decline of the Spotted Flycatcher is linked to there being fewer butterflies as well as other insects.

Birds begin to leave in late August, but September is the prime month for departure, with the average date of the last birds over sixty-four years being on the 28th. Occasional records during early October are not unusual, but those at Worcester on October 31st 1997 and Sandwell Valley on November 1st 1984 were exceptionally late. Prior to their departure, small groups up to 10, often family parties, can be seen feeding together, especially on elderberries. Occasionally larger groups occur, such as 35 at Napton Hill on August 25th 1997, whilst an unusually strong passage in August 1986 brought 24 to Willenhall Memorial Park and 50 to Sandwell Valley.

There have been two foreign recoveries. One that was ringed at Wolverton in May 1989 was recovered in the Netherlands, at Koverskooi, in the following May, whilst a nestling ringed in Warwickshire in June 1976 was recovered in Spain in September 1980.

Red-breasted Flycatcher   *Ficedula parva*
Very rare vagrant. One record.

Red-breasted Flycatchers breed from eastern Europe into Asia and winter in the Indian sub-continent and south-east Asia. In Britain, only 5% occur in spring, mainly in late May (Dymond *et al.* 1989) and they are rare inland, so this record was remarkable for two reasons.

The bird was discovered on a caravan site adjacent to where the Birdwatchers' Spring Fair was being set up, but, much to the frustration of others present, it could not be relocated. It was part of an exceptional spring passage that year, which brought 19 to Britain between May 25th and June 15th, including another one inland—at Ripon (N. Yorks) on May 31st.

Regional Record Number	County Record Number	Year	Locality, Date and Notes
1	Warks 1	1992	Kingsbury Water Park: adult male, May 28th-29th.

Pied Flycatcher   *Ficedula hypoleuca*

Frequent and increasing summer resident and passage migrant, though breeding regularly only in Staffordshire and Worcestershire.

The Pied Flycatcher is one of a trio of birds that are most closely associated with sessile oak-woods, the others being Common Redstart and Wood Warbler. In this region, such woods are largely confined to the Wyre Forest and the valleys of the Teme and its tributaries in west Worcestershire; and to the valleys of the Churnet, Dane and their tributaries in north Staffordshire. Breeding away from these areas is usually only sporadic. Passage birds might be seen almost anywhere, however, including suburban gardens, although many are seen around wetland habitats. The *Breeding Atlas* showed birds in 43% of 10-km squares, but this was much wider than the recognised range and some at least probably referred to passage birds.

The earliest arrival from the African wintering grounds was at Whatcote on April 2nd 1994, but the average date for the first birds to arrive, based on fifty-three years observations, was April 19th. Two-thirds of all passage birds are recorded in spring, when the resplendent black-and-white males arrive about a week ahead of the females.

Unusually there is more local than national information on population trends, mainly because birds freely use nest-boxes. *BWM* records Worcestershire, and more especially the Wyre Forest, as the species' regional stronghold, but the greater numbers are now found in north Staffordshire. The important population at Coombes Valley has been particularly well monitored. In 1967 there were four pairs, but by 1973 this had grown to nine (*BWM*) and numbers remained at about this level until the mid-1980s. Since then there has been a steady increase and now there are about 50 pairs—the largest colony in the region. In addition, at least another dozen pairs nest in the Churnet woods and smaller numbers do so in most years along the Dales, in the Dane valley woods and in the headwaters of the Trent at places such as Kypersley Reservoir. In south Staffordshire, there were two-to-four pairs on Cannock Chase in 1987, but this increased to seven pairs by 1992 before falling back again to three pairs in 1997 and just one breeding pair in 2002 (Bennett *et al*. 2002). Isolated nesting has also occurred at numerous, well-scattered localities across the county.

In Worcestershire, information from the Wyre Forest is less comprehensive, but *BWM* recorded a steady growth in numbers to a maximum of 20 pairs along 3.2 km of the Dowles Brook in 1961, while up to 15 pairs bred in the nest-boxes at the WoWT's Betts and Knowles Coppice reserves during the early 1970s. The best year appears to have been 1987, with 27 nesting attempts. Recent counts have been very random, but they give the impression that numbers overall may have fallen slightly, while in 2002 only six singing males were recorded at the two nest-box sites mentioned. In another part of the Wyre, twenty-nine nest-boxes were erected on one hectare of woodland at Lynall's Coppice and there is much detailed information from these. During 1981-92 between two and ten boxes were occupied each year and successful pairs raised an average of six young each, although in some seasons nests were abandoned, notably in 1986 because of the cold, damp weather. On the Malverns, breeding was first recorded in 1984 and, aided by the provision of nest-boxes, the numbers on Midsummer and Raggedstone Hills have now grown to 20 pairs. Up to five pairs also nest at the Knapp and probably in some of the dingle woods along the Teme Valley, although records from here are sparse. As with Staffordshire, there have also been a few breeding records from widely scattered sites. However, birds were lost from the isolated outpost of the Lickey Hills, where breeding was regular during the early 1990s, but the last record was of a male in song in 1997.

In the West Midlands county, at least one male held a territory in Sutton Park for two or three years in the early 1990s, whilst in Warwickshire birds also held territories at Coombe Abbey and in Bentley Park Woods, but there has been no successful breeding in either county. Overall, the current population is probably 100-200 pairs (*cf*. 30-50 pairs suggested in *BWM*).

Departing birds are less often recorded, but most leave during August and it is likely that some of those recorded in September are Scandinavian drift migrants. Thirty-five years of records show the average date for last birds to be September 12th, with the latest on Napton Hill on October 19th 1997. The geographical distribution of migrant birds is interesting. As might be expected, most were seen in Staffordshire (34%), but 27% appeared in the West Midlands—many of them in gardens—and 20% in Warwickshire, whilst Worcestershire, despite is good breeding population, attracted only 19%.

This species' willingness to use nest-boxes makes it easy to ring. Most are ringed as nestlings and recoveries are very often made within 40-60 km of the ringing site in subsequent years, indicating a high degree of site fidelity. Others show some interchange of birds between the region and Wales and Cheshire. Some idea of the true distances travelled is provided by a nestling ringed at Bewdley in June 1988 and found dead in April 1989 in Settat, Morocco, after a journey of 2,187 km.

Bearded Tit   *Panurus biarmicus*
Rare winter visitor, much reduced since 1994.

Bearded Tits are almost invariably found in extensive stands of common reed, which is an extremely scarce habitat in this region. Consequently they are rare winter visitors and those that do arrive are sometimes forced to resort to substitute habitats such as bulrush, reedmace and willow scrub.

Smith (1938) said that Bearded Tits may have resided in Staffordshire at one time, but in support could quote only two dubious records. The first of these involved two eggs taken from a couple of nests in gorse bushes at Aqualate c1850 and the other was of two birds shot at Chasetown in 1896, of which the author himself said it was doubtful they were truly wild!

The first definite record, which was inadvertently omitted from *BWM*, came in 1959, when three at Baginton Lagoons on November 1st coincided with an irruption along the East Coast. The period 1963-1978 then brought over 50 records involving more than 200 birds (*BWM*). The vast majority of these occurred during the 1970s, which was about the time Bearded Tits first started to erupt annually from their breeding areas in East Anglia and the Netherlands. Another 50 records followed during the winters 1978/79-2000/01, but these brought only 139 birds. In fact occurrences have almost ceased since 1993/94, with just single birds in November 1997, October 2001 and October 2002.

The majority of birds arrive in autumn, with the earliest being on September 11th 1988, at Kingsbury Water Park, and September 29th 1979, when 14 were at Chasewater. The bulk (70%) arrived during October and November, while the last to leave was a male that lingered at Westwood Pool until July 9th 1967. This was exceptional though, and the latest in recent times was one that remained at Church Lench until April 10th in 1989.

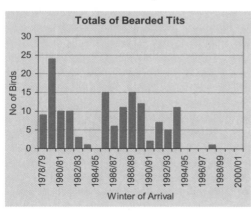

Hidden amongst reeds, Bearded Tits can be extremely elusive and often only the distinctive calls disclose their presence. This makes it difficult to know exactly when birds come and go and how many there are at any one time. Two-thirds of the records during 1978/79-2000/01 referred to just one or two birds, but parties up to eight were seen on several occasions. Brandon Marsh had as many as 10 in the winter of 1980/81 and 11 in 1988/89 and Chasewater, of course, had the flock of 14 mentioned above. These were all

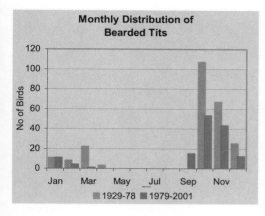

Monthly Distribution of Bearded Tits

No of Birds

120 100 80 60 40 20 0

Jan   Mar   May   Jul   Sep   Nov

■ 1929-78 ■ 1979-2001

surpassed, however, by the 35 at Brandon Marsh in October 1972 (*BWM*). The longest known individual stay was a wintering male that remained at Church Lench Pool from October 30th 1988 to April 10th 1989, but some birds (although not necessarily any particular individual) were present at Brandon Marsh from October 14th 1979 to April 3rd 1980. Over-wintering also occurred at Brandon Marsh on five other occasions, most recently in 1993/94, at Church Lench again in 1989/90 and at Oakley Pool in 1992/93 and 1993/94.

During 1978/79-2000/01 birds were reported from a total of twenty-one localities. Brandon Marsh remained the most consistently visited site (see *BWM*), accounting for 38% of records (49% of birds). Nowhere else attracted birds on more than three or four occasions, so it is not surprising that Warwickshire has proved the most favoured county, with 63% of birds, followed by Staffordshire with 19% and Worcestershire with 13%. The West Midlands share of 5% included its first ever record—a female at Wyken Slough on March 27th 1980.

What little ringing there has been in the region shows that birds ringed in summer at Minsmere (Suffolk), Ousefleet (Yorks) and Stodmarsh (Kent) wintered at Brandon Marsh, while wintering birds ringed at Brandon were recovered the following summer in Kent and Essex.

Long-tailed Tit *Aegithalos caudatus*
Common to very common resident.

Parties of Long-tailed Tits wandering through a wood or working their way along a tall hedgerow are a common sight throughout the region, except on the treeless northern moors and the most intensively built-up areas. They can also be found on shrubby heaths and commons, especially during the breeding season when gorse bushes are a favoured nest site.

Being largely insectivorous throughout the year, Long-tailed Tits can suffer great losses during cold weather and the winters of 1982,1986 and 1991 considerably reduced the population. They are especially vulnerable to glazed frosts and in a landlocked region such as the West Midlands, where the diurnal temperature range is greater than nearer the coast, even a relatively short cold snap can be potentially devastating. Fortunately, numbers are soon replenished, so the effects are not long lasting. More recently Long-tailed Tits have also begun to

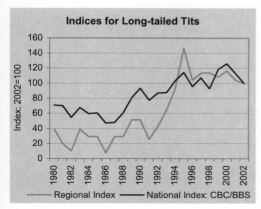

Indices for Long-tailed Tits

Index: 2002=100

160 140 120 100 80 60 40 20 0

1980 1982 1984 1986 1988 1990 1992 1994 1996 1998 2000 2002

—— Regional Index —— National Index: CBC/BBS

supplement their diet by visiting garden feeders and this, combined with a succession of mild winters, has seen a considerable growth in the population.

The pronounced annual fluctuations in the regional population index reflect both the impact of weather and the relatively small size of the sample prior to 1994. However, the dramatic growth shown between 1991 and 1995 seems to be a quirk in the data, which otherwise broadly reflects the national trend. As a consequence, the almost threefold increase implied by the chart, should be treated with extreme caution. Even so, it does seem the increase may have been above the national rate.

The *Winter Atlas* showed birds to be present in every 10-km square, whilst the *Breeding Atlas* showed them in 99%, with above average densities, especially in the south. The CBC/ BBS index rose by 40% during 1980-2002 and, based on all information, the regional population now is probably 8,000-15,000 pairs compared with the 5,000-9,000 estimated in *BWM*. The RSPB's Coombes Valley reserve showed little long-term change, with numbers during 1981-99 ranging between eight and ten pairs, apart from the occasional good years of 1983, 1997 and 1998 when 14 pairs were present on each occasion. This site has also produced some of the largest post-breeding counts, with 80-100 recorded quite regularly during the 1990s and over 150 in October 1996. Such large parties are exceptional, even in autumn, with flocks more commonly numbering 20-30 and consisting primarily of extended family groups. Nevertheless, gatherings up to 40 are not unusual and, with the population currently high, several recent counts have topped 60 and there were 85 at Coombe Abbey in 1993. Eventually these family units disperse as winter territories are established, although birds will still roost communally. At this season they may join with mixed flocks of other species to search the treetops for food, frequently favouring oak, ash and sycamore. Birds were first recorded coming to feeders in 1989, at Ladywalk, and they have now become a regular garden visitor is some areas, with several even reported close to the city centre in Birmingham in 1996.

Birds are usually sedentary, with movements mostly restricted to a few kilometres. However, ringing recoveries show they are capable of travelling considerable distances, with a bird ringed at Ladywalk moving 145 km to Snettisham (Norfolk) and another ringed at Southam travelling 159 km to Hadleigh (Essex). One remarkable record involves three juveniles caught in a flock of eleven birds at Coleshill on June 21st 1981. They were recovered 238 days later in Caldy on the Wirral, having remained together for the journey of 142 km.

Marsh Tit   *Parus palustris*
Fairly common resident.

Marsh and Willow Tits—the so called 'brown' tits—have declined markedly since *BWM* was published and both are now listed as Species of Conservation Concern. The Marsh Tit is on the *Red Alert List* (Gregory *et al.* 2002), its numbers having fallen nationally by more than 50% during 1974-99. Indeed, the species has been in long-term decline since 1965 and a major part of the population was lost prior to 1980 (Siriwardena 2001).

Broad-leaved woods, especially oak and beech, with a rich understorey are the preferred habitat of this species, but birds can also be found in parkland and large gardens with mature trees. Built-up areas are usually avoided, but where there are plenty of large trees birds can sometimes be found well within the urban environment at places such as Edgbaston and Sutton Park. In the woods, they spend much time searching for seeds in the shrub layer or on the ground, where beechmast is a favoured food. A very sedentary species, pairs are highly territorial throughout the year and ringing recoveries show only small local movements.

Within the West Midlands, there are signs that the decline has been more severe than nationally. In the *Winter Atlas* birds were recorded in 97% of 10-km squares, but by the time of the *Breeding Atlas* only 84% of squares were occupied and the abundance levels clearly showed the species to be on the periphery of its main range. Densities were below average everywhere except in the wooded districts of the Malverns and Teme Valley and the southernmost parts of Warwickshire and Worcestershire. Preliminary results from the two *Tetrad Atlases* indicate none within Birmingham and the Black Country and an average of just 27% of tetrads occupied in Warwickshire, the majority of them in the Feldon area. This is confirmed by the map of records during 1997-2001, which shows birds in just 64% of 10-km squares. The range contraction since the *Breeding Atlas* has been mainly in the northern half of the region. In Staffordshire the species seems to be confined to just a few sites in the Churnet Valley, Needwood and Meres and Mosses areas. Nationally the CBC/BBS index showed little overall change from 1980 to 2002 (the main decline having been before this period), while the regional sample was too small to indicate any trend. Taking account of the contraction in range, the limited data suggests a regional population towards the lower end of the range 600-2,000 pairs compared with the 2,000-4,000 suggested in *BWM*.

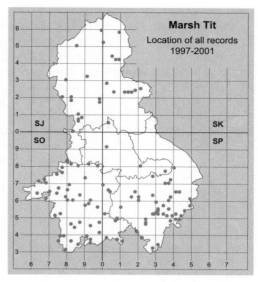

The first declines were reported from Packington and Westwood Parks back in 1980, although the following year numbers in Worcestershire were said to be increasing in the north. In the south a flock of 30 on Bredon Hill in November—the largest ever recorded in the region—gives some idea of the strength at that time, whereas more recently the largest party was 15 at Oversley Wood in November 1997. In the north of the region, numbers at Coombes Valley fell from 10 pairs in 1980 to seven pairs in 1982, five in 1986 and three in 1988. At other sites the collapse occurred in the late 1980s, with just seven territories on the Malvern Hills in 1988 compared with 31 in the previous year and birds said to be almost absent in the Churnet Valley, where five years previously they were fairly common. Although numbers on the Malverns did recover to around 15-18 pairs in 1989-90, birds were described in 1991 as becoming more difficult to find and they have remained at a low ebb ever since.

It seems Marsh Tits are now surviving best in a few traditional areas, but even so, numbers at most of these are too small to indicate long-term trends, with virtually no counts in double figures. Some stability is indicated by Coombe Abbey, with 11 pairs in 1992 and 10 in both 2000 and 2001.

Willow Tit   *Parus montanus*
Fairly common resident.

The Willow Tit was only recognised as being a different species to the similar Marsh Tit just over a hundred years ago and separating the two in the field still causes problems for some.

The best distinction is their respective calls, with the Willow Tit's nasal 'zee-zee' quite unlike the Marsh Tit's sharp 'pitchay'. Willow Tits are birds of damp or wet woodland, the scrubby margins around abandoned brick and gravel pits, streamside alders and willows and lowland conifer woods. Their main requirement is for decaying or rotten stumps into which they can excavate their nest-hole.

Adults defend their territories throughout the year and tend be sedentary, with ringing recoveries just showing small local movements. Birds may venture more widely in win-

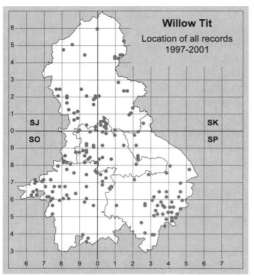

ter, but only rarely do they join foraging tit-flocks. Perhaps this is because their diet is mainly insects and fruits such as haws and honeysuckle, whereas the other tit species rely more on seeds, especially beechmast. Outside the breeding season small groups up to 10 are occasionally noted, particularly around good feeding sites such as those at Belvide Reservoir, Kingsbury Water Park, Ladywalk and Upton Warren.

Nationally the Willow Tit population declined by 80% during 1974-99, placing the species on the *Red Alert List* (Gregory *et al.* 2002). Their decline has been more recent than that of the Marsh Tit, however. In fact numbers actually increased between 1965-73, before falling back to their previous level during 1982-88, and it is only since then that the real decline has set in (Siriwardena 2001).

During the *Winter Atlas* birds were found in 94% of 10-km squares, whilst the *Breeding Atlas* showed them to be present in 90% (*cf.* 84% for Marsh Tit). Densities varied across the region, but were generally above average as opposed to those of the Marsh Tit. They were highest in Feldon, Birmingham, the Black Country, the Potteries and north-west Worcestershire, but lower along the valleys of the Severn and Avon and in the north Staffordshire uplands. The BBS also shows the highest densities to be within the West Midlands county, while early results from the two *Tetrad Atlases* reveal between a quarter and a third of tetrads to be occupied. The map of records for 1997-2001 confirms this distribution, with birds in 68% of 10-km squares.

Estimating the population is difficult. The CBC/BBS index shows a national decline of around 80% during 1989-2000 and this was also reflected by the only CBC plot in the region to hold Willow Tits in recent times, namely Mons Hill in Dudley, where numbers fell from three pairs to one during 1992-2002. However, this single sample may not be representative of the region as a whole. Figures from the BBS, however, suggest that it might be, as these show a decline of 69% in the regional population during 1994-2002 (*cf.* 72% nationally). If such figures are correct, the species could soon disappear from the region. On the other hand, it seems to be holding its own at favoured wetland localities, such as Chasewater, the Churnet Valley, Ladywalk and the Smestow Valley, although no site holds more than half-a-dozen pairs. It seems that the general countryside is where most birds have been lost and this accords with the national CBC, which shows declines in all but the wetland habitats, where numbers are more or less stable (Siriwardena 2001). Taking all factors into consideration, the regional population probably lies in the range 400-1,000 pairs compared with a suggested range of 2,000-4,000 pairs in *BWM*. This is a significant decline and the species must surely be a candidate for inclusion in future Local Biodiversity Action Plans.

Coal Tit   *Parus ater*
Common to very common resident and irruptive winter visitor.

The Coal Tit is mostly found around conifer trees, where it uses its fine bill to extract the seeds from cones. It was originally confined to a few areas of mixed woodland and the specimen conifers planted in landscaped parklands, large gardens and cemeteries. Since the second world war, however, large forestry plantations, together with the fashion for planting ornamental conifers in domestic gardens, have greatly increased the amount of suitable habitat and it has spread into many suburban areas. It can also be found in many of the larger deciduous woods and on occasions has been said to outnumber the Great Tit.

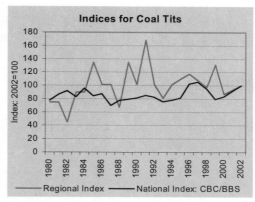

During the *Winter* and *Breeding Atlases* birds were recorded in 99% and 97% of 10-km squares respectively. Abundance was above average in the Churnet Valley, Cannock Chase and especially the Wyre Forest and Teme Valley and these areas remain the species' stronghold. The maturing conifers in suburban gardens, churchyards, cemeteries and town parks now support a substantial population too, but densities are below average over large parts of the region, such as the Meres and Mosses, Severn and Avon Vales and Dunsmore and Feldon areas, where there has been little large-scale afforestation. Early results from surveys for the two *Tetrads Atlases* show birds to be present in just under half of all squares in both urban and rural areas, whilst the BBS suggests the highest density is in Worcestershire.

Being very lightweight, the Coal Tit is one of several small birds that are vulnerable in cold weather and this is reflected by the sharp fluctuations in its numbers from year-to-year, with the severe winter weather early in 1982 clearly having a noticeable effect in this region. Apparently birds were scarce in southern Britain following the 'Great Storm' of 1987 (Buczacki 2002) and this could have accounted for the low numbers here in 1988, even though this region lost relatively few trees. The sample for the regional index is very small, so not too much credence should be given to the annual fluctuations. Overall the national CBC/BBS index increased by around 30% from 1980-2002 and the regional change was very similar. Current data points to a population of around 9,000-18,000 pairs, which, considering the increase in the CBC/BBS index, accords well with the 5,000-15,000 postulated in *BWM*.

Away from the CBC plots there is little information on density or trends and the following counts from Coombes Valley, in the Churnet, provide the only long-term data from the Coal Tit's strongholds. Based on three-yearly means, they show a 60% increase in numbers.

Year	1986	1987	1988	1989	1990	1991	1992	1993	1994	1995	1996	1997	1998	1999
No of Pairs	10	18	22	nk	21	19	nk	21	27	14	32	28	28	23

In winter, birds roam more widely in search of food, especially beechmast, but if natural food is scarce they will readily come to garden feeders. This often brings them into competition with Blue and Great Tits. In such situations, they barely have time to snatch a morsel before the larger birds chase them off, so they often carry food away and hoard it for later retrieval. They are gregarious and regularly form feeding flocks of up to 50 during the winter, with the larger gatherings being 65 in Oakley Wood in February 1997 and 300 in a huge mixed flock at Coldridge Wood in January 1984. Flocks totalling between 100-170 were also counted in Oversley Wood during 1998-2001.

British Coal Tits of the race *P. a. britannicus* move very little, but the nominate Continental race *P. a. ater* is prone to periodic irruptions. Such irruptions brought invasions into Britain in 1975 and 1996, although none were known to reach this region. The latter year, though, did see a large influx of birds in south-east Warwickshire, but none were specifically assigned to this race. However, there is one record of *P. a. ater*, at Jackson's Bank on February 2nd 1987.

Coal Tits are rarely recorded moving long distances. The exceptions include one ringed at Tring (Hertfordshire) that moved 140 km to Perry Barr and another ringed in Worksop (Notts) that was recovered in woodland bordering Blithfield Reservoir, 80 km from its ringing site.

Blue Tit   *Parus caeruleus*
Abundant resident.

The lively, acrobatic Blue Tit is a widespread and conspicuous species well known to almost everyone from its habit of coming to garden feeders. Although primarily a bird of deciduous woodland, especially oakwoods, it also occurs in a wide range of rural and urban habitats that offer suitable trees for nesting. These include conifer woods and well-timbered hedges, parks and gardens. It also takes readily to nest-boxes, even in busy urban situations.

It is certainly the commonest tit, being widespread and abundant right across the region. Both the *Winter* and *Breeding Atlases* recorded birds in every 10-km square, with abundance generally above average, except in the uplands of north Staffordshire, where suitable habitat is more restricted. In 1989 a pair even bred at Snow Hill Station, in the centre of Birmingham.

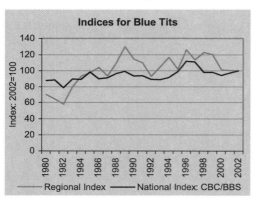

Well stocked feeders and milder winters have aided Blue Tit survival, with the result that numbers have generally increased. Periodic cold snaps, poor weather during the breeding season, or lack of food for nestlings still cause the occasional set-back as in 1986, 1996 and 2003 when breeding success was very low. The CBC/BBS indices show some variation between the national and regional trend during 1980-2002. Ignoring annual fluctuations, the national index increased by 12% during this time, whilst the regional one grew by about a half. This was partly due to the smaller sample size, but perhaps also reflected local conditions. The species was particularly hard hit by the freezing conditions in 1979 and 1982, so the rapid increase during the mid-1980s reflects a recovery from a low base. Judging from all data, both nationally and regionally, it seems likely that the regional population is in the range 100,000-130,000 pairs compared with the 80,000-100,000 estimated in *BWM*.

Examples of the annual fluctuations in numbers and variable breeding success are provided by the following data for two four-year periods at Lynall's Coppice in the Wyre Forest.

Year	1981	1982	1983	1984	1990	1991	1992	1993
No of occupied nest-boxes	5	1	6	3	5	4	2	7
No of young raised	35	nk	50	nk	35	28	Failed	nk
No of young per nest-box	7.0	nk	8.3	nk	7.0	7.0	0.0	nk

Despite the considerable differences from year-to-year, the long-term situation here remained relatively stable. At Coombes Valley, though, whilst numbers during 1981-98 showed similar yearly differences, ranging from 83-154 pairs, there was a general long-term increase from 98 pairs per annum during the 1980s to 130 pairs per annum during the 1990s. These figures represent woodland densities of 94-125 pairs per km^2, which is some 50% above the national CBC average. A survey at Hawkhurst Moor in 1987 also revealed a density above the CBC averages for farmland, with 23 pairs per km^2 compared with around 19 pairs per km^2 on

CBC plots. In Worcestershire, remarkable declines were recorded in 2000 at three regularly monitored sites, with numbers at Dog Hanging Coppice, Long Bank and Shelfheld down by 72%, 45% and 73% respectively. Although the BBS showed a significant decrease nationally in that year, there is no obvious explanation for such dramatic falls as these.

In autumn family groups begin to forage more widely for food and as winter progresses they merge with one another and with other species to form large, mixed flocks. Initially these flocks feed on insects, but as these become scarcer they turn to seeds, particularly those of beech and birch which are deftly taken from off the trees. *BWM* said winter flocks usually contained fewer than 100 Blue Tits and that is still the case. Nevertheless, there were five flocks of 100 during the current period and larger gatherings of 150 at the German Cemetery on December 18th 1988, 160 at Blithfield Reservoir on February 7th 1988 and 250 at Brandon Hall on January 1st 1981. However, 365 at Blithfield Reservoir on July 17th 1981 were exceptional. In 1983, one spent four days inside a Tesco's supermarket in Stafford, feeding on apples, cress, grapes, mustard and tomatoes, before it was caught and removed by local birders.

Blue Tits mostly make only local movements, but birds from the region have been recovered in the southern counties of Cambridgeshire, Hampshire, Berkshire and Wiltshire. The distances travelled were in excess of 80 km. The longest journey was made by one ringed at Titchwell (Norfolk) and recovered in Selly Park, Birmingham, a distance of 175 km. The vast majority of Blue Tits have short life spans of between one and two years, but there are exceptions such as one ringed at Malvern and found dead in a local sports hall seven and a half years later. There are also other records of birds between five and six years of age.

Great Tit *Parus major*
Abundant resident.

Although broad-leaved woodland is the Great Tit's favoured habitat, it is very versatile and will readily exploit anywhere that offers a suitable nest site, secure roost or source of food. Its adaptable nature means it can be found right across the region, from woods of all description to hedgerow trees and parks and gardens, even within urban areas where it makes full use of feeders and nest-boxes.

Both the *Winter* and *Breeding Atlases* showed birds to be present in every 10-km square and their abundance across most of the region was above average. The exception was the uplands of north Staffordshire, where suitable habitat is more restricted.

The CBC/BBS index shows that the Great Tit population increased both nationally and regionally by around 25% during 1980-2002. National and regional densities, however, suggest the current population is between 60,000-75,000 pairs compared with the 40,000-50,000 estimated in *BWM*. It seems possible, therefore, that the *BWM* figures were an under-estimate.

Two additional sets of data underline the strength of the regional population. Firstly, counts from the RSPB reserve at Coombes Valley during 1981-98 ranged from 61-94 pairs, with an average of around 70 pairs during the 1980s, rising to over 90 in the early 1990s, but then suddenly reverting to 70 again from 1994. These represent a woodland density of 67-87 pairs per km^2, which is some 70% above the national CBC average. Secondly, a survey at Hawkhurst Moor in 1987 revealed 11 pairs in 81 ha—a density of 14

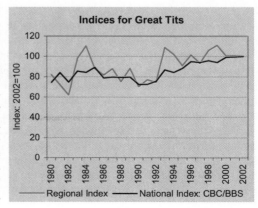

Indices for Great Tits

Index: 2002=100

—— Regional Index —— National Index: CBC/BBS

per km^2 compared with the national average for farmland of around 10 pairs.

As with Blue Tit, the nest-box scheme at Lynall's Coppice, in the Wyre Forest, again provides a good illustration of the breeding successes and failures over two four-year periods as can be seen from the table below. The blank years in 1990 and 1991 were the first time this species had failed to nest in twenty-two years.

Year	1981	1982	1983	1984	1990	1991	1992	1993
No of occupied nest-boxes	6	3	8	6	0	0	3	3
No of young raised	45	nk	32	43	0	0	10	nk
No of young per nest-box	7.5	nk	4.0	7.2	0	0	3.3	nk

BWM noted that most reports indicated two to four times as many Blue Tits as Great Tits, but the latest population estimates would put the ratio at only 1.7:1, which accords well with five winter walks in south Warwickshire in 2001 that produced a ratio of 1.8:1.

Small gatherings, mostly of juveniles, begin to form in late summer and by early winter many will have joined the roving flocks of tits and other species as they search for food. Males, though, tend to remain on their territory and only join such gatherings in severe weather. In late summer birds feed mainly on insects taken from foliage, but in autumn they turn increasingly to seeds and nuts. Being the heaviest of the tits, Great Tits are unable to feed from slender twigs and so are forced to forage more on the ground, where they seek beechmast and hazel nuts. Flocks up to 50 are not unusual and larger gatherings have included 98 at Blithfield Reservoir on February 7th 1998, 96 at the German Cemetery on Cannock Chase in the same year, 167 at Blithfield Reservoir on July 17th 1981 and 200 at Chase End Hill on December 31st 1997. The largest flock ever was an exceptional 500 at Brandon Hall in December 1974 (*BWM*). Unusual nest sites have included the offertory box in a Malvern churchyard in 1979 and a spent missile case at the DM Kineton army camp in 1993.

Although ringing recoveries show most Great Tits to be parochial in nature, several long distance movements have been recorded with birds travelling in excess of 100 km from the West Midlands to Norfolk and Lincolnshire. One bird from Dyfed in Wales travelled 116 km to Gnosall, while another, ringed in Lancashire, travelled 115 km to Penkridge. In 1997 there was an astonishing record of an adult female, ringed in Kidderminster and recovered alive just over two months later in Skagen, Jylland, Denmark—over 1,000 km away.

Eurasian Nuthatch   (European Nuthatch or Nuthatch)   *Sitta europaea*
Fairly common to common resident.

Mature broad-leaved woodland, parkland with gnarled old trees and gardens with large trees are the home of the Eurasian Nuthatch. It nests in holes and feeds along the trunks and main branches, especially of oak, beech and sweet chestnut. If natural holes are scarce, it will utilise nest-boxes, plastering the entrance with mud just as it would a natural hole. Birds also regularly visit garden bird tables and feeders close to their woodland territories. A very vocal bird, it has a wide repertoire of loud calls. The name derives from its habit of wedging a nut into a crevice in the bark and then hammering away at it to get at the kernel.

Ringing shows no movements over 10 km, indicating that birds are very sedentary and highly territorial throughout the year. This reduces their ability to exploit isolated habitats such as fragments of urban woodland. However, in a region with plenty of well-timbered hedgerows dispersal of the young is not too great a problem and the species has expanded its range and population in recent years. Indeed, it is quite common in the more sylvan suburbs of Birmingham, such as Edgbaston, and at places such as Sutton Park. It has also been observed along a tree-lined street in the centre of Leamington Spa.

The *Winter Atlas* shows birds were present in 97% of 10-km squares, whereas during the *Breeding Atlas* the figure was slightly lower at 90%. The gaps in their range largely coincided with the lower reaches of the Avon, Severn and Tame Valleys and the moors of Staffordshire, where woodland is generally scarce. Abundance levels were also below average in these areas, whereas they were above average in the well-wooded districts of the Churnet Valley, Wyre Forest, TemeValley and Arden. Surveys for the *Tetrad Atlases* reveal birds present in about 30% of urban tetrads and 40% of rural ones, whilst the BBS indicates that densities are highest in Worcestershire.

Nationally, the CBC/BBS index more than doubled during 1980-2002. Regionally, there was insufficient data to compile a comparative index, but anecdotal evidence points to a spread in range and an increase in numbers. This is especially so in Warwickshire, where as recently as 1990 the species was described as not common (Tasker *et al*. 1990), but today birds are being recorded for the first time in sub-optimal habitats such as Kingsbury Water Park. Whether this means the population in prime habitats has now reached saturation level is not clear. Certainly, while the population generally was increasing, numbers in both the Coombes and Churnet Valleys remained stable at around six pairs each between 1986-99. The best estimate of the current regional population is 2,000-4,000 pairs compared with the 700-1,400 suggested in *BWM*.

The only references to any declines came from Yoxall in 1990, Sutton Park in 1993 and Dog Hanging Coppice in 2000, but none was significant. Otherwise, there were several reports of birds using nest-boxes, with 40 young reared from six boxes on the Malvern Hills in 1995 indicative of productivity levels. Counts of 12 territories along the hills in 1987 and 1988 were also notable.

In winter birds sometimes join with the roving tit flocks in search of food, but their association with such flocks is seldom strong. At this season they rely heavily on hazel nuts, acorns and beechmast for food, but can also be seen in characteristic fashion working their way head-first down a tree trunk as they search for insects. Anything larger than a family party is unusual, but up to 10 have been seen on several occasions and 12 were at Chillington Lower Avenue in July 1981. Birds can be very confiding, with up to eight being fed from parked cars at Pipers Hill Common in 1980 and one even perching on a strategically placed telescope at Park Farm, Sandwell Valley, in 2001.

Eurasian Treecreeper   (Treecreeper)   *Certhia familiaris*
Common resident.

The Eurasian Treecreeper inhabits both broad-leaved and mixed woodland, from the smallest copses to the largest forests. It can also be found more sparingly in conifer plantations, along well-timbered hedgerows and in parklands and large gardens with trees. Adapted to spend almost its whole life on trees, its quiet, high-pitched call and habit of creeping mouse-like up trunks and along branches render detection difficult and it is easily overlooked. Even in flight it is hard to spot as it flits from one tree to the next.

Both the *Winter* and *Breeding Atlases* nevertheless revealed its presence in every 10-km square. Not surprisingly, the abundance was similar to that of Eurasian Nuthatch, with the lowest densities in the lower parts of the Avon, Severn and Tame Valleys and on the high ground of north Staffordshire, while the higher ones were in the well-wooded districts of Churnet Valley, Wyre Forest and Arden. More recent work for the *Tetrad Atlases* has shown that birds are present in about two-thirds of rural squares and one-third of urban ones, while the BBS suggests that densities are highest in Worcestershire.

Nationally, the CBC/BBS rose by about a third between 1980 and 2002, but again there was insufficient data to produce a comparable regional index. From the limited information available, however, it seems the regional population might be between 4,000-7,000 pairs compared with the 4,000-6,000 suggested in *BWM*.

An analysis of all comparative counts shows this species outnumbering Eurasian Nuthatch by a ratio of 2:1, which conforms well with the population estimates for both species. Interestingly, though, in only three years was it reported from more localities than Eurasian Nuthatch—a sure sign that it is less obtrusive.

There are very few data series from which to gauge changes over time, but at Coombes Valley the population during 1990-99 ranged from 11-19 pairs, with 18 pairs at both the beginning and end of the period indicating little long-term change. Otherwise 20 pairs in the Beaudesert area of Cannock Chase in 1986 was the only other concentration of note. Nests are usually constructed in a fissure or behind loose bark or a covering of ivy, but pairs will also use holes in buildings and specially designed nest-boxes, while in 2000 a pair at Ladywalk bred in a bat-box.

The species suffers high levels of mortality during cold winters such as that of 1978/79. It is most at risk when the trees have a covering of snow or glazed ice that prevents birds from feeding, but prolonged spells of severe cold will also take their toll. Fortunately populations generally recover quickly. A less customary hazard, at least for this species, was discovered at Farnborough in 2000, when one was found entangled in fishing line.

Birds sometimes loosely associate with roving tit flocks in winter, but mostly they feed alone, probing the bark for insects and their larvae. When food is very scarce they may be forced to extremes, with records of them pecking at concrete posts and searching larch-lap fencing for food. Groups up to ten, often family parties, are reported fairly regularly and 12 were noted at Wissetts Wood in February 1982 and the Churnet Valley in autumn 1985. They also roost communally in holes and fissures and behind loose bark, often excavating a hollow into the soft, spongy bark of Wellingtonias, many of which have been planted in the numerous landscaped parklands across the region.

Although influxes are occasionally reported, these probably involve only short journeys by local birds as the species is generally sedentary. This is confirmed by ringing recoveries, which also show low survival rates. The exception to the latter rule was a bird ringed in Sutton Park and re-trapped four years later, almost at the same spot where it was originally ringed.

Golden Oriole   *Oriolus oriolus*
Rare passage migrant.

Prior to 1979 there were 26 acceptable records involving 29 birds (*BWM*). These included one of possible nesting, at Kyre in 1868 (Prescott 1931), and two others that involved two birds—the last in 1905. Since then all records have been of single individuals. During 1979-2001 there were an additional 17 records as shown in the table opposite.

Typically, most were detected by their distinctive song, the birds themselves remaining well hidden in the canopy of trees. This probably explains the predominance of males, which accounted for 86% of those birds where the sex was specified. Indeed, the only female seen alive was that at Starts Green in 1997.

Records reached their peak in the 1970s and 1980s, when a small breeding population established itself in the poplar plantations of the East Anglian Fens, but have tailed off since the early 1990s in line with a national decline in breeding numbers (Ogilvie *et al.* 2003). Most birds (82%) arrived in spring, between April 25th-June 21st: otherwise there was one each in July, September and October. Few have remained for more than a couple of days, although the Hopwas Hays bird in 1979 was around for eight days and one lingered at Enville for about a month in 1960. The distribution between the three shire counties is remarkably even.

Regional Record Number	County Record Number		Year	Locality, Date and Notes
27	Staffs	9	1979	Hopwas Hays Wood: male singing, June 3rd-10th.
28	Warks	8	1979	Warwick: female, October 3rd. Found dead after flying into window.
29	W Mid	2	1980	Sutton Park: male singing, June 7th-8th.
30	Staffs	10	1982	Colwich: male, April 25th-26th.
31	Worcs	11	1982	Upton Warren: male singing, June 5th.
32	Warks	9	1984	Coleshill Woods: male, May 19th.
33	Staffs	11	1984	Eccleshall: male, July 23rd.
34	Staffs	12	1988	Hoar Cross: May 29th.
35	Warks	10	1988	Draycote Water: male, September 20th.
36	Worcs	12	1989	Nunnery Wood: June 21st.
37	W Mid	3	1990	Netherton Reservoir: male, May 13th.
38	Warks	11	1992	Kineton: male singing, May 19th.
39	Worcs	13	1993	Abberton: male singing, June 8th.
40	Warks	12	1994	Middleton Hall: male, May 15th.
41	Staffs Worcs	13 14	1997	Starts Green: female, May 31st. Also across boundary in Worcestershire.
42	Warks	13	2000	Ufton Fields: male singing, May 6th-7th.
43	Worcs	15	2000	Upton Warren: May 13th.

Red-backed Shrike   *Lanius collurio*
Rare passage migrant. Formerly bred.

Common and widespread in the nineteenth century, the Red-backed Shrike is now reduced to being nothing more than a rare passage migrant. It last bred in Staffordshire in 1948, Warwickshire in 1960, Worcestershire in 1962 and the West Midlands in 1966 (Teagle 1978). Thereafter there were just eight sightings between 1965 and 1978 *BWM*, while birds became even rarer during 1979-2001, with just the following six in twenty-three years.

Year	Locality, Date and Notes	Year	Locality, Date and Notes
1983	Bermuda: male, August 10th.	1997	Norton: immature, September 30th.
1984	Sandwell Valley: adult male, July 21st.	1999	Upton Warren: juvenile, October 3rd.
1988	Frankley: male, May 16th.	2000	Throckmorton: juvenile, October 8th-13th.

Although all recent records are listed, the large number of old records makes it impossible to determine regional and county record numbers. The southerly bias of these records is remarkable, with nothing north of Sandwell Valley. It is also interesting that only one was in spring and three of the five during return passage between July and October were in Worcestershire. At this time of year a more easterly bias might have been expected.

Lesser Grey Shrike   *Lanius minor*
Very rare vagrant. One record.

With, on average, less than two Lesser Grey Shrikes seen each year in Britain, this was an unexpected find in an unlikely situation.

Regional Record Number	County Record Number	Year	Locality, Date and Notes
1	Worcs 1	1987	Wythall: adult male, June 4th. *BB 81:586*

Presumably an overshooting migrant returning from wintering in southern Africa, this bird was observed feeding from raspberry canes at St Mary's Church. It arrived on a very typical date for this species to occur in Britain. Although the nearest Lesser Grey Shrikes are in southern France and Spain, analysis of records nationally suggests that most of those seen in Britain probably originate from the more substantial populations of eastern Europe rather than from nearer countries (Dymond *et al*. 1989).

Great Grey Shrike   *Lanius excubitor*
Rare or scarce passage migrant and winter visitor.

This species is a scarce winter visitor, presumably from the migratory populations in Fennoscandia. It is usually found in tracts of open countryside with scattered trees and bushes that are used as vantage points from which to watch for prey. Small birds, insects, reptiles and mammals are caught and then impaled on thorn bushes for later consumption. Despite frequently perching in prominent positions, birds can be surprisingly elusive.

Great Grey Shrikes were very scarce visitors to the region until the 1960s, with none at all during 1923-49 and barely more than one a year thereafter. Numbers then suddenly began to increase, leaping to 19 birds in 1966 and averaging around 10 a year during the 1970s, with peaks of 22 in the winters of 1973/74 and 1974/75. Since the early 1980s, they have virtually reverted to their former low levels, with just 60 during 1979-2001—an average of less than three a year. Indeed, only two winters since 1982/3 have brought more than three birds.

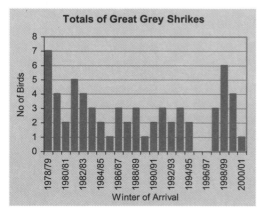

The monthly pattern prior to 1979 reflected that of many winter visitors, with a marked influx in October that gradually subsided through the winter and into spring, with the last birds in May. During 1979-2001, the pattern changed into one more typical of a passage migrant. The main arrival is still in October, with numbers then tailing off into early winter, but there has then been a secondary peak in March, which presumably represents a return passage. During this latter period the extreme dates were October 8th, at Sandwell Valley in 1986 and Sherbrook Valley in 1998, and May 6th, at Draycote Water in 1979. However, the earliest and latest records ever remain as quoted in *BWM*, namely September 6th, in 1970, and May 14th, in 1951 and 1972.

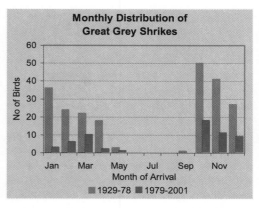

There have been numerous records of birds over-wintering, although they often appear to go missing for long periods of time. Cannock Chase remains the most favoured area, particularly the open heaths around Brocton Field and Sherbrook Valley, although clear-felled forestry plantations have also been visited. Even there, appearances have been patchy, but birds were present at some time during ten of the eleven winters from 1978/79-1988/89 and again in four of the five between 1997/98-2001/02, but not in any of the eight intervening ones. Usually only one individual was involved, but on occasions two were thought to have been present. This seemingly erratic pattern might be explained by the fact that Great Grey Shrikes often return to the same area, so perhaps just a few individuals are involved, coming back in consecutive years until they die. Elsewhere, Castlemorton Common has been visited on five occasions, but no other site has been especially favoured. Instead, it is site fidelity that accounts for sites having more than one or two records. For example, Newbold Comyn was visited in four successive winters from 1980/81-1983/84, presumably by the same bird as there were no other records from here either before or since. With Cannock Chase so dominant, 50% of the birds during 1979-2001 were in Staffordshire, while Warwickshire had 25%, Worcestershire 20% and the West Midlands 5%.

Woodchat Shrike   *Lanius senator*
Very rare vagrant. Two records

After waiting 106 years, the second appearance of this attractive shrike was a most welcome event. Fortunately the bird stayed long enough for all to enjoy it.

Regional Record Number	County Record Number		Year	Locality, Date and Notes
1	Worcs	1	1893	Weatheroak Hill: pair, May 14th.
2	W Mid	1	1999	Longmoor Valley, Sutton Park: June 1st-14th.

Woodchat Shrikes breed from Iberia and France eastwards to the Ukraine and Iran and winter in sub-Saharan Africa. Birds occur annually in Britain, with late May and early June a typical time for overshooting migrants to appear (Dymond *et al.* 1989).

Eurasian Jay   (Jay)   *Garrulus glandarius*
Fairly common to common resident.

The arboreal Eurasian Jay is a shy, wary bird, which makes it appear less common than it actually is. Birds are most conspicuous in autumn, when they fly more readily across open areas as they hoard acorns for the forthcoming winter. At other times their raucous, rasping calls are

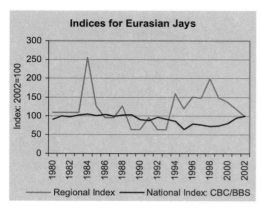

Indices for Eurasian Jays

Index: 2002=100

300
250
200
150
100
50
0

1980 1982 1984 1986 1988 1990 1992 1994 1996 1998 2000 2002

——— Regional Index ——— National Index: CBC/BBS

more likely to reveal their presence. Essentially a woodland bird, they have a special affinity with oaks, particularly favouring pedunculate oakwoods with a coppiced understorey. However, they can also be found in coniferous woods, along well-timbered hedgerows and in parklands and large gardens.

Both the *Winter* and the *Breeding Atlases* showed them to be present in every 10-km square, with above average densities in well-wooded districts such as the Churnet Valley, Wyre Forest and Arden. Conversely, they were below average in the more open country such as the lower parts of the Avon, Severn and Trent valleys and the higher ground of north Staffordshire. The BBS points to densities being lowest in Warwickshire, which is the least wooded county, but preliminary work for the *Tetrad Atlases* has recorded them in just over half of the squares in both Warwickshire and the West Midlands.

Nationally the CBC/BBS suggests numbers were fairly stable between 1980 and 2002—having recovered from a fall in the mid-1990s. Not too much reliance should be placed on the regional index, because of the small sample size, but it gives no hint of any significant long-term difference from the national trend. Taking account of all current data, the regional population is probably between 2,000-5,000 pairs, which is very similar to the 2,000-4,000 pairs estimated in *BWM*.

Further evidence of fluctuating fortunes, but long-term stability comes from Coombes Valley RSPB reserve, where there were ten pairs in 1990, only five in 1995, but ten again in 1998. Otherwise the only indication of breeding strength comes from random counts, with 18 pairs in Sutton Park in 1980 the most notable. Nesting attempts at Lichfield in 1992 and Solihull Station in 2001 both failed when the birds were either driven off or robbed by Magpies.

The most memorable event of recent times occurred in October 1983, when a huge invasion swept into southern Britain. Only modest numbers pervaded this region, but parties of a dozen or so were widely reported with maxima of 15 at Malvern on October 3rd and 18 at Wilden on October 9th. This alerted observers to the possibility of Continental birds occurring and one said to show the characteristics of the Continental race, *G. g. glandarius* was reported at Hollybush Lake on March 21st 1987, although the current consensus is that most birds are indistinguishable from the British race *G. g. rufitergum*. Small, but widespread, influxes were also reported in 1993, when 10 at Belvide Reservoir in October were said to be indicative of 'real migration', and again in 1996, when there were 15 at Priory Wood, Sandwell Valley, on October 30th and at Clent on November 1st, with 20 at Eymore Wood on November 8th. In addition, *BWM* mentions 30 at Bartley during the 1957 invasion.

Apart from these invasions, small 'social gatherings', which may involve as many as a dozen birds, quite frequently occur in spring. In autumn, small groups up to ten are regularly seen, but more than 15 together is a rare sight. However, the two largest gatherings in recent times were 18 moving between copses at Shawbury on August 17th 1986 and 27 at Grimley on August 15th 1993, but Harthan (1946) said he once saw 40 disturbed by foxhounds.

Eurasian Jays also frequently visit bird-feeders in both rural and urban situations. They had reportedly taken readily to nut holders at Ladywalk by 1987 and in 1996 were said to be regular garden visitors in many suburbs.

A bird ringed at Tamworth in January 1984 was found dead at Trowbridge (Wilts) in November 1985—a journey of 153 km. Otherwise most recoveries are local. The species' potential longevity is shown by a bird ringed in Edgbaston and shot at the same site 14 years later.

Magpie   *Pica pica*
Very common resident.

The chattering black-and-white Magpie needs little or no introduction—indeed it is the bird everyone loves to hate because of its reputation for predating the eggs and young of songbirds. The huge, domed nest can be found in trees, thickets or scattered bushes across a wide range of habitats including farmland, woods, parks and both suburban and urban gardens. However, birds are generally commonest in urban areas, or where there is mown or grazed grassland with overgrown hedgerows, copses and shelterbelts.

Villain or not, the question everyone asks is are Magpies on the increase? The answer is probably that it depends where you live. The Magpie's ability to exploit such a wide variety of habitats means it is widely distributed, with the *Winter* and *Breeding Atlases* both indicating a presence in every 10-km square, generally at above average abundance. Likewise, preliminary results for the *Tetrad Atlases* confirm that they are widespread, whilst the BBS shows the density in the West Midlands county to be more than double those of the three shires.

In many rural districts numbers are controlled, either directly by trapping or shooting, or indirectly through lack of cover in arable intensive areas. For example, in 1991 the use of live decoys to trap birds was said to have become a fairly competitive pursuit on several north Warwickshire farms, with 70 caught in just one trap in three months. The following year Larsen traps were being widely used in Staffordshire, seemingly in a concerted attempt to reduce numbers. So, whilst nesting pairs can be found in most tetrads, in rural areas it is frequently necessary to search village gardens to find them.

The CBC/BBS, which mainly monitors rural plots, showed an increase of almost 50% nationally between 1980 and 2002. The regional trend was broadly similar during the 1990s, but before then it was too variable to indicate any clear trend. Thus the popular perception that Magpies are perpetually on the increase seems to be borne out by the data. The wide fluctuations from year-to-year might be partly explained by the impact of hard winters on small birds, which means there are fewer eggs and young for Magpies to predate. Certainly both indices were relatively stable during the mild winters of the 1990s—a situation which was also reflected at Coombes Valley where there were consistently around 5-6 pairs. Current data suggest a population range of 20,000-25,000 pairs which, even allowing for the growth implied by the CBC/BBS index, is above the estimated 8,000-13,000 pairs in *BWM*. The difference is probably because the urban population has grown at a faster rate.

Whilst there is little comparative data on breeding, that for the winter is quite revealing. At this season Magpies become more gregarious and regularly gather together to roost. Parties of 30-40 are not unusual and 50 or more are reported annually. In the shire counties only four concentrations exceeded 70 birds, namely 106 at Oldington in December 1998, 120 at Apedale Country Park in November 2001 and roosts of 86 at Draycote Water in 1993 and 127 at Alvecote Pools in 1993.

In the cities and towns there is little to control numbers, so Magpies have flourished to the consternation of many and the majority of the larger flocks and roosts come from urban oases within the West Midlands county and the Potteries. Here there were 31 gatherings of over 70 birds at places such as Olton Reservoir, Sutton Park, Valley Park and Westport Lake and a maximum of 200 in Sandwell Valley in 2002. There were also roosts of 150 in Sutton Park in February 1986 and 170 at

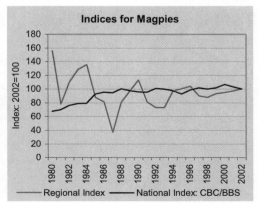

Indices for Magpies

Index: 2002=100

Regional Index   National Index: CBC/BBS

Westport Lake in 1995, while a total of 161 flew over Edgbaston to roost in 1988. Again the roosts show some conflicting trends, with that at Olton Mere being stable at around 100 birds, whilst the one at Westport Lake increased at least threefold, from 40-50 in the mid-1980s to 150-170 in the early 1990s. Overall, the average size of winter concentrations broadly doubled during 1979-2001, which was in line with the estimated population increase.

Magpies are sedentary and ringing recoveries show only local movements. Interestingly, birds were reportedly nest-building in different areas of Walsall at the unseasonable times of September 1993 and December 1995. They have also been noted eating water snails from a garden pond, stealing milk from a doorstep and optimistically trying to catch a bat and a weasel—the latter perhaps unwisely since another report refers to one being killed by a weasel!

Some idea of the toll Magpies inflict on songbirds can be gauged from a study at Willey in 1979-81. This found the remains of 135 predated eggs from at least eight species, with Blackbirds seemingly most vulnerable as they lost 50 or more eggs. Likewise, six Robin eggs, two clutches of Song Thrushes and several young Blackbirds were take from one suburban garden in 1986. Despite its reputation, studies have shown that eggs and nestlings form only a small part of the Magpie's diet (Tatner 1983) and its increasing population has apparently not affected songbird breeding success (Gooch *et al.* 1991).

Nutcracker *Nucifraga caryocatactes*
Very rare vagrant. Two records.

The first record coincided with a remarkable national invasion of unprecedented proportions that involved birds of the slender-billed race, *N. c. macrorhynchos* from Siberia *BWM*. The second, which was not assigned to a particular race, was less expected.

Regional Record Number	County Record Number	Year	Locality, Date and Notes
1	Staffs 1	1968	Stapenhill: October 27th-28th. *BB 63:372*
2	Staffs 2	1991	Cocknage Wood: October 14th to November 9th. *BB 85:548*

Nutcrackers reside in the mountains of central and south-eastern Europe and from Fennoscandia eastwards across Siberia, but the slender-billed race is prone to periodically erupt when an abundant crop of its favoured food, the Arolla pine, is followed by a poor crop the next year (Dymond *et al.* 1989).

Red-billed Chough (Chough) *Pyrrhocorax pyrrhocorax*
Very rare vagrant. One dubious record.

The only record concerns a bird killed whilst "perched on a building where it was resting after a long flight" (Hastings 1834).

Regional Record Number	County Record Number	Year	Locality, Date and Notes
1	Worcs 1	1826	Lindridge, near Tenbury Wells: unknown date, November. Killed.

Nothing can be added to the remark in *BWM* that "in the absence of a full knowledge of the status and distribution of the Red-billed Chough at that time, it is impossible to put this quite exceptional record into perspective."

Western Jackdaw (Eurasian Jackdaw or Jackdaw) *Corvus monedula*
Very common resident.

This, the smallest of our crows, occurs throughout the region. It nests colonially down chimneys or inside hollow trees, quarries, caves and old or ruined buildings. Although birds will feed on stubbles and ploughed fields, they prefer pastures grazed by sheep or cattle, where they predominantly take insects. The combination of pastures for feeding and veteran trees with plenty of nest-holes is best met by the region's many landscaped parklands and it is here that birds are often most numerous. In winter, they frequently join with other corvids, especially Rooks, to form large feeding flocks, while many also regularly feed at landfill sites. At the end of the day noisy flocks fly high to their communal roosts, which are usually in woods or quarries.

Both the *Winter* and *Breeding Atlases* showed birds in every 10-km square, with abundance levels at or below the national average except in the hilly country of the Dales, Malvern and Cotswold areas. This widespread distribution is confirmed at a finer grain by preliminary work for the *Tetrad Atlases*. These patterns are also confirmed by the BBS, which shows Worcestershire and Staffordshire to have very high densities, whilst that for the West Midlands county is very low.

The combined CBC/BBS index showed a national population growth of almost three-quarters during 1980-2002. Regionally the increase could have been even bigger, but this cannot be confirmed because of the small sample size and erratic nature of the data. However, current data suggest a regional population of 16,000-25,000 pairs, which compared with the estimate of 5,000-15,000 in *BWM*, implies a two to threefold increase.

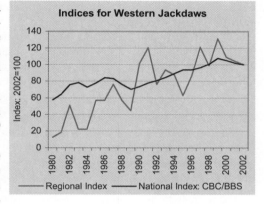

BWM said feeding flocks of 300-500 or so were common in winter and this is still the case. Birds are especially plentiful around Bredon Hill and the Malverns, with 1,500-2,000 on stubble at Little Malvern in December 1995 and 2,000-2,500, also on stubble, at Castlemorton Common in December 1996 comparing favourably with the largest flock of 2,000 mentioned in *BWM*. The number of roosts has increased in line with the population growth, but they have changed little in size, with 500-1,000 still quite normal, but there were more impressive gatherings of 1,200 at Bow Wood in 1993, 1,500 in a pre-roost at Blackmore Park in 1999 and 2,000 at Chillington in March 1981.

Though less favoured, urban areas are certainly not ignored. Indeed, the right conditions can result in some large gatherings. For instance, the huge corvid roost at Wightwick regularly holds around 500 birds, whilst the combination of nest-sites, food supply and a safe roost attracts similar numbers to Judkin's Quarry in Nuneaton.

British Western Jackdaws of the race *C. m. spermologus* are sedentary and most recoveries involve locally ringed birds, with the longest recorded movement being that made by an adult, ringed in Alcester, that travelled 30 km to Banbury (Oxfordshire). Some continental birds, however, are known to come to Britain in winter. Such movements were thought to account for the almost daily sightings at Westport Lake in the autumn of 1991, where birds were otherwise scarce at the time. One seen near Newborough on January 17th 1987 was said to have features of the continental race *C. m. monedula*, whilst a flock of 70 at Bromley Hurst on March 15th that year was thought to possibly be of the same race. However, the plumage variations in our native birds makes identification on sight alone extremely suspect.

Rook   *Corvus frugilegus*
Very common or abundant resident.

The Rook is one of the most numerous and familiar farmland birds, occurring right across the region except in highly urbanised situations. Clamorous and highly sociable, it nests colonially in rookeries built in the tops of the tallest trees, whether these be in small woods, copses or hedgerows. In winter feeding flocks probe for invertebrates amongst pastures, grass leys and stubbles, where they are often joined by Western Jackdaws and other corvids. They also roost communally, usually in woods.

The *Winter Atlas* showed birds in every 10-km square, whilst the *Breeding Atlas* showed them in all bar the two at the very heart of Birmingham and the Black Country. There are even a few rookeries in very urban situations, such as that in plane trees in the centre of Leamington Spa. Pastures and grass leys are very important during the breeding season and birds are most abundant in the south-east of the region, where these grasslands are more prevalent. This is confirmed by the BBS, which shows the highest densities to be in Warwickshire.

The CBC does not monitor Rooks, but the BTO did carry out a full survey in 1975 and a sample one in 1996, which showed a 40% increase in the national population. The BBS showed a fairly stable national population during 1994-2002, but regionally the sets of data were too erratic to draw any conclusions. A comprehensive regional survey, undertaken by the WMBC in 1973, revealed 19,079 nests in 1,022 rookeries (Dean 1974). Two years later, 22,478 nests were counted during the BTO national census. An attempt to repeat these surveys in 1991 met with such a disappointing response from the WMBC membership that only a third of the 10-km squares in the region were adequately covered (Winsper 1991). The following table compares the results from the two WMBC surveys.

Year	No of 10-km squares adequately surveyed	No of Rookeries	No of Nests	Average no of nests per rookery	Density of nests per km²
1973	64	995	18,570	18.7	2.90
1991	25	228	5,667	24.9	2.26

Using density as a guide, the regional population declined by 22% between 1973-1991. This was contrary to the national trend, but it did coincide with the spread of Dutch elm disease. Survey results were also variable as instanced by three 10-km squares in Warwickshire with a combined increase of 85%. The following table shows counts from other rookeries.

Year	81	82	83	84	85	86	87	88	89	90	91	92	93	94	95	96	97	98	99	00
Coombes Valley	116	59						92		57	65	63		46	52	58	54	52		
Sandwell Valley							12	16	20	25-30			44							
Sych Wood				65		81	76						60	77		120		100	90	150

These typify contrasting fortunes. At Coombes Valley many young perished in the blizzards and ice storms of late April 1981, with the result that numbers had halved by the following year. By 1988 they had almost recovered, but two years later they had fallen again, since when they have been reasonably steady. In contrast, the numbers at Sych Wood have increased significantly since 1994, whilst the Sandwell Valley rookery has grown steadily since it was first formed in 1987. Considering all the available data, it seems the regional population now is probably at the lower end of the range 16,000-31,000 pairs (*cf.* surveys above).

The 1973 survey found that 90% of nests were in just four species of trees—elm, oak, beech and ash—with 50% in elm alone. Following the outbreak of Dutch elm disease, which decimated the region's tree cover, birds were forced into alternative situations and, in addition to the trees already mentioned, the 1991 survey revealed nests in low streamside willows, hawthorn thickets and especially on electricity pylons.

In winter, when they feed on seeds, stubbles and invertebrates, Rooks are more catholic in their choice of habitat, preferring an equal mix of arable and pasture. At this time they regularly gather into flocks up to a thousand and frequently associate with other corvids, both to feed and roost. *BWM* said that over 1,000 had been noted on several occasions, with the largest flock being 1,500 in 1978. Subsequently, there have only been three gatherings larger than a thousand, namely two flocks of 1,300, one at Leacroft in June 1981 and another at Hopwas Hays in February 1984, and a roost of 2,000 at Willey in 1982. Rooks follow well-established flight lines to reach their traditional woodland roosts, which may be up to 20 km from their feeding areas, often stopping *en route* at pre-roost gathering points. These roosts begin to disperse in late winter as birds return to the rookeries (Lack 1986).

Rooks are largely sedentary as shown by one ringed at Draycote Water in May 1975 and found dead six kilometres away near Rugby. This one was at least seventeen-and–a-half years old when found, but most recoveries are of birds shot within one or two years of ringing. Immigrants from the Continent regularly arrive in Britain in late October and early November and, although there is no definite evidence that these immigrants penetrate as far inland as the West Midlands, one ringed at Spurn (Humberside) in November 1953 and recovered at Tamworth in February 1954 could have been a continental bird.

Carrion Crow   *Corvus corone*
Abundant resident.

The Carrion Crow is an extremely versatile opportunist. As its name implies, carrion forms an important part of its diet, but this is an omnivorous species that feeds principally on invertebrates in summer and cereal grain in winter. Small mammals, amphibians, birds and eggs are taken too and birds frequently scavenge at landfill sites. This crow is adaptable and inquisitive so there are few places where it cannot be seen, though it is perhaps most at home in a mosaic of grassland, copses and small woods. In urban areas it frequents parks, gardens and derelict sites. Pairs nest alone and usually remain on their territory throughout the year. However, they congregate at good feeding or roosting sites and young birds regularly flock together.

Carrion Crows were recorded in every 10-km square during both the *Winter* and *Breeding Atlas* surveys, mostly at an above average abundance, whilst the BBS shows densities to be highest in Staffordshire and lowest in the West Midlands county. The CBC/BBS indices show that the national population almost doubled over the past twenty years, whilst regionally there could have been an even greater growth, but the data are too sparse to be certain. Nevertheless the population now is probably 33,000-53,000 pairs compared with the 15,000-25,000 estimated in *BWM*.

Numbers seemed to noticeably increase during the late 1980s and early 1990s and three density counts in south-east Warwickshire during 1997-2000 ranged from 7-10 pairs per km^2. These imply densities slightly above the latest population estimate, whereas the density of 5-6 pairs per km^2 at Coombes Valley was about average.

During autumn and winter small flocks up

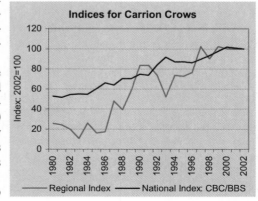

to 60 strong congregate around favoured feeding areas, such as the margins of reservoirs and gravel pits. As the population has expanded, so the number of flocks has increased. Several of these have been up to 300 strong, with even larger gatherings of 350 at the Queslett tip in 1990, 360 in the centre of the Potteries at Hanley Forest Park in 1984 and a huge flock of 1,000 corvids feeding on stubble at Holt in 1985, most of which were of this species. Some substantial roosts have also formed, with up to 350 a regular feature in Sutton Park, 500 at Chillington in 1984, a pre-roost gathering of 1,000 at Timberhonger in 1987 and 1,500 between the Hallow Road and the River Severn in 1986. Despite this, the regional record is still the roost of 3,000 at Bunkers Hill during the 1972/3 winter (*BWM*).

Ringing recoveries show only local movements, the maximum distance being 23 km from Wellesbourne to Banbury (Oxfordshire). The Carrion Crow's remarkable ingenuity is shown by a bird at Blithfield, which flew across the reservoir to catch a fish in its beak, and another at Upton Warren that dived like a tern to catch a fish. There are also records of birds flying up with freshwater mussels and then dropping them to break them open. Normally wary birds, five ventured up to a doorstep at Eccleshall in hard weather in 1981 to feed on dog biscuits.

Hooded Crow   *Corvus cornix*
Rare passage migrant or winter visitor.

Formerly a sub-species of the Carrion Crow, the Hooded Crow was accorded the status of a full species as recently as 2003 (Parkin *et al.* 2003). The British population, which is confined to the Scottish highlands and islands north-west of the Great Glen, is largely sedentary, as is that in Ireland. Those that breed in Scandinavia and eastern Europe, though, are migratory (Busse 1969) and used to regularly pass along the East Coast of Britain between autumn and spring (*BWM*). Occurrences in this region often coincided with easterly winds and presumably involved a westerly displacement of such birds, which during the 1970s were occurring at an average of four a year. Overall, *BWM* documented 95 individuals between 1929 and 1978, but since then this movement has virtually ceased. With just eight records during 1979-2001, all are listed separately, but some could have involved the same bird at more than one locality.

Year	Locality, Date and Notes	Year	Locality, Date and Notes
1981	Wren's Nest: March 3rd. Presume same, Sutton Park: March 6th-7th.	1984	Turners Hill: February 3rd.
1981	Beaudesert: March 17th.	1987	Kingsbury: April 12th.
1983	Stoke Works: December 27th.	1987	Dunstal: April 24th.
1983	Berry Mound: December 30th.	1994	Cannock Tip: January 8th.

Williamson (1975) suggested that this decline may be the result of climate change causing a northerly retreat in the range of this species. Certainly the monthly distribution of the above records is very different to that shown in *BWM*, with none during September-November compared to a significant passage in the earlier period.

Common Raven   (Raven)   *Corvus corax*
Frequent visitor and uncommon to frequent, but increasing, resident.

The popular image of the Common Raven as a bird of remote hills and windswept coasts is slightly misleading as it was once much more widespread, occurring even in lowland districts. Unfortunately, although birds are omnivorous, they feed mainly on carrion and especially on

dead sheep. This led to the belief that they were killing lambs and hence to their relentless persecution, which eradicated them from all but the remotest parts.

By the time *BWM* was published, the Common Raven had become a scarce wanderer and very scarce breeding species. Since then, however, its status has again changed dramatically and birds can once more be found sparingly across most of the region, with regular breeding recently becoming established in all three shire counties.

The increase in numbers is graphically illustrated by the accompanying chart, whilst an indication of the origins of the birds comes from a colour-ringed individual at Belvide Reservoir in 1999, which had been ringed as a chick three years earlier somewhere in mid-Wales or Shropshire. With a wandering species such as this it is impossible to avoid some duplication between records, so the annual totals cannot be precise. However, the long-term trend is very clear, with numbers having grown from around four a year during the early 1980s to over 200 a year now. Many place names, of course, testify to its former widespread distribution, although the species was never as common in Warwickshire as in the hillier country further north and west. By the middle of the nineteenth century breeding had ceased and, apart from four or five attempts during 1949-52—in the Teme Valley and at Malvern and Enville—it was 1979 before nesting was again reported.

The *Winter Atlas* (1981/2-1983/4), however, indicated a much more scattered distribution, with birds in five squares as far apart as Needwood, Arden and the Wyre Forest, as well as the Teme Valley. Even so, it was 1987 before birds bred again, but apart from 1988, they have done so in every year since. Predictably, recolonisation began in the west, along the Malvern Hills and Teme Valley. For the next seven years there was just one known pair, but in 1995 up to nine territories were reported in Worcestershire. A pair also attempted to breed in Staffordshire in 1995, for the first time in forty-three years, and birds were definitely breeding by 1999. By 1998 the expansion had spread eastwards to Warwickshire, where a pair was observed displaying, and two years later three pairs reared nine young—the first successful breeding in the county for perhaps around 200 years. At the turn of the century around 10 pairs were known to be breeding in the region, but by 2002 birds were recorded at up to 60 locations in the breeding season and the current population must now be at least 40-70 pairs.

Although birds are present throughout the year, numbers appear to increase steadily from late-summer until they peak in October. Thereafter, subsidiary peaks are evident in December and February—the latter perhaps a reflection of birds being more obvious as they prepare to nest. The prime habitats remain the open hills of the Malverns, the Teme Valley and north Staffordshire, and the heavily-wooded parts of the Wyre Forest, Enville, Cannock Chase and the Churnet Valley. However, birds are increasingly spreading into smaller woods and parklands with old trees, such as Packington Park. Not surprisingly, the three largest flocks were all in Worcestershire, with 16 over Sugarloaf Hill (Malverns) on December 23rd 1997, 18 at Grimley Old Workings on February 25th 2001 and 22 at North Hill (Malverns)

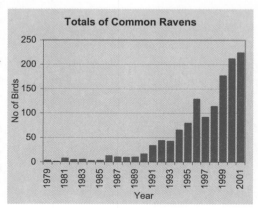

on October 19th 2000. The vast majority of birds (69%) have also appeared in the same county, with 19% in Staffordshire, 11% in Warwickshire and 1% in the West Midlands.

Common Starling   (Starling)   *Sturnus vulgaris*
Very common to abundant resident, passage migrant and winter visitor.

The opening statement in *BWM* says "the status of this well-known species appears to have changed little over the years." If only that were still true. Although still a very familiar bird in our cities, towns and countryside, the Common Starling has nevertheless declined alarmingly. So much so, in fact, that it is now on the *Red Alert List* of Species of Conservation Concern (Gregory *et al.* 2002). Many people associate it with cold winter evenings, when huge flocks would darken our city centre skylines at dusk as they wheeled round before settling to roost. Sadly, such evocative sights are becoming rarer, although noisy, quarrelsome parties still come to snatch every scrap of food from bird tables.

Common Starlings were recorded in every 10-km square in both the *Winter* and *Breeding Atlases*, with an abundance level well above average, except on the open moors of north Staffordshire. Densities were highest in the intensely developed urban cores of the Potteries, the Black Country, Birmingham and Coventry. Early results from the *Tetrad Atlases* confirm that birds are present in 93% of both urban and rural tetrads, whilst the BBS shows densities in the West Midlands county to be twice those of the rural shires.

Nationally, the CBC/BBS showed a steady decline of 60% in the population during 1980-2002. This decline was mirrored regionally by the BBS, but prior to that the sample was considered to be unrepresentative as few survey plots contained prime breeding habitat for Common Starlings. At a very tentative estimate, the regional population now is probably between 20,000-30,000 pairs, compared with the very wide range of 50,000-150,000 pairs suggested in *BWM*.

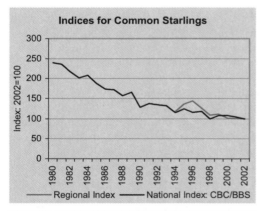

Two instances demonstrate the scale of declines at local sites. At Coombes Valley numbers collapsed from around 40 pairs in the early 1980s to seven in 1982 and just a single pair in 1999, whilst at the DM Kineton camp they dropped from around 200 in the late 1980s to 16 in 1998 and 28 in 2000. Apart from the CBC plots, there was little information on densities other than 15 pairs per km² at Chapel Green in 1998.

Similar declines have occurred across much of northern Europe, with the result that fewer Continental birds are now coming to Britain for the winter. The adjacent table shows the dramatic demise of the roost in Birmingham city centre. Although various physical measures had been taken to deter birds from roosting along cornices and pediments, these alone were certainly not responsible for this collapse, since many birds used to roost in trees and not on buildings.

As well as being attracted by the warmth

Common Starling Roosts in Birmingham City Centre			
Winter	No of Birds	Winter	No of Birds
1949/50	20,000	1984/85	57,620
1950/51	16,800	1985/86	36,888
1951/52	20,000	1989/90	1,949
1962/63	31,700	1990/91	64
1974/75	11,600	1991/92	1
1975/76	8,800		

from buildings and street lights, birds also roost in reedbeds and in conifers, thorn thickets and broad-leaved woods with a dense shrub layer. Comparison of the largest roosts provides yet more evidence of decline. *BWM* mentions several roosts of a quarter to one million birds, one of two million, at Newcastle-under-Lyme in 1961/62, and one of two-three million, at Drakes Broughton in 1970. By comparison, during 1979-2001, the largest roosts were a mere 100,000—at Lea Marston in 1979 and Aqualate in 1988. Moreover, the roost at Aqualate had shrunk to just 20,000 in 1998 and 15,500 by 2002.

In winter flocks also scour pastures, stubbles, freshly-ploughed fields and playing fields for invertebrates, or scavenge for food at landfill sites. Feeding flocks are generally smaller than roosts and *BWM* remarked that few counts were available. Of those that were, 2,000 in 1952 and 3,000 in 1973 were the best. The recent decline in numbers, however, combined with an article about the demise of the city centre roost that appeared in the *Birmingham Evening Mail* in 1991, appears to have prompted more reporting. As a result, there have been at least ten reports in the current period of gatherings in excess of 1,000 birds, with the larger being 3,000, at Hockley Heath on February 20th 1982 and Dunstall Park on August 15th 1990; and 5,000 at Doxey Marshes on November 18th 2001. Birds have also been noted feeding on windfall apples and on the larvae of craneflies and the green oak tortrix moth.

Although the first migrant birds may appear in September, the majority arrive between mid-October and mid-November and leave again during March. Visible evidence of migration in recent years has come from Wyken Slough, where 340 an hour moved NW on October 3rd 1994 and 400 an hour SW on November 3rd 1994, and from south Warwickshire, where 500 an hour passed SW over the gap in the hills at Fenny Compton/Wormleighton on October 19th 1997. Ringing tells us that many of these birds originate from as far afield as southern Scandinavia and western Russia, whilst others from the Low Countries indicate that their migration route is along the southern shore of the North Sea. Recoveries of our breeding birds show them to be mainly sedentary, with few long-distance movements recorded.

Rose-coloured Starling   (Rosy Starling)   *Sturnus roseus*
Very rare vagrant. Nine records.

BMW documented five records, all in the 1800s. Almost a century passed before the next in 1987, but this was followed by a total of three in 2001 and 2002.

Regional Record Number	County Record Number		Year	Locality, Date and Notes
1	Warks	1	1854	Barton: adult male, unknown date in summer. Shot.
2	Worcs	1	1855	Powick: female, August, date unknown. Killed.
3	Staffs	1	1875	Rushton Spencer: date unknown.
4	Warks	2	1890	Haselor: adult male, January 20th. Shot.
5	W Mid	1	1890	Sutton Park: immature female, November 10th. Shot.
6	Staffs	2	1987	Hockley: adult, July 27th. *BB 81:588*
7	Staffs	3	2001	Fradley: first-summer, June 9th-12th. *BB 95:518*
8	Warks	3	2001	Exhall (near Coventry): first-summer, June 21st-27th. *BB 96:602*
9	Worcs	2	2002	Aston Somerville: adult, August 23rd-25th.

Note: BBRC ceased to consider records of this species from January 1st 2002.

The Rose-coloured Starling breeds principally in Asia and winters in the Indian sub-continent. It is an irruptive species, however, and regularly reaches western Europe, with significant summer invasions in the three years 2000-2002 (Rogers *et al.* 2002). In addition to that listed above, there were other reports in 2002 of one or more birds in the West Midlands and Staffordshire, but no descriptive details have been received.

House Sparrow   *Passer domesticus*
Abundant, though declining, resident.

The humble House Sparrow has been associated with man's environment for so long that we tend to take its presence for granted. Consequently there is little quantitative data available, but it is known to have declined significantly since the 1970s and is now included on the *Red Alert List* of Species of Conservation Concern (Gregory *et al.* 2002). Nevertheless it is still widely distributed in areas of human habitation, from the very centres of our towns and cities down to the smallest settlements. Populations have become isolated, however, with birds maintaining a presence in some areas, but being inexplicably absent from others. They are highly sociable, nesting in colonies, roosting communally and feeding in flocks.

Both the *Winter* and *Breeding Atlases* showed birds to be present in every 10-km square, with abundance levels generally above the national average except in the more sparsely populated parts of north Staffordshire, Needwood and Feldon. Preliminary results from the two *Tetrad Atlases* have confirmed their presence in over 93% of urban tetrads and 85% of rural ones. As with Common Starlings, the BBS shows densities in the West Midlands county to be twice those in the shires, with Warwickshire having the lowest density of all.

With its focus on farmland and woodland, the CBC was not ideally suited to monitoring House Sparrows. However, it did show a 77% decline between 1977-99. Apart from the small populations on CBC plots, the only local indication of density came from Ladbroke, where at least 30 pairs were present in 1 km^2 of farmland and gardens in 1997.

The first mention of declining numbers came in 1990 and an indication of how rapidly populations could collapse was provided by the DM Kineton army camp, where breeding season numbers dropped by 25% in 1995, 60% the next year, and finished with none at all in 2000. Elsewhere numbers were 40% down on the five-yearly mean at Southcrest and 48% down at Webheath in 1999. In contrast, by 2001 there were some encouraging signs of recovery, with numbers at both Oddingley and Tibberton up by at least 50%. Nevertheless, the little data available point to a significant fall in the regional population, which is now probably in the range 25,000-50,000 pairs—down by two-thirds on the 75,000-150,000 in *BWM*.

Post-breeding flocks of 1,500 feeding on ripening corn in 1952 and 1976 were referred to in *BWM*, but it said that later in autumn, once they move to stubbles, plough or waste land, flocks seldom exceed 700. During the current period, there were 1,000 on stubble at Barr Common in September 1984 and 2,000 at Birchmoor on July 26th 2000, but these were exceptional and the only other flock since 1990 to exceeded 200 was one of 400 in stubble at Moat Hill in 1997. Although birds are known to roost communally, often behind ivy, in garden conifers or farm buildings, there are surprisingly no details of roost or pre-roost numbers.

In its urban strongholds the House Sparrow had become a scarce breeding bird in Coventry's suburbs by 1994 and three years later it had virtually disappeared from Willenhall Memorial Park. It had also ceased to visit suburban gardens in Dorridge. In contrast, it was still very common at the Harborne Nature Reserve in Birmingham in 1998, while small colonies were said to be thriving on Wolverhampton housing estates around Dunstall Park and Smestow Valley in 1999. This typifies the variable distribution, with none in some areas but elsewhere flocks up to 50 still reported from gardens, where they are frequent visitors to bird tables. Indeed, groups of 70 and 90 were reported in gardens in 2002. Surprisingly they were said to be out-numbered at times by Tree Sparrows in a garden at Little Stoke in 2000. As its name implies, this is a very parochial species and the only recovery is of a bird ringed at Malvern Link in December 1995 and found dead at the same place in September 1998.

Tree Sparrow   *Passer montanus*
Fairly common, but declining, resident.

According to *BWM*, colonies of Tree Sparrows occurred throughout the region wherever old, decaying trees or crumbling buildings provided suitable nest-holes and in winter large flocks gathered with finches and buntings to feed on weed-seeds. However, numbers declined nationally by a massive 95% between 1974-1999 and it is now on the *Red Alert List* of Species of Conservation Concern (Gregory *et al*. 2002). Today a few birds can still be found in their favoured haunts of hedgerows, parkland, ancient woodland and streamside pollards, but the distribution is much more patchy and only small flocks occur in winter.

At the time of the *Winter* and *Breeding Atlases*, Tree Sparrows were widely distributed, occurring in 95% of 10-km squares. The *Winter Atlas* found none on the uplands of the Dales or Malverns, suggesting that birds move to lower ground at this time of year, whilst during the *Breeding Atlas* they were absent from the centres of Birmingham and Coventry and the lower Avon valley. Conversely, they were most abundant in the Feldon, Dunsmore and Needwood districts. The major decline in the national CBC/BBS index occurred before 1990, but a slight recovery since has left an overall decline during 1980-2002 of 54%. Regionally, the survey plots held too few birds to reliably assess trends, but based on the BBS and falling average flock sizes, it seems the decline was similar to that nationally.

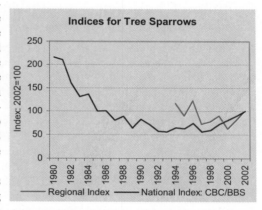

Since the *Breeding Atlas*, the range has contracted markedly as the accompanying map of all records during 1997-2001 shows, with birds in just 53% of 10-km squares. Moreover, they were present in only 12% of tetrads. In comparison, surveys for the two *Tetrads Atlases* show birds in 6% of urban squares and 25% of rural ones, excluding the Feldon area of south-east Warwickshire. The latter is a stronghold for the species, with a population of 250-300 pairs, or at least 125 pairs per 10-km square (J. J. Bowley *pers comm.*) Even here the population is much reduced. At Fenny Compton, for example, there were 60 pairs in 941 hectares in 1996, but just 11 pairs in 1998. Shortage of natural food in winter is a major cause of the decline and, aided by winter feeding, numbers there have since recovered to 40 pairs, while at nearby Farnborough they rose from nine pairs in 2000 to 25 in 2002.

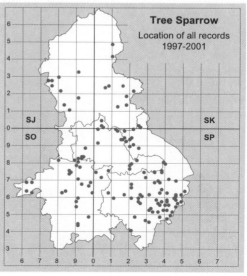

Loss of hedgerow trees for nesting has been offset by the use of nest-boxes at places such as Lutley Wedge and especially Pedmore, where occupancy increased from nine boxes in 1997 to 18 in 1999. Elsewhere the story is one of doom and gloom, with the once strong colony at Sandwell Valley said to be in terminal decline, none at Lower Moor in 1997 for the first time in fifteen years and none at traditional sites such as Doley Common, Dorridge, Hockley Heath and Stoke Bliss by 2000. Against this background it is difficult to envisage a regional population above the range 1,500-2,500 pairs, whereas *BWM* postulated 9,000-20,000 pairs.

Winter flocks have diminished accordingly. *BWM* gave a mean flock size of 164 and quoted three gatherings of over a thousand, of which the largest was 1,500 at Blithfield Reservoir in the winter of 1961/2. During 1997-2001, the average flock size was just 34, while the largest reported in recent years were both in the Feldon area in March 2001, when 150 were at Northend and 130 at Wormleighton Reservoir. Post-breeding flocks begin to form from late July and may then be seen at any time through to April, but they are generally larger and most frequent from December to March. Unlike the House Sparrow, the Tree Sparrow is more adventurous in its movements, with birds from Warwickshire moving over 100 km into Wiltshire and Surrey. Even so, about half of the recorded journeys are under 50 km.

Common Chaffinch   (Chaffinch)   *Fringilla coelebs*
Abundant resident, passage migrant and winter visitor.

The ubiquitous Common Chaffinch breeds everywhere where there are trees, bushes or hedges in which to build a nest. During the breeding season, when it is insectivorous, woodland is its favourite haunt, but it is also at home on farmland or in the parks and gardens of our towns and cities. Outside the breeding season it feeds on a variety of seeds and often wanders more widely to search for food around sheep troughs and manure heaps, or in stubbles and ploughed fields. Most British birds are sedentary and remain close to their territories throughout the year, but in winter they are joined by immigrants from the Continent, which tend to feed in flocks in more open situations. These immigrant birds also roost communally, especially in conifer plantations or woods with a dense shrub layer, such as rhododendrons.

Both the *Winter* and *Breeding Atlases* showed the Common Chaffinch to be present in every 10-km square, but with varied abundance. In winter, there were fewer in the Severn and Avon Vales and north Warwickshire, whereas breeding densities were below the national average in the urban cores of the Potteries, Black Country, Birmingham and Coventry. Notwithstanding this, preliminary results from the *Tetrad Atlases* show birds to be present in virtually all but the most urbanised areas.

The national CBC/BBS index grew by 12% during 1980-2002 and the regional index broadly followed this from the mid-1980s, but showed a faster rate of growth prior to that, giving an overall growth of over a third. In addition to the CBC data, counts of 139 pairs on the Malvern Hills in 1995 and 20, 35 and 37 territories per km^2 in south-east Warwickshire between 1997 and 2000 provide an indication of the populations in the general countryside. At Coombes Valley there were 53-88 pairs per km^2 in the species' favoured woodland habitat, with an average density during 1991-98 of 77 pairs per km^2. However, the densities in Kingsbury Wood were only half this level. The best estimate of the current re-

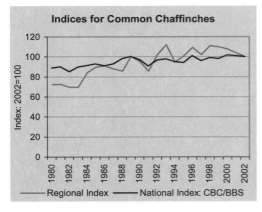

gional population is 160,000-200,000 pairs, compared with the 60,000-120,000 estimated in *BWM*.

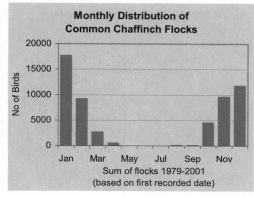

Monthly Distribution of Common Chaffinch Flocks

No of Birds

Sum of flocks 1979-2001
(based on first recorded date)

Although there is no evidence from ringing recoveries to suggest that British Common Chaffinches migrate, in autumn large numbers of migratory continental birds arrive here to over-winter. Foreign-ringed birds caught at our winter roosts and those ringed at these roosts, but recovered on the Continent, show that most are from southern Scandinavia, with some from northern Europe and Poland.

Small post-breeding flocks begin to form in August, when they feed on defoliating caterpillars in oakwoods, but it is usually late September, or more often October, before the above migrants arrive. Flocks continue to build up to a peak in January, but then quietly subside during February and March as birds begin their return journeys, largely unnoticed. *BWM* said flocks of 100-200 were commonplace and up to 500 by no means unusual, with the largest being 700 in 1972 and 1,000 in 1976. Little has changed, with almost 60% of flocks during 1978/9-2000/1 having up to 200 birds, while the largest were 700 at Blakedown in January and at nearby Island Pool in February 1994, and 900 at Warley in February 1983.

Roosts, however, appear to have declined. *BWM* refers to gatherings ranging from 800-3,000, whereas the best subsequent counts have all come from the Maer Hills, where there were 1,300 in March 1979 and 700 during January and February and again in November and December in 1981. Otherwise there was nothing above 400 and in very recent times there have been no reports of any roost larger than 200.

Brambling   *Fringilla montifringilla*
Fairly common passage migrant and winter visitor, but in variable numbers.

Bramblings breed in Fennoscandia and Russia and visit the region every winter, but in highly variable numbers. They are ground feeders and spend much of their time, often in the company of Common Chaffinches, searching for seeds on the woodland floor, where their plumage merges imperceptibly with the carpet of fallen leaves. Beech-mast is their favoured food and they travel widely to find it. Birds also feed in stubbles, crops and on wasteland and are reasonably regular garden visitors, especially in hard weather. Their communal roosts are in the same situations as Common Chaffinches, with which they often share the same site.

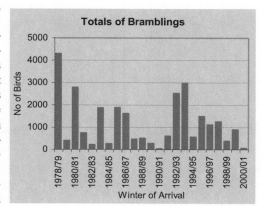

Totals of Bramblings

No of Birds

Winter of Arrival

Beech crops vary from area-to-area according to weather conditions, so the Brambling's preference for beech-mast often takes it to widely different areas, or even different countries, from one winter to the next. This is reflected in the winter totals, which have ranged from a meagre 47 in 1990/1 to 4,300 in 1978/9. Similarly, there were 8,000 in 1973/4 and 1975/6, but just 200-300 in the intervening winter (*BWM*).

Their preference for beech-mast also noticeably influences their distribution within

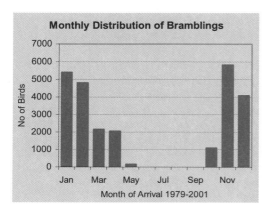

Monthly Distribution of Bramblings

Month of Arrival 1979-2001

the region, with 48% occurring in Stafford-shire and 38% in Worcestershire, which are the two counties with most beech trees, and only 7% each in Warwickshire and the West Midlands, where these trees are scarce. The most reliable site for the species in recent years has been the feeding station at the Marquis Drive Visitor Centre on Cannock Chase, where birds have been present most winters. Nowhere else can quite match this consistency, although small numbers fairly regularly follow the line of the Cotswold scarp or pass through the Malvern Hills via Happy Valley on their autumn migration. A few returning birds also gather on Cannock Chase in spring and one or two usually turn up at reservoirs.

The earliest autumn arrival was at Sheriffs Lench on September 3rd 1956, but it is usually early October before the first birds reach the region and November before appreciable numbers are recorded. Although some of these will stay for the winter, others move on to different parts of Britain or even Europe. Numbers then begin to increase again from mid-December, reaching a peak in January and February. This secondary influx is when most wintering birds come. It probably involves ones that arrived further north in Britain during the previous autumn and is often accompanied by hard weather.

BWM said most flocks comprise less than 50 birds, but that up to 300 were not uncommon. This remains the case, with 80% of groups comprising less than 50 birds, but several gatherings up to 350. The two largest flocks mentioned in *BWM* were 1,500 in February 1973 and 2,000 in February 1974, but the best in recent times were 1,000—at both Worcester refuse-tip and Summerfield in mid-February 1979 and at Rudyard on November 29th 1992. A gathering of 800 at Rudyard in November 1993 was also noteworthy. Gardens can also prove productive in winter, with a few reports of up to 30 and even 50 on one occasion, at Newcastle-under-Lyme in March 1987.

A small return passage occurs in March and April, with a few birds—occasionally including a resplendent, singing male—lingering into May. In 1981 an unseasonably large flock of 120 was still present on May 2nd at Stansley Wood. There have also been a handful of summer records. *BWM* quoted just two, but there have since been a further five, all of males—at Belvide Reservoir from August 3rd-9th 1980 and August 18th 1983; Chillington on June 14th 1981; Lineholt in August 1988; and Brocton Coppice from June 24th-July 2nd 1989.

Bramblings do not always figure prominently in ringing totals. They have nevertheless provided some interesting recoveries, with one ringed in the region being recovered in west Germany and others ringed in Belgium and Norway being caught in Worcestershire and Warwickshire respectively. Movements within this country are equally interesting, with a bird ringed in Liverpool in January 1981 and recovered in Sutton Coldfield in March of the same year—making its way home? Others ringed in Worcestershire in January and February 1979 were recovered on Anglesey in December 1981 and the Isle of Man in December 1980 respectively.

European Serin (Serin) *Serinus serinus*
Very rare vagrant. Six records.

European Serins bred in Britain for the first time in 1967 and colonisation was predicted, but a decade later occurrences had declined. The first regional record in 1978 was considered to be an isolated occurrence (*BWM*), but there have since been five more as shown opposite.

Regional Record Number	County Record Number		Year	Locality, Date and Notes
1	Worcs	1	1978	Near Evesham: two, possibly three, including one male in song, June 17th-18th.
2	Worcs	2	1981	Wilden: male, January 21st and April 1st.
3	Staffs	1	1992	Elford: July 26th.
4	Staffs	2	1995	Knypersley Reservoir: female, March 16th.
5	Staffs	3	2001	Swallow Moss: May 19th.
6	Warks	1	2002	Moreton Morrell: male, April 3rd.

The species breeds widely across the Continent, Turkey and north-west Africa and winters in southern Europe. The pattern of British records, mostly from the south coast, shows appearances in every month, but with distinct peaks in spring (April-May) and autumn (October-November) (Dymond *et al.* 1989). Only two of the above records fit into this pattern.

Greenfinch *Carduelis chloris*
Very common to abundant resident.

The Greenfinch breeds widely in loose colonies across the region in woodland glades and margins, scrub, hedgerows and a variety of urban situations including gardens, parks and churchyards. It feeds primarily on seeds, using its strong bill to prise these from trees, shrubs and herbaceous plants as well as gathering them from the ground. As the seed stocks diminish through the winter, so it increasingly forms mixed flocks with other finches to roam ploughed fields, stubbles and waste ground in search of food, whilst some visit garden feeders. It also roosts communally, usually in rhododendron bushes, holly or dense conifer plantations.

Birds were recorded in every 10-km square in both the *Winter* and *Breeding Atlases*, with above average abundance in many districts, but especially in the market gardening area of the Vale of Evesham. The BBS confirms that densities are highest in Worcestershire, while the early results from the *Tetrad Atlases* reinforce the widespread distribution, with birds in 90% of urban squares and nearly all rural ones.

Apart from the CBC data, the only information on density showed an extremely wide range, with 5 pairs per km² at Hawkhurst Moor in 1987 and an exceptional 23 territories per km² at Ladbroke in 1997. Data from individual sites showed stable situations at Alvecote and Doxey Marshes, with 4-6 pairs during 1984-96 and 2-4 pairs during 1984-99 respectively, whereas at Coombes Valley numbers increased sharply from one pair in 1992 to five pairs in 1997 and 1998.

The best estimate of the current population is 21,000-35,000 pairs compared with 25,000-50,000 pairs in *BWM*. However, the national CBC/BBS index increased by 20% in the interim, whilst the regional index more than doubled. This suggests that the figures in *BWM* may have been too high and Gibbons *et al* (1993) acknowledge the difficulty of estimating numbers with any accuracy.

Post-breeding flocks are regularly seen during August and September, when they of-

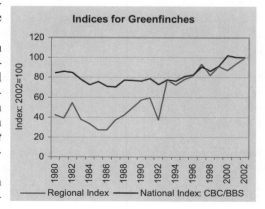

Indices for Greenfinches

Index: 2002=100

—— Regional Index —— National Index: CBC/BBS

ten feed on the seeds of any un-harvested crops, especially oilseed rape. As modern farming practices made seeds harder to find, so Greenfinches increasingly turned to gardens for food in winter. They have become particularly adept at feeding from suspended peanut feeders and are very partial to sunflower seeds. Gradually more and more are now remaining within the confines of cities, towns and villages to breed, turning the emphasis from a rural to an urban species. Indeed, a pair bred right in the heart of Birmingham, at Chamberlain Square, in 1989.

Winter flocks reach their maximum size and abundance during December and January. Despite the population increase, flock size remains much as described in *BWM*, with numbers frequently reaching 100 and up to 300 not unusual. There have been twenty larger gatherings, with the two biggest being 750 feeding on linseed at Blakeshall on December 8th 1996 and 1,000 in a huge finch flock of 2,500 birds at Cotes Heath on January 7th-8th 1994. The latter eclipsed the previous regional bests of 700 and 750 set in the 1970s (*BWM*). Amongst the feeding areas noted, oilseed rape fields, stubbles and set-aside featured prominently, but gardens were mentioned most often, with some impressive counts including 85 in a Kineton garden in 1992. Many also visit feeding stations, such as those at the WMBC's reserves at Belvide Reservoir and Ladywalk (*e.g.* 170 in 1997), and a few are attracted by the food put down at game rearing stations.

Roosts tend to increase in size as winter advances until they finally disperse around March. *BWM* said few were smaller than 200 and mentioned three occasions when numbers reached 1,000. During 1979-2001 there was little information, but they appeared to be fewer and smaller (mean size just 125), with the largest being 500—at Packington back in February 1979. In more recent times the best was an impressive 425 roosting in evergreen bushes at Dudley in the cold weather of January 1997.

Although ringing indicates that large numbers remain during the winter months, it also shows that some British Greenfinches are partial migrants, moving south-westwards during autumn. These migrants presumably account for the small movements that are occasionally noted in the region, such as those in 1995 when 40 passed south-westwards over Fenny Compton on October 10th and 32 moved westwards through the Malverns at Happy Valley on October 22nd. This is confirmed by a bird ringed in Staffordshire in May that appeared 155 km south in Christchurch (Hampshire) the following January. Ringing also indicates there is a north-easterly spring passage as birds return to their breeding grounds. This is illustrated by one ringed in Sutton Coldfield in February and recovered in Doncaster (Yorkshire) during April of the same year.

Goldfinch   *Carduelis carduelis*
Very common summer visitor and partial migrant: increasingly common in winter.

The Goldfinch favours open habitats, where it nests in trees and bushes. Typical haunts include farmland and parkland; scrub, orchards and the edges and rides of woodland; and garden shrubberies, even in urban areas. Outside the breeding season, twittering 'charms' of this brightly-coloured finch search open and waste land for weed seeds. The Goldfinch specialises in feeding from plants in the daisy family, such as knapweed and ragwort, but is best known for using its pointed beak to extract seeds from thistles and teasels. Recently it has become more common as a winter visitor to garden feeders, where it is especially attracted to black Nyjer seed.

The *Winter Atlas* indicated a presence in every 10-km square, but the *Breeding Atlas* showed birds in only 97% of squares. Many are found in the main towns and cities, even right into the centre of Birmingham and in 1981 singing males were at Holliday Street and nearby Brindley Walk, where a small 'charm' was feeding on ragwort, whilst a flock of 40 visited the old Snow Hill railway station in 1983. Indeed, at the latter site breeding was recorded annually

during the Black Redstart surveys of 1987-91
(J. Winsper *pers comm.*)

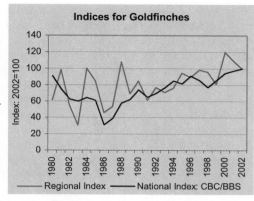

Indices for Goldfinches

The two *Atlases* showed abundance to be above average in south Worcestershire, but around the norm elsewhere and this is confirmed by the BBS. Preliminary results from the *Tetrad Atlases* show around 60% of urban squares to be occupied compared with 85% of rural ones.

The CBC/BBS index indicated a national decline prior to 1986, which was thought to be due to the increased use of herbicides to control thistles. Thereafter it grew at a steady rate. In comparison, the regional index was very erratic through the 1980s, but then closely followed the national trend through the 1990s. Overall, the national growth between 1980-2002 was about 10%, but regionally it might have been much greater. Despite the steady growth, numbers at individual sites, such as Alvecote Pools, Coombes Valley, Doxey Marshes and Upton Warren have changed very little. Other than the CBC, the only density data was a very high 6 pairs per km^2 at Ladbroke in 1997. The current population is estimated at 10,000-16,000 pairs compared with the 6,000-10,000 suggested in *BWM*.

After breeding, birds gather into flocks, 56% of which occur between July and October, with the majority in September. At this time the average flock size is about 65, although up to 300 were at Grimley in September 1988 and 320 at Throckmorton on October 3rd 1999 (*cf.* 600 at Wilden in October 1974 *BWM*). In years when thistledown is plentiful, flocks tend to be smaller, but more widespread.

Although some birds are resident, with many ringing recoveries showing movements of less than 30 km, most migrate south to winter in France and Spain as there is often insufficient natural food to sustain the entire population through the winter (Newton 1972). This is illustrated by two birds ringed during August and September that were recovered in November of the same year in Spain. Winter flocks here are therefore fewer and slightly smaller, with an average size around 50 and a maximum of 200. Those birds that do remain, roam quite widely from one feeding site to the next, gradually dispersing as winter progresses and food becomes harder to find. It is at this time that many visit garden feeders. By early spring many birds have turned to taking seeds from birches and alders and to opening conifer cones (Newton 1972). Flocks then increase slightly in size again during April as emigrant birds return to breed, although a gathering of 500 at Hanchurch on April 29th 1985 was unusually large. Passage is seldom apparent, but 30 flying north over Belvide Reservoir on April 24th 1993 were possibly returning migrants. Equally, there is little information on winter roosts in the region, but small numbers are known to gather in dense thickets or conifers and 134 roosted in holly at a Stoke Bliss garden in December 1991.

Siskin *Carduelis spinus*
Fairly common passage migrant and winter visitor. Rare or scarce breeding species.

Siskins are primarily winter visitors that arrive in the region from October onwards and leave again in the following March or April. When they first arrive, acrobatic flocks cling precariously to the end of slender twigs as they deftly take the seeds from alders, or less often birch and then larch. By the following spring, these food sources are mostly exhausted and so they turn to their summer diet of seeds prised from the cones of spruce and pine. This is also when

they most often visit garden feeders, although they may appear at any time in hard weather. Maturing conifer plantations in areas such as Cannock Chase, Enville, Hanchurch, Keele and the Wyre Forest have also created ideal breeding habitat and a few pairs now nest.

Winter numbers are governed by the availability of food, both here and on the breeding grounds. Siskins nest in the spruce forests of Fennoscandia and Russia, where their population fluctuates according to the two-yearly cycle of the spruce crop (Haapanen 1966). The effect of these cycles on numbers visiting the region was clearly demonstrated in *BWM*. It can also be traced in the accompanying chart, although it is gradually being obscured by the growing British breeding population. The abundance of spruce seed also governs the scale of immigration, with the largest numbers following an abundant crop that will have enabled many second broods to be raised. The biggest irruption of all occurred in 1985/86, when birds began to arrive exceptionally early. The first one on July 21st was followed by a flock of 40 in the Churnet Valley on the 29th and unprecedented numbers occurred in many areas during September. A similar, but smaller mid-summer influx, associated with Common Crossbills, occurred in 1997.

Normally the first birds appear in September and numbers then steadily increase to a January peak before declining during February and March. These days it is impossible to separate migrants from residents, but prior to 1991 the average date for first birds to arrive, based on fifty-two years of observations, was September 30th. Many Siskins move into, or through, the region in late summer and early autumn as they make their way from northerly breeding sites to their southerly wintering quarters and birds ringed in Kildarry (Scotland) and Lancashire in April have appeared here in the following February. Others ringed here in February have been recovered in Cumbria and the Central Region of Scotland in April, while evidence of breeding in the far north comes from a bird ringed in Tamworth in February and recovered in April of the same year in Ostfold, Norway—a distance of 1,077 km. In some years a small return passage is evident in March and April and, over fifty-one years, the average date for last birds was April 16th. By mid-May only potential breeding birds remain.

The *Winter Atlas* showed birds in 97% of 10-km squares. Analysis of wintering flocks shows an uneven distribution, however, with the number of birds in Staffordshire and Worcestershire, respectively, being 36% and 34% of the total, whereas Warwickshire attracted only 19% and West Midlands 11%. By comparison, the *Breeding Atlas* showed birds to be present in just nine 10-km squares (12%), all but one of them in Staffordshire. Ironically, the only confirmed breeding came from SP34, on the Warwickshire/Oxfordshire

Totals of Siskins

No of Birds (y-axis: 0, 1000, 2000, 3000, 4000, 5000, 6000)

Winter of Arrival (x-axis: 1978/79, 1980/81, 1982/83, 1984/85, 1986/87, 1988/89, 1990/91, 1992/93, 1994/95, 1996/97, 1998/99, 2000/01)

border, in one of just two squares where birds were not recorded in winter!

As the plantations of conifers have matured and their seed crops have become more reliable, so Siskins have spread rapidly in western and northern Britain. In the West Midlands suitable habitat is still restricted and colonisation has been slow and sporadic. The first breeding records came from Cannock Chase and the Stour Valley in 1973 and the Wyre Forest in 1974, since when a few pairs, or singing males, have been seen or heard most years. More positive proof of breeding has proved hard to obtain, but probably or definitely did occur in the Wyre Forest in 1982 and 1984; on Cannock Chase in 1987, 1990, 1992 and 1999; and at Lordsley in 1988, Packington Park in 2000 and Eymore Wood in 2001. These few records almost certainly understate the true situation, however, and there are probably up to ten pairs breeding most years.

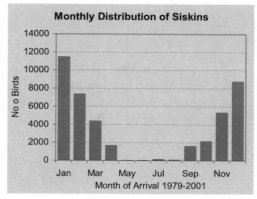

Monthly Distribution of Siskins

Winter flocks of 50 or so are quite common and once a good food supply has been located they may remain in the same area for several days or even weeks. They seldom stay long in birches or larches, but will remain in their favoured alders for as long as the seed crop lasts. Larger gatherings up to 200 are reasonably frequent, and in recent years 400 were recorded on four occasions, whilst the maximum was a staggering 1,300-1,700 at Coldridge Wood in March 1993 (*cf.* a maximum of 'well over 400' quoted in *BWM*).

Of 38 suburban gardens surveyed in Staffordshire in 1986, 20 were visited at least once and 12 had regular visits. The average number of birds per garden was three and the maximum eight, but the garden record stands at 75, at Solihull in 1981. Siskins often consort with Lesser Redpolls and at the time *BWM* was written they were much the scarcer of the two. Fortunes have changed, however, and today Siskins outnumber Lesser Redpolls by 1.7:1.

Linnet   *Carduelis cannabina*
Very common resident and partial migrant, with fewer in winter.

Gorse-clad heaths, commons, areas of scrub and thick hedgerows are where the Linnet is most at home, but it also occurs in young plantations and occasionally suburban gardens. Pairs generally nest in loose colonies. Between 1974-99 numbers nationally fell by more than half, causing it to be included on the *Red Alert List* of Birds of Conservation Concern (Gregory *et al.* 2002). After breeding, large flocks assemble to search for seeds in freshly cultivated ground, stubbles and on waste ground, but in autumn many birds leave the region, so wintering flocks are smaller.

The Linnet's decline can be attributed to the loss of heathland, removal of hedges and reduction in arable weeds. As a breeding species it is still widely distributed, being recorded in every 10-km square during the *Breeding Atlas* survey. Its levels of abundance were generally about average, but tended to be slightly higher on the heaths south of the Potteries, on Cannock Chase and around Brownhills. Above average densities were also apparent in the open countryside of the Avon Valley and Feldon areas. Conversely, densities were below average in mid-Staffordshire and in the more heavily timbered areas such as Arden and Wyre Forest.

The *Winter Atlas* showed a more restricted distribution, with only 87% of 10-km squares occupied. The highest densities were again around the concentrations of heathland and in the Avon Valley and Feldon areas. This suggests that the best breeding sites are also capable of

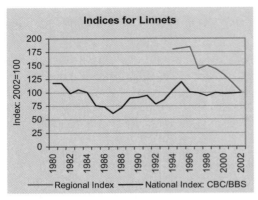

Indices for Linnets

Index: 2002=100

——— Regional Index ——— National Index: CBC/BBS

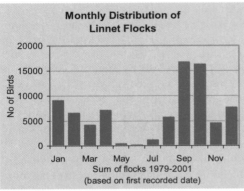

Monthly Distribution of
Linnet Flocks

No of Birds

Jan Mar May Jul Sep Nov
Sum of flocks 1979-2001
(based on first recorded date)

sustaining birds through the winter, although they do tend to move down to lower altitudes. This similarity between breeding and wintering areas gives rise to the misconception that the Linnet is a resident, whereas it is a partial migrant. The BBS shows the highest densities still to be in Staffordshire and Warwickshire, but the Linnet has continued to decline in the region since the BTO atlases were compiled and preliminary work for the *Tetrad Atlases* has recorded breeding in only half of urban squares and three-quarters of rural ones.

The national CBC/BBS index continued to decline until the late 1980s, but has since shown some recovery. Overall it fell by 15% during 1980-2002. Regionally, the BBS shows a very sharp decline since 1994, but there was insufficient data to compute an index prior to then. From the available data the regional population is judged to be around 13,000-25,000 pairs compared to the 15,000-30,000 pairs estimated in *BWM*.

Linnets flock together from late summer, when they are especially attracted to the ever increasing fields of oilseed rape, through to spring. In summer they feed directly from herbaceous plants, but in winter food is taken from the ground (Newton 1972). Numbers show three distinct peaks, but flocks are largest and most widespread in September and October, when they average around 160 birds.

Many birds depart to winter on the Continent and ringing recoveries show movements chiefly through western France into Spain. Interestingly, 70% of the recoveries were for birds that were ringed as nestlings or juveniles and 20% of those recovered had been shot. By November far fewer remain here, but numbers increase again to a second peak in December and January, when the average flock size is around 140. They then subside in February and March, but return passage in April sees flocks increase in frequency once again, though they are smaller, with a mean size of about 100. Examples of visible migration include several parties of 20-50 birds at Bittell Reservoir on November 12th 1986, 500 moving south through Fens Pools in five hours on October 1st 1996 and 120 moving SSW in an hour at Ilmington Downs on October 3rd 2001.

Overall, flocks up to 250 are regular and up to 600 by no means unusual, while the most impressive counts have been 1,200, at Summerfield in February 1979 and Fenny Compton in October 2001, at least 1,250 at Kingsbury Rifle Range in October 1994 and 1,500 at Draycote Water in December 1991, when the water-level had been lowered. Indeed, the abundance of seed exposed around reservoir margins by low water levels often attracts huge feeding flocks. Weed seeds, such as those of crucifers, fat-hen and chickweed, form an important component of the Linnet's diet and parties are often seen foraging on waste ground in urban areas as well as in field margins, verges and set-aside. Feeding flocks have also been noted in a variety of crops, including cereals, linseed, millet, mustard, vegetables and especially oilseed rape. Often they associate with other species, but usually stay together as a group within the larger flocks. There is little information on roosts, but up to 50 regularly did so in gorse at Netherton Hill in 1998, which, along with thorn thickets, is a typical site.

Twite   *Carduelis flavirostris*

Scarce summer visitor to the North Staffordshire Moors. Scarce and much declined winter visitor.

Traditionally the Twite, named after its distinctive call, has occupied two distinct habitats in the West Midlands. During the summer a few pairs breed on the high heather moorlands of north Staffordshire, whilst in winter a regular flock used to visit the old colliery spoil banks to the north of Chasewater. The latter is no longer the case, however, and winter sightings are now confined to occasional birds detected initially by call, or by diligently searching through flocks of feeding Linnets.

The north Staffordshire moorland population, at the southern end of the Pennines, is the most southerly in England. Here the density was estimated at 7.8 pairs per tetrad (Davies 1988), but numbers have fallen significantly since that time, along with those of other species associated with the heather moors. However, it is known that populations at the edge of their range tend to fluctuate markedly (Waterhouse 1985).

The first birds begin to arrive back on their territories in April, but most do not appear until May and it can even be the end of June before birds are really evident (Waterhouse 1985). On arrival, they rely heavily on the seeds in burnt patches of purple moor-grass before moving into the heather and bracken dominated areas to nest (Orford 1973). They then continue to feed in upland pastures throughout the breeding season, flying up to three miles from their moorland nests to do so, and Gribble (2000) considered the loss of such meadows may have led to a decline in breeding success. He also said numbers tend to run in cycles, as with Linnets and Lesser Redpolls. The population apparently declined in the first half of the twentieth century, but then showed a strong resurgence from the late 1960s, as the following table shows. Since 1994, however, there appears to have been a dramatic collapse (McKnight *et al.* 1996, Gribble 2000).

Year	1968	1971	1973	1974	1978	1985	1992	1994	1996	Post 1996
No of Pairs	2 or 3	20	40	50	c40	95	88	80	64	5-10

There has also been some contraction in range, with birds present in four 10-km squares during 1966-72 (*BWM*), whereas they were only recorded in one square during 1988-91. Most recent records have come from the Knotbury area. Birds normally leave the moors in September or mid-October, with one on November 12th 1961 the latest mentioned in *BWM*, but an unusually late flock of 28 was at Roach End on December 1st 1981.

At Chasewater, a wintering flock was present annually from 1948/9 until 1984/5, by which time habitat reclamation work, commenced in 1974, had rendered the area unsuitable. Numbers varied widely, reaching a peak of 200 in November 1977, after which there was a sharp decline as the following table shows.

Winter	1978/9	1979/80	1980/1	1981/2	1982/3	1983/4	1984/5	1989/90	1990/1	1991/2	1995/6
Birds	6	60	12	10	8	6	11	2	1	2	1

Just what attracted them to the area in the first place remains obscure, but they used to feed on the seeds of tall herbs such as fat-hen and wormwood. With no regular wintering site, few birds are now seen at this season and, away from Chasewater and the Moors, the twenty-four winters 1978/9-2001/2 produced just 120 birds—an average of five a year—and not surprisingly, Blithfield and Tittesworth Reservoirs have had most records with nine each. However, this involved far more birds at Blithfield with 30 as opposed to 13 at Tittesworth. Draycote Water was the next most visited site with five records of seven birds.

Lesser Redpoll   (Common Redpoll or Redpoll)   *Carduelis cabaret*
Fairly common passage migrant and winter visitor. Uncommon or frequent breeding species, mainly in Staffordshire.

Redpolls used to be divided into two species, Common and Arctic, with five races of the former and two of the latter. However, in 1999 the BOURC decided to split the former into two separate species, with the nominate race (*C. f. flammea*) becoming Common Redpoll *C. flammea* and the British race (*C. f. cabaret*) becoming Lesser Redpoll *C. cabaret*.

The fortunes of the Lesser Redpoll have fluctuated markedly over time. In the first quarter of the twentieth century it was described as little more than a winter visitor to birch woods in the region, although historical evidence points to its once having been more numerous. There was then a resurgence during the 1960s and 1970s, accompanied by an expansion in the breeding range. This established it as a regular winter visitor to birches and alders and a familiar breeding species in birch and thorn scrub, young conifer plantations and even rank hedgerows (*BWM*). Since then it has again become much scarcer, especially as a breeding species.

Between the two BTO *Breeding Atlases*, which covered 1968-72 and 1988-91 respectively, the percentage of occupied 10-km squares fell from 79% to 57%. Staffordshire, with its birch-clad heaths and conifer plantations on Cannock Chase, in the Churnet Valley and at Enville, Hanchurch, Highgate Common and Kinver, has always been the species' stronghold in the region—the birds nesting in the young conifers and feeding on the birch seeds. By the early 1990s any previously occupied sub-optimal habitat, notably most of Worcestershire, central Warwickshire, west Staffordshire and the Dales, had been deserted.

The initial population explosion was typical of an irruptive species and is thought to have correlated with the maturing of the birch scrub that regenerated following wartime fellings

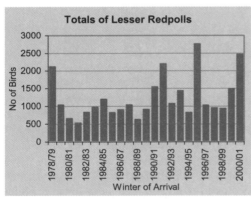

Totals of Lesser Redpolls

(Gibbons *et al.* 1993). The national CBC peaked around 1977 (Marchant *et al.* 1990), but then declined by two-thirds between 1980 and 2000. The decline between 1974-99 was even higher (96%), but due to the south-easterly bias of the CBC this is considered to be possibly unrepresentative of the UK as a whole. As a result, the species is included only on the *Amber Alert List* of Species of Conservation Concern (Gregory *et al.* 2002).

Regionally there were too few birds to compute a comparable index, but by 1998 there was no indication that it still bred in Warwickshire and the following year it was said to possibly no longer breed in Worcestershire. Breeding still occurs in the West Midlands, most notably at Sutton Park where the population seems stable at around two or three pairs, whilst in Staffordshire breeding has been recorded in most years, mainly in the north of the county. Nevertheless, the regional population is probably no higher than 50-100 pairs and might even be less, whereas 2,000-5,000 pairs were estimated in *BWM*.

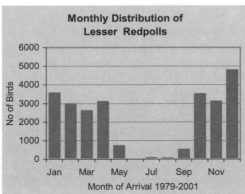

Monthly Distribution of Lesser Redpolls

Always more numerous and widespread outside the breeding season, the *Winter Atlas* showed Lesser Redpolls to be present in 95%

of 10-km squares. Flocks begin to form in September as the first migrants arrive and reach an initial peak in October. Numbers then fall slightly in November as some passage birds move onwards, but peak again in December with the arrival of more migrants. Thereafter they steadily decline as birds begin to disperse, but there is a subsidiary peak in April that marks a return spring passage. Winter flocks, often accompanied by Siskins, feed predominantly on birch and alder seeds, which they take from the trees as well as the ground, but as these food supplies dwindle they will join other finches in searching weedy fields and wastes for food. Overall during 1978/9-2000/1 there were nearly twice as many Siskins as Lesser Redpolls.

Flocks up to a 100 are quite regular and 250 is not unusual, whilst larger numbers were noted on half-a-dozen occasions during the current period, with maxima of 500 at Oldacre Valley in December 1984, 550 at Kinver Edge in February 1979 and an incredible 800-1,000 at Chasewater during December 2000. The geographical distribution of wintering birds is heavily skewed towards Staffordshire and Worcestershire, with 37% and 32% respectively, whereas the Warwickshire and West Midlands shares were only 16% and 15%.

Most Lesser Redpolls migrate southwards in autumn and recoveries show an influx of summer-ringed birds from the more northerly counties of Nottinghamshire, Lancashire and Dumfries during subsequent winters. Some birds may winter in the region, but evidence of others moving on to the Continent is shown by three Warwickshire ringed birds recovered in Belgium during subsequent Novembers and one ringed in Staffordshire in September 1970 that was recovered in France in October 1971. A corresponding northerly movement has been recorded for winter-ringed West Midland birds, with recoveries from Northumberland, Yorkshire, Lancashire and Cheshire in the following and subsequent summers.

Common Redpoll   (Mealy Redpoll)   *Carduelis flammea*
Rare or scarce winter visitor in fluctuating numbers.

In Europe Common Redpolls are chiefly found in open, scrubby woodland in Fennoscandia and Russia. Small numbers arrive in Britain every autumn and a few usually reach this region. Periodic irruptions also occur when the Scandinavian birch crop fails, bringing considerably greater numbers. Prior to 1979 they had occurred just seventeen times (*BWM*), but during 1978/9-2000/1 there were a further 76 records involving a staggering 1,050 birds at least. Incredibly, some 950 or so of these appeared during a massive invasion of redpolls into Britain in the winter of 1995/6 (see also Arctic Redpoll). To put this into perspective, seven records involving 17 birds in 1975/6 was regarded as 'quite exceptional' (*BWM*). Excluding the 1995/6 invasion, the average was about four a year, but there were five winters with none at all, whilst the second highest total was 21 in 1997/8.

A very early bird was seen on September 22nd 1976 (*BWM*), but the earliest date in the current period was November 1st, when birds were at Ladywalk in 1988 and Upton Warren in 1998. Peak numbers are generally attained during December-February, after which they fall away as birds begin to leave for their breeding grounds. The latest record came from Doulton's Claypit on April 16th 1996.

Geographically most birds have occurred in Staffordshire (53%) and Worcestershire (37%), with Warwickshire's share a meagre 8% and the West Midlands 2%. Interestingly, if the 1995/6 influx is excluded, then this pattern changes somewhat, with 52% in Worcestershire and 31% in Staffordshire, whilst the West Midlands had 13% and Warwickshire just 4%. The pre-eminence of Staffordshire and Worcestershire is to be expected, since these are the counties with most heathland and birch scrub. During the 1995/6 winter at least seven flocks of 50 or more were reported, with the largest being 150 in the Wyre Forest on January 15th and 200 on Cannock Chase on March 2nd. In normal years, however, just a few birds mingle with flocks of Lesser Redpolls, but numbers seem to be increasing.

Arctic Redpoll   *Carduelis hornemanni*
Rare vagrant.

With fourteen records, this is strictly a rare vagrant, though very rare would more accurately reflect its true status, since all but one record occurred during the unprecedented national invasion of redpolls during the 1995/6 winter.

Regional Record Number	County Record Number	Year	Locality, Date and Notes
1	Staffs 1	1995	Tittesworth Reservoir: December 10th to January 5th, 1996. *BB 90:508*
2	Staffs 2	1995	Rudyard Reservoir: December 17th. *BB 90:508*
3	Staffs 3	1995	Near Newborough: first-winter, December 24th and 28th. *BB 91:512*
4	Staffs 4	1995	Hanchurch: male, December 27th. *BB 89:524*
5	Worcs 1	1996	Lodge Hill Farm, Wyre Forest: up to four, January 14th-26th, including male, 14th probably to 26th. *BB 90:508*
6	Staffs 5	1996	Stepping Stones, Cannock Chase: adult, February 16th-17th. *BB 91:512*
7	Staffs 6	1996	Stepping Stones, Cannock Chase: another adult, February 20th. *BB 91:512*
8	Staffs 7	1996	Westport Lake: male and first-winter, February 22nd-25th., one or other until 28th. *BB 90:508*
9	Staffs 8	1996	Stepping Stones, Cannock Chase: another adult, March 7th-11th. *BB 91:512*
10	Staffs 9	1996	Stepping Stones, Cannock Chase: first-winter, March 8th. *BB 91:512*
11	Staffs 10	1996	Westport Lake: at least one first-winter, March 11th-13th. *BB 90:508*
12	Staffs 11	1996	Westport Lake: adult, March 21st-28th. *BB 90:508*
13	Staffs 12	1996	Chasewater: two, March 23rd, one to 24th. *BB 90:508*
14	Worcs 2	2001	Habberley Valley: December 30th to January 24th, 2002. *BB 96:602* (recorded only to January 22nd in *BB*).

Arctic Redpolls breed in the high Arctic and make short-distance movements south in winter (*BWP*). Periodical irruptions have resulted in several reaching Britain before (*e.g.* around 80 in 1990/1 Rogers *et al.* 1991, 1992), but the scale of this invasion, which totalled about 400 birds was quite exceptional. Several others were allegedly in the region at this time, including some in Warwickshire, but documentary evidence was not forthcoming.

Two-barred Crossbill   *Loxia leucoptera*
Very rare vagrant. One record.

The only record is that quoted in *BWM*, namely:

Regional Record Number	County Record Number	Year	Locality, Date and Notes
1	Staffs 1	1979	Beaudesert: male, December 16th to April 1st, 1980. *BB 73:527*

The Two-barred Crossbill is a resident of the larch forests from northern Russia eastwards into Siberia, from where its irruptive dispersal leads to irregular breeding in Fennoscandia and vagrancy in western Europe. Its arrival in Britain often coincides with those of Common

Crossbills and towards the end of its stay, on March 9th, this particular individual was observed mating with a Common Crossbill.

The above record refers to the Eurasian race *L. l. bifasciata*, but Tomes (1901) also mentioned an earlier record of a female, killed near Worcester in 1838, which Harthan included in his original *Birds of Worcestershire* (1946). In his 1961 revision, though, Harthan said "Professor Newton examined this skin at Cambridge and a label attached to it states that it seemed in all respects to resemble the American race *L. l. leucoptera* (White-winged Crossbill). It is doubtful if this was a genuine wild bird. *The Handbook* does not admit this subspecies to the British list." Following the precedent in *BWM*, it is excluded from the above list.

Common Crossbill   (Crossbill)   *Loxia curvirostra*
Frequent, though variable, irruptive visitor. Rare and erratic breeding species.

Feeding flocks of Common Crossbills rarely roam far from mature coniferous woods, where their presence can often be detected by half-eaten cones scattered on the ground, or by their excitable 'chip, chip' flight calls. Spruce seeds are their preferred diet, but in this region many feed on the seeds of larch and pine, which they extract from the cones with their specially adapted crossed bills. They lead a nomadic life, ranging widely in search of the heaviest cone crop, remaining till the food runs out and then moving on again. This heavy dependence on a limited range of food makes them vulnerable to crop failures and when this happens they irrupt in huge numbers from the Continent soon after breeding, becoming evident in Britain from mid-summer onwards. At such times they are sometimes forced to exploit other food sources and have been noted feeding on chrysalides in oaks and on beech mast.

Although the Common Crossbill is an annual visitor, its irruptive nature results in dramatically fluctuating numbers from year-to-year, as the accompanying chart shows. To accommodate the early breeding season this chart is based on years running from June-May. The period 1978/9-2000/1 witnessed the two biggest irruptions ever recorded—in 1990/1 and 1997/8. Being a highly mobile species, double-counting is always a danger, and it is almost impossible to arrive at precise figures, but the respective totals for those years were at least 1,400 and 2,200. In complete contrast, 1978/9 and 1984/5 produced just three and four respectively!

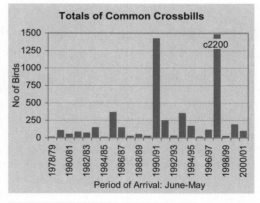

The monthly distribution shows three arrival peaks. By far the heaviest influx occurred in June and July, slightly earlier than the late July peak noted in *BWM*. A second, smaller wave of immigrants then often followed during October-December and finally there was a small build up of numbers during March-May.

Common Crossbills used to be solely erratic visitors, coming to the region only during major irruptions, but they have become more regular as the region's conifer plantations have matured and their seed crops have be-

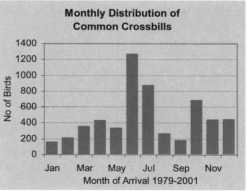

come more reliable. After major irruptions a few pairs will even nest, but as yet breeding remains erratic, although it probably occurred in twelve seasons during 1979-2001, but with no more than three or four pairs in any one year.

The *Breeding Atlas*, which embraced the 1990/1 invasion, recorded birds in 14% of 10-km squares, all of them in Staffordshire or Worcestershire, and included areas such as the Hanchurch and Maer Hills, Cannock Chase, Needwood Forest, Enville and Kinver, and the Wyre Forest. Almost 90% of all probable breeding records were shared equally between Cannock Chase and the Wyre Forest woodland complex.

The *Winter Atlas*, undertaken during three average years, showed a more restricted distribution than the *Breeding Atlas*, with birds in just 8% of 10-km squares covering the Hanchurch Hills, Cannock Chase, Kinver, Enville and the Wyre Forest. These have certainly been the most frequented places, along with the Lickey Hills, Maer Hills and some smaller woods around the Wyre Forest, especially Eymore and Coldridge Woods. Birds are more widely spread during major irruptions, when parties appear in quite small conifer plantations, or are seen moving across open country, such as the Malvern Hills. Single birds have even been seen twice in a Grendon garden. Inevitably, there is a clear bias towards the more heavily wooded counties, with 44% of birds in Staffordshire and 39% in Worcestershire compared with just 13% in Warwickshire and 4% in the West Midlands.

Flocks are generally small, with 80% comprising less than 20 birds, although up to 60 are not unusual during major irruptions. During the current period, there were six instances of flocks exceeding 100, with the two largest both coming in 1997, when 120 were at Bentley Park Wood on June 29th and 200 gathered on the Lickey Hills on July 15th-16th. The only ringing record relates to a juvenile female, ringed in Norway on September 11th 2002 and recorded in Worcestershire, 889 km away, twelve days later.

Bullfinch   (Common Bullfinch)   *Pyrrhula pyrrhula*
Common resident.

The Bullfinch is widely, but thinly, spread across the entire region, frequenting woods and copses with a rich shrub layer, thick hedges and garden shrubberies. It feeds on a variety of flowers, buds, berries, soft fruit and seeds, which are taken directly from plants such as oak, ash, birch, rowan, fruit trees, hawthorn, clematis and honeysuckle. Flocks of Bullfinches were once the scourge of fruit growers in the Vale of Evesham, where they stripped the orchards of blossom, but with much reduced numbers and new growing techniques this is no longer the problem it once was. On the moors of north Staffordshire birds also feed on heather capsules.

Fieldwork for both the *Winter* and *Breeding Atlases* revealed birds in every 10-km square. The latter showed abundance to be below average across north Warwickshire and most of Staffordshire, but above average in parts of Feldon, the Dales and especially the fruit and market gardening areas of the Vale of Evesham and the Teme Valley. At one time Bullfinches used to cause serious damage to commercial orchards in these latter areas, mainly in those springs when ash seed and other natural foods were scarce. In 1962 at least 400 were shot and many more were trapped in three parishes in the Vale of Evesham and the following year 163 were trapped on a single fruit farm (*BWM*). Although we are unaware of any such instances since then, there might be some significance in the fact that flock sizes in Worcestershire tend to be smaller than in the other counties.

Nationally the decline of Bullfinches began in the mid 1970s and has continued ever since. The CBC/BBS index fell by 57% during 1974-99, resulting in it being placed on the *Red Alert List* of Species of Conservation Concern (Gregory *et al.* 2002), and continued to fall at a similar rate through to 2002. The decline was more severe on farmland than in woodland and has been attributed to the removal of hedges and scrubby wasteland. Early results from the *Tetrad*

Atlases suggest around three-quarters of tetrads are occupied in rural areas and a half in urban districts. The BBS shows densities in Warwickshire and Worcestershire to be more than twice those in Staffordshire.

Samples were too small to produce a reliable regional index prior to the BBS, which since 1995 has shown a trend not dissimilar to that nationally. Apart from the CBC, the only data on densities showed two pairs on 81 ha of farmland at Hawkhurst Moor in 1987. Trends varied considerably between sites, with places such as Alvecote Pools, Coombes Valley and Westport Lake having stable populations, but

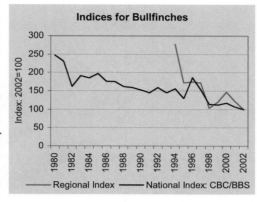

other areas such as Bredon Hill referring to significant declines. Numbers were even said to have increased around Fenny Compton and Wormleighton in 1999. Nevertheless, most quantitative data point to a decline in the mid-1990s and indicate a current population around 2,500-4,500 pairs. This suggests the population at the end of the *BWM* period was at the lower end of the range of 10,000-15,000 pairs. However, even that estimate might have been too high.

Bullfinches are neither colonial nor territorial, but do gather into small, loose flocks at favoured feeding sites during autumn and winter, when they not infrequently visit gardens. From the mid-1950s to 1979 the average size of reported groups was 15 or 16 birds, with maxima of 50 on half-a-dozen occasions, mostly between 1970-73 (*BWM*). With the population shrinking, the average group size dropped to 11 during the late 1990s, whilst the largest single flock was 45 feeding on haws at Brandon Marsh on December 2nd 1993. Although not a single flock, 50 at Coombes Valley in December 1995 was an excellent count. Birds often visit gardens to feed on rowan and honeysuckle berries, whilst in the urban areas generally, at least 20 were at the Harborne Reserve in 1997 and 26 were along the Smestow Valley in 1995.

The British Bullfinch, *P. p. pileata*, is probably the most parochial of our finches, with no record of those ringed in the region travelling more than 9 km from their place of ringing. However, the nominate northern race *P. p. pyrrhula* is a regular migrant. It seldom reaches this region, however, but there were claims of three males and a female at Lickey in January 1949 (*BWM*) and up to four at various places around Needwood Forest on seven occasions between 1986 and 1989.

Hawfinch   *Coccothraustes coccothraustes*
Scarce to uncommon, but declining, resident.

The Hawfinch is a bird of mixed broad-leaved woods, parkland and orchards, where it feeds mostly on the fruit of trees. It is extremely scarce and localised in the West Midlands, being largely confined to the well wooded districts on the western side of the region. The species is best known for its ability to crack open cherry stones with its massive bill and for its liking of hornbeam seed, but these, along with wych elm and holly, are only components of its autumn and winter diet. In spring it feeds on beech buds and the terminal shoots of yew, while in summer it resorts to caterpillars, especially those of the oak roller moth. Despite its name, haws are generally taken only when these other foods have been exhausted.

For those unfamiliar with the explosive 'tik' calls, detection can be extremely difficult as these are shy, elusive birds. In summer especially, they spend much time hidden high in the canopy and the best time to locate them is during their noisy display fights in March and April. In winter they will warily drop to the ground to feed on fallen seeds, but at the slightest

sound or movement they catapult back into the canopy and are most reluctant to return.

The *Winter Atlas* showed birds to be present in 18% of 10-km squares, but most of these involved scattered individuals that were probably just passage birds. The only concentrations to occur were along the Tettenhall Ridge, including the Chillington area, and in the Wyre Forest. These were also the only areas where birds were found during the *Breeding Atlas*. Interestingly this Atlas shows the West Midlands as a desert surrounded by four core populations centred on Shropshire, the Forest of Dean, the north Cotswolds and, more remotely, Sherwood Forest and the southern Peak District. Most regional records occur around the periphery in places closest to these core areas and it seems probable that birds move into the region in search of food, or when numbers are high, only to retreat again later. At least this would partly explain their unpredictable comings and goings. Since 1980 there has been a steady decline from just over 50 a year to about 15 a year, with a marked drop after 1980, which is when a regular flock at Chillington disappeared.

In the Wyre Forest and the surrounding woods the population appeared to peak in the early 1980s, when birds bred in several years and flocks up to 20 were not unusual. Finding this secretive species in a large woodland complex is difficult, but numbers now seem to be much reduced, with only irregular breeding records and no count above eight in recent years. A flock of 22 in nearby Bewdley during the 1994/5 winter, however, suggests reasonable numbers are still present in the area. Meanwhile, a new wintering population has been discovered at the southern end of the Malvern Hills.

At these regular localities most records fell between December and April, with a pronounced peak in March when birds are most active and vocal. Elsewhere, many records have involved single birds on passage during October and November. There have also been one or two reports of birds visiting gardens.

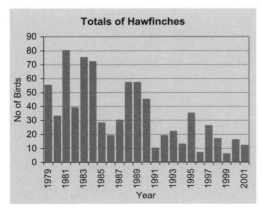

It is hard to establish the true picture for such a retiring species, but breeding occurred in every year bar one during 1979-89, with the best year being 1981 when a colony of five pairs was discovered in Douglas firs in the Wyre Forest. Since 1989 there have been only three instances of probable breeding, namely three in song at Chase End Wood in April 1991, a possible family party in Wellesbourne

Wood in July 1995 (the first evidence of possible breeding in Warwickshire since 1976) and three juveniles in a party of eight in the Wyre Forest in July 1997. Even allowing for its unobtrusive nature, it is doubtful if the regional population exceeds 10 pairs.

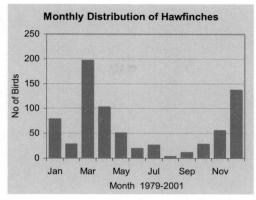

During the winter months, Hawfinches gather into small feeding flocks, especially where there are hornbeams. For years the Lower Avenue at Chillington was the best place to watch them. From 1979/80-1984/5 the flock there averaged 16 (range 9-24) and birds were noted collecting nest material in 1984—the last evidence of possible breeding in Staffordshire. They all but vanished for three years, before returning with maxima of 57 in 1988/9 and 30 in 1989/90. What happened to these substantial numbers remains a mystery, but just three appeared the following year and the only subsequent record was of one or two in 1993/4. Other sightings from the nearby Tettenhall Ridge also ceased about this time. These had included groups of 31 and 20 at an undisclosed locality in 1979 and 1981 respectively, plus 19 in a wood near Wolverhampton in 1983. During the 1990s, birds also appeared at Belvide Reservoir on a couple of occasions, presumably on passage.

On a brighter note, the few remaining old cherry orchards of the Teme Valley have always proved attractive and occasional sightings from the Knapp and Old Storridge, including breeding records in 1986 and 1987 respectively, confirmed their continued presence in this area and on the Malvern Hills. In 1987/8, a flock of 16 was discovered on Chase End Hill. Since then this locality has taken on the mantle of the most regular haunt in the region for this species, although records were only received for nine of the fourteen winters up to 2000/1 and numbers were small, with an average of just five a year. Modest as these figures are, it is comforting to know the species is at least maintaining its presence in the region.

Lapland Bunting   (Lapland Longspur)   *Calcarius lapponicus*
Rare passage migrant and winter visitor.

There have been fifteen records of Lapland Buntings, involving 26 birds. Eight of these records were documented in *BWM*, namely the first in 1904 and seven during 1948-79, whilst a further seven have occurred since.

Regional Record Number	County Record Number		Year	Locality, Date and Notes
1	W Mid	1	1904	Acock's Green: male, October 21st, caught in a clap net.
2	Staffs	1	1948	Chasewater: one, probably a first-winter, December 5th-8th.
3	Staffs	2	1956	Belvide Reservoir: October 28th.
4	Staffs	3	1959	Belvide Reservoir: November 22nd-29th.
5	Staffs	4	1973	Chasewater: November 3rd.
6	Warks	1	1978	Kingsbury Water Park: three from January 8th to February 19th, increasing to four, including at least two males, from January 14th to February 18th: at least two remained until February 26th. Ladywalk: a male, presumed one of these, January 25th.

Regional Record Number	County Record Number		Year	Locality, Date and Notes
7	Staffs	5	1979	River Trent south of Burton-on-Trent: male and female, January 21st-28th.
8	W Mid	2	1979	Bartley Reservoir: female or immature, January 21st.
9	Warks	2	1981	Draycote Water: January 17th.
10	Staffs	6	1986	Needwood Airfield: three, October 19th.
11	Staffs	7	1987	Chasewater: October 29th.
12	Staffs	8	1993	Belvide Reservoir: November 2nd.
13	W Mid	3	1996	Forge Mill Lake, Sandwell Valley: two, October 1st.
14	Staffs	9	1997	Apedale CP: immature male, February 28th intermittently to March 12th.
15	Staffs	10	2002	Westport Lake: five, October 18th.

Lapland Buntings breed in Greenland and Scandinavia and migrate south-westwards and south-eastwards to winter respectively in North America and Asia. Those that arrive along the East Coast of Britain during autumn are therefore presumed to be drift migrants, their numbers varying according to the weather (*Winter Atlas*). The majority of the above conform to this pattern. Those at Kingsbury in 1978 followed a major East Coast influx in the preceding autumn and the two in 1979 arrived during an exceptionally cold winter. It is interesting that ten of these records have been in Staffordshire, including a party a five that flew over Westport Lake calling in 2002, whilst the West Midlands has claimed three and Warwickshire two.

Snow Bunting   *Plectrophenax nivalis*
Scarce passage migrant, mainly in autumn, and winter visitor.

In Britain most Snow Buntings winter around the sandy shores and dunes of the East Coast and inland occurrences are rare. Yet a few visit this region most years, usually in autumn when they appear on the summits of hills or around the margins of reservoirs. Mostly they come in ones or twos, but occasionally a small flock flutters across the ground, like snowflakes driven by the wind, before settling to feed in a patch of short, sparse vegetation.

Snow Buntings breed in North America, Greenland, Iceland and northern Europe and the numbers visiting Britain vary considerably according to climatic and weather conditions. In this region, after a blank winter in 1958/9, there was a sudden, dramatic upsurge in occur-

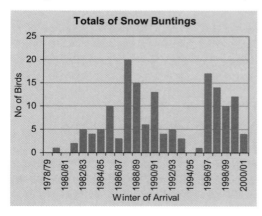

rences and for the next two decades the species became an annual visitor with the number of birds increasing from just over one a year to seven a year. Since then the annual average has remained at this level, although some winters have produced very few whereas there were 20 in 1987/8 and 17 in 1996/7.

The earliest birds to arrive were three on the Malvern Hills on September 29th 1996, but the vast majority (77%) came during October-December, with 46% in November alone. Most birds pass swiftly on elsewhere, with 79% leaving within two days and only 10% remaining for longer than a week. One on the Sheepwalks at Enville from February 2nd to March 21st 1992—a period of 49 days—is the longest known stay for an individual bird. Small groups have also lingered more than once on the Malvern Hills, but as they were not seen daily and numbers varied it is impossible to assess the extent to which birds came and went. Similar circumstances also occurred at Boarsgrove in 1989. Prior to 1979 there was no evidence of any spring passage (*BWM*), but the current period has produced slight signs of a meagre movement, with the latest date being one at Belvide Reservoir on May 2nd 1987.

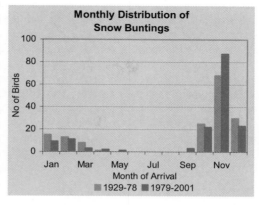

Most records involve just single birds or small groups up to three, but during 1978/9-2000/1 parties of eight were recorded on three occasions—on North Hill, Malvern, on November 2nd 1987, flying over Tolladine Golf Course, Worcester, on February 9th 1991 and on the Worcestershire Beacon, Malvern, on November 15th 1996. These three records say much about the species' distribution, which was dominated during the current period by just two localities. The Malvern Hills, especially Worcestershire Beacon, were most productive, with 38 records involving 58 birds, whilst Draycote Water produced 17 records of 21 birds. Between them, these two sites accounted for 47% of records and 49% of birds. The remaining records were spread around forty localities, none of which produced more than half-a-dozen reports. As a consequence of Malvern's pre-eminence, Worcestershire dominates the county totals, with 46% of birds, but Staffordshire (28%) surprisingly eased Warwickshire (23%) into third place, with the West Midlands producing the other 3%.

Pine Bunting *Emberiza leucocephalos*
Very rare vagrant. One Record.

This was certainly a surprise addition to the regional avifauna.

Regional Record Number	County Record Number	Year	Locality, Date and Notes
1	Worcs 1	1996	Bibby's Hollow, Halesowen: adult male, February 6th-20th. *BB 90:510*

Pine Buntings, which breed in Siberia and winter in Pakistan, north-west India and northern China, are rare visitors to Britain and this superb male was only the 34th to be recorded (Rogers *et al.* 1997). Much to the delight of many, it made periodic visits to a feeding station favoured by Yellowhammers during spells of snowy weather, but, to the frustration of others, it disappeared with every thaw.

Yellowhammer *Emberiza citrinella*
Very common to abundant, though declining, resident.

The Yellowhammer is one of our most familiar farmland birds, its characteristic song continuing late into summer, well after most other species have stopped singing. It has a widespread distribution and can be found in almost any tract of open countryside with elevated song-posts, although it is most common in productive arable areas. Like so many species, its population is decreasing on farmland. It is also declining in sub-optimal habitats such as woodland margins and roadside verges, but appears to be holding up in other favoured habitats, such as heaths, commons and scrub. Birds feed on the ground and outside the breeding season they gather in flocks to take the seeds of cereal grain and other large grasses.

Both the *Winter* and *Breeding Atlases* recorded Yellowhammers in every 10-km square, with an abundance that was generally above average, except in the more urbanised areas such as Birmingham, the Black Country and Potteries. On the higher ground of north Staffordshire, the density was no more than average. These differences are reinforced by an analysis of flocks, which shows 35% of birds in Warwickshire and 32% in Worcestershire, but only 24% in Staffordshire despite the latter being the largest county. Preliminary results from the two *Tetrad Atlases* show just a quarter of the squares to be occupied in Birmingham and the Black Country compared with over 80% in Warwickshire.

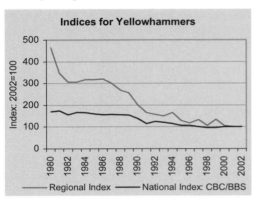

Nationally the CBC/BBS showed a steady decline over the period 1980-2002 of 40%, whilst longer-term it was more than half during 1974-99, which resulted in the species' inclusion on the *Red Alert List* (Gregory *et al.* 2002). Regionally the decline since 1980 appears to have been even greater, but with only limited data this should be treated with caution. Taking all available data into account, the current regional population is estimated to be 20,000-32,000 pairs compared with the range of 30,000-50,000 pairs in *BWM*, which is now thought to be a slight under-estimate.

Numbers halved between 1980 and 1982 at Sutton Park, mirroring the steep decline shown by the regional index and perhaps indicating that local factors, such as the cold winters at that time, were affecting the population. Thereafter they showed little change at around 15 pairs. Relative stability was also evident at Alvecote Pools (five or six pairs 1983-95), Sandwell Valley (around 12 pairs 1987-93) and Park Lime Pits (four or five pairs 1988-94). At Timberhonger the population during 1993-2001 was highly variable, ranging from five to 12 pairs with no clear trend, whilst at Brandon Marsh there were only five sightings in 2001 whereas twenty years previously there had been 10 breeding pairs. Perhaps the most interesting data comes from the Malvern Hills and commons, where larger populations are involved. On the Hills numbers rose from 14 pairs in 1987 to 39 in 1989, but then fell back to 19 in 1995. On Castlemorton Common during 1986-2001 they were more stable, generally ranging from five to eight pairs, but with a peak of 11 in 1987, but at Old Hills Common during 1983-96 numbers were more variable (ranging from seven in 1984 and 1985 to 19 in 1996), but with a generally upward trend. Elsewhere, counts at Berkswell, Bulkington, Fenny Compton, Ladbroke and Lutley Wedge revealed densities ranging from 8-12 pairs per km^2.

Outside the breeding season birds readily gather around good food sources, such as cereal stubbles and set-aside, often in company with finches. Flocks begin to form in October and persist until birds return to their breeding territories in March and early April, but they are most frequent and largest in December and January, when days are short and food hard to find. During 1978/9-2000/1, the average flock size in these latter months was 68 compared to 80 during 1929-78 (*BWM*)—a surprisingly small reduction considering the fall in the population. Birds tend to congregate more in cold weather, with, for example, 200 at Chasewater during snow on December 30th 2000. Over 80% of flocks contain fewer than 100 birds, but up to 150 are not unusual. During the current period around twenty larger concentrations were reported, but the only one to exceed 200 was at Grimley on January 23rd 1982, when an exceptional

600 had gathered—by far the most ever recorded in the region. Some idea of the general numbers on farms is provided by surveys in 2000 that revealed densities of 29, 32 and 53 per km² respectively on three Warwickshire farms. A further indication of how this species can be helped to survive comes from the Marsh Lane reserve, where 100 in December 2001 came to feed on wheat planted there specifically to attract farmland birds.

Yellowhammers will also come to rural and suburban gardens in search of food, particularly during hard weather. However, the 70 feeding on seed put down in a Southam garden on January 15th 1998 was fairly exceptional. They also penetrate urban areas and have been recorded in the centre of Birmingham (*BWM*), whilst a singing male in the centre of Kidderminster on March 22nd 1996 found itself having to compete with the noise from a nearby construction site. There is little information on roosts, which are generally in dense vegetation, with bracken, reeds and conifers having been recorded. Yellowhammers show little movement, but *BWM* mentions one ringed at Wellesbourne in January 1963 and recovered some 19 km away at Finham five days later.

Cirl Bunting   *Emberiza cirlus*
Formerly a very scarce resident, now a very rare vagrant.

The small population of Cirl Buntings in the West Midlands region appeared to have finally become extinct in 1977 and the species was described in *BWM* as no longer present—a slightly premature statement as it turned out since the following bird appeared in 1983.

County	Year	Locality, Date and Notes
Worcs	1983	Hartlebury: female, February 27th.

The species' distribution was always restricted. It was recorded only once in Staffordshire—at Kinver in May 1951—and twice in the West Midlands county area—at Northfield in 1888 and Bartley Reservoir in 1950. In Warwickshire it was formerly very local and uncommon, but had died out by 1931, apart from an isolated record from Shipston-on-Stour in 1959. In Worcestershire it was confined to the Lower Severn Valley and Malvern area, where it was said to be common until 1910. The last records from there were in 1972, when birds were reported from four sites with singing males at three of them. Another was also further up the Severn Valley, at Northwick Marsh just north of Worcester, in January of that year. Records then ceased and the species was assumed to be lost to the region, but in 1976 a quite unexpected report emerged of a pair thought to have bred at nearby Hallow, where birds had apparently been present for at least five years. This pair was last seen in 1977, prompting the above statement in *BWM*. It is interesting that the 1983 record came from Hartlebury, which is only seven miles north of Hallow. Could it be that some went undetected in the intervening years?

Rustic Bunting   *Emberiza rustica*
Very rare vagrant. One record.

This remarkable record was the first in Britain away from the coast or an island since one at Doncaster (South Yorkshire) in September 1958 (Rogers *et al.* 1989).

Regional Record Number	County Record Number	Year	Locality, Date and Notes
1	Worcs 1	1987	Upton Warren: immature, November 7th.. *BB 82:558*

Rustic Buntings breed from Fennoscandia eastwards across Russia and winter principally in eastern China, Korea and Japan. Even so, they are almost annual visitors to Britain, mostly to the East Coast in May or September-October. This was the first acceptable record for the region, an earlier claim of one at Chasewater on August 17th 1958, placed in square brackets in the *WMBC Annual Report*, having later been rejected by the BBRC (*Brit. Birds* 53:157).

Little Bunting   *Emberiza pusilla*
Very rare vagrant. Four records.

After a ninety year gap between the first two records, there were then three in four years.

Regional Record Number	County Record Number		Year	Locality, Date and Notes
1	Warks	1	1902	Pailton: male, early October. Caught with bird lime and kept in cage.
2	Staffs	1	1992	Kingswood Bank, Trentham: November 8th. *BB 89:526*
3	Worcs	1	1994	Near Defford: male, May 25th-26th.
4	Staffs	2	1995	Belvide Reservoir: April 21st.

Note: BBRC ceased to consider records of this species as from January 1st 1994.

Little Buntings breed from Fennoscandia eastwards across Siberia and winter in eastern Asia. A few reach Britain every year, mostly along the East and South Coasts and chiefly in autumn, so it is surprising that two of the above occurred in spring.

Reed Bunting   *Emberiza schoeniclus*
Common, though declining, resident.

Wetlands are the Reed Buntings' preferred habitat and they can be found from moorland mosses to damp hollows in urban wastes and parks. Numbers have fallen greatly over the past thirty years, however, and the distribution is now patchy. The strongholds are along the scrubby banks of rivers and canals, or around lakes, gravel pits and reservoirs where there are stands of reed or reedmace. Following the wetland drainage of last century, however, many have now moved into drier situations, such as young forestry plantations and crops of oilseed rape, beans and winter-sown wheat. Outside the breeding season, they roost together at night, usually in reedbeds, then disperse during the day as they search crops, stubbles, set-aside and waste ground for grain and weed seeds. At such times they often wander into urban situations, visiting garden bird tables, especially when lying snow denies them access to natural food.

During the *Winter* and *Breeding Atlas* surveys, birds were recorded in 94% of 10-km squares. The main gaps were in the well-wooded parts of the Churnet Valley, Wyre Forest and Teme Valley, where the hills and fast-flowing rivers provide little suitable habitat, and in the drier parts of south Warwickshire and Worcestershire. Abundance levels were mostly around, or slightly below, average, except in east Warwickshire, south Staffordshire and the moorland fringe, where they tended to be just above average. The BBS suggests densities are lowest in Worcestershire and highest in Warwickshire, whilst initial results from the two *Tetrad Atlases* show birds to be present in a third of urban tetrads and just over half of rural ones.

The national CBC data showed a 62% decline in the Reed Bunting population during 1974-99, resulting in its being included on the *Red Alert List* of Species of Conservation Concern (Gregory *et al.* 2002), whilst during 1980-2002 the CBC/BBS index fell by about half.

Much of this decline occurred in the early 1980s and the WBS index showed little long-term change from 1984-2002. Unfortunately the regional data was too sparse to produce a comparable regional index, but data from certain core centres of population give an indication of local trends. At Brandon Marsh numbers were down to a single pair by 1991, but have since recovered to around a dozen; at Doxey Marshes they ranged widely between 18 and 48 pairs during 1984-2001, but with little long-term change; while at Belvide Reservoir, Upton Warren and Sandwell Valley they have fluctuated considerably without showing any clear trend. Other notable counts were 34 pairs at Tittesworth Reservoir in 1995 and an estimated 60 pairs along the lower Avon Valley in 1988, while sustained ringing, such as that at Betley Mere in 1990s, shows how the population fluctuates markedly from year-to-year. The general impression is that numbers were at their lowest in the late 1980s, but have since recovered slightly, at least at the main sites. Current data suggest there are between 8,000-9,000 pairs in the region, whereas the population was said in *BWM* to be at least 15,000 pairs.

Winter flocks are most numerous from December to February and tend to reach their maximum size towards the end of this period. They reinforce the scale of decline shown by the CBC/BBS as the average size halved, from 60 during 1929-78 (*BWM*) to 30 during 1978/9-2000/1. The proportion of flocks over 100 also dropped, from 25% to 5%. They have been fewer and smaller during the current period, too, with maxima of 150 at Bramcote on March 2nd 1992 and 250 at Elford on February 8th 1991 compared with five flocks up to 250 and one of 300 mentioned in *BWM*. Likewise roosts have been much smaller, with the largest being 120 in the reedbed at Belvide Reservoir on January 23rd 1994. At Brandon Marsh there have been no more than 100, which pales into insignificance compared to the phenomenal 1,000 that roosted there from January to March 1974 (*BWM*). There have been numerous reports of up to ten in gardens, with a maximum of 15 at Coventry during a snowy spell in December 1981. Reduced seed crops due to the increased use of herbicides have been cited as a cause of population decline and may also explain the increased use of feeders, both in gardens and on reserves such as Ladywalk, where up to 30 were noted in 1996. Amongst other food sources to be exploited, 35-40 were feeding in an area of purple moor-grass on Cannock Chase in January 1986, while, in December 2001, 30 frequented wheat specifically planted to attract farmland birds at the Marsh Lane reserve.

Although numbers appear to increase slightly in March and April, when birds are returning to their breeding grounds, there has been no real evidence in the recent period of the noticeable spring passage mentioned in *BWM*. However, a study at Betley Mere in 1994 did reveal some movement in September and October. Only 25% of the ringing recoveries for this species involve birds moving within the region, with a further 38% going into adjacent counties. Of the remainder, half were wintering movements to the southerly counties of Devon, Dorset, Wiltshire and Hampshire, while the other half were birds moving northwards back to their breeding areas in Lancashire, Yorkshire and Cheshire. Interestingly, one bird ringed as a juvenile in the Channel Islands in August 1984 was recorded in the West Midlands in April 1986.

Corn Bunting   *Emberiza calandra*
Fairly common, though much declined, resident.

Open arable country, with fence posts and overhead wires for song-posts, but few trees and hedges, is the Corn Bunting's usual home. It is a gregarious species, nesting in loose colonies where it is both polygamous and polyandrous, and forming small feeding flocks in winter, of-

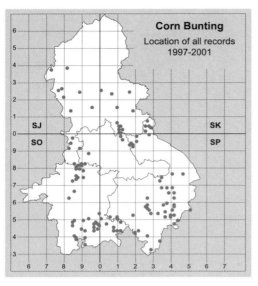

ten with other bunting species. It also roosts communally, usually in reedbeds, but sometimes in dense conifers.

The *Winter Atlas* showed birds to be present in 69% of 10-km squares, whilst the *Breeding Atlas* recorded them in 64%. The gaps in distribution were on the higher ground of north Staffordshire; in the Wyre Forest, Teme Valley and Arden areas; and in the major towns and cities. Two subtle differences were that breeding was recorded from the northern part of the Meres and Mosses, where none were seen in winter, but there was a thin scatter of winter sightings across Arden where birds were absent in the breeding season. As can be seen on the map, the distribution is still much the same as that shown in *BWM*, with the populations concentrated into the main arable districts around Lichfield, across the Mid-Severn Sandstone Plateau, and in the Vale of Evesham and Feldon areas. Overall there has been some contraction of range, but a slight spread northwards in the mixed farming areas of the Meres and Mosses.

Numerically, the CBC/BBS shows a catastrophic decline of 89% between 1974 and 1999, which not surprisingly places the species very firmly on the *Red Alert List* of Species of Conservation Concern (Gregory *et al.* 2002). However, the Corn Bunting's population has often shown marked fluctuations in response to agricultural change. In the late nineteenth century it was considered common and well distributed, but declined considerably during the early twentieth century, when cereal growing was much reduced as a result of the agricultural depression. Earlier writers in the 1940s said it had almost disappeared in Worcestershire and Warwickshire, but agricultural policy changes in the 1950s and 1960s brought about more barley growing and the population expanded rapidly. *BWM* drew attention to the very strong lapsed correlation between the two—an association since remarked upon by others (*e.g.* Thompson and Gribbin 1986, O'Connor and Shrubb 1986)—although subsequent evidence suggests that this may have been a spurious correlation (*Breeding Atlas*).

Certainly Corn Buntings require a mixed habitat mosaic that includes grass leys and not simply an arable monoculture, so the current trend towards single-crop specialisation does not suit them. *BWM* also cited other reasons for the recovery, including hedgerow removal and the loss of elms, which reduced competition from other species. Unfortunately a BTO survey in 1993 has not been repeated to indicate trends, but the current decline appears to relate more to reduced densities than to range contraction. During 1980-2002 the national CBC/BBS index fell by about three-quarters. There was insufficient data to compile a regional index, but an analysis of the average size of wintering flocks showed a remarkably similar decline. The BBS suggests that densities are highest in Warwickshire, whilst early indications from the *Tetrad Atlas* for that county show birds in 13% of tetrads compared with just 4% in Birmingham and the Black Country, which have very little arable land. Estimating numbers is difficult since the most obvious indicator, namely the number of singing males, is of limited value for a polygamous species, but current information suggests between 400-1,100 singing males, whereas *BWM* says the population was possibly in the range 1,000-5,000.

Counts of some populations in core areas of Warwickshire during 2000 revealed 19 territories at Milcote, 14 between Marton and Long Itchington and 13 between Charlecote Park and Wasperton, but sadly there are no directly comparable counts for earlier years. The story from elsewhere, however, is mostly one of decline. For example, the number of singing birds at Alvecote Pools fell from two or three in 1980 to one in 2000; at Kempsey from 4 in 1997 to one in 2000; at Throckmorton from eight in 1998 to two in 2001; and at Whitemoor Haye from 22 in 1993 to one in 2000. Two populations to have maintained their strength so far are those at High Offley, where numbers fell from five in 1981 to one in 1986, but have since re-covered to four in 1998 and Wasperton, where there have generally been five to seven, but eight in 1987 and nine in 2001.

During the winter, feeding flocks search cultivated land, stubbles, set-aside and waste ground for cereal and weed seeds. Flocks are most numerous between November and Febru-ary, increasing slightly in size as the winter progresses, but averaging just under 30 birds over-all. About 85% of flocks comprise less than 50 birds, but up to 100 (the maximum recorded in *BWM*) were encountered at times during the current period, with the most being 140—at Lenchwick in February 1989 and Wilnecote in February 1991. For a species so closely tied to arable land, it is perhaps surprising that 50 were in Sutton Park in 1979 and 67 in 1981, while earlier appearances in inner city Birmingham, at Nechells and Saltley, were quite remarkable (*BWM*). So too were 10 which came to seed put down in a Southam garden in 1996.

Roosts, by comparison, have been smaller than during the *BWM* period, when up to 100 were said to be by no means unusual and the largest count was an exceptional 500 at Exhall, near Alcester, on December 31st 1973. During the current period, the average roost size was 50 and there were just half-a-dozen instances of 90 or more, all of them in January or Febru-ary. The numbers roosting at any particular site vary considerably, but maxima among the ten more consistently used sites were 90 at Eathorpe in 1990 (*cf.* 150 in 1975), 156 at Rous Lench in 1985 and 190 at Brandon Marsh in 1981.

Corn Buntings are extremely sedentary and 80% of recoveries show movements of less than 8 km. The only journey of any distance was made by a bird ringed in Northampton and recovered in Warwickshire, having travelled 63 km.

Hopefully the new proposals for payments under the Environmental Stewardship scheme will lead to more wildlife friendly farming. If this happens, then perhaps the populations of Corn Buntings and other farmland birds will increase again.

Baltimore Oriole   (Northern Oriole)   *Icterus galbula*
Very rare vagrant. One record.

This is the only North American passerine to have been recorded in the region.

Regional Record Number	County Record Number	Year	Locality, Date and Notes
1	W Mid 1	1968	Coventry: first-winter male, found dead, December 16th. *BB 76:527*

Greeted with some incredulity at the time because of the late date and the extreme rarity of Nearctic passerines inland, this record was initially regarded as probably relating to an escape. However, it was reviewed in the light of modern attitudes to such records by the BBRC and finally gained acceptance in 1982 (Rogers *et al.* 1982). The skin is now in the Herbert Art Gal-lery and Museum, Coventry. As is normal with Transatlantic vagrants, September and October are the usual months of arrival, so it is possible this individual had gone undetected for some time before its death. Interestingly, its date of discovery and inland, urban location closely mirror those of another Baltimore Oriole in Oxford during 2003/4.

Postscript

Compiling a book of this magnitude inevitably takes a long time, during which records continue to amass. The last year of the main analysis was 2001, but we have attempted to update the species accounts by including as many as possible of the more interesting 2002 records, together with accepted BBRC records and any new species for the region to the end of 2003. However, full details of some were received too late to be incorporated in the Systematic List and so are listed below.

Bean Goose   *Anser fabalis*

Staffs   2002   Croxall: two, January 31st and February 9th-10th. Both of the race *A. f. rossicus*.

Green-winged Teal   *Anas carolinensis*

Staffs   2002   Blithfield Reservoir: male from 2001 till January 1st.
Staffs   2002   Blithfield Reservoir: male, October 20th to November 4th.

Ring-necked Duck   *Aythya collaris*

Worcs   2002   Beckford: adult female, April 3rd. Same as Abbots Salford, Warks, in 2002 (see Systematic List).

Golden Pheasant   *Chrysolophus pictus*

Worcs   2002   Upton Snodsbury: male, May 5th
Worcs   2002   Nash End: male, May 5th.

Lady Amherst's Pheasant   *Chrysolophus amherstiae*

Worcs   2002   Grimley: May 9th-15th.
Warks   2002   Lower Radbourne: July 1st. Feathers found, probably from predated male.

These constitute the first records for the region, though presumably they relate to escaped or released birds.

White Stork   *Ciconia ciconia*

Worcs   2002   Throckmorton Tip: May 11th. Left to the NW, so probably same as Staffs below.
Staffs   2002   Belvide Reservoir , June 4th; same near Brownhills, June 30th; Cheadle, July 21st and 22nd; Blithfield Reservoir, August 6th; Stoke-on-Trent, August 19th; and Cresswell, August 26th.

Least Sandpiper   *Calidris minutilla*

Warks   2002   Fisher's Mill GP: May 25th. Same as Drayton Bassett, Staffs.

This bird briefly crossed from Staffordshire into Warwickshire, where it was seen by several observers, but adequate documentation is still required for its addition to the County List.

Red-necked Phalarope   *Phalaropus lobatus*

Staffs   2002   Doxey Marshes: juvenile moulting into first-winter, September 12th-18th.

Common Rosefinch   (Scarlet Rosefinch)   *Carpodacus erythrinus*

Warks   2003   Alcester: May 29th.

This constitutes the first acceptable regional record. There is an earlier record, under the name Scarlet Grosbeak, of one shot at Powick in December 1855. However, Harthan (1946) placed this in square brackets, denoting some doubt about its authenticity or origin.

Species not fully admitted to the British List

The following species do not form part of the official *British List*, but fall within the British Ornithologists' Union Category D. This category comprises species that would otherwise appear in Categories A or B except that:

i   there is reasonable doubt that they have ever occurred in a wild state;
ii   they have certainly arrived with ship or human assistance;
iii   they have only ever been found dead on the tideline; or
iv   species that would otherwise appear in Category C, except that their feral populations may or may not be self-supporting.

Five species have occurred in this region. The sequence and nomenclature used is the same as for the Systematic List.

Falcated Duck (Falcated Teal)
Anas falcata
East Palearctic; winters Iran , India, Burma.

Warks   1981   Kingsbury WP: October 25th to December 6th.
Worcs   1985   Holt Fleet: February 20th-21st.
Warks   1989   Middleton Hall: November 5th.

Marbled Duck (Marbled Teal)
Marmaronetta angustirostris
Canary Islands, Mediterranean basin to south-west Asia.

Staffs   1973   Belvide Reservoir: April 30th.
Warks   1990   Dosthill Lake: July 7th. Also Kingsbury same day until August 19th. Returned to Dosthill for one day on August 12th.
Staffs   1993   Chasewater: June 26th, November 6th, December 4th and 24th.
W Mid   2001   Dunstall Park Lake: August 30th, fully winged female, believed to be from West Park Lake, Wolverhampton.

White Pelican
Pelecanus onocrotalus
South-central Eurasia, south Asia & Africa.

Warks   1975   Leamington Spa Reservoir: October 26th,.
Staffs   1981   Blithfield Reservoir: October 28th
Worcs   2001   Stourport-on-Severn: October 25th. An unidentified pelican at Ombersley, November 20th, was possibly the same bird.

Greater Flamingo
Phoenicopterus roseus
Southern Palearctic, southern Asia, Africa, Madagascar, Caribbean, Galapogos.

Staffs   1881   Manifold Valley: September.

W Mid   1909   Warley: December 22nd.
Warks   1962   Wormleighton Reservoir: October 14th
Warks   1968   Ladywalk: April and May.
Warks   1968   Kingsbury: June
Warks   1968   Brandon Marsh: August.
Worcs   1968   Bittell Reservoir: late November.
Staffs   1968   Blithfield Reservoir: December
Worcs   1978   Wilden: September 22nd.

Some, if not all, of the 1968 records probably involved the same wandering individual. With the increasing number of escapees, it is also possible that some of these individuals were of the American race *P. r. ruber*, or the Chilean Flamingo *P. chilensis*.

Red-headed Bunting
Emberiza bruniceps
South-central Eurasia; winters India.

Warks   1976   Draycote Water: May 6th, possibly same Barston (W Mid), May 11th-12th.
Staffs   1977   Wheaton Aston: male in song, July 19th to August 3rd.

The following is strictly a Category C species on the strength of the self-supporting population in the Scottish highlands. However, its history in the West Midlands makes it more appropriate to follow the precedent set in *BWM* and include it here.

Capercaillie
Tetrao urogallus
Coniferous forests of northern Eurasia.

Staffs   1970s   Cannock Chase: male and two females, unsuccessfully introduced early 1970s.

Exotic Species

The following are records of species within the British Ornithologists' Union's Category E that are known to have occurred in the West Midlands during 1979-2001. This category comprises introductions, transportees or escapees from captivity and whose breeding populations (if any) are thought not to be self-sustaining.

The order and nomenclature generally follow the BOU, augmented by Clements (2000) for additional species. Full details are given only for those species with ten or less records—the others being summarised. Hybrids are not included.

Fulvous Whistling Duck
Dendrocygna bicolor
Southern US, to Argentina; eastern Africa,
Madagascar and southern Asia.

Warks 1992 Dosthill Lake: April 19th-20th.
Warks 1992 Packington Park: three, September 27th, with one throughout October.
Worcs 1992 Westwood Pool: March 31st.
Warks 1993 Coombe Abbey: March 21st-31st and April 15th-16th.

White-faced Whistling Duck
Dendrocygna viduata
Tropical America and Africa.

Warks 1994 Brandon Marsh: April 22nd.

Black Swan
Cygnus atratus
Australia and Tasmania.

The records during 1979-2001 could have involved between 60-75 birds, but many exotic species are very mobile and so the number of individuals could be considerably less. Appearances have been almost annual since 1989, with just over 40% of records coming from Staffordshire. The largest herd was five at Chasewater in February 1992. Most birds have been seen on lakes and reservoirs, but a few have occurred on rivers.

Swan Goose
Anser cygnoides
Eastern Eurasia.

Warks 1979 Packington: pair bred.
Worcs 1987 Bredon's Hardwick: two, November 22nd.
Warks 1990 Polesworth: January 7th, on R. Anker.
W Mid 1991 Bilston: December 29th.
W Mid 1993 Hydes Road Pool: November 15th.
W Mid 1995 Handsworth Park: two, September 28th.

W Mid 1995 Walsall Arboretum: November 11th.
W Mid 1996 Handsworth Park: two, January 5th.
W Mid 1996 Walsall Arboretum: February 3rd.
Worcs 2000 Pirton: May 10th.
W Mid 2000 Walsall Arboretum: October 25th.

There is probably some duplication in the above records. Some birds were recorded as being of the domesticated form known as the Chinese Goose, which is common in captivity.

Bar-headed Goose
Anser indicus
Central Asia; winters India and Burma.

This, the commonest of the exotic wildfowl, was seen in eighteen of the twenty-three years 1979-2001, often amongst flocks of Canada Geese. Around 100 were recorded, but again birds are mobile so some duplication is inevitable. Almost 40% of them were in Worcestershire and 30% in Warwickshire. Most of Staffordshire's records came from Westport Lake, where breeding occurred in 1999 and 2001, though no young survived. Another, paired with a Barnacle Goose, was seen at several localities in the West Midlands county during 1998. The largest gaggle was 11 at Draycote Water in June 1999.

Ross's Goose
Anser rossii
Canadian tundra; winters south to US.

Since 1990, there have been around a dozen reports, which could have involved up to 16 individuals. A pair remained in Worcestershire for two to three years, breeding in 1992 when they were seen with a juvenile, and one frequented Blithfield intermittently from 1991-94. The pattern of occurrences suggests one or two birds are wandering around the region.

Emperor Goose
Anser canagicus
NE Siberia to western Alaska; winters southern Alaska to California.

Warks 1981 Near Hams Hall: June 12th.
Staffs 1998 Westport Lake: December 12th.
Warks 1999 Draycote Water: June 13th.
Warks 2000 Kingsbury Water Park: January and again June-December.
Warks 2001 Dosthill Lake/ Kingsbury Water Park: May-August, a free-flying bird from Drayton Manor Park, Staffs.

Hawaiian Goose (Nene)
Branta sandvicensis
Upland lava flows of Hawaii.

Worcs 1999 Captain's Pool: August 18th.

Cape/South African Shelduck
Tadorna cana
Karoo of southern Africa.

Warks 1983 Seeswood Pool: October 5th.
Staffs 1987 Branston GP/WP: flying over, August 30th.
Staffs 1990 Barton GP: August 24th to September 22nd.
Warks 1998 Dosthill Lake: January 1st.

Paradise/New Zealand Shelduck
Tadorna variegata
New Zealand.

Staffs 1995 Blithfield Reservoir: ten, July 20th, and one, October 5th.
Warks 1996 Middleton: male, May 5th.
Staffs   Same, Drayton Bassett GP, May 5th and probably same Blithfield Reservoir, September 29th to December 15th.
Warks 1997 Dosthill Lake: possibly same as above, May 18th, and at many sites in the north of the county on various dates in 1998.
Staffs 1999 Blithfield Reservoir: September 12th.
Staffs 2001 Blithfield Reservoir: August 12th.

Muscovy Duck
Cairina moschata
Southern Mexico to Argentina and Brazil.

This locally common resident occurs on many farm ponds and urban parks, but is seldom reported. Of around a dozen records during 1988-2001, at least half occurred in the West Midlands county. Breeding was confirmed at Walsall Arboretum in 1988 and 1989, with 23 young being raised in two broods during the latter year. A group of up to 11 remained at Blithfield for several months during 1990.

Ringed Teal
Callonetta leucophrys
Southern Brazil to Bolivia, Paraguay, Uruguay and north-east Argentina.

Birds were present in 13 of the 17 years 1985-2001, with perhaps 15 individuals involved. This unexpected frequency suggests a few were wandering around the region. Individuals made regular, sometimes protracted, visits to Upton Warren during 1985-1989 and Chasewater from 1992-96. There were two pairs at Lower Moor in 2001.

Wood Duck
Aix sponsa
Canada to northern Mexico; and Bahamas.

Originally a Category D species, *BWM* listed five records. Since 1979 this species, which is often kept in wildfowl collections, has been seen most years and breeding occurred at Dowles Brook in 1982, Broadway in 1984 and Tunstall Park in 1990. Excluding ducklings, approximately 40 birds were recorded, distributed fairly evenly between the four counties. Coombe Abbey and Westport Lake were both favoured localities, although birds at the latter site often went absent for long periods. The most seen together were four.

Maned (Australian Wood) Duck
Chenonetta jubata
Australia and Tasmania.

Staffs 1984 Blithfield Reservoir: November 25th to December 16th.
Staffs 1986 Himley: during January.
W Mid 1997 Edgbaston Res: unspecified date, May.

Chiloe Wigeon
Anas sibilatrix
Cent. Chile, Argentina to Tierra del Fuego, Falklands; winters to south-east Brazil.

Staffs 1991 Tittesworth Reservoir: female, May 31st to June 2nd.

W Mid 1993 Cornets End: September 12th.
Warks 1993 Draycote Water: October 17th. Same, Brandon Marsh, November 2nd.
Staffs 1997 Blithfield Reservoir: July 6th to August 17th.
Warks 1999 Brandon Marsh: May 25th, intermittently to May 17th 2000.
Worcs 2001 Grimley: May 1st-3rd.

Speckled (Chilean) Teal

Anas flavirostris
Andes of Venezuela to Tierra del Fuego.

Warks 1989 Brandon Marsh: September to December 8th.
W Mid 1990 Sandwell Valley: three, September 15th.
Warks 1991 Brandon Marsh: November 24th.
Staffs 1991 Blithfield Reservoir: November 13th. Presumed same, Belvide Reservoir, December 23rd.
Worcs 1995 Mill Pond, Malvern: September 22nd.
W Mid 1997 Sandwell Valley: May 16th-20th, August 2nd-10th and September 28th.
Staffs 1998 Belvide Reservoir: December 5th-9th.
Warks 2001 Brandon Marsh and Coombe Abbey: September 29th to November 25th.

Cape Teal

Anas capensis
Locally in eastern and southern Africa.

Worcs 1989 Bittell Reservoir: July 27th to October 25th. Same, Upton Warren: September 5th-11th and 16th.
Worcs 1991 Bredon's Hardwick: February 17th.
Worcs 1991 Pirton: pair, March 17th and September 30th; also Wilden, intermittently June 4th to October 28th.
Warks 1993 Draycote Water: April 4th.

Grey Teal

Anas gracilis
Australia to New Guinea and the Solomon Islands.

Staffs 1994 Blithfield Reservoir: July 23rd and 31st.

Chestnut Teal

Anas castanea
Australia and Tasmania.

Staffs 1983 Perton: pair, February 10th. until end of year.
Staffs 1987 Westport Lake: adult drake, January 23rd.
Warks 1988 Draycote Water: two, October 8th.
Worcs 1993 Mill Pond, Malvern: three on an unspecified date.
Worcs 1996 Upton Warren: July 21st-26th.
Worcs 1998 Upton Warren: August 14th-24th.

African Yellowbill (Yellow-billed Duck)

Anas undulata
Locally in eastern and south-eastern Africa.

Worcs 1992 Westwood Park: July 8th to October 28th.

Spot-billed Duck

Anas poecilorhyncha
Eastern Asia and India: winters Indochina and Philippines.

Warks 2000 Lower Radbourn: October 22nd.

White-cheeked (Bahama) Pintail

Anas bahamensis
Locally , southern America, West Indies and Galapagos islands.

Birds escape fairly regularly from wildfowl collections and just over 20 were recorded in fourteen of the twenty-three years during the current period. Most were singles, but two were seen together on a couple of occasions. Almost half of the birds were in Worcestershire, whereas only one was seen in the West Midlands county.

Hottentot Teal

Anas hottentota
Africa south of the Sahara.

Worcs 1989 Bittell Res.: July 27th to November 20th, intermittently. Same, Upton Warren, September 4th- 11th.

Cinnamon Teal

Anas cyanoptera
West and north America (Southern Canada) to Tierra del Fuego and Falkland Islands.

Staffs 1992 Blithfield Reservoir: June 5th.
Warks 2001 Wormleighton Reservoir: October 11th.

Red (Argentine) Shoveler

Anas platalea
Lowlands of southern Peru and south Brazil to Tierra del Fuego.

Staffs 1979 Belvide Reservoir: June 23rd.

Australian (New Zealand) Shoveler

Anas rhynchotis
Australia, Tasmania and New Zealand.

Worcs 1985 Bittell Reservoir: April 6th.

464

Rosy-billed Pochard

Netta peposaca
SE Brazil to southern Argentina and Chile.

Warks 2001 Ladywalk: three during December. Two of these visited Lea Marston, December 29th.

Southern Pochard

Netta erythrophthalma
Patchily distributed Africa and S. America.

Worcs 1986 Evesham: female, March 2nd. Presume same, Larford March 23rd to May 21st and Upton Warren May 29th.

Baer's Pochard

Aythya baeri
Eurasia; winters to India, south-east Asia & south-east China.

W Mid 1999 Marsh Lane GP/NR: September 12th to October 11th..

White-eyed Duck

Aythya australis
Australian region and south-west Oceania.

Worcs 1984 Upton Warren: August 21st and 22nd.

New Zealand Scaup

Aythya novaeseelandiae
Lagoons, lakes and ponds of New Zealand.

Staffs 1980 Belvide Reservoir: male, October 25th, November 15th and intermittently until November 1981.

Maccoa Duck

Oxyura maccoa
Locally, highlands of east and south Africa.

Worcs 1993 Westwood Park: May 17th, then Upton Warren, May 22nd-23rd, returning to Westwood Park, where it remained until August 9th.

Chukar

Alectoris chukar
Balkans to Tibet, Mongolia & north China.

Staffs 1987 Gib Torr: two, April 5th.
Worcs 1988 Bredon's Norton: May 14th.
Staffs 1989 Needwood Airfield: pair, April 24th, with male again May 2nd.
Worcs 1991 Bittell Reservoir: present all year.
Warks 1992 Shustoke: May 3rd.
Warks 1997 Ilmington: April 12th.

Indian Peafowl

Pavo cristatus
India and Sri Lanka.

W Mid 1999 Smestow Valley: male, first noted in August and recorded intermittently until at least the end of 2002.
W Mid 2001 Sandwell Valley: male, during February.

Often kept at stately homes from where they wander, but are not always reported.

Pelican sp.

Pelecanus sp.

Worcs 2001 Ombersley: November 20th.

Sacred Ibis

Threskiornis aethiopicus
Sub-Saharan Africa to Iran; Madagascar.

Staffs 1989 Whiston Mill: October 11th-13th. Same near to Cannock M6 junction on November 13th and Belvide Reservoir, December 11th and 19th.
Warks 1997 Stratford-upon-Avon: adult, May 13th, on R. Avon near to town centre.
W Mid 1999 Minworth Sewage Works: June 22nd. Same, Castle Vale, July 4th.

Flamingo sp.

Phoenicopterus sp.

Warks 1979 Alvecote Pools: April 11th.
Staffs 1983 Blithfield Reservoir: two, August 27th.
Staffs 1988 Blithfield Reservoir: June 7th-12th.
Warks 1991 Brandon Marsh: November 28th-29th.

Chilean Flamingo

Phoenicopterus chilensis
Andes of southern S. America; pampas of south Brazil, Paraguay to south Argentina.

Staffs 1980 Gailey Reservoir: November 29th. Disturbed and moved to Belvide Reservoir for rest of day.
Staffs 1984 Blithfield Reservoir: March 21st.
Warks 1988 Draycote Water: July 8th-24th.
Worcs 1992 Lower Moor: July 18th.
Warks 1992 Draycote Water: September 25th to October 4th.

Lesser Flamingo

Phoenicopterus minor
Locally in Africa and Madagascar to north-west India.

Worcs 1989 Upton Warren: August 26th to September 27th. Same, Wilden, September 11th. Wearing blue plastic ring.

Harris's Hawk

Parabuteo unicinctus
South-west United States to northern Argentina, Chile and Brazil.

Staffs 1990 Hampton Valley, Enville: February 23rd.
W Mid 1994 Edgbaston Park/Winterbourne: January/
          February.
Worcs 1999 Strensham: November 28th.
Worcs 2000 Dowles Brook: May 14th.

Red-tailed Hawk

Buteo jamaicensis
North and central America and West Indies.

Warks 1998 Packington: throughout year. Believed to
          be an escapee from owner in Hampton-
          in- Arden , 1996.
Warks 1999 Fenny Compton Hills: white phase
          (Krider's Hawk), March 11th-12th.

Lanner Falcon

Falco biarmicus
Savannah and deserts of western Palearctic and Africa.

Worcs 1993 Bredon Hill: July 28th to September 18th
          (without jesses).
Worcs 1996 Broadway: October 1st.
Warks 1997 Draycote Water: in December.

Saker Falcon

Falco cherrug
South-central Eurasia; winters from eastern Mediterranean to India and Tibet.

Worcs 1993 Bredon Hill: May 6th (with jesses).
Warks 1999 Riversley Park, Nuneaton: November 3rd.

Crowned Crane

Balearica regulorum/pavonina
Africa.

Worcs 1980 High Green: two, October 5th.

Grey-headed Gull

Larus cirrocephalus
Africa and Madagascar; southern and western South America.

Worcs 1996 Bredon's Hardwick: April 5th-13th.
Warks 1997 Draycote Water: September 1st.
Warks 2000 Kingsbury Water Park: June 5th.

These three records almost certainly refer to the same individual, which has been wandering around the wider Midlands area for several years.

Barbary Dove

Streptopelia 'risoria' (domestic hybrid)

W Mid 1980 Kingstanding: April 4th.
Worcs 1986 Little Comberton: February 24th.
Worcs 1986 Evesham: different to above, February
          25th.
Worcs 1988 Eckington: April 23rd.
Worcs: 1988 Cropthorne: June 16th.
W Mid 1989 Willenhall: April 24th.

The four records in 1986 and 1988 all came from the lower Avon Valley.

Parrot sp.

Psittacidae

Warks 1993 Draycote Water: August 31st.
Warks 1993 Ladywalk: November 20th.
Warks 2001 Hampton Lucy: July 24th.
W Mid 2001 Pype Hayes Hall: two, February 2nd.
W Mid 2001 Marston Green: another, or one of the
          above two, September 28th-30th.

Lorikeet sp.

Psittacidae

Worcs 1988 Evesham: December 30th.

Sulphur-crested Cockatoo

Cacatua galerita
New Guinea and adjacent islands to Australia and Tasmania.

Staffs 1976 Chillington: one from March until 1990,
          when found dead. Also on occasions at
          Brewood and Belvide Reservoir.
Warks 1989 Seeswood Pool: September 20th.
Worcs 1992 Bredon: May 6th
W Mid 1994 Sheepwash Urban Park: September 2nd
          and again August 3rd 1996. Apparently
          seen almost annually in the area since
          about 1986.

Amazingly, the Chillington bird survived in the wild for at least fourteen years.

Cockatiel

Nymphicus hollandicus
Interior of Australia.

Around 70 Cockatiels were reported between 1983 and 2001, with records in every year. All were of singles, and the best years were 1988 and 1992, with approximately 10 birds in each. The West Midlands county and Staffordshire each had a third of the records. There was an urban bias to many of the localities where birds were seen in these two counties, reflecting its popularity as a cage or aviary bird.

Crimson Rosella
Platycercus elegans
Queensland to Victoria, Australia and Tasmania.

Staffs 1994 Harpfields, Stoke-on-Trent: September 30th to late December.
W Mid 1999 Marston Green: July 12th--16th

Red-rumped Parrot
Psephotus haematonotus
Scrub and riverine woodlands of interior south-eastern Australia.

Worcs 1992 Bishampton: October 24th.

Budgerigar
Melopsittacus undulatus
Australia.

One or two of these most popular of pet birds escape each year and there were reports in twenty of the twenty-three years 1979-2001. Overall, 37 were recorded, but many others doubtless went unreported. As with Cockatiels, most were seen in the West Midlands county and Staffordshire. Apart from three at Doxey in 1998, all records were of single birds.

Parakeet sp.
Psittacidae

In nine years of the current period there was a total of eleven records of Parakeets that were not specifically identified. All were of single birds, except for three at Evesham in 1996.

Moustached Parakeet
Psittacula alexandri
Forests of northern India to south-east Asia, Andamans and Greater Sundas.

Worcs 1990 Bredon Hill: November 29th to years end.

Lovebird sp.
Agapornis sp.
Africa

W Mid 1999 Smestow Valley: October 30th.

Peach-faced (Rosy-faced) Lovebird
Agapornis roseicollis
Northern Tanzania.

W Mid 1989 Park Lime Pits: May 7th.

Fischer's Lovebird
Agapornis fischeri
Northern Tanzania.

W Mid 1988 Walsall: July 23rd.

African Grey Parrot
Psittacus erithacus
West and central Africa.

Staffs 1993 Lichfield: June 22nd.
Staffs 1997 Chasewater: November 1st.

Senegal Parrot
Poicephalus senegalus
Senegal to Cameroon and south-west Chad.

W Mid 1986 Sandwell Valley RSPB Reserve: February 21st-22nd.
W Mid 1995 Aldridge: intermittently from April until April 21st 1998.

Scarlet Macaw
Ara macao
Tropical southern Mexico to north Bolivia, Amazonian Brazil.

W Mid 1984 Darlaston: from early in year to September 16th.

Monk Parakeet
Myiopsitta monachus
Central Bolivia to central Argentina and southern Brazil.

Staffs 1983 Porthill area of Newcastle-under-Lyme: pair, April 26th, with completed nest. Nestlings later found dead, but five birds on November 17th, so presumably bred successfully nearby. Nesting was also reported in 1984, 1985, 1989 and 1991, although only one bird seen in latter year. It was thought that birds nested most years between 1983-91, though usually unsuccessfully. The last record was of a bird on December 6th 1994.

Blue-fronted Amazon (Blue-fronted Parrot)
Amazona aestiva
Lowlands of eastern Brazil to Bolivia, Para-

guay and northern Argentina.

Staffs 1976 Chillington: present until 1990 when
           found dead.
Warks 1989 Seeswood Pool: September 20th.

Yellow-crowned Amazon (Yellow-crowned Parrot)
Amazona ochrocephala
Tropical north Honduras; Panama to Bolivia, Amazonian Brazil.

Worcs 1996 Frankley: one of the race *oratix*, August
           3rd.

Eurasian Eagle Owl
Bubo bubo
Palearctic.

W Mid 1990 Willenhall: December 9th.
Warks 1999 Dassett Hills: present from February
           through to February 3rd 2002. Local residents intimated it had been present in the
           district since 1993.
W Mid 1999 Wolverhanpton: several months prior to
           June, close to town centre.
W Mid 2001 Sandwell Valley: during May.

Red-whiskered Bulbul
Pycnonotus jocosus
Oriental.

Worcs 1993 Hewell Grange: June to November 20th.
Staffs 1993 Fradley: November 15th.

Waxwing sp.
Bombycilla sp.

Warks 1998 Lighthorne: June 14th, from sketchy details it seemed more likely that this bird
           was either *B. japonica* or *B. cedrorum*
           rather than *B. garrulus.*

Red-billed Leiothrix (Pekin Robin)
Leiothrix lutea
Mountains of north India, south-east Tibet, south China, Burma and north Tonkin.

Staffs 1991 Rushton Spencer: May 13th.
Warks 1996 Southam: pair, April 1st-7th.

Sunbird sp.
Nectariniidae

Worcs 1999 Martin Hussingtree: August 9th.
Warks 2000 Moreton Morrell: July 12th to August
           26th—an unusually long time for a subtropical nectar feeder to survive outside in
           Britain.

Myna sp.
Probably *Acridotheres sp.*

Worcs 1993 Little Comberton: August 7th.

Glossy Starling sp.
Lamprotornis sp.
Africa.

W Mid 1987 Sutton Coldfield: November 8th.

Black-headed Weaver
Ploceus melanocephalus
West-central and north-east Africa.

Worcs 1986 Bittell Reservoir: August 16th.

Red-billed Quelea
Quelea quelea
Africa south of the Sahara.

W Mid 1979 Sutton Coldfield: October 10th-12th.

Red Bishop
Euplectes orix
East and Central Africa.

Worcs 1995 Lower Moor: October 29th.

Black-rumped Waxbill
Estrilda troglodytes
Sub-Saharan Africa.

Worcs 2001 Upton Warren: August 23rd to September
           16th.

Common Waxbill
Estrilda astrild
Africa south of the Sahara

Warks 1999 Kenilworth: October 13th.

Zebra Finch
Poephila/Taeniopygia guttata
Australia and Lesser Sundas.

Staffs 1983 Blithfield Reservoir: August 30th.
Warks 1993 Brandon: May 2nd.
Staffs 1992 Belvide Reservoir: late July.
Worcs 1996 North Hill: October 23rd.

Island Canary (Canary)
Serinus canaria
Madeira, Azores and west Canary Islands.

Staffs 1980 Belvide Reservoir: male in song, August
           16th.

W Mid 1985 Willenhall Memorial Park: November
　　　　　　　10th.
Warks 1988 Ladywalk: December 29th into 1989.
Warks 1991 Ryton-on-Dunsmore, July 21st.
Worcs 1997 Evesham: October 17th.
Staffs 1997 Little Stoke: August 18th-31st.
Worcs 2000 Lower Moor: January 9th.
Staffs 2000 Etruria: a 'Crested Norwich' form bird,
　　　　　　　July 17th.

Yellow-throated Bunting
Emberiza elegans
South-east Siberia, China, northern Korea;
winters to northern SE Asia and Japan.

Warks 2000 Shipston-on Stour: male, March 23rd

Rufous-collared Sparrow
Zonotrichia capensis
Southern Mexico to Argentina.

Worcs 1996 Finstall: early February for two weeks.
　　　　　　　Presume same, Upton Warren, February
　　　　　　　15th-22nd
Worcs 1998 Walton Hill: April 24th.

In addition the *WMBC Annual Reports* for 1979-2001 include several records of exotic birds under English names that could not be specifically traced in any publications available to us and for which no scientific names were given namely:

Australian Pochard
(possibly White-eyed Duck
Aythya australis)
Grey Cockatiel
Pied Cockatiel
Black-headed Starling
Red-headed Cardinal

The following additional Category E species were recorded in *BWM*, but without full details.

Marabou Stork
Leptoptilos crumeniferus

Red-billed Whistling Duck
Dendrocygna autumnalis

Black-necked Swan
Cygnus melanocorypha

Australian (Pacific) Black Duck
Anas superciliosa

Red-billed Teal (Duck)
Anas erythrorhyncha

Chilean (Yellow-billed) Pintail
Anas georgica

Indian White-backed Vulture
Gyps bengalensis

Red-headed (Red-necked) Falcon
Falco chicquera

Laggar
Falco jugger

California Quail
Callipepla (Lophortyx) californica

Northern Bobwhite
Colinus virginianus

(A Category D species in *BWM*, but now in Category E. The only mention is from Staffordshire prior to 1878).

Silver Pheasant
Lophura nicthemera

Sarus Crane
Grus antigone

Demoiselle Crane
Anthropoides virgo

Diamond Dove
Geopelia cuneata

Red-billed Blue Magpie
Urocissa erythrorhyncha

Common Myna
Acridotheres tristis

Pin-tailed Whydah
Vidua macroura

Paradise Whydah
Vidua paradisaea

Unacceptable Published Records

A few records that gained a measure of acceptance through being published in earlier authoritative works are no longer considered admissible. Those relating to species included in the *Systematic List* are mentioned there, but the following refer to species not so far recorded in the region. Records which have been submitted, but not officially accepted and published are excluded.

Lesser Kestrel
Falco naumanni

Staffs   1973   Chasewater: male, November 4th.

Originally accepted by BBRC (*Brit. Birds* 67:319), but subsequently considered to have been inadequately documented (*Brit. Birds* 88:505-506).

Greater Yellowlegs
Tringa melanoleuca

W Mid   1907   Sutton Park: three, of which one was shot, November 22nd.

This record was initially viewed with some incredulity (*Brit. Birds* 4:109) and both Witherby *et al.* (1938-41) and Norris (1947) cast doubts on its authenticity by placing it in square brackets.

Eurasian Scops Owl
Otus scops

Worcs pre1834 Near Fladbury.
Worcs c1860   Worcester: brought to a taxidermist.
Staffs C19th   Chillington: said to have been obtained locally.

Harthan (1946) considered the first two to be dubious and placed them in square brackets, but Smith (1938) included the latter without question. None, however, appeared in *The Handbook* (Witherby *et al.* 1938-41).

Snowy Owl
Nyctea scandiacus

Staffs pre 1881 Near Burton-on-Trent: killed.
(May have been in Derbyshire).
Staffs   1917   Near Pipe Ridware: December 28th.

Smith (1938) placed both in square brackets and Witherby *et al.* (1938-41) included neither.

Crested Tit
Parus cristatus

Staffs   1954   Cannock Chase: April 11th.

The *WMBC Annual Report* (21:45) included this record within square brackets "as there was only one observer and this was felt to be inadequate for such an unusual occurrence."

Pine Grosbeak
Pinicola enucleator

Hastings (1834) included this species in his list for Worcestershire, but gave no description or details of capture.

List of Plants and Animals (other than birds) mentioned in the text

Plants

These are listed in alphabetical order of vernacular names. The names generally follow those in *Wild Flowers of Britain and Ireland* (Blamey, Fitter and Fitter 2003), who in turn used the Botanical Society of the British Isles for English names and the *New Flora of the British Isles* (Stace, second edition, 1997) for scientific names. For plants not covered by the above, a variety of specialised books have been used.

Adderstongue	*Ophioglossum vulgatum*	Cedar	*Cedrus spp.*
Alder	*Alnus glutinosa*	Chenopodium	
Italian	*Alnus cordata*	(goosefoot family)	*Chenopodiaceae*
Anemone, Wood	*Anemone nemorosa*	Cherry, Bird	*Prunus padus*
Apple	*Malus domestica*	Wild	*Prunus avium*
Crab	*Malus sylvestris*	Chestnut, Sweet	*Castanea sativa*
Archangel, Yellow	*Lamiastrum galeobdolon*	Chickweed	Probably *Stellaria spp.*
Ash	*Fraxinus excelsior*	Clematis	*Clematis spp.*
Aspen	*Populus tremula*	Clover	*Trifolium spp.*
		Clubmoss	Lycopsida
Balsam, Himalayan	*Impatiens glandulifera*	Cotoneaster	*Cotoneaster spp.*
Barley	*Hordeum vulgare/distichon*	Cotton-grass	*Eriophorum spp.*
Bean	*Vicia spp.* or	Cowberry	*Vaccinium vitis-idaea*
	Phaseolus spp.	Cowslip	*Primula veris*
Bedstraw, Heath	*Galium saxatile*	Cow-wheat	*Melampyrum spp.*
Beech	*Fagus sylvatica*	Cress	*Lepidum sativum*
Beet, Sugar	*Beta vulgaris spp.*	Crowberry	*Empetrum nigrum*
Bellflower, Nettle-leaved	*Campanula trachelium*	Crucifer	
Bent, Common	*Agrostis capillaris*	(cabbage family)	Cruciferae
Bilberry	*Vaccinium myrtillus*	Currant, Mountain	*Ribes alpinum*
hybrid	*Vaccinium myrtillus x vitis-*	Cypress	Cupressaceae
(Bilberry x Cowberry)	*idaea*		
Birch	*Betula spp.*	Daffodil, Wild	*Narcissus pseudonarcissus*
Birdsfoot (Bird's-foot)	*Ornithopus perpusillus*	Daisy family	Asteraceae / Compositae
Birdsnest, Yellow	*Monotropa hypopitys*	Dittander	*Lepidium latifolium*
Blackthorn	*Prunus spinosa*	Dodder, Greater	*Cuscuta europaea*
Bladderwort	*Utricularia spp.*	Dogwood	*Cornus sanguinea*
Blanket weed	Cladophora		
Bluebell	*Hyacinthoides non-scriptus*	Eel-grass	*Zostera spp.*
Bogbean	*Menyanthes trifoliata*	Elder	*Sambucus nigra*
Bracken	*Pteridium aquilinum*	Elm	*Ulmus spp.* usually *Ulmus*
Bramble	*Rubus fruticosus* agg.		*procera*
Brassica		Wych	*Ulmus glabra*
(cabbage family)	Cruciferae		
Broom	*Cytisus scoparius*	Fat Hen	*Chenopodium album*
Buddleia	*Buddleia spp.*	Fern	Filicopsida
Bulrush (Reedmace)	*Typha latifolia*	Maidenhair	*Adiantum capillus-veneris*
Bulrush (Sedge)	*Scirpus spp.*	Fescue, Sheep's	*Festuca ovina*
Burnet, Great	*Sanguisorba officinalis*	Fir	*Abies spp.* or *Pseudotsuga*
Butterbur	*Petasites hybridus*		*spp.*
		Douglas	*Pseudotsuga menziesii*
Catchfly, Sand	*Silene conica*	Flax (Linseed)	*Linum spp.*

Forget-me-not, Field	*Myosotis arvensis*
Fritillary	*Fritillaria meleagris*
Fuchsia	*Fuchsia spp.*
Gorse	*Ulex europaeus*
Western	*Ulex gallii*
Grape (vine)	*Vitis vinifera*
Greenweed, Dyer's	*Genista tinctoria*
Guelder-rose	*Viburnum opulus*
Hair-grass, Grey	*Corynephorus canescens*
Wavy	*Deschampsia flexuosa*
Harebell	*Campanula rotundifolia*
Hawthorn	*Crataegus monogyna or*
	C. laevigata
Hazel	*Corylus avellana*
Heath, Cross-leaved	*Erica tetralix*
Heather (Ling)	*Calluna vulgaris*
Helleborine, Marsh	*Epipactis palustris*
Herb Paris	*Paris quadrifolia*
Holly	*Ilex aquifolium*
Honeysuckle	*Lonicera periclymenum*
Hornbeam	*Carpinus betulus*
Iris, Yellow	*Iris pseudacorus*
Ivy	*Hedera helix*
Knapweed, Common	*Centaurea nigra*
Knotgrass	*Polygonum aviculare*
Lady's Mantle	*Alchemilla spp.*
Larch	*Larix spp.*
European	*Larix decidua*
Lichen	*Lichenes*
Lime, Large-leaved	*Tilia platyphyllos*
Small-leaved	*Tilia cordata*
Ling (Heather)	*Calluna vulgaris*
Linseed (Flax)	*Linum spp.*
Liverwort	*Bryophyta*
Madder, Field	*Sherardia arvensis*
Maize	*Zea mays*
Maple, Field	*Acer campestre*
Marigold, Marsh	*Caltha palustris*
Meadowsweet	*Filipendula ulmaria*
Millet (Common)	*Panicum miliaceum*
Mistletoe	*Viscum album*
Moonwort	*Botrychium lunaria*
Moor-grass, Purple	*Molinia caerulea*
Moss	*Bryophyta*
Sphagnum	*Sphagnum spp.*
Mustard	*Sinapis spp.*
Nettle, usually Stinging	*Urtica dioica*
Oak	*Quercus spp.*
Pedunculate	*Quercus robur*
Sessile	*Quercus petraea*
Oat	*Avena sativa*
Orchid	*Ochidaceae*
Bee	*Ophrys apifera*
Green-winged	*Anacamptis morio*
Marsh	*Dactylorhiza spp.*

Orchid cont.	
Pyramidal	*Anacamptis pyramidalis*
Southern marsh	*Dactylorhiza praetermissa*
Osier	*Salix viminalis*
Pansy, Field	*Viola arvensis*
Wild	*Viola tricolor*
Pear	*Pyrus communis*
Pimpernel, Scarlet	*Anagallis arvensis*
Pine	*Pinus spp.*
Arolla	*Pinus cembra*
Corsican	*Pinus nigra*
Scots	*Pinus sylvestris*
Plane, usually London	*Platanus x hispanica*
Plum	*Prunus spp.*
Poplar	*Populus spp.*
Black	*Populus nigra*
Poppy	*Papaver spp.*
Potato	*Solanum tuberosum*
Primrose	*Primula vulgaris*
Pyracantha (Firethorn)	*Pyracantha spp.*
Ragwort	*Senecio spp.*
Rape, Oilseed	*Brassica napus*
	var. oleifera
Raspberry	*Rubus idaeus*
Rattle, Yellow	*Rhinanthus minor*
Reed, Common	*Phragmites australis*
Reedmace (Bulrush)	*Typha latifolia*
Rhododendron	*Rhododendron ponticum*
Robin, Ragged	*Lychnis flos-cuculi*
Rock-rose, Common	*Helianthemum*
	nummularium
Rose	*Rosa spp.*
Rowan	*Sorbus aucuparia*
Rush	*Juncus spp.*
Saffron, Meadow	*Colchicum autumnale*
Sallow	*Salix spp.*
Sedge	*Cyperaceae*
Thin-spiked Wood	*Carex strigosa*
Service Tree, Wild	*Sorbus torminalis*
Skimmia	*Skimmia spp.*
Sorrel, Sheep's	*Rumex acetosella*
Sprout	*Brassica oleracea*
	gemmifera
Spruce	*Picea spp.*
Spurge, Dwarf	*Euphorbia exigua*
Strawberry	*Fragaria spp.*
Sugar-beet	*Beta vulgaris spp.*
Sundew, Round-leaved	*Drosera rotundifolia*
Sunflower	*Helianthus spp.*
Sweet-grass, Reed	*Glyceria maxima*
Sycamore	*Acer pseudoplatanus*
Teasel	*Dipsacus spp.*
Thistle	Asteraceae / Compositae
Tomato	*Lycopersicon esculentum*
Toothwort	*Lathraea squamaria*
Tussock Sedge, Greater	*Carex paniculata*
Umbellifer	
(Carrot family)	Umbelliferae

Venus's Looking-glass	*Legousia hybrida*	Wheat	*Triticum aestivum /*
Viburnum	*Viburnum spp.*		*turgidum*
Virginia creeper	*Parthenocissus spp.*	Willow	*Salix spp.*
		Willowherb	*Epilobium spp.*
Water-plantain,		Wisteria	*Wisteria spp.*
Ribbon-leaved	*Alisma gramineum*	Wood-rush, Great	*Luzula sylvatica*
Waterwort,		Wormwood	*Artemisia absinthium*
Eight-stamened	*Elatine hydropiper*		
Wayfaring-tree	*Viburnum lantana*	Yew	*Taxus baccata*
Wellingtonia	*Sequoiadendron giganteum*		

Animals

These are listed in alphabetical order of their vernacular names. A wide variety of reference books have been used and as far as is known both the vernacular and scientific names follow current usage.

Adder	*Vipera berus*	Fritillary (butterfly)	Nymphalidae
Amphibians		Frog	Ranidae
(frogs, toads & newts)	Amphibia		
Ant	Formicidea	Goldfish	*Carassius auratus*
		Grayling (butterfly)	*Eumenis semele*
Badger	*Meles meles*		
Bat	Chiroptera	Hairstreak (butterfly),	
Bee	Apoidea	Brown	*Thecla betulae*
Solitary	Apoidea	White-letter	*Strymonidia w-album*
Beetle	Coleoptera	Hare, Brown	*Lepus capensis*
Cabbage-stem Flea	*Phyllotreta sp.*		
Blackfly	Aphididae	Ladybird	Coccinellidae
Bullhead	*Cottus gobio*	Leaf-beetle	Chrysomelidae
Bumblebee, moorland	*Bombus sp.*	Lemming	Microtidae
(possibly Heath or		Norway	*Lemmus lemmus*
Bilberry Bumblebee)		Wood	*Myopus schisticolor*
Heath	*Bombus jonellus*	Lizard	Lacertidae
Bilberry	*Bombus monticola*	Common (viviparous)	*Lacerta vivipara*
Butterfly	Lepidoptera		
		Mayflies	Ephemeroptera
Caddis-fly	Trichoptera	Mink (American)	*Mustela vison*
Cat	*Felis silvestris* (domestic)	Molluscs (Snails)	Mollusca
Caterpillar	Lepidoptera (larva)	Moth	Lepidoptera
Cattle	*Bos taurus* (domestic)	Green Oak Tortrix	
Click Beetle, Violet	*Limoniscus violacea*	(Oak Roller Moth)	*Tortrix viridana*
Cranefly	Tipulidae	Mouse, Wood	*Apodemus sylvaticus*
Crayfish	*Austropotamobius pallipes*	Mussel, freshwater	Lamellibranchia
Deer	Cervidae	Newt	Triturus
Dog	Canidae (domestic)		
Dormouse	*Muscardinus avellanarius*	Otter	*Lutra lutra*
Dragonfly	Odonata		
	(sub-order Anisoptera)	Peacock (butterfly)	*Inachis io*
Dutch Elm Disease		Pig	*Sus* (domestic)
(Elm Bark Beetle)	*Scolytus scolytus*	Pike	*Esox lucius*
		Poultry	*Gallus gallus* (domestic)
Earthworm	Oligochaeta		
		Rabbit	*Oryctolagus cuniculus*
Fish	Pisces	Reptiles	
Fly	Diptera	(lizards and snakes)	Reptilia
Foxhound	Canidae (domestic)		

Sawfly	Symphyta	Toad	Bufonidae
Sheep	*Ovis aries* (domestic)	Trout	*Salmo spp.*
Shrew, Common	*Sorex araneus*	Brown	*Salmo trutta*
Pygmy	*Sorex minutus*		
Snail	Mollusca	Vole	Microtidae
Snail, Water	Gastropoda	Bank	*Clethrionomys glareolus*
Snake	Ophidia	Field	*Microtus agrestis*
Spider	Araneae	Water	*Arvicola amphibius*
Wolf	*Pisaura mirabilis*		
Squirrel, Grey	*Neosciurus carolinensis*	Wasp, Solitary	Pompiloidea and Vespoidea
Stag Beetle	Lucanidae	Weasel	*Mustela nivalis*
		White, Wood (butterfly)	*Leptidea sinapis*

Gazetteer

This Gazetteer gives the county and Grid Reference of places referred to in this book that are within the Region, plus the page numbers where sites are described. Names for parts of larger sites, *e.g.* Cliff Pool at Kingsbury Water Park, are excluded. For most localities a four-figure Grid Reference is given. For rivers, canals and large areas a two-figure reference is used (sometimes just for a central length). No reference is included for the longest rivers as these are shown on the map on page 12. Place names are generally as on the *Ordnance Survey 1:50,000* maps. Alternative names, spellings or extra identification for places with the same name are also given.

Place	County	Grid Ref	Page	Place	County	Grid Ref	Page
Abberley Hill	Worcs	SO7566		Baginton	Warks	SP3474	
Abberton	Worcs	SO9953	106	Baginton Lagoons	Warks	SP3573	
Abbey Fields, Kenilworth	Warks	SP2872		Bagot's Park	Staffs	SK0927	
Abbots Bromley	Staffs	SK0824		Bagots Wood	Staffs	SK0727	79
Abbots Salford Pool	Warks	SP0749		Baldstones NR	Staffs	SK0164	
Acock's Green	W Mid	SP1183		Balsall Common	W Mid	SP2476	
Acton	Staffs	SJ8328		Barford	Warks	SP2760	
Adams Hill	Worcs	SO9279		Barnards Green	Worcs	SO7845	
Alcester	Warks	SP0957		Barnt Green	Worcs	SP0073	
Aldridge	W Mid	SK0500		Barr Beacon	W Mid	SP0697	
Alfrick	Worcs	SO7453	110	Barr Common	W Mid	SP0699	
Allimore Green Common	Staffs	SJ8519	61	Barston	W Mid	SP2078	
Alne, River/ Valley	Warks	SP16	55	Bartley Reservoir	W Mid	SP0081	56
Alrewas	Staffs	SK1715		Barton	Warks	SP1051	
Alton Towers	Staffs	SK0743		Barton GP	Staffs	SK2017	
Alvecote Pools	Warks	SK2504	86	Bascote	Warks	SP3864	
Alveston	Warks	SP2356		Bateswood CP	Staffs	SJ7947	67
Amblecote	W Mid	SO8985		Beaconwood	Worcs	SO9775	
Amington	Staffs	SK2304		Bearda/ Hill	Staffs	SJ9664	
Anker, River/ Valley	Staf/Wks	SK02/SP39		Beaudesert/ Old Park	Staffs	SK0313	44
Ansley	Warks	SP3091		Beckford GP	Worcs	SO9836	
Anson's Bank	Staffs	SJ9816		Bedworth	Warks	SP3586	
Ansty	Warks	SP4083		Bedworth Slough	Warks	SP3587	
Apedale CP	Staffs	SJ8047	67	Beech	Staffs	SJ8538	
Aqualate Mere	Staffs	SJ7720	60	Belfry, The	Warks	SP1895	
Aquamoor	Staffs	SJ8214		Belvide Reservoir	Staffs	SJ8610	62
Arbury Park	Warks	SP3389	54	Bemersley Tip	Staffs	SJ8854	
Arley	Warks	SP2890		Bengeworth	Worcs	SP0443	
Arley	Worcs	SO7680		Bentley	Warks	SP2895	
Arley Wood	Worcs	SO8082		Bentley Park/ Woods	Warks	SP2895	54
Arrow Valley Park	Worcs	SP0567		Berkswell	W Mid	SP2479	
Arrow, River/ Valley	Wks/Wor	SP05/06	55	Bermuda	Warks	SP3589	
Ashley Heath	Staffs	SJ7436	61	Berrow Hill (Martley)	Worcs	SO7458	
Ashmoor Common	Worcs	SO8446		Berry Hill	Staffs	SJ8946	
Aston	W Mid	SP0889		Besford	Worcs	SO9144	
Aston Mill	Worcs	SO9435		Betley Mere	Staffs	SJ7548	
Aston Somerville	Worcs	SP0438		Betts Reserve/ Coppice	Worcs	SO7276	
Astwood Bank	Worcs	SP0462		Bewdley	Worcs	SO7875	
Atherstone	Warks	SP3097		Bibby's Hollow	Worcs	SO9682	
Austrey	Warks	SK2906		Bickford Meadows	Staffs	SJ8814	61
Avon Dassett	Warks	SP4149		Biddulph	Staffs	SJ8857	
Avon River/ Valley	Wks/Wor		99	Biddulph Moor	Staffs	SJ9058	
Back Forest	Staffs	SJ9865		Bignall End	Staffs	SJ8051	
Baddesley	Warks	SP2798		Bilbrook Sewage Works	Staffs	SJ8803	
Baddesley Clinton	Warks	SP2071	54	Billesley Common	W Mid	SP0880	
Badsey	Worcs	SP0743		Bilston	W Mid	SO9496	
Baggeridge CP	Staffs	SO8992	51	Binton	Warks	SP1453	

Place	County	Grid Ref	Page	Place	County	Grid Ref	Page
Birchfield	W Mid	SP0690		Brund Hill	Staffs	SK0264	71
Birchmoor	Warks	SK2501		Buckpool/ Dingle	W Mid	SO8987	47
Birdingbury	Warks	SP4368		Budbrooke/ Barracks	Warks	SP2565	
Birlingham	Worcs	SO9343		Bulkington	Warks	SP3986	
Birmingham Airport	W Mid	SP1784		Burmington	Warks	SP2637	
Birmingham University	W Mid	SP0483		Burnt Wood	Staffs	SJ7433	61
Birmingham/ City Centre	W Mid	SP0686	57	Burslem	Staffs	SJ8749	
Bishampton	Worcs	SO9851		Burton Dassett Hills	Warks	SP3951	
Bishampton Vale Pool	Worcs	SP0050		Burton Hastings	Warks	SP4189	
Bishop's Hill	Warks	SP3958		Burton-on-Trent	Staffs	SK2423	
Bishop's Tachbrook	Warks	SP3161		Bushbury	W Mid	SJ9202	
Bishops Wood	Staffs	SJ7531		Byrkley Park	Staffs	SK1623	
Bittell Reservoir	Worcs	SP0174	55	Calcutt	Warks	SP4664	
Black Bank/ Hill	Staffs	SJ8147	67	Caldon Canal	Staffs	SJ95/SK04	65
Black Brook	Staffs	SK0064	71	Calf Heath	Staffs	SJ9309	
Black Firs & Cranberry Bog	Staffs	SJ7450	61	Calton	Staffs	SK1050	75
Black Heath/ Casey Bank	Staffs	SK0549	71	Cannock	Staffs	SJ9810	
Blackbrook Sewage Works	Staffs	SO8398		Cannock Chase	Staffs	SJ91/SK01	41/3
Blackbrook Valley	Staffs	SK0064	71	Cannock Tip	Staffs	SJ9909	
Blackmore Park	Worcs	SO7943		Captain's Pool	Worcs	SO8474	
Blakedown	Worcs	SO8878		Castern Wood	Staffs	SK1153	74
Blakeshall	Worcs	SO8381		Castle Hill, Dudley	W Mid	SO9490	
Bleak House	Staffs	SK0311	44	Castle Vale	W Mid	SP1491	
Blithe, River/ Valley	Staffs	SK02/03		Castlemorton Common	Worcs	SO7839	104
Blithfield Reservoir	Staffs	SK0623	78	Catholme	Staffs	SK2015	
Blythe Valley Business Park	W Mid	SP1475		Caunsall	Worcs	SO8680	
Blythe, River/ Valley	Wks/WM	SP28/17	55	Chad Brook	W Mid	SP0385	
Boarsgrove	Staffs	SK0462		Chadbury	Worcs	SP0246	
Bodymoor Heath	Warks	SP2095		Chaddesley Wood	Worcs	SO9073	54
Bordesley	W Mid	SP0886		Chadshunt	Warks	SP3452	
Bourne, River/ Valley	Warks	SP28/29		Chapel Ascote	Warks	SP4157	
Bow Wood	Worcs	SO9455		Chapel Green	Warks	SP4660	
Bowshot Wood	Warks	SP3053		Charlecote	Warks	SP2656	
Bradley Green	Worcs	SO9861		Charlecote Park	Warks	SP2556	106
Bradnock's Marsh	W Mid	SP2179		Chartley Moss	Staffs	SK0228	80
Brailes	Warks	SP3337		Chase End Hill/ Wood	Worcs	SO9073	
Bramcote	Warks	SP4088		Chasetown	Staffs	SK0408	
Brandon Hall	Warks	SP4076		Chasewater	Staffs	SK0307	45
Brandon Marsh	Warks	SP3875	93	Chateau Impney	Worcs	SO9164	
Branston	Staffs	SK2221		Cheadle	Staffs	SK0143	
Branston GC	Staffs	SK2320		Chell Heath	Staffs	SJ8852	
Branston GP/WP	Staffs	SK2120	85	Cherington	Warks	SP2936	
Bredon	Worcs	SO9136		Cheslyn Hay	Staffs	SJ9707	
Bredon Hill	Worcs	SO9139	96	Chesterton	Warks	SP3558	92
Bredon's Hardwick	Worcs	SO9135	101/3	Chesterton Wood	Warks	SP3457	
Bredon's Norton	Worcs	SO9339		Cheswick Green	W Mid	SP1275	
Brereton	Staffs	SK0516		Childswickham	Worcs	SP0738	
Brewood	Staffs	SJ8808		Chillington	Staffs	SJ8606	
Bridgtown	Staffs	SJ9708		Chillington Lower Avenue	Staffs	SJ8807	
Brierley Hill	W Mid	SO9187		Church Eaton	Staffs	SJ8317	
Broad Green	Worcs	SO7756		Church Lawford	Warks	SP4476	
Broadway	Worcs	SP0937		Church Lench	Worcs	SP0251	
Broadway Hill	Worcs	SP1136		Church Lench Pool	Worcs	SP0250	
Brocton	Staffs	SJ9619		Church Pool Covert	Warks	SP2092	
Brocton Coppice	Staffs	SJ9819	44	Churnet Valley	Staffs	SJ95/SK04	63/4
Brocton Field	Staffs	SJ9817		Claverdon	Warks	SP1964	
Bromford	W Mid	SP1390		Clay Mills	Staffs	SK2625	
Bromley Hurst	Staffs	SK0822		Clayhanger	W Mid	SK0404	
Bromsgrove	Worcs	SO9570		Clent	Worcs	SO9379	
Brookleys Lake	Staffs	SK0943	65	Clent Hills	Worcs	SO9380	57
Brookvale Park	W Mid	SP0991		Clifford Chambers	Warks	SP1952	
Brownhills	W Mid	SK0405		Clifton-upon-Teme	Worcs	SO7161	

Place	County	Grid Ref	Page	Place	County	Grid Ref	Page
Clowes Wood	Warks	SP0973	54	Doley Common	Staffs	SJ8121	
Cocknage Wood	Staffs	SJ9140		Dorridge	W Mid	SP1675	
Codsall	Staffs	SJ8603		Dosthill	Staffs	SK2100	
Cofton Hall Farm	Worcs	SP0175		Dosthill GP	Staffs	SP2099	
Cofton/ Reservoir	Worcs	SP0075		Dosthill Lake/ Pool	Warks	SP2098	84
Coldmeece	Staffs	SJ8532		Doulton's Claypit	W Mid	SO9387	45
Coldmeece Pools	Staffs	SJ8432		Dove, River/ Valley	Staffs	SK13/15	76
Coldridge Wood	Worcs	SO8082	50	Dovedale	Staffs	SK1452	
Cole, River/ Valley	Wks/WM	SP08/18	55	Dowles Brook	Worcs	SO77	50
Coleshill	Warks	SP2089		Doxey	Staffs	SJ9023	
Coleshill Gasworks (site of)	Warks	SP1990		Doxey Marshes	Staffs	SJ9024	62
Coleshill Woods	Warks	SP2086		Drakes Broughton	Worcs	SO9148	
Colwich	Staffs	SK0121		Draycote Meadows	Warks	SP4470	91
Compton Verney	Warks	SP3152		Draycote Water	Warks	SP4669	93
Compton Wynyates	Warks	SP3341		Drayton Bassett GP	Staffs	SP2099	84
Conderton	Worcs	SO9636		Drayton Field	Warks	SP1555	106
Consall	Staffs	SJ9748		Drayton Manor Park/ Zoo	Staffs	SK1901	
Consall Nature Park	Staffs	SJ9948	65	Droitwich (Spa)	Worcs	SO8963	
Consallforge	Staffs	SJ9949		Droitwich Canal	Worcs	SO86	104
Cookley	Worcs	SO8480		Dudley	W Mid	SO9490	
Coombe Abbey	Warks	SP4079	93	Dudley GC	W Mid	SO9688	
Coombes Valley	Staffs	SK0052	64	Dumbleton Dingle	Worcs	SP7069	112
Copmere	Staffs	SJ8029		Dunchurch	Warks	SP4871	
Copston Magna	Warks	SP4588		Dunhampstead	Worcs	SO9160	
Corley	Warks	SP3085		Dunstall Park/ Lake	W Mid	SJ9000	51
Cornets End	W Mid	SP2381		Dydon Wood	Staffs	SK1344	
Coseley	W Mid	SO9494		Eades Meadow	Worcs	SO9864	104
Cotes Heath	Staffs	SJ8335		Eardiston	Worcs	SO6968	
Coton Clanford	Staffs	SJ8723		Earlswood/ Lakes	Warks	SP1174	55
Coton Pools	Warks	SP2194	84	Eathorpe /Marsh	Warks	SP3868	
Coton-in-the-Clay	Staffs	SK1629		Eccleshall	Staffs	SJ8329	
Cotton Dell	Staffs	SK0545	65	Eckington	Worcs	SO9241	
Cotwall End	W Mid	SO9192		Edgbaston	W Mid	SP0584	
Coventry	W Mid	SP3378		Edgbaston Park/ Pool	W Mid	SP0584	56
Coventry Airport	Warks	SP3574		Edgbaston Reservoir	W Mid	SP0486	57
Cradley Heath	W Mid	SO9585		Edge Hill	Warks	SP3747	97
Cresswell	Staffs	SJ9739		Edingale	Staffs	SK2112	
Crews Hill Wood	Worcs	SO7353		Elford GP	Staffs	SK1809	
Croome Court/ Park	Worcs	SO8844		Elmley Castle	Worcs	SO9841	
Cropthorne	Worcs	SO9844		Enville	Staffs	SO8286	49
Crossplains	Staffs	SK1624		Etruria	Staffs	SJ8647	
Crowle	Worcs	SO9256		Ettington	Warks	SP2649	
Croxall GP/ Pool	Staffs	SK1914	85	Evesham	Worcs	SP0343	
Cuckoo Bank	Staffs	SK0310	44	Evesham, Vale of	Worcs	SP04/14	104
Curdworth	Warks	SP1892		Exhall (near Alcester)	Warks	SP1055	
Dane, River/ Valley	Staffs	SJ96/SK06	72	Exhall (near Coventry)	Warks	SP3384	
Danebridge	Staffs	SJ9665		Eymore Wood	Worcs	SO7779	50
Darlaston	W Mid	SO9697		Farnborough	Warks	SP4349	
Dassett Hills	Warks	SP5050		Farnborough Park	Warks	SP4249	97
Daw Mill Colliery	Warks	SP2689		Feckenham	Worcs	SP0061	
Deep Hayes CP	Staffs	SJ9653	65	Feckenham Wylde Moor	Worcs	SP0160	104
Deepfields	W Mid	SO9494		Fenny Compton	Warks	SP4152	
Deers Leap Wood	W Mid	SP0286		Fens Pools	W Mid	SO9188	47
Defford	Worcs	SO9143		Fenton	Staffs	SJ8944	
Dene, River/ Valley	Warks	SP25		Festival Park	Staffs	SJ8647	
Denford	Staffs	SJ9553		Fillongley	Warks	SP2887	
Denstone	Staffs	SK0940		Finham	Warks	SP3374	
Devil's Spittleful	Worcs	SO8875	49	Finstall	Worcs	SO9769	
Dick Brook	Worcs	SO76/86		Fisher's Mill GP	Warks	SP2098	84
Digbeth	W Mid	SP0786		Fisherwick	Staffs	SK1709	
DM Kineton	Warks	SP3651		Flash	Staffs	SK0267	
Dog Hanging Coppice	Worcs	SO7374		Foot's Hole	W Mid	SO9087	

Place	County	Grid Ref	Page	Place	County	Grid Ref	Page
Ford Green/ Marsh	Staffs	SJ8950	66	Haselor	Warks	SP1257	
Fordhouses	W Mid	SJ9002		Hatherton	Staffs	SJ9510	
Foster's Green	Worcs	SO9865	104	Hawkhurst Moor	Warks	SP2679	
Fowlea Brook	Staffs	SJ84		Hay Wood	Warks	SP2171	54
Fradley	Staffs	SK1513		Hayhead Wood	W Mid	SP0498	
Fradley Wood	Staffs	SK1313		Hazelstrine	Staffs	SJ9420	
Frankley	Worcs	SO9980		Hednesford	Staffs	SK0012	
Frankley Reservoir	W Mid	SP0080		Henley-in-Arden	Warks	SP1565	
Frog Hall GP	Warks	SP4173		Herefordshire Beacon (part)	Worcs	SP7639	
Fullmoor Wood	Staffs	SJ9411		Hewell Grange	Worcs	SP0069	
Furnace End	Warks	SP2491		High Cross	Warks	SP4788	
Gadbury Bank	Worcs	SO7931		High Green	Worcs	SO8645	
Gailey Reservoir	Staffs	SJ9310		High Offley	Staffs	SJ7826	61
Gaydon	Warks	SP3654		Highgate Common	Staffs	SO8389	49
German Cemetery	Staffs	SJ9815		Hillmorton	Warks	SP5373	
Gib Torr	Staffs	SK0264	71	Himbleton	Worcs	SO9458	
Gnosall	Staffs	SJ8220		Himley/ Hall	Staffs	SO8891	51
Goldsitch Moss	Staffs	SK0164		Hinton-on-the-Green	Worcs	SP0240	
Goosehill Wood	Worcs	SO9360		Hixon	Staffs	SK0025	
Goscote Valley	W Mid	SK0102		Hixon Airfield	Staffs	SJ9926	
Gradbach Hill	Staffs	SJ9965	72	Hoar Cross	Staffs	SK1223	
Grafton Wood	Worcs	SO9756	105	Hockley	Staffs	SK2200	
Grandborough	Warks	SP4965		Hockley	W Mid	SP0588	
Great Haywood	Staffs	SJ9922		Hockley Heath	W Mid	SP1572	
Great Malvern	Worcs	SO7745		Hodnell	Warks	SP4257	
Great Witley	Worcs	SO7566		Holly Bush			
Great Wyrley	Staffs	SO7566		(Hollybush)/ Lake	Staffs	SK1326	
Greenway Bank CP	Staffs	SJ8855	65	Hollywood	Worcs	SP0777	
Grendon	Warks	SP2799		Holt Fleet	Worcs	SO8263	
Grimley	Worcs	SO8360	102	Holt Heath	Worcs	SO8163	
Grove End	W Mid	SP1695		Holt/ GP	Worcs	SO8262	102
Gullet, The	Worcs	SO7638		Honeybourne	Worcs	SP1143	
Gun Hill	Staffs	SJ9761		Hopwas/ Hays Wood	Staffs	SK1705	86
Gwen Finch NR	Worcs	SO9341	102	Hornhill Coppice/ Wood	Worcs	SO9558	
Habberley Valley	Worcs	SO8078	49	Horsepasture Covert	Staffs	SK0413	44
Hagley	Worcs	SO9180		Hulme End	Staffs	SK1059	
Halfpenny Green	Staffs	SO8291		Hunthouse Wood	Worcs	SO7070	112
Hallow	Worcs	SO8258		Hydes Road Pool	W Mid	SO9994	
Hamps, River/ Valley	Staffs	SK05		Ilam	Staffs	SK1350	
Hampton Lucy	Warks	SP2557		Ilmington	Warks	SP2143	
Hampton Valley	Staffs	SO8485		Ilmington Downs	Warks	SP1942	
Hampton-in-Arden	W Mid	SP2080		Ipstones	Staffs	SK0249	
Hams Hall	Warks	SP2091		Ipstones Edge	Staffs	SK0251	
Hamstall Ridware	Staffs	SK1019		Island Pool (Islandpool)	Worcs	SO8580	
Hanbury	Staffs	SJ9661		Itchen, River/ Valley	Warks	SP35/46	
Hanchurch	Staffs	SJ8441		Jackson's Bank	Staffs	SK1423	
Hanchurch Hills	Staffs	SJ8340	61	Jackson's Coppice & Marsh	Staffs	SJ7830	61
Hanchurch Water Tower	Staffs	SJ8439		Jewellery Quarter	W Mid	SP0687	
Handsacre/ Flash	Staffs	SK0915		Jubilee Pools	Warks	SP3873	
Handsworth/ Park	W Mid	SP0590		Judkins Quarry	Warks	SP3492	
Hanley	Staffs	SJ8847		Katyn Memorial	Staffs	SJ9816	
Hanley Dingle	Worcs	SO6866	112	Keele	Staffs	SJ8045	
Hanley Forest Park	Staffs	SJ8848		Kemerton/ Pool	Worcs	SO9437	102
Happy Valley	Worcs	SO7645		Kempsey	Worcs	SO8549	
Harborne	W Mid	SP0284		Kempsey Lower Ham/ SW	Worcs	SO8448	
Harborne NR	W Mid	SP0285	57	Kenilworth	Warks	SP2971	
Harborne Walkway	W Mid	SP0385/6	57	Kidderminster	Worcs	SO8376	
Harbury	Warks	SP3760		Kidsgrove	Staffs	SJ8354	
Harston Wood	Staffs	SK0347	65	Kineton	Warks	SP3351	
Hartlebury	Worcs	SO8470		Kings Bromley	Staffs	SK1216	
Hartlebury Common	Worcs	SO8270	49	King's Norton	W Mid	SP0478	
Haseley	Warks	SP2368		Kings Wood	Staffs	SJ8639	66

Place	County	Grid Ref	Page	Place	County	Grid Ref	Page
Kingsbury	Warks	SP2196		Lordsley	Staffs	SJ7437	
Kingsbury Rifle Range	Warks	SP2296		Lower Gailey	Staffs	SJ9310	
Kingsbury Water Park	Warks	SP2097	84	Lower Kempsey	Worcs	SO8448	
Kingsbury Wood	Warks	SP2397		Lower Moor	Worcs	SO9847	
Kingsford/ CP	Worcs	SO8281		Lower Radbourne	Warks	SP4456	
Kingstanding	W Mid	SP0794		Lower Smite Farm	Worcs	SO8858	
Kingswinford	W Mid	SO8888		Loxley	Warks	SP2552	
Kingswood Bank	Staffs	SJ8540	66	Loxley Green	Staffs	SK0630	
Kinsham	Worcs	SO9335	102	Loynton Moss	Staffs	SJ7824	60
Kinver/ Edge	Staffs	SO8383	49	Lutley Gutter	W Mid	SO9584	
Knapp, The & Papermill NR	Worcs	SO7451	112	Lutley Wedge	W Mid	SO9483	58
Knavenhill	Warks	SP2449		Lydiate Ash	Worcs	SP9775	
Knightcote	Warks	SP4055		Lyme Valley Park	Staffs	SJ8544	
Knighton Reservoir	Staffs	SJ7328		Lymedale (Business) Park	Staffs	SJ8348	
Knightwick	Worcs	SO7355		Lynall's Coppice	Worcs	SO7375	
Knotbury	Staffs	SK0168		Madeley Heath	Worcs	SO9577	
Knowle	W Mid	SP1876		Maer Hills	Staffs	SJ7739	61
Knowles Coppice	Worcs	SO7676		Maer/ Pool	Staffs	SJ7938	
Knypersley Reservoir	Staffs	SJ8955	65	Majors Green	Worcs	SP1077	
Kyre	Worcs	SO6263		Malvern	Worcs	SO7745	
Kyre Pool	Worcs	SO6364		Malvern Hills/ The Malverns	Worcs	SO73/74	107/8
Ladbroke	Warks	SP4158		Malvern Link	Worcs	SO7847	
Ladywalk NR	Warks	SP2191	83	Malvern Wells	Worcs	SO7742	
Ladywood	W Mid	SP0586		Manifold, River/ Valley	Staffs	SK05/15	74
Langdale Wood	Worcs	SO7943		Marquis Drive Visitor Centre	Staffs	SK0015	
Larford	Worcs	SO8169		Marsh Lane GP/ NR	W Mid	SP2180	55
Lawford Heath Tip	Warks	SP4473		Marston Green	W Mid	SP1781	
Lea Marston/ Pools	Warks	SP2093	84	Martin Hussingtree	Worcs	SO8860	
Leacroft	Staffs	SJ9909		Marton	Warks	SP4068	
Leam, River/ Valley	Warks	SP36/46		Maxstoke	Warks	SP2386	
Leamington Hastings	Warks	SP4467		Mease, River/ Valley	Staffs	SK11/21	
Leamington Spa	Warks	SP3165		Meerbrook	Staffs	SJ9960	
Leamington Spa Reservoir	Warks	SP3365		Meon Hill	Warks	SP1745	
Leasowes, The	W Mid	SO9783		Merevale/ Park	Warks	SP2997	54
Leek	Staffs	SJ9856		Meriden	W Mid	SP2481	
Leek Wootton	Warks	SP2868		Merry Hill Shopping Centre	W Mid	SO9287	
Leigh Brook	Worcs	SO7652	111	Middle Tame Valley	Staf/Wks	SK20/SP29	83
Lenches, The	Worcs	SP0251		Middleton	Warks	SP1798	
Lenchwick	Worcs	SP0347		Middleton Hall	Warks	SP1998	
Lichfield	Staffs	SK1109		Midsummer Hill	Worcs	SO7637	
Lickey/ Hills/ Woods	Worcs	SO9975	54/8	Milcote	Warks	SP1852	
Lighthorne	Warks	SP3355		Milford	Staffs	SJ9721	
Lighthorne Quarry	Warks	SP3456	92	Mill Pond	Worcs	SO7737	
Lindridge	Worcs	SO6769		Milldale	Staffs	SK1354	
Lineholt	Worcs	SO8166		Million Wood/ Plantation	Staffs	SO8486	
Little Aston	Staffs	SK0900		Minworth/ Sewage Works	W Mid	SP1592	
Little Comberton	Worcs	SO9643		Moat Hill	Staffs	?	
Little Malvern	Worcs	SO7640		Moneymore GP	Staffs	SK1302	
Little Stoke	Staffs	SJ9132		Monks Park	Warks	SP2996	54
Little Wyrley	Staffs	SK0105		Monkspath	W Mid	SP1474	
Littleton	Worcs	SP0746		Monkwood	Worcs	SO8060	105
Lodge Hill Farm	Worcs	SO7576		Mons Hill	W Mid	SO9392	47
Long Bank	Worcs	SO7674		Moreton Morrell	Warks	SP3155	92
Long Compton	Warks	SP2832		Morridge	Staffs	SK0257	
Long Itchington	Warks	SP4165		Moseley	W Mid	SP0783	
Long Lawford	Warks	SP4776		Mottey Meadows	Staffs	SJ8313	61
Longbridge	W Mid	SP0077		Mount Segg	Worcs	SO8675	
Longdon	Staffs	SK0814		Mow Cop	Staffs	SJ8557	
Longdon Marsh	Worcs	SO8236	101	Musden Low	Staffs	SK1150	
Longsdon Marsh	Staffs	SJ9655		Mushroom Green Marsh	W Mid	SO9386	
Longsdon Mill/ Pool	Staffs	SJ9555		Mythe Bridge	Worcs	SO8833	
Longton	Staffs	SJ9043		Nafford	Worcs	SO9441	101

Place	County	Grid Ref	Page	Place	County	Grid Ref	Page
Napton	Warks	SP4661		Patshull Hall	Staffs	SJ8000	
Napton Hill	Warks	SP4561		Pedmore	W Mid	SO9182	
Napton Reservoir	Warks	SP4759		Pelsall	W Mid	SK0203	
Nash End	Worcs	SO7781		Pelsall (Nth.) Com./ Wood	W Mid	SK0103	
National Exhibition Centre	W Mid	SP1983		Pendeford Mill NR	Staffs	SJ8904	
National Mem. Arboretum	Staffs	SK1814		Penk, River/ Valley	Staffs	SJ91/92	
Naunton Beauchamp	Worcs	SO9652	106	Penkridge	Staffs	SJ9214	
Nebsworth/ Hill	Warks	SP1942		Penn	W Mid	SO8996	
Nechells	W Mid	SP0989		Perry Hall	W Mid	SP0591	
Needwood	Staffs	SK1824		Pershore	Worcs	SO9045	
Needwood Airfield	Staffs	SK1624		Perton	Staffs	SO8598	
Needwood Forest	Staffs	SK12	77	Piccadilly	Warks	SP2298	
Nether Whitacre	Warks	SP2392		Pillaton	Staffs	SJ9413	
Netherton	W Mid	SO9488		Pipers Hill (Common)	Worcs	SO9565	
Netherton Hill	W Mid	SO9388		Pirton/ Pool	Worcs	SO8747	
Netherton Reservoir	W Mid	SO9387		Polesworth	Warks	SK2602	
New Fallings Coppice	Warks	SP1074	54	Pool Dam Marsh	Staffs	SJ8346	
Newbold Comyn	Warks	SP3365		Porthill	Staffs	SJ8548	
Newbold Quarry	Staffs	SK2019		Powick	Worcs	SO8351	
Newborough	Staffs	SK1325		Princethorpe	Warks	SP4070	
Newcastle-under-Lyme	Staffs	SJ8445		Priors Hardwick	Warks	SP4756	
Newnham	Worcs	SO6468		Priors Marston	Warks	SP4957	
Norbury	Staffs	SK1242		Pype Hayes Hall/ Park	W Mid	SP1392	
North Hill	Worcs	SO7646		Queslett Tip/ NP	W Mid	SP0694	
North Littleton	Worcs	SP0847		Quinton	Warks	SP1747	
North Staffs Moors	Staffs	SJ96/SK06	69	Radway	Warks	SP3748	
Northend	Warks	SP3952		Raggedstone Hill	Worcs	SO7536	
Northfield	W Mid	SP0279		Ramshaw Rocks	Staffs	SK0162	
Northwick Marsh	Worcs	SO8357		Randan Wood	Worcs	SO9272	54
Norton	Worcs	SP0447		Ratley	Warks	SP3847	
Nuneaton	Warks	SP3691		Rea, River	Worcs	SO66/67	
Nunnery Wood	Worcs	SO8754		Red Hill	Warks	SP1356	
Oakley Wood	Warks	SP3059		Redditch	Worcs	SP0467	
Oakley/ Pool	Worcs	SO8960		Ribbesford Wood	Worcs	SO7872	50
Oakwood Pasture	Staffs	SK1621	80	Rickerscote	Staffs	SJ9320	
Ocker Hill	W Mid	SO9793		Ripple	Worcs	SO8736	
Ockeridge Wood	Worcs	SO7962	105	Roach End	Staffs	SJ9964	
Oddingley	Worcs	SO9159		Roaches, The	Staffs	SK0063	70
Offchurch	Warks	SP3565		Rocester	Staffs	SK1139	
Offenham Cross	Worcs	SP0645		Rocester, JCB Pool	Staffs	SK1039	
Old Hills Common	Worcs	SO8246		Rock Wood	Worcs	SO7163	50
Old Nun Wood	Warks	SP3870	91	Rod Wood	Staffs	SJ9953	65
Old Storridge	Worcs	SO7451		Rolleston-on-Dove	Staffs	SK2427	
Oldacre Valley	Staffs	SJ9718		Rough Hay	Staffs	SK2023	
Oldbury	W Mid	SO9889		Rough Hills	W Mid	SO9296	
Oldington	Worcs	SO8274		Rous Lench	Worcs	SP0153	
Oliver Hill	Staffs	SK0267		Rowley Regis	W Mid	SO9687	
Olton	W Mid	SP1382		Rudyard Reservoir	Staffs	SJ9459	65
Olton Mere/ Reservoir	W Mid	SP1381		Rugby	Warks	SP5175	
Ombersley	Worcs	SO8463		Rugeley	Staffs	SK0418	
Overbury	Worcs	SO9537		Rushall	W Mid	SK0201	47
Oversley Wood	Warks	SP1056		Rushton Spencer	Staffs	SJ9362	
Packington/ Park	Warks	SP2284	54	Ryall/ GP	Worcs	SO8639	102
Packington Ford	Warks	SP2185		Ryton Pools CP	Warks	SP3772	93
Packington GP/ Tip	Warks	SP2085		Ryton Wood	Warks	SP3872	90
Packington Hall/ Great Pool	Warks	SP2283		Ryton-on-Dunsmore	Warks	SP3874	
Packwood House	Warks	SP1772	54	Sale Green	Worcs	SO9358	
Pailton	Warks	SP4781		Salford Bridge	W Mid	SP0990	
Park Banks	Staffs	SK0742		Salford Coppice	Warks	SP0451	
Park Hall CP	Staffs	SJ9244	66	Salford Priors GP	Warks	SP0752	102
Park Lime Pits	W Mid	SP0299		Saltley	W Mid	SP0987	
Pasturefields Saltmarsh	Staffs	SJ9924	78	Saltwells LNR/ Wood	W Mid	SO9387	45

Place	County	Grid Ref	Page	Place	County	Grid Ref	Page
Salwarpe, River/ Valley	Worcs	SO86/96		Stepping Stones	Staffs	SJ9820	
Sandwell GC	W Mid	SP0200		Stoke Bliss	Worcs	SO6562	
Sandwell Valley	W Mid	SP0291	46	Stoke Floods	W Mid	SP3778	56
Saredon	Staffs	SJ9407		Stoke Prior	Worcs	SO9467	
Scounslow Green	Staffs	SK0929		Stoke-on-Trent	Staffs	SJ8745	
Seabridge	Staffs	SJ8343		Stone	Staffs	SJ9034	
Seckington	Warks	SK2607		Stone	Worcs	SO8575	
Seeswood Pool	Warks	SP3290		Stoneleigh	Warks	SP3732	
Seighford	Staffs	SJ8824		Stoneleigh Park	Warks	SP3171	54
Selly Oak	W Mid	SP0482		Storridge Common (Old)	Worcs	SO7451	
Selly Park	W Mid	SP0582		Stour, River/ Valley	Warks	SP23/24/25	
Seven Springs	Staffs	SK0020	44	Stour, River/ Valley	Wor/Staf/WM	SO87	50
Severn Stoke	Worcs	SO8544		Stourbridge	W Mid	SO8983	
Severn, River/ Valley	Worcs		99	Stourport-on-Severn	Worcs	SO8171	
Shard End	W Mid	SP8815		Stourvale Marsh	Worcs	SO8277	
Shawbury	Warks	SP2588		Stratford-upon-Avon	Warks	SP2055	
Shebdon	Staffs	SJ7625		Strensham	Worcs	SO9139	
Sheepwalks	Staffs	SO8185	50	Stretton Hall	Staffs	SJ8811	
Sheepwash UP	W Mid	SO9791	47	Stretton-on-Fosse	Warks	SP2238	
Sheldon	W Mid	SP1483		Stubbers Green	W Mid	SK0401	
Shelfheld	Worcs	SO7575		Studley	Warks	SP0763	
Shelsley Walsh	Worcs	SO7263		Suckley	Worcs	SO7251	
Shenstone	Staffs	SK1004		Suckley Hills/ Wood	Worcs	SO7351	
Sherbourne	Warks	SP2661		Sudbury, near	Staffs	SK1531	
Sherbrook Valley	Staffs	SJ9818	44	Sugnall	Staffs	SJ7930	
Sheriffs Lench	Worcs	SP0249		Summerfield	Worcs	SO8473	
Shipston-on-Stour	Warks	SP2640		Sutton Coldfield	W Mid	SP1296	
Shirley	W Mid	SP1279		Sutton Park	W Mid	SP0997	44
Shortwood Roughs	Worcs	SP0270		Swallow Moss	Staffs	SK0660	70
Shotteswell	Warks	SP4245		Swarbourn, River/ Valley	Staffs	SK11/12	
Shrawley Wood	Worcs	SO8066	105	Swift, River/ Valley	Warks	SP57/58	
Shropshire Union Canal	Staffs	SJ80/81/72		Swineholes Wood	Staffs	SK0450	71
Shuckburgh Hills/ Park	Warks	SP4961		Swinfen	Staffs	SK1306	
Shugborough/ Hall	Staffs	SJ9922		Swythamley	Staffs	SJ9764	
Shustoke	Warks	SP2290		Sych Wood	Warks	SP2092	
Shustoke Reservoir	Warks	SP2291	93	Tame River/ Valley	Staf/Wks/WM		81
Silverdale Colliery	Staffs	SJ8146		Tamworth	Staffs	SK2003	
Sling Pool	Worcs	SO9477		Tardebigge	Worcs	SO9868	
Small Heath	W Mid	SP0985		Tatenhill	Staffs	SK1624	
Smestow Valley	W Mid	SO8899	51	Tean, River/ Valley	Staffs	SK2022	
Smethwick	W Mid	SP0288		Teddesley Park	Staffs	SJ9515	
Snow Hill Station, B'ham	W Mid	SP0687		Teme, River/ Valley	Worcs	SO66/76	107/11
Solihull	W Mid	SP1579		Tenbury Wells	Worcs	SO5968	
Solihull Lodge	W Mid	SP0978		Tettenhall/ Ridge	W Mid	SJ8800	
Somers, The	Warks	SP2282		Tewkesbury, near	Worcs	SO8833	
Southam	Warks	SP4162		Thickbroom	Staffs	SK1203	
Southcrest	Worcs	SP0366		Thicknall	Worcs	SO9079	
Sow, River/ Valley	Staffs	SJ73/82/92		Thorpe Cloud, Derbys		SK1551	
Sowe, River/ Valley	Wks/WM	SP37/38	56	Three Shires Head	Staffs	SK0068	
Spaghetti Junction	W Mid	SP0990		Throckmorton	Worcs	SO9849	
Spernall Ash	Warks	SP0762		Throckmorton Tip	Worcs	SO9748	
Spetchley	Worcs	SO8953		Thurlaston	Warks	SP4671	
Springslade	Staffs	SJ9716		Tibberton	Worcs	SO9057	
Springslade Pool	Staffs	SJ9616		Timberhonger	Worcs	SO9170	
Stafford	Staffs	SJ9223		Tipton	W Mid	SO9592	
Staffs & Worcs Canal	Staf/WM/Wor	SO89		Tittensor	Staffs	SJ8738	
Stanford Bridge	Worcs	SO7165		Tittesworth Reservoir	Staffs	SJ9959	72
Stanley Pool	Staffs	SJ9351		Tividale	W Mid	SO9790	
Stansley Wood	Staffs	SK0524	78	Tixall	Staffs	SJ9722	
Stanton Dale	Staffs	SK1048		Tolladine GC	Worcs	SO8757	
Stapenhill	Staffs	SK2522		Trench Wood	Worcs	SO9258	105
Starts Green	Staf/ Wor	SO8083		Trent, River/ Valley	Staffs		81

Bibliography

Allsopp K. and Dawson I. 1988. March reports. *Brit. Birds* 81: 347-351.

Amphlett J. and Rea C. 1909 (republished 1978). *The Botany of Worcestershire*. EP Publishing Ltd., Wakefield.

Anon. Undated. Staffordshire Wildlife Trust: *Nature Reserve Guide*. Staffordshire Wildlife Trust, Sandon, Stafford.

Atkinson P., Conway G., Fuller R. and Vickery J. 2004. Grassland management and bird food resources. *BTO News* 250: 16-17.

Austin G. 2001. Estimating naturalised goose numbers … … precisely! *BTO News* 237: 8-9.

Baskerville N. B. 1992. Nightjars of Cannock Chase. *WMBC Annual Report* 58: 20-27.

Batten L. A., Bibby C. J., Clement P., Elliott G. D. and Porter R. F. 1990. *Red Data Birds in Britain*. T & A. D. Poyser, London.

Beebee T. J. C. and Griffiths R. A. 2000. *Amphibians and Reptiles*. The New Naturalists No 87. Harper Collins, London.

Bennett J. S., Welch S. and Jennett R. J. 2002. *The Breeding Birds of Cannock Chase in 2002*. West Midland Bird Club, Staffordshire Branch.

Bird Reports (mostly annual):
Banbury Ornithological Society Annual Report.
Belvide Reservoir Nature Reserve Annual Report. WMBC, Studley.
Brandon Marsh Nature Reserve Report. Warwickshire Wildlife Trust, Coventry.
Ladywalk Nature Reserve Annual Report. WMBC, Studley.
Birds on the Malvern Hills and Commons. (see Parr D): (covering 1986-95 and 2003).
Upton Warren Bird Report. J. T. Belsey and M. I. Wakeman.
WMBC Annual Reports 1934-2002. WMBC, Studley.

Blamey M., Fitter R. and Fitter A. 2003. *Wild Flowers of Britain and Ireland*. A & C Black, London.

Bourne W. R. P. 1970. Field characters and British status of Mediterranean Gulls. *Brit. Birds* 63: 91-93.

Breeding Atlas. Gibbons D. W., Reid J. B. and Chapman R. A. (Eds). 1993. *The New Atlas of Breeding Birds in Britain and Ireland: 1988-1991*. T. & A. D. Poyser, London.

Brindley E., Lucas F. and Waterhouse M. 1992. *North Staffordshire Moors Survey 1992*. RSPB report, RSPB Midlands Office, Droitwich.

Brit. Birds. 1997. *List of Birds of the Western Palearctic*. British Birds, Bedford.

Brit. Birds (Eds). 2004. The British List of English names for Western Palearctic birds. *British Birds* 97: 2-5.

Brown L. 1976. *British Birds of Prey*. The New Naturalist No 60: Collins, London.

Brown S. C. 1994. Intended predation of Lesser Spotted woodpecker nestlings by Great Spotted Woodpecker. *Brit. Birds* 87: 274-275.

Brown S. C. and Skeates R. W. 2003. An Orchard of Fieldfare? *WMBC Annual Report* 68: 222-224.

Buczacki S. 2002. *Fauna Britannica*. Hamlyn, London.

Busse P. 1969. Results of ringing European *Corvidae*. *Acta. Orn. Warsz.* X1 8: 263-328.

BWM. Harrison G. R., Dean A. R., Richards A. J. and Smallshire D. 1982. *The Birds of the West Midlands*. West Midland Bird Club, Studley.

BWP. Cramp S. *et al*. (Eds). 1977-1994. *Handbook of the Birds of Europe, the Middle East and North Africa: The Birds of the Western Palearctic*. Vols I-IX. Oxford University Press, Oxford.

Cadbury D. A., Hawkes J. G. and Readett R. C. 1971. *A Computer-mapped Flora: a study of the county of Warwickshire*. Academic Press, London.

Central Science Laboratory 2002. *UK Ruddy Duck control trial final report*. Report to the Department for Environment, Food and Rural Affairs.

Character Area. Countryside Agency 1999. *Countryside Character Volume 5: West Midlands. The character of England's natural and man-made landscape*. Countryside Agency, Cheltenham.

Chinery M. 1976 (2nd edition). *A Field Guide to the Insects of Britain and Northern Europe*. Collins, London.

Christie D. A. 1975. October reports. *Brit. Birds* 68: 86.

Clarkson J. 1988. Caring for the Cole Valley. *WMBC Annual Report* 55: 27-32.

Clements J. F. 2000. *Birds of the World—A Check List*. (5th edition). Ibis, USA.

Clements R. 2001. The Hobby in Britain: a new population estimate. *Brit. Birds* 94: 402-408.

Clifton D., Coleman J. T. and Coleman A. E. 2001. A preliminary analysis of Canada Goose *Branta canadensis* movements from the West Midlands. *WMBC Annual Report*: 68: 213-216.

Coleman A. E. 1987. Movement of (Common) Chaffinches and (Lesser) Redpolls to and from the West Midlands. *WMBC Annual Report*: 54: 40-45.

Coleman A. E. 2002. Ringing Notes. *WMBC Bulletin* 414: 5.

Coleman A. E. 2004. Barn Owl Monitoring Programme. *WMBC Bulletin* 421: 7.

Coleman A. E. and Coleman J. T. 1994. Movements of Grey Heron to and from the WMBC area with special reference to breeding success at the Gailey Heronry during 1960-70 and 1980-90. *WMBC Annual Report*: 61: 20-24.

Coleman A. E., Coleman J. T. and Clifton T. 1998. Population trends in three south Staffordshire Mute Swan herds. *WMBC Annual Report*: 65: 33-36.

Coleman J. 2002. Barn Owl nest box scheme in Staffordshire. *WMBC Bulletin* 413: 14-15.

Coulson J. C, Monaghan P., Butterfield J. E. L., Duncan N., Ensor K., Shedden C. and Thomas C. 1984.

Scandinavian Herring Gulls wintering in Britain. *Ornis Scand.* 15: 79-88.

Countryside Agency 1999. *Countryside Character Volume 5: West Midlands. The character of England's natural and man-made landscape.* Countryside Agency, Cheltenham.

Countryside Agency. 2000. *The state of the countryside 2000: The West Midlands.* Countryside Agency, Wetherby, West Yorkshire

Craddock B. and Dedicoat P. 2001. (European) Nightjars on Cannock Chase—year 2000. *WMBC Annual Report* 67: 210-212.

Craddock B. and Lawson B. D. 1980. (European) Nightjars of Cannock Chase, 1976. (unpubl.) but summarised in *BTO News* 111-2.

Cramp S. *et al.* (Eds). 1977-1994. *Handbook of the Birds of Europe, the Middle East and North Africa: The Birds of the Western Palearctic.* Vols I-IX. Oxford University Press, Oxford.

Crick H. 1999. Global Warming and Early Birds. *BTO News* 223: 2-3.

Davies, M. 1988. The importance of Britain's Twites. *RSPB Conservation Review* 2: 91-94.

Dawson I. and Allsopp K. 1994. The Ornithological Year 1993. *Brit. Birds* 87: 457.

Dean A. R. 1973. The Rookeries of Warwickshire, Worcestershire and Staffordshire. *WMBC Annual Report* 40: 11-21.

Dean A. R. 1982. A Profile of Blithfield Reservoir. *WMBC Annual Report* 49: 14-22.

Dean A. R. 1987. Seasonality of Herring Gulls in the West Midlands. *Brit. Birds* 80: 632-633.

Dean A. R. 1988. Status of Mediterranean Gull *Larus melanocephalus* in the West Midlands Region. *WMBC Annual Report* 55: 34-39.

Dean A. R. 1988. Herring Gulls, Glaucous Gulls and gulls in-between. *WMBC Annual Report* 55: 32-34.

Dean A. R. 1989. Wintering *Aythya* ducks at Coton and Lea Marston . *WMBC Annual Report* 56: 31-39.

Dean A. R. 2002. Caspian Gull *L. (a.) cachinnans* at Bartley and Frankley Reservoirs. *WMBC Annual Report* 67: 215-218.

Dean A. R. 2005. Status of Yellow-legged Gull *Larus michahellis* in the West Midlands region. *WMBC Annual Report* 69: 234-249.

Dean A. R., Fortey J. E. and Phillips E. G. 1977. White-tailed Plover: new to Britain and Ireland. *Brit. Birds* 70: 465-471.

DETR 1998. *Sustainability Counts.* Department of the Environment, Transport and Regions, London.

DoE 1994a. *Sustainable Development: The UK Strategy.* Department of the Environment. HMSO, London.

DoE 1994b. *Biodiversity: The UK Action Plan.* Department of the Environment. HMSO, London.

DoE 1994c. *Climate Change: The UK Programme.* Department of the Environment. HMSO, London.

DoE 1994d. *Sustainable Forestry: The UK Programme.* Department of the Environment. HMSO, London.

Donald P. F., Wilson J. D. and Shepherd M. 1994. The decline of the Corn Bunting. *Brit. Birds* 87: 106-132.

Dymond J. N., Fraser P. A. and Gantlett S. J. M. 1989. *Rare Birds in Britain and Ireland.* T. & A. D. Poyser Ltd, Calton.

Easterbrook T. G. (Ed). 1983. *Birds of the Banbury Area 1972-1981.* Banbury Ornithological Society, Banbury.

Edees E. S. 1972. *Flora of Staffordshire: flowering plants and ferns.* David and Charles, Newton Abbot.

Elkins N. 1988. *Weather and Bird Behaviour.* Poyser, Calton.

Emley D. W. and Low W. J. 1982. The Birds of Westport Lake. *Staffordshire Biological Recording Scheme, Publication No 9.* Stafford.

English Nature. 1998. *Natural Areas. Nature conservation in context.* (CD-ROM). Version 1.1. Peterborough: English Nature. Available from: www. english-nature.org.uk

Evans I. M. & M. W. Pienkowski, 1991. World Status of the Red Kite: A background to the experimental reintroduction to England and Scotland. *Brit. Birds* 84: 171-187.

Evans K. L. and Robinson R. A. 2004. Barn Swallows and agriculture. *Brit. Birds* 97: 218-230.

Ferguson-Lees I. J. 1971. Studies of less familiar birds 164, Wood Sandpiper. *Brit. Birds* 64: 114-117.

Fitter R. and Fitter A. 1984. *Collins Guide to the Grasses, Sedges, Rushes and Ferns of Britain and Northern Europe.* Collins, London.

Flegg J. 1981. Swifts on the wing. *The Living Countryside* 2: 349-351.

Forbes P., Hackett P. and Hextell T. 2000. *Birds of the Sandwell Valley.* Sandwell Valley Naturalists' Club, Sandwell.

Forestry Commission 2002. *National Inventory of Woodland and Trees: County Reports for Hereford-Worcester, Staffordshire, Warwickshire and West Midlands.* Forestry Commission, Edinburgh.

Fraser P. A. and M. J. Rogers 2003. Report on scarce migrant birds in Britain in 2001. *Brit. Birds* 96: 626-649.

Fraser P. A. and Rogers M. J. 2004. Report on scarce migrant birds in Britain in 2002. *Brit. Birds* 97: 647-664.

Frost R. A. 1978. *The Birds of Derbyshire.* Moorland Publishing Company, Buxton.

Fuller R. J. 1982. *Bird Habitats in Britain.* T. & A. D. Poyser, Calton.

Fuller R. 2004. Why are woodland birds declining? *BTO News* 253: 5-7.

Garcia E. F. J. 1983. An experimental test of competition for space between Blackcaps *Sylvia atricapilla* and Garden Warblers *Sylvia borin* in the breeding season. *J. of Anim. Ecol.* 52: 795-805.

Garner M. 1997. Identification of Yellow-legged Gulls in Britain. *Brit. Birds* 90: 25-62.

Garner M., Quinn D. and Glover B. 1997. Identification of Yellow-legged Gulls in Britain, Part 2. *Brit. Birds* 90: 369-383.

Garner R. 1844. *Natural History of the County of Staf-*

ford, with supplement 1860. London.

Gibbons D. W., Reid J. B. and Chapman R. A. (Eds). 1993. *The New Atlas of Breeding Birds in Britain and Ireland: 1988-1991*. T. & A. D. Poyser, London.

Gillham E., Harrison J. M. and Harrison J. G. 1966. A study of certain *Aythya* hybrids. *The Wildfowl Trust 17th Annual Report*: 49-65.

Gillham E. and Gillham B. 2002. *Hybrid Ducks*. B. L. Gillham, Bury St. Edmunds.

Glue D. 2003. Late finishes and early starters. *BTO News*. 246: 6.

Glue D. E. and Morgan R. 1972. Cuckoo hosts in British habitats. *Bird Study* 19: 187-192.

Gooch S., Baillie S. and Birkhead T. R. 1991. The impact of Magpies *Pica pica* on songbird populations. Retrospective investigation of trends in population density and breeding success. *J. Applied Ecology* 28: 1068-1086.

Green G. H. 1995. *A Year in the Life of Worcestershire's Nature Reserves*. Pices Publications, Nature Conservation Bureau Ltd., Newbury.

Green G. H. and Westwood B. 1991. *The Nature of Worcestershire. The Wildlife and Ecology of the old County of Worcestershire*. Barracuda Books Ltd., Buckingham.

Gregory R. D., Wilkinson N. I., Noble D. G., Robinson J. A., Brown A. F., Hughes J., Procter D., Gibbons D. W. and Galbraith C. A. 2002. The population status of birds in the United Kingdom, Channel Islands and Isle of Man: an analysis of conservation concern 2002-2007. *Brit. Birds* 95: 410-448.

Gribble F. C. 1983. (European) Nightjars in Britain and Ireland in 1981. *Bird Study* 30: 165-176.

Gribble F. C. 1993. Survey of Breeding Waders of Lowland Wet Meadows in Central Staffordshire 1993. *WMBC Annual Report*. 60: 21-25.

Gribble F. C. 2000 Changes affecting Staffordshire's Breeding Birds from 1800 to 2000. *WMBC Annual Report* 67: 14-37.

Gribble F. C. and Jennett R. 1998. Survey of Breeding Waders in Staffordshire. *WMBC Annual Report* 65: 11-15.

Haapanen, A. 1965, 1966. Bird fauna of the Finnish forests in relation to forest succession. *Ann. Zool. fenn*. 2: 153-196; 3: 176-200.

Hale W. G. 1980. *Waders*. The New Naturalist No 65: Collins, London.

Handbook, The. Witherby, H. F., Jourdain, Rev. F. C. R., Ticehurst N. F. and Tucker, B. W. 1938-41, reprinted with revisions 1943-44. *The Handbook of British Birds*. London.

Harbird, R. E. 1998. Common Buzzards in Worcestershire. *WMBC Annual Report* 65: 26-32.

Harbird R. and Gribble F. C. 1997. European Nightjars and other breeding birds of Cannock Chase 1997. *WMBC Annual Report* 64: 11-27.

Harrison G. R. 1996. *Draycote 25—A Review of Wildfowl and Waders at Draycote Water*. West Midland Bird Club, Studley.

Harrison G. R., Dean A. R, Richards A. J. and Smallshire D. 1982. *The Birds of the West Midlands*. West Midland Bird Club, Studley.

Harrison G. R. and Normand R. 1984. *The Birds of Saltwells Local Nature Reserve, Dudley—1983*. Nature Conservancy Council, Banbury. (Reprinted in *WMBC Annual Report* 53: 28-53).

Harrison G. R. and Sankey J. 1987. *Where to Watch Birds in the West Midlands*. Christopher Helm, London.

Harrison G. R. and Sankey J. 1997 *Where to Watch Birds in Herefordshire, Shropshire, Staffordshire, Warwickshire, Worcestershire and the former West Midlands County*. Christopher Helm, A & C Black, London.

Harthan A. J. 1946. *The Birds of Worcestershire*. Worcester.

Harthan A. J. 1961. A Revised List of Worcestershire Birds. *Transactions of the Worcestershire Naturalists Club* XI: 167-186.

Hastings, Sir C. 1834. *Illustrations of the Natural History of Worcestershire*. London.

Hay S., Lewington I., Thomson S. and Uren J. 2001. *Birds of Oxfordshire 2001*. Oxford Ornithological Society.

Henderson I. 2004. SAFFIE – enhancing biodiversity. *BTO News* 250: 11.

Hubbard C. E. 1968 (2nd Edition). *Grasses*. Penguin Books, Harmondsworth.

Hudson R. 1965. The spread of the Collared Dove in Britain and Ireland. *Brit. Birds* 58: 105-139.

Hudson R. 1973. *Early and Late Dates for Summer Migrants*. BTO Guide 15, British Trust for Ornithology, Tring.

Hudson R. 1976. Ruddy Ducks in Britain. *Brit. Birds* 69: 132-143.

Hume R. A. 1976. Inland flocks of Kittiwakes. *Brit. Birds* 69: 62-63.

Hume R. A, 1978. Variations in Herring Gulls at a Midland roost. *Brit. Birds* 71: 338-345.

Hunt A. E. 1977. Lead poisoning in Swans. *BTO News* 90: 1-2.

Hutchinson C. D. and Neath B. 1978. Little Gulls in Britain and Ireland. *Brit. Birds* 71:563-582.

Hywel-Davies J. and Thom V. 1984. *The Macmillan Guide to Britain's Nature Reserves*. Macmillan London Ltd., London.

Kington B. L. 1989 *Birds in a Manmade Land: The story of Ladywalk Nature Reserve*. Central Electricity Generating Board and West Midland Bird Club, Chadderton.

Kramer D. 1995. Inland spring passage of Arctic Terns in southern Britain. *Brit. Birds* 88: 211-217.

Lack, P. (Ed.) 1986. *The Atlas of wintering birds in Britain and Ireland*. British Trust for Ornithology. Poyser, Calton.

Lawrence J. A. 1997. Breeding Northern Lapwings on the North Staffordshire Moors. *WMBC Annual Report* 64: 172.

Lord J. and Blake A. R. M. 1962. *The Birds of Staffordshire*. West Midland Bird Club, Studley

Lord J. and Munns D. J. (Eds.) 1970. *Atlas of Breeding Birds of the West Midlands*. Collins, London.

Lovenbury G. A., Waterhouse M. and Yalden D. W. 1978. The status of Black Grouse in the Peak District. *The Naturalist.* 1978: 3-14.

Mackney D. and Burnham C. P. 1964. *The Soils of the West Midlands. Soil survey of Great Britain: England and Wales Bulletin No 2.* Agricultural Research Council, Harpenden.

Madge S. and Burn H. 1988. *Wildfowl—an identification guide to ducks, geese and swans of the world.* Christopher Helm, London.

Marchant J. H., Hudson R., Carter S. P and Whittington P. 1990. *Population trends in British breeding birds.* British Trust for Ornithology, Tring.

Marquiss M. and Newton, I. 1982. The Goshawk in Britain. *Brit. Birds* 75: 243-260.

Marren P. 2002. *Nature Conservation.* Harper Collins, London.

Matthews, L. Harrison 1982. *Mammals in the British Isles.* The New Naturalists No 68. Collins, London.

McKnight A. J., O'Brien M., Waterhouse M. and Reed S. 1996. *The North Staffordshire Moors Upland Breeding Bird Survey 1996.* English Nature and RSPB, Peterborough and Sandy.

Mead C. 2000. *The State of the Nations' Birds.* Whittet Books, Stowmarket.

Migration Atlas. Wernham C., Toms M., Marchant J., Clark J., Siriwardena G. and Baillie S. (Eds.) 2002 *The Migration Atlas: Movements of the Birds of Britain and Ireland.* British Trust for Ornithology, T. & A. D. Poyser, London.

Minton C. D. T. 1969. Movements of thrushes to and from the West Midlands. *WMBC Annual Report* 36: 15-24.

Minton C. D. T. 1970. The Gailey Heronry 1960-1970. *WMBC Annual Report* 37: 24-29.

Mitchell A. 1974. *A Field Guide to the Trees of Britain and Northern Europe.* Collins, London.

Moeller A. P. 1989. Population dynamics of a declining Swallow *Hirundo rustica* population. *J. Anim. Ecol.* 58: 1051-1063.

Mosley Sir Oswald 1863. *Natural History of Tutbury.* London.

Moss S. 1995. *Birds and Weather.* Hamlyn, London.

Murton R. K. 1965. *The Woodpigeon.* Collins, London.

National Trust, The 2004. *Handbook for Members and Visitors 2004.* Also individual property booklets. The National Trust, London.

Natural Areas. English Nature. 1998. *Natural Areas. Nature conservation in context.* (CD-ROM). Version 1.1. Peterborough: English Nature. Available from: www. english-nature.org.uk

Newton I. 1972. *Finches.* The New Naturalist No 55: Collins, London.

Nightingale B. and Allsopp K. 1995. The ornithological year 1994. *Brit. Birds* 88: 470.

Noble D. and Robinson R. 2000. Your data used to produce a measure of the quality of life! *BTO News* 231: 14-15.

Norris C. A. 1947 *Notes on the Birds of Warwickshire.* Cornish Bros Ltd., Birmingham.

Norris C. A. 1951. *West Midland Bird Distribution*
Survey, 1946-50. (printed for private circulation).

O'Connor R. J. and Shrubb M. 1986. *Farming and Birds.* Cambridge University Press, Cambridge.

Oddie W. E. 1983. *Bill Oddie's Gone Birding.* Methuen, London.

ODPM 2004. *Regional Planning Guidance for the West Midlands: RPG11.* Office of the Deputy Prime Minister, The Stationery Office, London.

Ogilvie Dr M. and the Rare Breeding Birds Panel 1994–2004. Rare breeding birds in the United Kingdom (1991-2002). *Brit. Birds* Vols 87 -97.

Ogilvie M and the Rare Breeding Birds Panel 2002. Non-native birds breeding in the United Kingdom in 2000. *Brit. Birds* 95: 631-635.

Ogilvie M and the Rare Breeding Birds Panel 2004. Non-native birds breeding in the United Kingdom in 2002. *Brit. Birds* 97: 633-637.

Orford, N. 1973. Breeding distribution of the Twite in central Britain. *Bird Study* 20: 50-62 and 121-126.

Ormerod S. J. and Tyler S. J. 1986. The diet of Dippers wintering in the catchment of the River Wye, Wales. *Bird Study* 32: 33-39.

Ormerod S. J and Tyler S. J. 1987. Dippers *Cinclus cinclus* and Grey Wagtails *Motacilla cinerea* as indicators of stream acidity in upland Wales. *ICPB Technical Publication No 6.*

Osborne 1982. Some effects of Dutch elm disease on nesting farmland birds. *Bird Study* 29: 2-16.

Parkin D. T., Collinson M., Helbig A. J., Knox A. G. and Sangster G. 2003 The taxonomic status of Carrion and Hooded Crows. *Brit. Birds* 96: 274-290.

Parr D. and Mrs J. D. (Eds.) 1987-96. *Birds on the Malvern Hills and Commons.* Annual Bird Reports covering 1986-95 and 2003. Published privately, Malvern.

Pearce E. A. and Smith C. G. 1998. *The Hutchinson World Weather Guide.* Helicon, Oxford.

Perrins C. 1979. *British Tits.* The New Naturalist No 62: Collins, London.

Piotrowski S. 2003. *The Birds of Suffolk.* Christopher Helm, London.

Plot R. 1686. *Natural History of Staffordshire.* Oxford.

Pollitt M. S., Cranswick P., Musgrove A., Hall C., Hearn R., Robinson J. and Holloway S. 2000. *The Wetland Bird Survey 1998-99: Wildfowl and Wader Counts.* BTO/WWT/RSPB/JNCC, Slimbridge.

Pollitt M. S., Hall C., Holloway S.J., Hearn R.D., Marshall P.E., Musgrove A. J., Robinson J. A. and Cranswick P. A. 2003. *The Wetland Bird Survey 2000-01 Wildfowl and Wader Counts.* BTO/WWT/RSPB/JNCC, Slimbridge.

Prater A. J. 1975. The Wintering Population of the Black-Tailed Godwit. *Bird Study* 22: 169-176.

Prescott F. E. 1931. List of Birds in Bockleton and the Neighbourhood. *Tenbury.* F. Joyce, Oxford.

Rackham, O. 1986. *The History of the Countryside.* Dent, London.

Ratcliffe D. 1999. Wintering Blackcaps in Worcestershire 1998/99. *WMBC Annual Report* 66: 17-22.

Ratcliffe D. A. 1963. The Status of the Peregrine in

Great Britain. *Bird Study* 10: 56-90.

Ratcliffe D. A. (Ed) 1977. *A Nature Conservation Review*. Vols 1 and 2. Cambridge University Press, Cambridge.

Ratcliffe D. A. 1980. *The Peregrine Falcon*. Poyser, Calton.

Ray J. 1678. *The Ornithology of Francis Willughby*.

Richards A. 1980. *The Birdwatcher's A-Z*. David and Charles, Newton Abbot.

Rogers M. J. and the British Birds Rarities Committee. 1978-2004. Rare birds in Great Britain in (1977-2003). *Brit. Birds* Vols 71-97.

Sainter J. D. 1878. *Scientific Rambles Round Macclesfield*.

Sharrock J. T. R. 1974. *Scarce Migrant Birds in Britain and Ireland*. T, & A. D. Poyser, Berkhamsted.

Sharrock J. T. R. (Ed.) 1976. *The Atlas of Breeding Birds in Britain and Ireland*. British Trust for Ornithology, T. & A.D. Poyser, Calton.

Sharrock J. T. R. and the Rare Breeding Birds Panel. 1978-83. Rare breeding birds in the United Kingdom (1976-81). *Brit. Birds* Vols 71-76.

Shrubb M. 2003. Farming and birds: an historic perspective. *Brit. Birds* 96: 158-175.

Simms E. 1978. *British Thrushes*. The New Naturalist No 63: Collins, London.

Simms E. 1985. *British Warblers*. The New Naturalist No 71: Collins, London.

Simms E. 1992. *British Larks, Pipits and Wagtails*. The New Naturalist No 78: Collins, London.

Simms E. A. 1949. An Overland Migration Route, *WMBC Annual Report* 15: 10-11.

Siriwardena G. 2001. Why are 'brown tits' declining? *BTO News* 235.

Smallshire D. 1986. The frequency of hybrid ducks in the Midlands. *Brit. Birds* 79: 87-89.

Smallshire D. 1987. *Belvide Bird Reserve: A Natural History*. West Midland Bird Club, Studley.

Smith F. R. and the Rarities Committee. 1975. Report on rare birds in Great Britain in 1974. *Brit. Birds.* 68: 317.

Smith T. 1938. The Birds of Staffordshire. Issued as Appendices 1-9 of the *Transactions and Annual Report of the North Staffordshire Field Club*, LXIV, 1930 to LXXII, 1938.

Spencer K. G. 1969. Overland migrations of Common Scoter. *Brit. Birds* 62: 332-333.

Spencer R. and the Rare Breeding Birds Panel. 1985-93 Rare breeding birds in the United Kingdom (1982-90). British Birds Vols 78-86.

Stanley P. I., Brough T., Fletcher M. R., Horton N. and Rochard J. B. A. 1981. The origins of Herring Gulls wintering inland in south-east England. *Bird Study* 28: 123-132.

Stone B. H., Sears J., Cranswick P. A., Gregory R. D., Gibbons D. W., Rehfisch M. M., Aebischer N. J. and Reid J.B. 1997. Population estimates of birds in Britain and in the United Kingdom. *Brit. Birds* 90: 1-22.

Sugrue A. 2002. *Lapwing and Wader Survey 2002: Peak District and surrounding area*. RSPB North West Regional Office, Huddersfield.

Tasker, Dr. A. (Ed.) 1990. *The Nature of Warwickshire. The Wildlife and Natural History of Warwickshire, Coventry and Solihull*. Barracuda Books Ltd., Buckingham.

Tatner P. 1983. The diet of urban Magpies *Pica pica*. *Ibis* 125: 90-107

Teagle W. G. 1978. *The Endless Village*. Nature Conservancy Council, Shrewsbury.

Thomas C. A. and Minton C. D. T. 1976. Movements of (Common) Starlings to and from the West Midlands. WMBC Annual Report 43: 11-14.

Thompson A., Clark P. and Tasker A. 1998. Warwickshire Wildlife Trust: *Nature Reserves Handbook*. Warwickshire Wildlife Trust, Brandon Marsh, Coventry.

Thompson, D. B. A. and Gribbin, S. 1986. Ecology of Corn Buntings *Miliaria calandra* in NW England. *Bull. Brit. Ecol. Soc.* 17: 69-75.

Tomes R. F. 1901. Birds. In the *Victoria County History of Worcestershire*. London.

Tomes R. F. 1904. Aves. In the *Victoria County History of Warwickshire*, 1. London.

Toms M. P., Crick H. Q. P and Shawyer C. R. 2001. The status of breeding Barn Owls *Tyto alba* in the United Kingdom 1995-97. *Bird Study* 48: 23-37.

Tucker G. M. and Heath M. F. 1994. *Birds in Europe: their conservation status*. Cambridge: BirdLife International (BirdLife Conservation Series no. 3).

Tucker J. J. 1980. The decline of six typically heathland bird species at two Worcestershire heathlands. *WMBC Annual Report* 47: 13-21.

UK Biodiversity Steering Group. 1995. *Biodiversity: The UK Steering Group Report*. HMSO, London.

Vernon J. D. R. 1970 and 1972. Feeding habitats and food of the Black-headed and Common Gulls. Parts I and II. *Bird Study* 17: 287-296 and 19: 173-186.

Vinicombe K., Marchant J. and Knox A. on behalf of the BOURC. 1993. Review of status and categorisation of feral birds on the British List. *Brit. Birds* 86: 605-614

Vinicombe K. E. and Harrop A. H. J. 1999. Ruddy Shelducks in Britain and Ireland, 1986-94. *Brit. Birds* 92: 225-255.

Vinicombe K., Marchant, J. and Knox, A. 1993. Review of status and categorisation of feral birds on the British List. *Brit. Birds* 86: 605-614.

Walker S. W. and Day J. J. 1984. The Dipper in Worcestershire. *WMBC Annual Report* 51: 14-22.

Warmington K. and Vickery M. 2003. *Warwickshire's Butterflies—their habitats and where to find them*. The Warwickshire Branch of Butterfly Conservation, Atherstone.

Warren A. 2004. Scandinavian Song Thrushes in South Warwickshire. *WMBC Annual Report* 69: 263-264.

Waterhouse M. 1985. *North Staffordshire Moors Survey 1985*. RSPB Midlands Office, Droitwich.

WCC 1978. Warwickshire County Council: *County Landscape Plan*. County Planning Department, Warwick.

Wernham C., Toms M., Marchant J., Clark J., Siriwardena G. and Baillie S. (Eds.) 2002 *The Migration Atlas: Movements of the Birds of Britain and Ireland.* British Trust for Ornithology, T. & A. D. Poyser, London.

West Midlands Round Table for Sustainable Development 2000. *Quality of Life: the future starts here—a sustainable strategy for the West Midlands.* Government Office for the West Midlands, Birmingham.

West Midlands Wildlife Trusts. 2001. *The West Midlands Wildlife Trusts' Premium Programme: Managing for wildlife in the West Midlands countryside.*

Whitlock F. B. 1893. *Birds of Derbyshire.* London and Derby.

Williamson K. 1975. Birds and climatic change. *Bird Study* 22: 143-164.

Winsper J. R. 1991. WMBC Research Committee Black Redstart Survey 1987-1991. *WMBC Annual Report* 57: 25-30.

Winsper J. R. 1991 WMBC Research Committee Rook Survey 1991. *WMBC Annual Report* 58:39-41.

Winstanley D., Spencer R. and Williamson K. 1974. Where have all the Whitethroats gone? *Bird Study* 21: 1-14.

Winter Atlas. Lack, P. (Ed.) 1986. *The Atlas of wintering birds in Britain and Ireland.* British Trust for Ornithology. Poyser, Calton.

Witherby, H. F., Jourdain, Rev. F. C. R., Ticehurst N. F. and Tucker, B. W. 1938-41, reprinted with revisions 1943-44. *The Handbook of British Birds.* London.

WMBC Annual Reports 1934-2002. West Midland Bird Club, Studley.

Wood J. D. 2003. *Horace Alexander: 1889 to 1989 - birds and binoculars.* Ebor Press, York.

Wyllie I. 1981. *The Cuckoo.* Batsford, London.

Yalden D. W. 1979. An estimate of the number of Red Grouse in the Peak District. *The Naturalist.* 104: 5-8.

Yalden D. W. 1984. Bird populations of The Roaches Estate, 1978-84. *WMBC Annual Report* 51: 23-27.

Yalden D. W. 1992. The influence of recreational disturbance on Common Sandpipers *Actitis hypoleucos* breeding by an upland reservoir. *Biol. Conservation* 61: 41-49.

Yalden Dr. D. W. 1994. The Red Grouse in Staffordshire. *WMBC Annual Report* 60: 19-21.

Yapp W.B. 1962. Birds and Woods. Oxford University Press, London.

Yapp W.B. 1969. The bird population of an oakwood (Wyre Forest) over eighteen years. *Proc. Birm. Nat. Hist. Soc.* 21: 199-216.

Index to Birds